Electronics for Scientists

Electronics for Scientists

Principles and Experiments for Those Who Use Instruments

H. V. Malmstadt
University of Illinois

and

C. G. Enke
Princeton University

with the assistance of
E. C. Toren, Jr.
Duke University

W. A. Benjamin, Inc.   *New York*   *1963*

ELECTRONICS FOR SCIENTISTS
Principles and Experiments for Those Who Use Instruments

Library of Congress Catalog Card Number: 62-15645
Manufactured in the United States of America

First printing, September 1962;
    Second printing, with corrections,
    March 1963.

The publisher is pleased to acknowledge the assistance
    of Russell F. Peterson, who produced the illustrations,
    and William Prokos, who designed the cover,
    dust jacket, and end papers

W. A. BENJAMIN, INC.
2465 Broadway, New York 25, New York

Preface

This book is a practical book for scientists and science students. It is written expressly for *chemists, physicists, engineers, medical researchers, biologists,* and other science students and research workers who have little or no background in electronics but who need to gain a working knowledge of electronic devices and circuits. The text begins with *electronic principles, basic circuits,* and *components.* It leads systematically into *servo systems, operational amplifiers, feedback control, digital circuits,* and other devices used in current laboratory research and engineering control problems. The liberal use of diagrams attests to the authors' belief that a picture can speak louder than a thousand words.

The order of presentation is laboratory-centered. There is a natural progression from the basic measurement techniques necessary to start experimentation toward the complete instruments and systems. Specific components are usually introduced in the chapter where the most common or important applications are first described. Circuits with *new and special devices* are presented as well as the widespread *transistor and vacuum-tube circuits.* Most circuit diagrams contain actual component values so that they can be used as working drawings. A selected list of references with specific comments concerning the nature of the contents is included at the end of each chapter.

The three supplements at the end of the book serve several functions. Supplement 1 introduces and gives specifications on the universal experimental system used to perform the experiments in the book, and the pictures acquaint the reader with the individual components. Supplements 2 and 3 serve primarily as review of and reference to the *basic laws* and *component characteristics* which are usually introduced in basic courses of college physics. For scientists who do not remember or have had little exposure to these basic relationships, Supplements 2 and 3 are a good starting point.

This book should be especially useful as a text for a one-semester course at the junior-senior level in various physics, chemistry, or engineering college curricula, or as a self-teaching text for scientists on the job. For those who already have a good basic training in electronics, the chapters on comparison measurements, operational amplifiers, feedback control, servo systems, and digital circuits should provide both new information and reference material, because all these topics are presented in a way that the authors believe to be unique. As explained in the introduction, the authors have also found the material in this book to provide a practical working background in electronics for both graduate and postdoctoral students, especially if combined with thorough discussions of specific systems related to individual disciplines.

There have been many people influential in the start, preparation, and completion of this book. Professor H. A. Laitinen encouraged us from the beginning, both in support of the course from which this book developed and by his enthusiasm for the experimental system that we originated. The staff of the Heath Company (Benton Harbor, Michigan), especially W. Kooy, E. B. Mullings, and A. Robertson, was responsible for taking our original system and ideas and developing them into the completely integrated system of components and laboratory instruments now available for performing the experiments. Several valuable discussions took place with Professors Harry Pardue and Robert Kerr concerning portions of the manuscript. Great appreciation goes to Professor D. Lazarus of the University of Illinois Physics Department. He read all the chapters and made many important suggestions that greatly influenced our presentation of several topics. Mr. Verle Walters contributed in many ways to the construction of the original experimental system. Julia Zvilius, Frances Watson, and Linda Leahy were all very helpful in typing and assembling various parts of the manuscript. We are especially grateful for the help and encouragement of our wives, Gay Malmstadt and Mary Enke.

H. V. MALMSTADT
C. G. ENKE

Urbana, Illinois
Princeton, New Jersey
July 1962

Contents

Electronics for Scientists

Introduction

Go into a clinical laboratory, a chemistry, biological, or soil-science laboratory—in fact, go into laboratories in all areas of science and technology—and you will find them loaded with instruments that depend upon electronic circuits for operation. Talk to the experimental personnel, the people who do the research and accumulate the data, and you learn that these scientists are using a powerful array of tools with considerable success to probe the mysteries of their specialties. But you also learn of problems! Problems of how to put a new instrument into operation, how to modify a commercial instrument for a new research problem, how to increase sensitivity, how to eliminate electrical noise, how to prevent inaccuracies because of interaction between the measurement device and the system under test, how to automate a process or analytical method.

Unless answers to these questions can be readily provided by the available scientific personnel, a research project might be stalled, a breakthrough in science or production delayed. At the University we have observed research students waste weeks and months of valuable time because of the improper use of perfectly good instruments or the use of inadequate ones. Seldom do they understand what instrument changes should be made to keep pace with the developments in their research. Reports from several industrial-research directors indicate that the same situation prevails among many scientists on the job. This is to be expected, of course, because electronics has come of age since many of them completed their formal training.

Fortunately, however, there is an increasing awareness among experimental scientists that instruments can be used more effectively and that

more reliable measurements can be obtained if some basic understanding
and working ability in electronics can be "picked up along the way." It
is the purpose of this book to help the already trained scientist or advanced
college science student to acquire this understanding and working ability.

Obviously, if unlimited time were available, a thorough program of
study in an electronics department over a period of years would be desirable. However, the number of courses in most scientific curricula are
already overwhelming, and the scientist at work is generally overloaded
with his regular responsibilities. It was therefore a major concern to develop a course of study and experimentation that would permit a breakthrough of the "electronics barrier" in a minimum amount of time.

In the Chemistry Department at the University of Illinois many
different ideas were tested with chemistry graduate students. The senior
author of this book presented lectures, special seminars, and various laboratory courses over several years. It became increasingly apparent that a
laboratory-oriented course was essential to provide the desired results.
Finally a set of experiments evolved, together with descriptive material
and a new, unique, and rapid method of connecting electronic circuits; the
three proved to be an efficient and effective combination in taking scien-
tifically trained students across the "electronics barrier"—to the point
where they were working not with "magic boxes" but with scientific instruments. As would be hoped and expected, it also paved their way for further
study and furnished a new awareness of how electronics might be useful in
their work. It was found that this could be accomplished in 15 half days
of laboratory work with at least an equivalent amount of time for study.
This amounts to about one very full day per week during the regular 15-
week college semester.

Many scientists throughout the country heard of our semester course
and asked whether it would be possible to have a special concentrated
course. Therefore a 3-week course was arranged for the summer of 1960,
covering the same material as that in the semester course. All in attendance had scientific B.S., M.S., or Ph.D. degrees. Some were research group
leaders with their companies; others were relatively new college graduates
or Ph.D.'s. Upon completion of the course this group left no doubt that
the venture was successful, and the scientists in attendance encouraged us
to repeat the course. The second year there were more applicants than
the course could accommodate. There are now requests by applicants to
be put on waiting lists for future summer classes. Inquiries concerning
both the regular and concentrated courses come from industries, colleges,
and medical laboratories throughout the United States and many other
countries as well. Several schools would like to set up similar courses.
Some individuals in laboratories would like descriptive material, experiments, equipment, and parts to work with in their spare time on the job

or at home. The many indications of interest demonstrate a need and desire for a special type of training in experimental electronics and have prompted the writing of this book.

Concentrating so much in a 3-week period does not mean that one is "getting something for nothing." Rather, an all-out effort is required. The important point is that the material can be absorbed, and absorbed effectively, in this short period of time. The schedules and responsibilities of many thousands of scientists and engineers are such that a longer period away from their regular jobs is impossible.

The authors' experience has indicated that the experiments can be performed most efficiently and the basic concepts grasped most easily by working in small laboratory sections of five or six students per instructor. As in the regular semester course, each student works at a desk complete with test equipment, parts, and tools which are for his individual use throughout a 4- to 5-hr laboratory period. With an instructor available throughout this period, the give-and-take certainly stimulates the thinking and performance of each person.

There are many who find it necessary to get such training either at home or on the job or not at all. Therefore the problems and experiments have been presented with the hope that the book could serve as a self-teaching text. The circuits could be successfully built, tested, understood, and used by a scientist or engineer working in his home or laboratory. The disadvantage of missing the discussions with instructors and other students could be compensated for by additional reading from the references supplied and by allowing somewhat longer times for the experiments.

As sketched in the following paragraphs, an electronics-instrumentation laboratory made up of relatively inexpensive units is a unique feature of the courses and is described in the book. This carefully planned and tested laboratory setup, which is described in detail, provides the possibility for efficient experimentation either for self-training at home or on the job or in an organized course.

The construction of the circuits described in this book would take much longer than the scheduled 15 half days if only conventional soldering techniques were used. Therefore, many available "breadboarding" schemes were tested to speed up the construction of the circuits. Unfortunately, all had shortcomings, primarily because they were not typical of good wiring practice and the connected circuits had characteristics considerably inferior to those with soldered joints. Therefore a scheme was devised which has subsequently proved completely satisfactory. It increases the speed of construction, testing, and component interchange in circuits at least threefold.

Parts and wires are connected point to point as in conventional practice, but spring clips permit the same parts and wires to be used over and over again, hundreds of times. The clips bind tightly so that circuit characteristics are, in general, quite similar to those with soldered joints. Component placement and the finished circuit are very similar to that of standard chassis wiring. The complete laboratory system is described in Supplement 1.

The preparation of the original experimental setup was a long and tedious job. The hand making of the parts was very time-consuming and a deterrent to others who wished to use the system. Fortunately, however, all parts and chassis are now commercially produced. All the basic experiments described in this book, including servomechanisms and operational amplifiers for computation and control, can be performed by using the commercially available kits and inexpensive instrumentation laboratory. Hundreds of other useful circuits can also be constructed with the same parts.

Many of those who have taken the course have expressed a keen desire to have a similar complete system at their work or at home and always available for rapidly testing new ideas before permanent construction is attempted. Needless to say, such a system is an excellent aid in building or modifying instruments.

The order in which topics were introduced was changed many times so that the most systematic presentation might be achieved. Discontinuities in the order were revealed by the troubles and questions of the students working in the laboratory. For 3 years now the order has remained essentially unchanged because the response of the students indicated that each experiment and its descriptive material followed logically from previous experiments and descriptive material. On the basis of this experience, it is recommended that anyone unfamiliar with electronics start at the beginning and proceed consecutively through the chapters. To do otherwise would be to risk wasting time in studying and working with the more complex circuits in the later chapters. Those who have some background in electronics may want to delve immediately into the later chapters on servomechanisms, operational amplifiers, and digital systems. For convenient reference and review on basic d-c and a-c circuits, Supplements 2 and 3 have been provided. In these sections the basic laws of electricity, such as Ohm's and Kirchhoff's laws, are presented. Resistors, capacitors, and inductors and their simple networks are discussed. Important tables are included in the Appendix.

Each chapter opens with a discussion of the important basic principles. This is followed by a section of experiments that emphasize the most important aspects of each subject. Although valuable information can be obtained by reading only the discussion sections, there is no doubt that it is by working the experiments that great strides can be made in exploring the new possibilities of electronics in one's own research.

chapter one

Electrical Measurements

The operation of electronic circuits and systems which make up most modern scientific instruments depends on correct values for the components, such as resistors and capacitors, and on the use of suitable voltages and currents of proper phase and frequency within the circuits. To test and study operational characteristics or to trouble-shoot (i.e., determine the cause of instrument failure), it is especially important to make accurate measurements of current, voltage, resistance, phase angle, and frequency. It is the purpose of the discussion and experiments in this chapter to introduce the various test instruments and show how they can be used to obtain reliable information.

Some of the test equipment is relatively simple, and the methods of operation follow directly from a few well-known basic laws of electricity. In such cases, a thorough understanding of the equipment is possible at this point. However, some test equipment, for example, the oscilloscope, is an assemblage of several more or less complex electronic circuits, many of which are the subject of study and experimentation in subsequent chapters. Therefore a detailed understanding of the oscilloscope is not possible at this time; yet it is important to learn now the general functions of its basic circuits and components and how to use it to obtain reliable measurements. With this indispensable test instrument, as well as the other meters available, it is possible to measure the most important variables in all the circuits that are to follow. Since many of the circuits to be studied are the general building blocks for the oscilloscope as well as most scientific instruments, a greater appreciation and understanding of this test instrument will develop with the completion of subsequent chapters.

1-1 Measurement of Voltage and Current

The purpose of a *voltage* measurement is to determine the *potential difference*[1] between two points in a circuit. The potential difference between any two points in a circuit is measured by connecting the two voltmeter leads to these points (see Fig. 1-1). Thus the voltmeter is connected "across" or in *parallel*[2] with the circuit whose potential is to be measured.

Because the voltmeter *resistance*[3] is not infinite and is connected between two points of unequal potential, a *current*[4] will occur in the voltage-measuring circuit. The application of the voltmeter to the test points may change the current magnitudes in the circuit enough to cause a considerable change in the potential being measured. If a voltmeter has a resistance of 60 kilohms when switched on the 3-volt scale and its leads are connected across a 10-kilohm resistor in the circuit, the potential across the combination of 10 kilohms and 60 kilohms will no longer be 2.5 volts. The parallel resistance $= (10K* \times 60K)/(10K + 60K) = 8.6K$. The potential that the voltmeter will indicate is 10 volts $\times [8.6K/(30K + 8.6K)] = 2.23$ volts. *To avoid this kind of error, a voltmeter of sufficiently high internal resistance must be used to make the measurement.* The method of determining a voltmeter's resistance is discussed in Sec. 1-2. The slide-wire potentiometer, which makes a potential measurement under conditions approaching zero current through the instrument, is discussed in Chap. 6.

[1] *Voltage* is the difference in electric pressure between two points. The *potential difference* between two points is the work required to transfer a unit quantity of electricity from one point to the other. Between any two points the voltage and the potential difference are the same and are measured in volts. Both terms are commonly used interchangeably and are abbreviated V, E, or emf, although voltage (V) usually implies that if the two points were connected in a closed circuit a flow of current would result. A potential difference (E or emf) may exist between two electrically isolated points simply because of a difference in electrostatic charge. For this reason the terms potential or potential difference are sometimes used to indicate the zero-current or open-circuit potential between two points.

[2] Circuit components are said to be arranged in *parallel* when each component has both terminals in common with the two terminals of the other components. The voltage is the same across all components connected in parallel.

[3] *Resistance* is the opposition to the flow of current offered by a device or circuit element. Resistance (R) has for units ohms, abbreviated Ω.

[4] *Current* is the rate of electric charge transfer from one point to another. Current (I or i) is measured in amperes, abbreviated A. The current in a circuit is related to the voltage and resistance by Ohm's law ($E = IR$), as explained in Supplement 1.

* When kilohms are used in calculations, the symbol K is often employed.

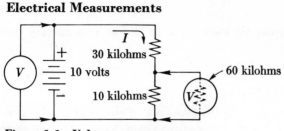

Figure 1-1 Voltage measurement.

The purpose of a current measurement is to determine the rate of electron flow in any given branch of a circuit. The usual current meter must be put in *series*[5] with the components in that branch so that the electrons flow through the meter coil (see Fig. 1-2). The circuit must be broken to connect the ammeter; therefore the ammeter becomes an essential part of the circuit being measured. Since the ammeter has some internal resistance, its insertion into the circuit may considerably decrease the current in the measured branch. Consider the effect of introducing a milliammeter which has a resistance of 100 ohms in the circuit of Fig. 1-2. The resistance in the R_3 branch will increase to 1.1 kilohms. This will cause only a small change in the potential across R_2 and R_3. The resistance of R_2 in parallel with R_3 and meter = 525 ohms. The potential across R_2 and R_3 is 1.5 volts (525/1525) = 0.517 volt. The current through the meter is then 0.517 volt/1.1 kilohms = 0.468 ma,[6] instead of the 0.5 ma that would be read if the meter had zero resistance. The determination of the resistance of a meter is discussed in the next section. This information is important

---

[5] Components are said to be in *series* when there is only one point of connection between them. The current through all components arranged in a simple series circuit is the same.

[6] *Milliampere*, thousandth of an ampere, is abbreviated ma.

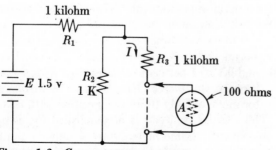

Figure 1-2 Current measurement.

because the meter resistance must be allowed for in connecting current meters into circuits.

1-2 The Moving-Coil Meter

Of all the devices (meters) that convert an electrical quantity to the physical displacement of a pointer or light beam, the moving-coil meter is by far the most common. The moving-coil meter owes its popularity to its great versatility, combined with reasonable ruggedness, accuracy, and simplicity. Discussion of other types of meters, which are used mostly in heavy-duty and special applications, will be found in the References.

The usual D'Arsonval moving-coil meter used in test instruments is shown in Fig. 1-3*a*. A coil of fine wire, wound on a rectangular aluminum frame, is mounted in the air space between the poles of a permanent horseshoe magnet. Hardened-steel pivots attached to the coil frame fit into jeweled bearings so that the coil rotates with a minimum of friction. An indicating pointer is attached to the coil assembly, and springs attached to the frame return the needle (and coil) to a fixed reference point. When electrons flow through the coil a magnetic field is developed that interacts with the magnetic field of the permanent magnet to force the coil to rotate as in an electric motor. The direction of rotation depends on the direction of electron flow in the coil. The magnitude of the pointer deflection is proportional to the rate of flow of electrons (the current). The laboratory galvanometer is a very sensitive moving-coil meter; it is discussed in Sec. 6-2. A recording galvanometer is shown in Fig. 1-3*b*. A writing stylus is used instead of a pointer. The stylus can have an ink tip, or it can have a tip that is the contact for an electro-sensitive, heat-sensitive, or pressure-sensitive paper. The roll of chart paper is usually driven by a constant-speed motor. If a writing arm of fixed length is used, the ordinate will be curved. In order to convert the curvilinear motion of the writing tip into rectilinear motion, various writing mechanisms have been devised to change the effective length of the writing arm as it moves across the chart.

The meter movement has three characteristics which are used to determine its effectiveness for a given measurement. These characteristics are sensitivity (milliamperes full scale, microamperes per centimeter, microamperes per degree, etc.), internal resistance (the d-c resistance of the coil in ohms), and accuracy (normally $\frac{1}{2}$ to 3 per cent of full scale deflection for general-purpose meters, and 0.1 to 1 per cent for laboratory types).

When the current through the meter changes value suddenly, it is desirable that the indicator move quickly to its new position with no overshoot or oscillations. This desired behavior is accomplished by *damping* or braking the meter movement. Some meters have a damper built in; others, particularly galvanometers, need to be damped by adjusting the re-

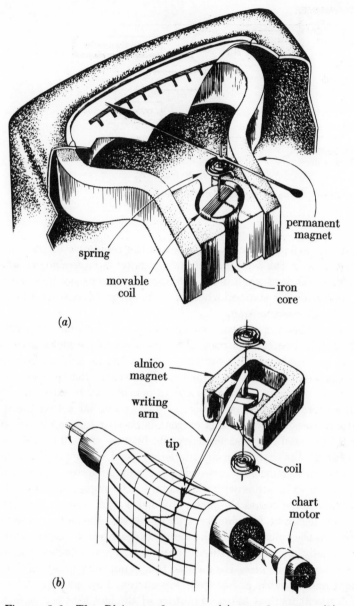

spring

movable
coil

permanent
magnet

iron
core

(a)

alnico
magnet

writing
arm

tip

coil

chart
motor

(b)

*Figure 1-3 The D'Arsonval meter: (a) panel meter; (b) recording
galvanometer.*

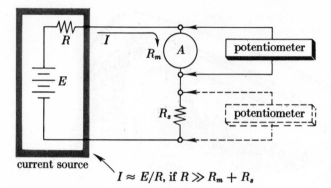

$$I \approx E/R, \text{ if } R \gg R_m + R_s$$

Figure 1-4   Measurement of meter resistance.

sistance in the external circuit. The lower the resistance in the external circuit, the greater the damping action. A meter is *underdamped* when it overshoots, *overdamped* when it takes longer than necessary to reach equilibrium, and *critically damped* when it reaches equilibrium as quickly as possible without overshooting.

The sensitivity and accuracy of a meter can be determined by calibration with standard current sources. The resistance of the meter movement should not be measured with ordinary ohmmeters or bridges because of probable damage to the coil and pointer. To measure the resistance R_m of the meter coil, a current source is wired to provide nearly full-scale deflection of the current meter, as in Fig. 1-4; the potential across the meter movement is measured when this current is passing through it (a potentiometer is suggested for good accuracy and because only 10 to 100 mv are to be measured); the current on the ammeter is read, or for greater accuracy the current is determined by measuring the voltage across a standard resistor R_s which is in series with the meter. The meter resistance R_m is equal to the voltage across the meter divided by the current through the meter. A less accurate, but simpler, way to measure the meter's resistance, which relies on the calibration of the meter, is described in Experiment 1-2.

Occasionally meters are fused to protect them against accidental current overload. For sensitive meters, this is not very practical because of the high and variable resistance a low-current fuse adds to the meter circuit. A recent method takes advantage of the fact that a *p-n* diffused-junction *diode*[7] requires a few tenths of a volt of forward bias before it is conductive. The circuit is shown in Fig. 1-5. A resistance R is put in series with the meter resistance R_m so that when the current through the

---

[7] A *diode*, or rectifier, is a device that has a much higher resistance to current in one direction than the other.

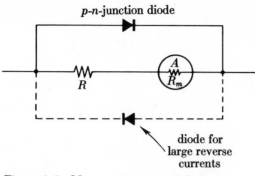

Figure 1-5   *Meter protection with diodes.*

meter is two or three times the full-scale deflection the potential across $R + R_m$ will be sufficient for the diode to conduct and bypass some of the current around the meter. Assume that a 50-μa[8] meter is to be protected. This meter would typically have a resistance of 2000 ohms. With a double overload ($i = 100$ μa), the voltage across the meter movement would be $(0.1 \times 10^{-3}$ amp$)(2 \times 10^{3}$ ohms$) = 0.2$ volt, and at this potential the diode begins to conduct and shunts the current around the meter. A 1000-ohm series resistor would be required if the diode begins to conduct around 0.3 volt instead of 0.2 volt. Another diode could be added to protect against accidentally imposed large reverse currents.

1-3   The Ammeter

The moving-coil meter described in the last section is sensitive to current and is therefore an ammeter. However, it is often necessary to increase the range (synonymous with decreasing the sensitivity) of a meter in order to measure larger currents. This is done by *shunting* part of the current around the meter so that only a fraction of the total current passes through the meter, as in Fig. 1-6a. The voltage across the *shunt*[9] and the meter must be equal; so $(I_{shunt})(R_{shunt}) = (I_{meter})(R_{meter})$, and $R_{shunt} = (R_{meter})(I_{meter})/I_{shunt}$. If the range of the meter is to be increased tenfold, then only one-tenth of the total current in the circuit must pass through the meter and nine-tenths through a shunt, so that $I_{meter}/I_{shunt} = \frac{1}{9}$ and $R_{shunt} = \frac{1}{9}R_{meter}$. If a 1-ma meter movement which is to read 100 ma full scale has a resistance of 46 ohms, the shunt resistance should be $\frac{1}{99} \times 46 = 0.455$ ohm. This resistance need be accurate to only 1 per cent to

---

[8] *Microampere*, millionth of an ampere, is abbreviated μa.

[9] A *shunt* is a component, in this case a resistor, which is connected in parallel with a device to provide an alternate current path around the device.

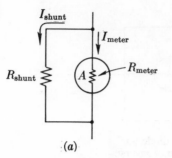

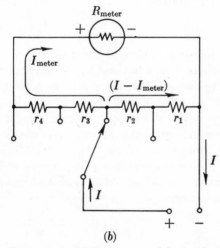

Figure 1-6   *Meter shunts: (a) simple shunt; (b) Ayrton shunt.*

take advantage of the accuracy of most panel meters. Accurate low-resistance shunts must be wired so that the resistances of the connections to the meter and shunt are not part of the shunt resistance. The shunt strips are often made of manganin (an alloy with nearly zero temperature coefficient), and the ends are embedded in large copper blocks to which the meter and circuit leads are attached.

The Ayrton Shunt. The shunt shown in Fig. 1-6*b* enables a meter to be used for several different current ranges, and the meter sensitivity is readily changed by exact increments. This type is usually referred to as an "Ayrton shunt." The circuit current I divides between two resistance branches, the resistance r (which is $r_1 + r_2$ when the switch is in position, as shown in Fig. 1-6*b*), and the resistance in parallel with it, which is $R - r + R_{meter}$, where R is the sum of $r_1 + r_2 + r_3 + r_4$. Since the voltage drop is the same across both resistance branches,

$$I_{meter}(R_{meter} + R - r) = (I - I_{meter})r$$

This reduces to

$$\frac{I}{I_{meter}} = \frac{R + R_{meter}}{r} \tag{1-1}$$

Therefore, if a 50-μa meter is used and it is desired to have current ranges of 15 ma, 150 ma, 0.5 amp, and 15 amp, then the ratios $(R + R_{meter})/r$ should be 300, 3000, 10,000, and 300,000, respectively. If $R_{meter} = 5000$ ohms, the correct ratios are obtained if $r = R = r_1 + r_2 + r_3 + r_4 = 16.7$ ohms for the 15-ma range; and $r = r_1 + r_2 + r_3 = 1.67$ ohms, $r = r_1 + r_2 = 0.5$ ohm, and $r = r_1 = 0.0167$ for the 150-ma, 0.5-amp, and 15-amp ranges, respectively. It follows that $r_2 = 0.483$ ohm, $r_3 = 1.17$ ohms, and $r_4 = 15$ ohms.

Measurement of Alternating Current with Moving-Coil Meter. The operation of the moving-coil meter depends on the unidirectional flow of electrons through its coil. Therefore, if it is to be used to measure *alternating current*,[10] certain meter circuits must be devised. The meter circuit must permit the flow of electrons in only one direction through the meter coil and yet not prevent the bidirectional flow of electrons in the measured circuit. Two meter circuits are shown in Fig. 1-7

[10] An *alternating current* is one in which the direction of charge flow reverses at regular intervals. The period required for two current reversals is one cycle. The frequency is the number of cycles per second. See also Supplement 3.

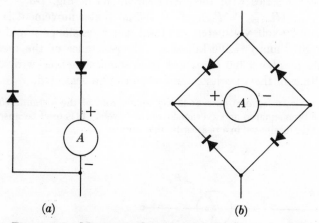

(a) (b)

Figure 1-7   Moving-coil meter circuits for a-c current measurements: (a) half-wave; (b) full-wave.

which accomplish these objectives. A shunt could be used across the meter or across the whole meter circuit to extend the current range. Most a-c current meters are not made this way but, rather, use a different kind of meter movement whose pointer deflects in one direction regardless of the direction of electron flow. Presumably, since high-quality, high-current, inexpensive diodes are now available, more rectifier-type meters will be used for a-c measurements.

The meter circuits of Fig. 1-7 will respond to the *average value* of the rectified alternating current (i.e., the average rate of flow of electrons from the rectified current pulses). If the meter is calibrated in amperes rms,[11] the manufacturer has assumed that sine waves are being measured and has included the factor 0.707/0.637 in the dial calibrations. (For an explanation of the relationships among peak, average, and rms values for sine and other waveforms, see Supplement 3.) If some waveform other than a sine wave is being measured, so that the rms/average factor is different, the meter will not read the true rms value of the current. The quality of the rectifiers imposes an upper limit to the frequency that can be measured. At frequencies over 1 kc, it is important to consider the possibility of error from this source.

1-4 The Voltmeter

The moving-coil meter has a constant resistance, so that the current through the meter is proportional to the voltage across it. In this sense, the current meter can be used to measure voltage. The full-scale deflection sensitivity in volts is the full-scale deflection current times the resistance of the meter. To extend the voltage range of the meter, it is necessary only to add resistance in series with the meter circuit as in Fig. 1-8. Now $E_{\text{full scale}} = I_{\text{full scale}}(R_{\text{series}} + R_m)$. If a 200-$\mu$a meter movement is to be used for a 0-to-20-volt voltmeter, the total meter resistance would be 20 volts/$(0.2 \times 10^{-3}$ amp$) = 100$ kilohms. The resistance of the meter movement would be about 300 ohms and is so small compared with the total resistance that in this case its contribution can be neglected.

[11] The rms (*root mean square*) current is the square root of the instantaneous currents that have been squared and averaged over one cycle. It is used because it is related to the power dissipated in a resistor by this current.

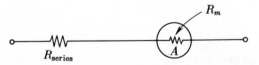

Figure 1-8   A d-c voltmeter.

Note that $(R_{\text{series}} + R_m)/E_{\text{full scale}}$ is a constant. This constant is the ohms per volt rating of the voltmeter. The resistance of the voltmeter is the ohms per volt rating times the full-scale deflection voltage. A 20,000-ohms/volt meter will have a resistance of 30,000 ohms on the 1.5-volt scale and 600 kilohms on the 30-volt scale. The current sensitivity of the meter with a 20,000-ohms/volt rating is $50\mu a$ full-scale deflection. As explained in Sec. 1-1, it is important to have a meter resistance which is high compared with those in the circuit being measured. The ohms per volt rating of the meter will be higher if a moving-coil meter of greater current sensitivity is used.

To measure a-c voltages, rectification is required, but, because ideally the meter is not part of the circuit being measured, only the effects of the *rectifier*[12] on the meter circuit need be considered. Two a-c voltmeter circuits are shown in Fig. 1-9. As in the case of a-c current meters, a-c voltmeters respond to the *average* value of the rectified voltage but are calibrated in volts rms for a sine wave. If a nonsinusoidal voltage is measured, a factor other than $0.707/0.637$ will have to be used to determine the rms value of the voltage.

Most diodes do not work well at very low current values. Therefore very sensitive meters are not used in a-c voltmeters, and the ohms per volt rating of a-c voltmeters is usually much lower than is typical for a d-c voltmeter. The diodes also impose a frequency limitation, and care should be

---

[12] A *rectifier* is a circuit, usually containing diodes, which converts bidirectional current to unidirectional current. Many such circuits are described in Chap. 2.

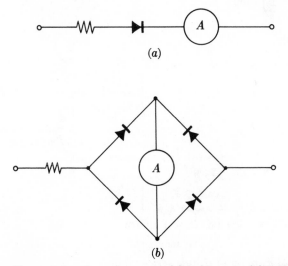

(a)

(b)

Figure 1-9   A-c voltmeters: (a) half-wave; (b) full-wave.

taken to be sure that accuracy is maintained when an a-c voltmeter is used
to measure frequencies over 1 kc.

1-5   The Ohmmeter

A series-type ohmmeter circuit is shown in Fig. 1-10. With the test
prods short-circuited ($R_u = 0$), the "ohms adjust" control is turned so that
the current I_1 through the total circuit resistance $R_m + R_f + R_a$ deflects
the meter exactly full scale. Now, by connecting the test prods across the
unknown resistance R_u, the current is decreased to a value I_2 which depends on the value of R_u. The 1.5-volt battery is across the total resistance
in the two cases; so

$$I_1(R_m + R_f + R_a) = 1.5 \text{ volts}$$

and $$I_2(R_m + R_f + R_a) + I_2 R_u = 1.5 \text{ volts}$$

from which it follows that

$$R_u = \left(\frac{I_1}{I_2} - 1\right)(R_m + R_f + R_a) \tag{1-2}$$

Since a 1-ma meter movement is used and the battery is 1.5 volts, the total
resistance $R_m + R_f + R_a$ will have to be set to 1500 ohms for full-scale
deflection; so, from Eq. (1-2),

$$R_u = \left(\frac{I_1}{I_2} - 1\right)1500$$

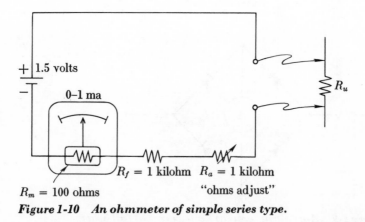

Figure 1-10   An ohmmeter of simple series type.

With $I_2 = \frac{1}{2}I_1$ (midscale deflection), the unknown resistance $R_u = 1500$ ohms; with $I_2 = \frac{1}{3}I_1$, $R_u = 3000$ ohms, etc. It is apparent that the scale is nonlinear. Values of R_u much higher than 1500 ohms become crowded on the "infinite ohms" end of the scale, and values much lower become indistinguishable from zero. The resistance at midscale could be decreased tenfold to 150 ohms by shunting the meter to make it 10 ma full scale and decreasing the series resistance (with test prods short-circuited) to 150 ohms. The resistance at midscale could be increased to 15 kilohms by increasing the supply voltage to 15 volts and the circuit resistance $R_m + R_f + R_a$ to 15,000 ohms. This system of changing ranges is, of course, rather cumbersome and is not too suitable for a practical multirange ohmmeter. It has the serious disadvantage of not maintaining a constant zero adjustment when switching ranges.

The principle of operation for a practical multirange ohmmeter is illustrated in Fig. 1-11. This ohmmeter is referred to as the "voltmeter type" or "potentiometer type" because the voltage is measured across a resistance that is in series with the unknown resistance R_u. The voltmeter branch has a total resistance R_v that is in parallel with R_s, so as to give an effective resistance $R_p = R_s R_v/(R_s + R_v)$, which is in series with R_r and any unknown resistance R_u. When the test leads are short-circuited, a current I_1 flows through the series circuit of $R_p + R_r$. This resistance is across a battery of E volts. When the unknown resistance R_u is connected into the circuit by the test leads, the current is reduced to a value I_2. In

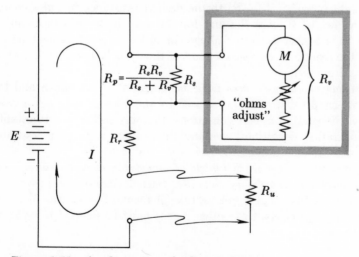

Figure 1-11   An ohmmeter of voltmeter type.

each case the sum of the voltage drops in the circuit is equal to the supply voltage, so that

$$I_1 R_p + I_1 R_r = E$$

$$I_2 R_u + I_2 R_p + I_2 R_r = E$$

and solving these two equations for R_u, one obtains,

$$R_u = (R_p + R_r)\left(\frac{I_1}{I_2} - 1\right) \tag{1-3}$$

Note that the currents in the meter path will be proportional to the circuit currents I_1 and I_2. If the "ohms adjust" resistance is varied until the meter reads full scale with the test leads short-circuited, the meter will have a midscale reading ($I_2 = I_1/2$) when $R_u = R_p + R_r$, a one-third full-scale reading when $R_u = 2(R_p + R_r)$, etc.

If $R_p = 11.5$ ohms and $R_r = 1.0$ ohm, then $R_u = 12.5$ ohms for a midscale meter reading. The meter would be calibrated to read ohms directly. If $R_p + R_r$ is increased to 1250 ohms, the ohms value will equal the meter reading $\times$ 100. In this case, $R_u = 1250$ ohms for a midscale reading if the "ohms adjust" was previously varied so that the meter current was full scale (zero ohms) with the test leads short-circuited.

As the circuit resistance $R_p + R_r$ is increased for measuring larger values of R_u, the circuit current decreases. Consequently, the fraction of circuit current sent through the meter branch must be increased in order for it to read full scale. The range switch, therefore, not only switches the absolute value of $R_p + R_r$ to the desired resistance but also changes relative values of R_s and R_v; and for the very high resistance range it switches in a higher battery voltage, in order to get sufficient current through the meter. A complete circuit of this type is described in Sec. 1-6 for the multimeter.

An ohmmeter is never used while the circuit is in operation, and thus there is no circuit distortion introduced by the measurement. For resistances that depend on circuit conditions, the only solution is to establish normal operating conditions, measure the voltage across the resistance, measure the current through the resistance, and calculate.

The resistance of devices that might be damaged by moderate currents cannot be measured with an ordinary ohmmeter. Such devices include meter movements and some fuses, lights, relays, tube filaments, diodes, etc. When the danger of damage exists, some other means must be devised to make the measurement.

1-6 The Multimeter

The multimeter, or VOM (volt-ohm-milliammeter), is usually a moving-coil meter, which, by switching and the proper selection of probe jacks, can be a d-c voltmeter, an a-c voltmeter, a d-c milliammeter, or an ohmmeter. Sometimes a-c current scales are present, and occasionally no a-c scales at all are included. When the device is switched to perform a particular function, the active part of the circuit is similar if not identical to the circuits described in the previous sections. The limitations, precautions, and errors mentioned for each measurement circuit apply to the multimeter as well. In addition, the batteries should be checked frequently, and the instrument should be stored away from corrosive atmospheres for the sake of the switch contacts. The function selector switch of the VOM should always be kept on a high d-c volts scale to avoid: (1) draining batteries by accidental short-circuiting of leads during storage; (2) burning out the rectifier by accidentally connecting to the d-c voltage when on the a-c scale.

The diagrams of all the functions of a commercial VOM (Heathkit VOM, model MM-1) are presented in Fig. 1-12. The "d-c volts" function is shown in Fig. 1-12a. R_{series} is composed of precision resistors in series with the meter. The resistor for the 5-kv d-c range is connected to a separate jack to avoid placing a high voltage directly across the switch contacts. A reversing switch is provided to measure voltages of either polarity without reversing the test leads.

Figure 1-12b illustrates the "a-c volts" function. Metallic instrument rectifiers are connected as a double half-wave rectifier, as explained in Sec. 1-3. The finite resistances of these rectifiers will reduce the ohms per volt rating of the meter for a-c measurements. The 2725-ohm resistor is used to reduce further the ohms per volt rating to the convenient value of 5000 ohms/volt and to correct the scale to rms instead of average values for sine-wave voltages.

Figure 1-12c illustrates the "d-c current" function. Note that this is the Ayrton-shunt arrangement described in Sec. 1-3. The 2484-ohm resistor is *shorted*[13] out for all current ranges except the 150-μa range. On this range, the 5000-ohm meter branch is shunted by 2500 ohms (2484 + 16), so that one-third of the current goes through the 50-μa meter. To measure the 0.5- and 15-amp currents, the meter is set on the 150-ma range, and separate jacks are used for the leads to avoid passing large currents through the switch contacts.

Figure 1-12d illustrates the "ohms function." It is the voltmeter-type circuit described in Sec. 1-5 and illustrated in Fig. 1-11. The battery volt-

---

[13] A *short* (short circuit) between two points is a direct, no-resistance connection. To short out a component, a wire is connected in parallel with it.

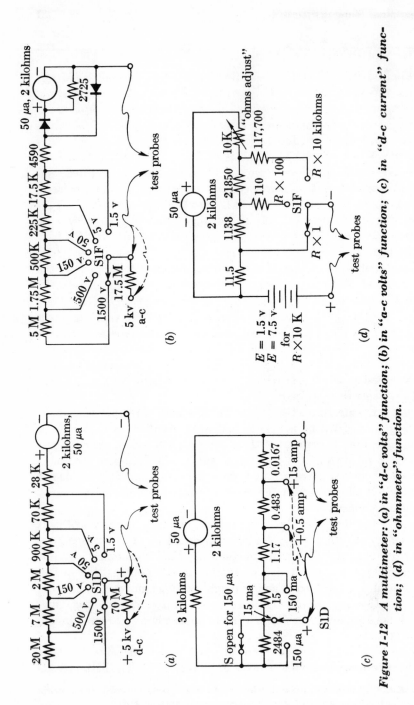

Figure 1-12 A multimeter: (a) in "d-c volts" function; (b) in "a-c volts" function; (c) in "d-c current" function; (d) in "ohmmeter" function.

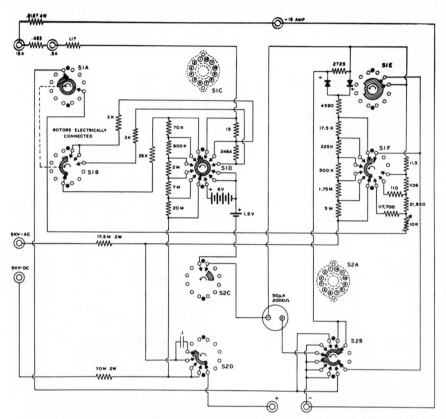

Figure 1-13   Circuit diagram of a multimeter. (Courtesy of Heath Co., Benton Harbor, Mich.)

age is 1.5 volts for the $R \times 1$ and the $R \times 100$ positions, and it is 7.5 volts for the $R \times 10K$ position. The resistance values at midscale deflection are 12.5 ohms, 1.25 kilohms, and 125 kilohms, respectively. At these readings, the current through the meter is 25 μa.

The complete diagram of the Heathkit multimeter is given in Fig. 1-13, showing all the circuits of Fig. 1-12 combined in one figure, and showing the connections to the rotary switches. This diagram will provide good practice in "reading" circuit diagrams.

1-7   The Vacuum-Tube Voltmeter (VTVM)

The error in voltage measurements discussed in Sec. 1-1 is due to the fact that the voltage source to be measured must supply the power to move

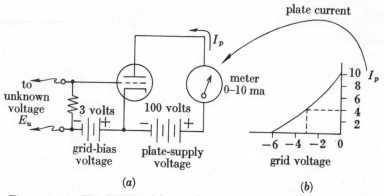

Figure 1-14   The VTVM: (a) simple vacuum-tube voltmeter; (b) triode plate current vs. grid voltage.

the needle of the voltmeter. It is possible to use an *amplifier*[14] so that the measured voltage is used only to control the current supplied to the meter from another source of power. If a vacuum-tube amplifier is used, the resulting device is called a vacuum-tube voltmeter (VTVM). A simple d-c vacuum-tube voltmeter is shown in Fig. 1-14a. The plate current as a function of the grid voltage for a typical vacuum triode is shown in Fig. 1-14b. It can be seen from this transfer characteristic that the voltage applied between the grid and the cathode will control the current through a meter that is inserted in the plate circuit. Note also that the control-grid voltages are all negative with respect to the cathode. If the meter is to indicate zero volts at the left, it is necessary to add a bias voltage in series with the unknown voltage. The bias voltage is negative and is adjusted so that, when the unknown voltage is zero, no current flows in the plate circuit and the meter reads zero.

The circuit described has a limited range of input voltages, is nonlinear at the ends of the transfer characteristic, and, once calibrated, requires that the tube maintain constant characteristics. These limitations can be overcome to a great extent by more complex circuits. However, the principle of the operation of all VTVM's is the same as that of Fig. 1-14a. It is characteristic of VTVM's that the zero adjustment must be made rather frequently.

The *loading*[15] effect on the circuit to be measured is greatly reduced by using a vacuum-tube voltmeter, but it is not entirely eliminated. The grid,

[14] *Amplifiers* are defined and described in detail in Chaps. 3 and 4.
[15] A *load* is a device or element which will draw current from a voltage source. As explained in Sec. 1-1, the connection of a load will have the effect of reducing the voltage.

because of its physical placement, collects a small percentage of the electrons as they stream past it to the plate. These electrons must be returned to the cathode through the external circuit, because, if they were allowed to accumulate on the grid, their negative charge would change the potential of the grid. Therefore, a resistor is placed in the circuit between the grid and the bias voltage to accommodate the "grid current." The value of this resistor becomes the input resistance of the meter. Fortunately this resistance can be quite high. In most VTVM's it is 10 megohms and is constant for all voltage ranges. This is a considerable improvement over even a commercial VOM of 20,000 ohms/volt, whose resistance on the 3-volt scale would be only 60,000 ohms.

The VTVM can measure a-c voltages as well as d-c by rectifying the input voltage. Many VTVM's also measure resistance using the circuit described in Sec. 1-5. Most VTVM's use vacuum diodes to rectify the a-c voltage for the a-c scales. The vacuum diode will rectify much higher frequencies than the rectifiers used in most a-c voltmeters. Therefore, the range of frequencies that can be measured with the VTVM is much greater (up to the order of 5 Mc) than that of ordinary a-c voltmeters.

Because of the very high input resistance of the VTVM, it is possible to make the meter *respond to the peak* value of the a-c voltage being measured. The scale, however, is often *calibrated in rms* values as in the case of the a-c voltmeter. For this reason the scale calibration of the VTVM will be correct only for sinusoidal a-c voltage. The correct peak value of any shape of alternating current can be determined by multiplying the indicated value by 1.414. The effective *capacitance*[16] between the input terminals of the VTVM must be considered when one measures a-c voltages of very high frequency. It is possible at high frequencies that this capacitance can lower the effective input *impedance*[17] of the VTVM considerably. This will result in an error of measurement of the type discussed in Sec. 1-1.

The vacuum-tube electrometer is a vacuum-tube voltmeter which uses a special tube for the input. This tube is constructed and operated in such a way that the fraction of electrons that encounter the grid is extremely small. Such a tube is called an electrometer tube. Commercial electrometers are available with input resistances over 10^{14} ohms. Electrometers are much more expensive than and not so rugged as an ordinary VTVM. However, they are essential for voltage measurements where even small currents cause difficulties in the measured circuit. Such measurements include the voltage across a charged capacitor and the determination of the potential of a high-impedance glass pH electrode. Electrometers can also be used to measure the values of very high resistances (up to 10^{14} ohms).

[16] *Capacitance* and capacitive circuits are discussed in Supplement 3.

[17] *Impedance* is the opposition to the flow of *alternating* current offered by a circuit or component. Impedance is a complex quantity as described in Supplement 3, is often a function of frequency, and is measured in ohms.

1-8   The Oscilloscope

The cathode-ray tube (CRT) is the indicating device for an oscilloscope in the same sense that the moving-coil meter is the indicating device for a voltmeter. The tube consists of the so-called "electron gun," shown in Fig. 1-15a, and the deflection plates (Fig. 1-15c) combined in a vacuum tube with a fluorescent screen on the enlarged end, as shown in Fig. 1-15b. The purpose of the electron gun is to produce a beam of electrons that are focused to a sharp point at the fluorescent screen. The end of the tube is coated with various phosphors which emit visible phosphorescent radiation at the point of bombardment with electrons. The intensity of the emitted visible light depends on the number of electrons per unit time striking a given area of the screen; the larger the number, the more intense the light. By partially surrounding the cathode with a metal grid, and applying a voltage so that the grid is negative with respect to the cathode, the rate of electron flow through the grid can be regulated. The more negative the grid potential, the greater the repulsion of electrons, the fewer the electrons reaching the fluorescent screen, and the lower the intensity of the visible light spot. In other words, a variable grid-cathode voltage supply acts as the "intensity control."

To obtain the point source of electrons on the screen, it is necessary to focus and accelerate the electrons by two anodes that are at high positive potentials with respect to the cathode. For a typical 5-in. tube, the second anode is often 2000 volts more positive than the cathode, and the first anode about 350 to 750 volts more positive. The electrostatic field that exists between the two hollow cylindrical anodes provides the necessary focusing of the electron beam. The diverging electrons entering the first hollow anode are forced to converge because of the field that exists between the first and second anode. The desired focus point is, of course, the fluorescent screen, and the correct focus can be obtained by varying the voltage on one anode with respect to the other. The "focus control" is another front-panel adjustment on the oscilloscope.

The electron beam then passes through the first set of deflection plates that are mounted in the horizontal plane, as shown in Fig. 1-15c. When a voltage is applied across the plates, the electron beam will be deflected toward the more positive plate to provide a vertical deflection on the fluorescent screen. These plates are referred to as the "vertical deflection plates." Next, the beam passes between two plates mounted perpendicular to the first set, and a voltage difference between these plates causes a horizontal deflection of the beam. Therefore, the position of the electron beam (and the light spot on the screen) at any moment depends on the instantaneous voltages across the two sets of plates.

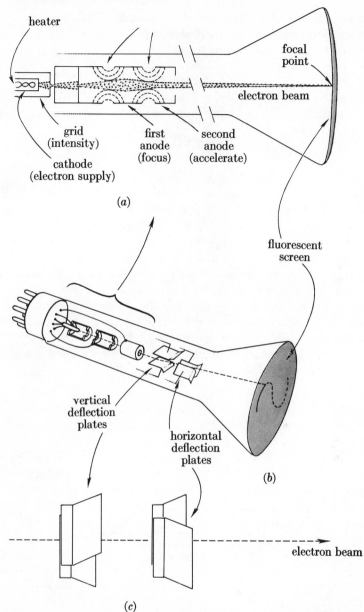

heater

focal
point

electron beam

grid
(intensity)

first
anode
(focus)

second
anode
(accelerate)

cathode
(electron supply)

(a)

fluorescent
screen

vertical
deflection
plates

horizontal
deflection
plates

(b)

electron beam

(c)

*Figure 1-15   The cathode-ray tube: (a) electron gun; (b) cathode-ray
tube; (c) deflection plates.*

Linear Sweep for Horizontal Deflection Plates. For most applications of the oscilloscope, the voltage applied between the horizontal deflection plates produces a "linear trace." That is, the light spot is moved horizontally across the face of the tube at a uniform rate. The linear trace is important because it provides a uniform time scale against which another voltage can be plotted, by applying it across the vertical deflection plates. This is illustrated in Fig. 1-16, where a "sawtooth" voltage provides the linear horizontal movement of the electron beam, the voltage applied to the vertical deflection plates is plotted vs. time, and the curve is displayed on the screen.

It is often stated that the electron beam is swept across the screen at a uniform rate, and it is customary to refer to the sawtooth waveform as a "sweep." The oscillator circuit that produces the sweep is called the "sweep generator." Various types of sweep generators will be discussed in subsequent chapters. It is apparent, though, that the rate of change of voltage must be very uniform in order to obtain a reliable time base. Good linearity of the sweep is a major requirement for a reliable oscilloscope. At the end of the sweep the electron beam is moved back across the screen to the starting point by lowering the sweep voltage back to zero. The finite time required to change the sweep voltage back to the starting value can cause a visible trace of low intensity, known as the "retrace" or "flyback." It is possible to blank out the retrace by applying a negative grid voltage during this short time interval.

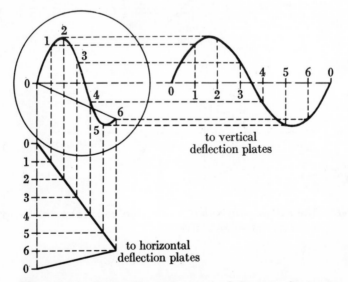

Figure 1-16   Sawtooth vs. sine wave of the same frequency.

Basic Components of an Oscilloscope.   Besides the cathode-ray tube and sweep generator, other circuits are required to make up an oscilloscope.   A block diagram is shown in Fig. 1-17.   The voltage required to give a sensible deflection of the electron beam is usually much higher than the voltage levels that are measured.   For this reason, amplifiers are used to increase the signal voltage to a level required by the deflection plates. The quality and type of oscilloscope are greatly dependent on its amplifiers.   A frequency response of 20 cycles to 1 Mc is common.   Very high frequency and d-c amplifiers are also available in some oscilloscopes, usually for a considerable increase in cost.   Since the oscilloscope uses a vacuum-tube input circuit, its effect on the circuit being measured is the same as for a VTVM with respect to resistance and capacitance.   The input resistance is usually 1 to 10 megohms.

The amplitude-time curve (called the waveshape) can be continuously displayed on the CRT screen only if the measured voltage is continuous and repetitive.   So that repetitive displays are superimposed, the sweep generator must oscillate at exactly the same frequency as the repetition rate of the signal, or some submultiple thereof.   The sweep generator is synchronized to the signal frequency by feeding the input waveform to the sweep generator in such a way that it controls the repetition rate.   This type of sweep generator is called a *synchronized sweep* and is found in many oscilloscopes.   The "sync" control is often a front-panel adjustment. The relationship of the sweep signal and the input waveform is shown in Fig. 1-18.   The sweep rate for a stable display depends on the frequency of the signal, and thus the exact time relationship between various parts of the trace is not known.   Coarse and fine adjustments to vary the sweep rate are on the front panel.

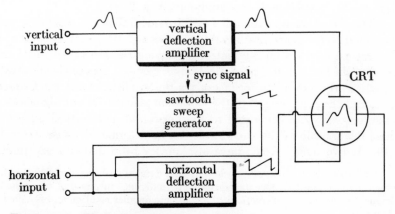

Figure 1-17   Block diagram of an oscilloscope.

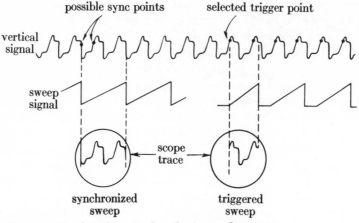

Figure 1-18   *Synchronized and triggered sweeps.*

For measurements of time, a *triggered sweep* is desirable. With this type of sweep, you select the particular voltage and slope of the incoming waveform which you would like to have "trigger" the sweep. When this point in the waveform occurs, the electron beam moves horizontally across the CRT at a rate which you have selected. When the scan is complete, the sweep circuit is receptive to the next trigger point in the wave train (see Fig. 1-18). This type of sweep is calibrated in time per division and can be used for time measurement. It can also be used to observe single, as well as repetitive, phenomena. Many general-purpose research oscilloscopes today have a triggered sweep, because of its great usefulness.

Although the power supplies are not shown on the block diagram, they are essential for the operation of the scope. Their characteristics will be more readily appreciated after studying Chap. 2.

The Oscilloscope as an *x-y* Plotter. When a second signal is connected to the horizontal amplifier, instead of the sweep generator, the oscilloscope becomes an *x-y* plotter displaying the functional relationship between the horizontal- and vertical-input signals. This mode of operation is particularly convenient for measuring the amplitude ratio, the frequency ratio, and the *phase angle*[18] of the two input signals. If two signals of the same frequency are connected to the horizontal and vertical inputs, the phase relationship of the two signals can be determined, as shown in Fig. 1-19. If two signals which have a frequency ratio that can be expressed

[18] *Phase* is the fraction of a cycle that an a-c signal is at any instant away from some reference point on the waveform. The difference in phase of two signals is measured in degrees or in fractions of a complete angular rotation and is called the *phase angle*.

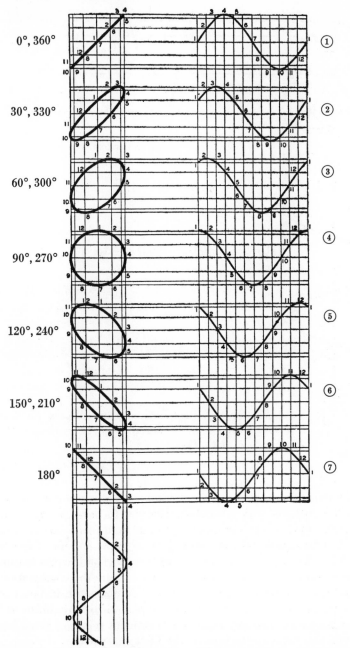

Figure 1-19 Lissajous figures indicating phase difference. (From "Radar Electronic Fundamentals," U.S. Government Printing Office, Washington, D.C., 1944.)

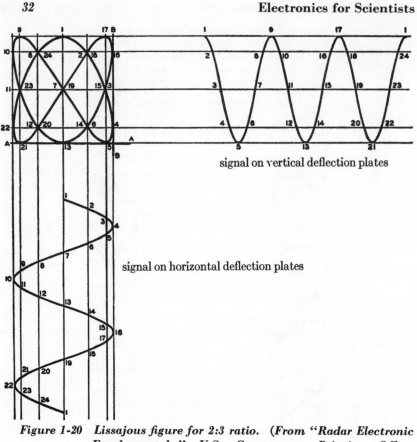

signal on vertical deflection plates

signal on horizontal deflection plates

Figure 1-20   Lissajous figure for 2:3 ratio.   (From "Radar Electronic Fundamentals," U.S. Government Printing Office, Washington, D.C., 1944.)

in a small whole number or a simple fraction are applied to the horizontal and vertical inputs, patterns are obtained similar to those of Figs. 1-20 to 1-22.   Patterns of this type are called Lissajous figures and can be used to determine the frequency ratio, as shown.   For example, in Fig. 1-20 each of the points (1, 2, 3, ..., etc.) indicates an identical time for the signals applied to the horizontal and vertical deflection plates.   Since the combination of the horizontal and vertical applied voltages determines the instantaneous position of the electron beam, it is possible to plot the beam position at the equal-time points and thereby trace the movement of the electron beam across the face of the scope to provide the Lissajous pattern.   In Fig. 1-20 there are two complete sine waves on the horizontal plates over the same time in which there are three complete sine waves on the vertical plates, to provide a pattern that indicates a 2:3 frequency ratio.

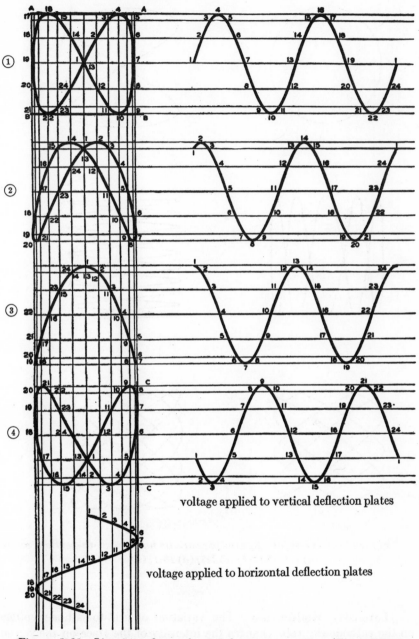

voltage applied to vertical deflection plates

voltage applied to horizontal deflection plates

Figure 1-21 Lissajous figure for 1:2 frequency ratio. (From "Radar Electronic Fundamentals," U.S. Government Printing Office, Washington, D.C., 1944.)

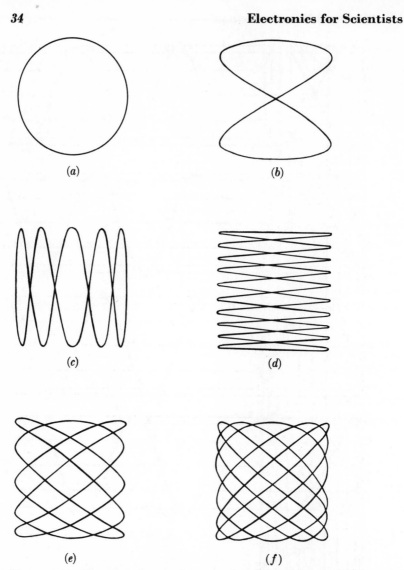

Figure 1-22   Lissajous figures for various horizontal-to-vertical ratios:
(a) 1:1; (b) 2:1; (c) 1:5; (d) 10:1; (e) 5:3; (f) 6:5.

Intensity Modulation. The variation of grid-to-cathode voltage on the cathode-ray tube changes the intensity of the trace on the screen. This intensity modulation of a CRT can be a useful variable in laboratory instrumentation, as well as in the popular television. One application is "blanking" from the screen an unwanted portion of the pattern. An il-

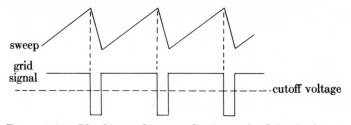

Figure 1-23 *Blanking voltage to eliminate the flyback of sweep voltage from the oscilloscope screen.*

lustration, already mentioned, is the elimination of the flyback of a sweep voltage, as shown in Fig. 1-23. A negative pulse is applied to the grid so that electrons do not reach the screen for the time interval of the flyback. Another useful application of intensity modulation is the display of time markers on the screen. Either positive pulses or negative pulses could be applied to the grid at known time intervals. If positive pulses are applied to the grid, the intensity of a sweep will be increased periodically, to make a trace with bright spots, as shown in Fig. 1-24.

Intensity modulation has also been used in determining frequency ratios. As shown in Fig. 1-19, when two sine waves are the same frequency

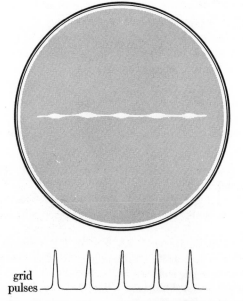

Figure 1-24 *Time markers displayed on a screen by grid modulation.*

Figure 1-25   *Frequency-ratio determination by intensity modulation of circular sweep.*

and are 90° out of phase, they can trace a circle on the screen, if one is applied to the horizontal input and the other to the vertical input. The time for the electron beam to travel once around the circle is the reciprocal of the oscillator frequency. Now, if an alternating voltage is applied to the grid, the beam will be cut off when the grid goes negative and will make a visible trace when the grid swings positive. If the frequency of the grid-voltage signal is four times the frequency of the circular trace, a pattern will be obtained as shown in Fig. 1-25. It is easy to determine from the trace that the frequency ratio for this example is 4:1.

References
The following books contain additional information. The first two are written on a moderately advanced level.

Hill, W. R., "Electronics in Engineering," McGraw-Hill, New York, 1961. Especially for its section on the oscilloscope.

Soisson, H. E., "Electronic Measuring Instruments," McGraw-Hill, New York, 1961. Describes meter movements, recording galvanometer, multimeters, and the VTVM.

"Theory and Use of Electronic Test Equipment," TM 11-664, U.S. Government Printing Office, Washington, D.C., 1952. Especially good and thorough coverage of the basic meter movements and their applications.

"Cathode-Ray Tubes and Their Associated Circuits," TM 11-671, U.S. Government Printing Office, Washington, D.C., 1951.

"Radar Electronic Fundamentals," NAVSHIPS 900,016, U.S. Government Printing Office, Washington, D.C., 1944. Contains 65 pages on the CRT, the oscilloscope, and oscilloscopic measurements.

"The Radio Amateur's Handbook," published annually by the American Radio Relay League, West Hartford, Conn. The chapter on measurements presents the most basic information in an easily understood form.

Problems

1-1 A current meter has a resistance of 200 ohms and deflects half-scale when a 50-mv source is applied across its terminals. What is the full-scale current sensitivity? *Ans.:* 500 μa full scale

1-2 Variations in the voltage across the load shown in Fig. P1-2 will seriously disturb the load. The load has a nominal resistance of about 12 ohms. The following three current meters are available; all are accurate to 2 per cent. Which meters should be used to obtain the best accuracy with the least disturbing effect? Calculate the internal resistance and voltage error for each: (*a*) properly shunted 50-μa, 2-kilohm meter movement; (*b*) the multimeter of Fig. 1-12*c*; (*c*) a 1-amp, 0.1-ohm meter movement.

Ans.: (*c*) 0.1 ohm, 0.05 volt. (*a*) and (*b*) have 0.1-volt and 0.25-volt errors, respectively.

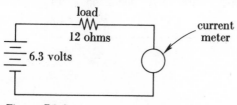

Figure P1-2

1-3 For an Ayrton shunt similar to that shown in Fig. 1-6*b*, what values of r_1, r_2, and r_3 must be used with a 500-μa, 200-ohm meter movement to provide scales of 1 ma, 10 ma, and 100 ma? (r_4 in Fig. 1-6*b* is not used for a 3-range shunt.)

Ans.: $r_3 = 180$ ohms; $r_2 = 18$ ohms; $r_1 = 2$ ohms

1-4 (*a*) What is the basic current sensitivity of the meter movement in a 100,000-ohms/volt voltmeter? (*b*) The meter movement reads 5 μa when connected to a source having a voltage of 0.1 volt and an internal resistance of 10 kilohms. What is the meter resistance? (*c*) What value of R_s must be used to make this meter a 1-volt voltmeter? (*d*) For the voltmeter constructed in (*c*), what is the percentage error observed when measuring a 1-volt source whose resistance is 10 kilohms? *Ans.:* (*a*) 10 μa; (*b*) 10 kilohms; (*c*) 90,000 ohms; (*d*) 9 per cent

1-5 Show that the simple ohmmeter of Fig. 1-10 changes scale calibration as the battery voltage decreases.

1-6 Show that the multimeter circuit of Fig. 1-12*a* has the voltage ranges indicated. For example, verify the 5-kv and the 1.5-volt ranges.

1-7 Using the 5-kv rms setting of Fig. 1-12*b*, calculate the full-scale rms current sensitivity of the circuit consisting of the meter, the two diodes, and the 2725-ohm resistor.   *Ans.:* 200 μa rms

1-8 A Heathkit VTVM, model 1M-11, is shown in the "ohms" position in Fig. P1-8. When $R_x = \infty$, the voltmeter indicates the battery reading as full scale. When $R_x = 0$, the voltmeter reads 0. (*a*) In the "$R \times 1000$" position, what numerical reading is indicated on the dial at the one-half deflection point? (*b*) To obtain the same reading on the "$\times 1$ meg" position, what must R_x be? (*c*) The resistance of the voltmeter must be greater than what value to obtain 2 per cent accuracy? (*d*) If the voltmeter deflects half scale with $R_x = 10$ ohms on the "$R \times 1$" position, what is the internal resistance of the battery and test leads? What difficulties would be encountered in designing an "$R \times 0.1$" position? (*e*) Is the half-scale deflection value independent of E when the meter is properly adjusted?

Ans.: (*a*) 10; (*b*) 10 megohms; (*c*) 500 megohms; (*d*) 0.9 ohms; (*e*) yes

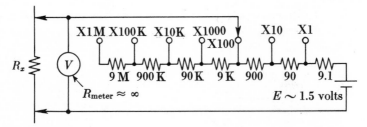

Figure P1-8

1-9 In the measurement of pH of a solution, a glass electrode whose internal resistance may be from 10 to 1000 megohms is used. Various types of electrometer circuits are used for these measurements. The full-scale meter deflection is usually about 500 mv. What is the maximum allowable input current and minimum input resistance that the electrometer may have to avoid errors greater than 1 per cent?

Ans.: $I_{max} = 5 \times 10^{-12}$ amp; $R_{min} = 100 \times 1000$ megohms $= 10^{11}$ ohms

1-10 An oscilloscope is calibrated for vertical sensitivity by a 1-kc sine-wave source whose output resistance is 10 kilohms. The scope has an input impedance of 1 megohm shunted by 47 pf. At what frequency will a 30 per cent error result?

Ans.: When $X_c = 10$ kilohms a 30 per cent error results, and $f = 1/(2\pi \times 10^4 \times 47 \times 10^{-12}) = 340$ kc

1-11 Show by drawing the sweep and signal waveforms that a triggered-sweep oscilloscope can be used to observe a fraction of the cycle while a recurrent-sweep oscilloscope cannot.

1-12 If the 60-cps line frequency is considered to be a standard, approximately what upper and lower frequency limits may be measured by using Lissajous figures? What are the limiting factors?   *Ans.:* 600 and 6 cps

1-13 Figure P1-13 indicates a Lissajous figure obtained in phase measurements. To calculate the phase angle ϕ from a given pattern, the following equation may be used:

$$\phi = \arcsin (a/b) - 2n\pi$$

where $n = 0, 1, 2$, etc. Verify this equation.
[*Hint:* Consider that the vertical voltage is given by $V = b \sin (2\pi ft + \phi)$, the horizontal voltage is given by $H = c \sin (2\pi ft)$ and, when $H = 0$, $V = a$.]

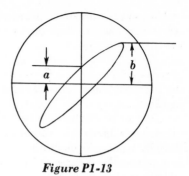

Figure P1-13

EXPERIMENTS

The vacuum-tube voltmeter, volt-ohm milliammeter, oscilloscope, sine-square signal generator, and voltage reference source are introduced in the following experiments, and all devices are checked for calibration. These test instruments are used repeatedly for experiments in subsequent chapters and a familiarity with their capabilities, shortcomings, and accuracy should be obtained now. An expanded-range current meter and a voltmeter are made from a basic 1-ma meter. The constructed voltmeter is compared with the standard meters in respect to loading a measured source. Some problems of a-c measurements are experimentally observed with the various meters. The oscilloscope is used as an x-y plotter, and several Lissajous figures are observed in the process of calibrating the signal generator.

Expt. 1-1 Equipment Check

a. Vacuum-Tube Voltmeter (VTVM) Check. Put the VTVM in operating position. Before turning on, check to see that the meter reads zero. If not, carefully turn the set screw on the meter face using a screwdriver. This adjustment is only made with the meter turned off and is required very infrequently.

Turn the vacuum-tube voltmeter on. Set the function selector switch on the d-c+ position. Wait a minute until the meter needle comes to a steady position. Adjust the meter zero with the zero adjust control. This adjustment is required frequently.

b. The Voltage Reference Source (VRS). In the experiments to follow, the voltage reference source will be used for four very important functions, as described in Supplement 1. The circuit is basically a voltage divider across a regulated d-c voltage. It has four basic voltage ranges of 100, 1000, 10^4, and 10^5 mv, which are selected by the range switch. The actual output voltage in millivolts is the sum of the voltages indicated by the coarse and fine voltage controls times the factor on the range switch. The coarse and fine dials are labeled so that in the ×1 position they are direct reading in millivolts and in the ×1000 position they are direct reading in volts. The polarity of the voltage at the output terminals may be reversed by a polarity switch. The position of the output switch determines the function of the unit. The voltage reference source will be used to provide a standard d-c voltage for calibration in STD VOLT position, compare the reference voltage with a d-c signal voltage in the SUM-DIFF position, provide a low-voltage bias supply in the STD VOLT position, and provide a calibrated bucking voltage in the SUM-DIFF position.

In the SIGNAL position the signal voltage is connected directly to the output terminals; by depressing the spring-return ZERO switch, the output is shorted in all function positions. This ZERO switch is for convenience of operation in many applications.

The a-c on-off switch of the VRS is part of the OUTPUT selector switch. For maximum stability, the unit should be left on during the entire working period. Very little power is consumed.

Adjust the voltage of the VRS to +12 volts. (RANGE ×1000, COARSE voltage control at 10, FINE voltage control at 2.0, POLARITY "normal," OUTPUT at STD VOLT.) Switch the VTVM to the 15-volt range, and readjust the zero. Measure the output voltage of the VRS with the VTVM. Connect the common lead to the black output terminal and the probe to the red output terminal. (Be sure that you have the proper leads, or that your probe switch is in the proper position for a d-c voltage measurement.) Don't be concerned about small errors, because the calibration of neither unit has been checked.

c. Oscilloscope Check. An oscilloscope with the following characteristics is required for these experiments: identical horizontal and vertical amplifiers for x-y plotting; d-c coupled amplifiers for d-c measurements, sensitivity of at least 1 volt full-scale deflection. Other required characteristics are common to all standard scopes.

The check-out procedure is described for the Heathkit IO-10. For other oscilloscopes, refer to your instruction manual. Turn the FREQUENCY control to the 50—500 position. Turn the HORIZONTAL attenuator to ×1 and the HORIZONTAL gain control full clockwise. Turn the INTENSITY control through half its rotation. Put the HOR CEN control approximately at its midpoint. Turn the VERT CEN control until a horizontal line appears on the screen. If none appears, increase the INTENSITY adjustment and repeat.

Turn down the HORIZONTAL gain until the sweep line is confined to the screen. Use the FOCUS control to obtain a sharp line. Use the HOR CEN control to center the line horizontally.

Connect the output of the VRS to the VERT IN terminals of the oscilloscope, using banana plug patch cords. Adjust the VRS output voltage to 0 volts, on the RANGE ×1000, and in the STD VOLT position. Turn the oscilloscope VERTICAL attenuator to ×10 DC, the VERTICAL gain control full clockwise, and the VERT CEN control so that the line is in the center of the screen. Now vary the FINE control of the VRS until the sweep moves from the center to the top ruled line on the screen. Press the ZERO switch and note the vertical deflection of the line back to the center. Reverse the polarity of the VRS output and note the vertical displacement of the line from the top to the bottom ruled lines: The magnitude of the deflection is proportional to the magnitude of the input voltage and VERTICAL gain of the oscilloscope.

Disconnect the horizontal sweep by switching the FREQUENCY switch to HOR IN. Connect the reference voltage output to the HOR IN terminals, adjust the HORIZONTAL attenuator and gain controls, and observe the horizontal deflection of the dot as done above for the line.

d. Sine-Square Wave Generator Check. The sine-square generator contains a sine-wave oscillator (Chap. 5) whose frequency is determined by the position of the FREQ MULTIPLIER and FREQUENCY controls. The sine-wave output is divided, and the fraction of voltage available at the output is selected by a RANGE switch and the AMPLITUDE control. These controls are roughly calibrated in volts rms. The output of the sine-wave oscillator is also fed to a squaring circuit (Chap. 9) to provide a square-wave signal that is divided so that the magnitude of the square wave at the output can be selected in a similar manner as the sine-wave output. The square-wave output is roughly calibrated in volts peak-to-peak. The sine- and square-wave outputs are electrically independent but necessarily the same frequency.

Turn on the signal generator. Turn the FREQ MULTIPLIER switch to 10, the FREQUENCY control to 100, the sine-wave RANGE switch to 10 volts and the AMPLITUDE control about two-tenths of full amplitude. Turn the scope FREQUENCY control to the 50—500 position. Adjust the HORIZONTAL and VERTICAL controls so that the sweep line is confined to the screen and roughly centered. Connect the sine-wave output terminals to the VERT IN terminals of the scope. Adjust the scope FINE frequency control until the sine-wave pattern is stationary. Count the number of cycles observed. Rotate the FINE frequency control clockwise until the signal is again stationary. Note the new number of cycles observed. Note that the signal voltage alternates equally each side of zero.

Transfer the scope leads to the square-wave output terminals and observe the output waveform. Note that the waveform is not symmetrical about the zero line. Vary the square-wave AMPLITUDE control and observe that the bottom of the square wave remains on the zero line. Turn the VERTICAL attenuator to ×10 AC and observe that the square wave is symmetrical about the zero line. Again vary the square-wave AMPLITUDE control. The AC position on the scope input attenuator places a capacitor in series with the input signal and thus blocks any d-c signal.

Expt. 1-2 D-C Calibration

To take full advantage of measurement equipment, it is necessary to put it and keep it in calibration. Even the calibration of new equipment should be checked; and the aging of components causes the equipment to drift out of calibration. The following calibration procedure is recommended for the measurement equipment used in these experiments.

a. Calibration of the Voltage Reference Supply. The voltage of mercury cells (Sec. 2-8) is very reproducible at 1.34 volts from one unit to the next and is very constant during its life. As such it is a good standard for calibrating test equipment to within 1 per cent. The mercury cell will be used to calibrate the voltage reference source. The voltage regulator in this source is very stable and will require only infrequent checks once calibrated. The voltage reference source then becomes a suitable secondary standard for the continuing calibration of the other test equipment. Thus the danger of calibrating the equipment with an exhausted cell is avoided. Because precision resistors are used in the reference supply, the calibration at one value calibrates all values indirectly. Thus standard voltages from zero to 100 volts are available for calibrating the various ranges of the test equipment.

Connect the mercury cell to the signal terminals of the VRS. (Observe the polarity markings.) Adjust the VRS to 1.34 volts (RANGE ×100, COARSE at 10, FINE at 3.4). Switch the OUTPUT function to the SUM-DIFF position, and the POLARITY to DIFF position. Connect the VTVM to the output terminals. Put the VTVM on the 1.5-volt d-c range; depress the ZERO switch on the VRS and move the ZERO adjust knob on the VTVM so that its zero is at an arbitrary reference position near midscale. If there is any difference voltage between the mercury cell and the 1.34 volts from the VRS, adjust the VRS CALIBRATE control (screwdriver adjust on back of unit) so that the VTVM returns to the arbitrary preset zero position. Alternately depress and release the ZERO switch to detect any small difference voltage. When properly calibrated, the VTVM reading should remain constant when the ZERO is alternately depressed and released. Return the VRS voltage to zero and remove the mercury cell.

b. Calibration of the VTVM. Select a range on the VTVM between 1 and 3 volts, and set the VTVM ZERO adjust at the zero dial reading. Switch the POLARITY of the VRS to the NORMAL position, turn the OUTPUT function to STD VOLT position, and adjust the RANGE, COARSE, and FINE controls to the nominal full-scale voltage of the VTVM. If the VTVM does not read the applied full-scale voltage, adjust the d-c calibrate control so that it does. (See the instruction manual for the location of this control.)

c. Checking the Accuracy of the VOM. Multimeters are made with precision resistors and a calibrated meter movement. Often no provision is made for calibration adjustment. Still, it is desirable to check the accuracy of the meter from time to time. Measure several d-c voltages from the reference voltage source to check the meter accuracy.

d. Calibration of the Oscilloscope Deflection. The position of zero signal deflection, as set by the VERT CEN control, should not change when the VERTICAL attenuator and gain controls are varied. If the zero does shift, an adjustment of the vertical d-c balance control is required. If this adjustment is not on the front panel, its position can be determined by reference to the instruction manual. To adjust the d-c balance, turn the VERTICAL gain control completely counterclockwise and adjust the zero position with the VERT CEN control to the center horizontal line. Turn the VERTICAL gain control full clockwise and adjust the d-c balance control to return the beam to the zero position. The d-c balance of the horizontal amplifier is done similarly, with the horizontal sweep disconnected.

Use the reference voltage source to calibrate the vertical deflection of the oscilloscope to 1 volt per division. (Use the VERTICAL attenuator and gain controls. Recheck the zero often.) Thus the vertical deflection of the oscilloscope may be calibrated for any voltage range. The calibration of the oscilloscope will be done in this way throughout the experiments prior to each measurement.

e. Calibrated Range Extension for a Basic Current Meter. In order to calculate the correct shunt resistance for the range extension of a current meter (Sec. 1-3), it is necessary to know the resistance of the meter movement. In preparation for the shunting of a meter, the resistance of the movement will be determined. *An ohmmeter should not be used.* One method of making the measurement is to determine the shunt resistance necessary to double the current range of the meter. The variable reference voltage is used as a current source; the decade resistance box is used as the meter shunt. The procedure is described for a 1-ma meter movement.

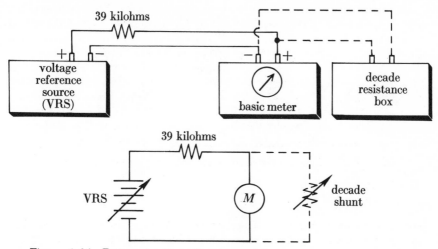

Figure 1-26   Determination of meter resistance.

Connect the meter to the reference source as shown in Fig. 1-26. For information on the method of connecting components within the recommended system, see Supplement 1. For a physical description and an explanation of the markings on standard electrical components, see Supplements 2 and 3.

Adjust the output of the reference source so that a full-scale current flows through the unshunted meter. Now connect the decade box to shunt the meter movement. Find the setting of the decade box for a meter reading of exactly half scale. R_{meter} will then equal R_{decade}.

Calculate the value of the shunt resistance necessary to give a full-scale deflection sensitivity of either 1.5 or 2 ma (depending on the markings on the meter face for convenience of reading). Locate a resistor of the right size and connect it as a shunt. If the exact size is not available, calculate the error in using the closest available size. Remember most composition resistors have a tolerance of ±10 per cent, unless specified as precision resistors; the meter movement is generally accurate to 2 per cent. Note the meter reading of the 1-ma current from the reference voltage source. If the shunt resistance is too large (shunted meter reading too high), the shunt value may be trimmed with a parallel resistance.

Prepare a 5-ma shunt using resistance wire, following the same general procedure. The calculated length of resistance wire may be wound around an insulating plastic or phenolic support to which leads are attached for connection to the meter. The length of resistance wire may be carefully adjusted before final connection by noting the 1-ma deflection of the meter.

Label and set aside these shunts for use in later experiments.

f. Calibrated Voltage Scale for the Basic Current Meter. Calculate the series resistance necessary to make a voltmeter of 10 or 15 volts full-scale deflection from the unshunted 1-ma meter movement. Set the decade resistance box at this value and connect the decade resistance in series with the meter. Use the resulting low-resistance voltmeter to measure 2, 5, and 10 volts from the voltage reference

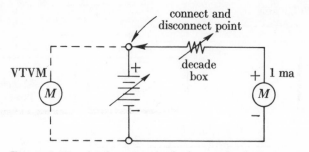

Figure 1-27   A voltmeter made from a basic 1-ma meter.

source, as shown in Fig. 1-27. The readings will be in error due to the 1-ma drain through the internal resistance of the VRS. Connect the VTVM at the output of the VRS, with the low-resistance voltmeter still connected, and compare voltage readings of the two meters for various outputs from the VRS. Now alternately connect and disconnect the low-resistance voltmeter while keeping the VTVM connected to the output of the VRS and observing its reading. Determine the percentage error at each of the above voltages caused by the loading of the low-resistance voltmeter. What is the "ohms/volt" figure of merit for the low-resistance voltmeter constructed above? Note that the observed voltage values on the VTVM should check closely with the dial readings on the VRS when the low-resistance voltmeter is disconnected.

Using the 150-μa current range of the VOM and a 100-kilohm precision resistor in series with one lead, construct a 15-volt full-scale voltmeter. Measure several voltages from the VRS with this voltmeter, and determine the percentage error introduced by its loading the VRS. What is its ohms/volt rating?

Disconnect the 100-kilohm resistor you connected to the VOM lead and switch to the 5-volt scale. Measure 2 and 5 volts with the VOM and VTVM, and observe the change in the VTVM reading when the VOM is alternately connected and disconnected. Note the ohms/volt rating of this voltmeter as printed on the meter face of the VOM. Compare this value with the figures of merit for the other two voltmeters constructed with current meters of 1-ma and 150-μa full-scale sensitivity.

It is important to keep in mind during subsequent experiments two facts demonstrated by the above experiment:

1. The resistance of a VOM at a given range must be sufficiently high compared to the output resistance of the measured source. For sources of high output resistance, the VOM can change the output voltage to give erroneous results.

2. For the voltage at the terminals of the VRS to be accurate within 1 per cent of the dial values, the load should not draw more than about 50 μa on the low ranges.

Expt. 1-3   Resistance Measurements

Measure a wide range of resistances in the resistance *decade* box using the VOM and VTVM. Compare the accuracy of the two meters. Measure some high resistances within the resistance *substitution* box. Which meter is better for this? Be sure the meters are properly adjusted using first an *open* circuit and then a *short* circuit to set ∞ and 0, respectively.

Expt. 1-4   A-C Calibration

a. Oscilloscope. Calibrate the oscilloscope vertical deflection to 20 volts full-scale deflection. Turn the universal power supply (Supplement 1) to the POWER ON position. Always use the least sensitive attenuator position possible to avoid distortion in the scope amplifiers. Switch the scope to A-C INPUT and measure the peak-to-peak voltage from the FILS terminals of the power supply. For convenience of calibration and zero adjustment, the signal from the FILS terminals may be connected to the scope through the SIGNAL terminals on the reference source as shown in Fig. 1-28.

b. VTVM. Switch the VTVM to the 15-volt a-c scale. (Be sure to use the proper leads or probe switch position.) Use the VTVM to measure the voltage at the FILS terminals of the power supply. (It is desirable to leave the scope connected.) Compare the readings from the scope and the *p-p* scale of the VTVM. If they do not agree, adjust the A-C CALIBRATE control of the VTVM. Refer to instruction manual for location.

c. VOM. Calculate the rms value of the voltage at the FILS terminals. Check this with the reading of the rms scale of the VTVM and the VOM.

Expt. 1-5   Nonsinusoidal A-C Measurements

Adjust the frequency of the sine-square generator to 1 kc. Set both the square-wave and sine-wave output voltages at 10 volts peak-to-peak by measuring the outputs with the calibrated oscilloscope. Measure the peak-to-peak value and the rms value of both sine and square waves with the VTVM. Compare the rms readings of the VTVM with those of the VOM. Note the great discrepancy of the VOM reading of the square wave. This is due to the nonsinusoidal wave shape and the d-c component in the square-wave signal. *The VOM should only be used for pure a-c signals, and it is calibrated for sinusoidal wave shapes only.*

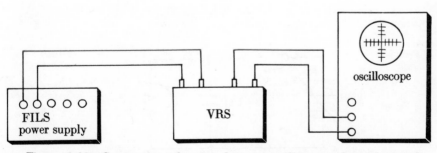

Figure 1-28   Connection of a signal to an oscilloscope through signal input of VRS.

Expt. 1-6   The Oscilloscope as an *x-y* Plotter

In this experiment the frequency dial of the sine-square generator is calibrated
using the line frequency as a standard and the oscilloscope as a comparator. Connect the voltage from the power supply FILS terminals to the scope vertical input
terminals. Connect the sine-wave output of the signal generator to the horizontal
input terminals. Turn the FREQUENCY switch to HOR IN to connect the
generator signal to the horizontal deflection system. Adjust the signal generator
FREQUENCY to about 60 cycles. A circular or elliptical pattern will be observed
when the signal generator frequency is equal to that of the power line. For the
calibration adjustment of the signal generator, refer to the instruction manual.
Vary the frequency of the signal generator and observe the Lissajous figures. Check
whether the observed frequency reading on the signal generator corresponds to the
theoretical multiples or submultiples of the 60-cps line frequency.   The shapes of
the Lissajous patterns for multiples and submultiples of the line frequency are
described in Sec. 1-8 and Figs. 1-20 to 1-22.

Expt. 1-7   Determination of the Input Resistance of a VTVM

Measure the input resistance of the VTVM by observing the rate of discharge
of a 1-μf capacitor through the input resistance of the VTVM, as shown in Fig. 1-29.
Connect point S and adjust the reference supply so that the VTVM reads 8 volts.
Disconnect contact S and measure the time required for the capacitor voltage to
decay to 3 volts, or 37 per cent of the initial value. This time is given by the time
constant τ of the circuit, which is equal to RC (Supplement 3). Therefore, R_{VTVM}
$= \tau/C$.

Repeat the above procedure to measure the input impedance of the oscilloscope.

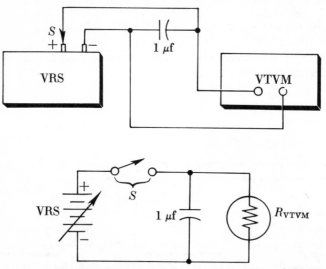

**Figure 1-29   Connections for the determination of the input resistance
of a VTVM.**

chapter two

Power Supplies

In order to operate electronic equipment, it is necessary to have electrical power. This power is provided by a variety of sources. Because of convenience and economy, most instruments are designed to operate from conventional (in the United States) 115-volt and 220-volt 60-cycle a-c voltages. The instrument power supply must convert the a-c line voltage to the d-c voltages and other a-c voltages necessary to operate the devices and circuits within the specific instrument. Since the operation of the instrument depends on the proper supply of voltages and currents, it is important to learn the characteristics of the power sources most commonly encountered. Instrument troubles are frequently found to be failures in the power supply.

2-1 General Considerations

Power supplies used for the operation of transistor circuits usually provide only low d-c voltages of about 5 to 30 volts. Power supplies used for the operation of vacuum-tube circuits generally provide 5-volt a-c and/or 6.3-volt a-c for the tube filaments and d-c voltages of a few hundred volts. The low a-c filament voltages are readily obtained by step-down windings on the *transformers*.[1] The important methods and problems in-

[1] *Transformers* are used to change the voltage level of a-c power with very little power loss. Their operation and characteristics are discussed in Supplement 3.

herent in the conversion of a-c *line*[2] voltages to useful d-c voltages are the major topics for the following discussion and experiments.

For some instruments it is feasible, desirable, or even necessary to use batteries as sources of d-c voltages. Therefore, the characteristics of the common battery types are also presented.

An ideal d-c power supply would have: (1) a constant output voltage regardless of variations in the current required by the load (good *regulation* or low output resistance); (2) a constant output voltage regardless of variations in temperature, a-c line voltage, age of power supply, etc. (good *stability*); and (3) no noise voltage of line or other frequency superimposed on the d-c output (low *ripple*). In addition to these characteristics, the d-c output voltage and the current capability of the power supply must meet the operational requirements of the electronic devices.

2-2   Scheme for Converting A-C Line Voltage to D-C Voltage

The block diagram in Fig. 2-1 illustrates the basic components and functions usually required to convert a-c to a useful d-c voltage. First, a transformer is used to convert the a-c line voltage to more nearly the desired voltage. Next, a rectifier circuit converts the a-c to a *pulsating d-c*[3] voltage. To smooth out the pulsating d-c voltage, a filter network is employed. Sometimes a regulator circuit is added to improve the stability and regulation and further to reduce the ripple of the output voltage. In the following sections, each component of the power supply is discussed.

[2] *Line* is an abbreviation of the a-c power distribution line. *Line voltage* is the rms voltage available at the power socket; *line frequency* is its frequency, etc.

[3] Direct current is a net flow of charge in one direction. If a direct current or voltage is discontinuous or varies in magnitude, it is called *pulsating d-c.*

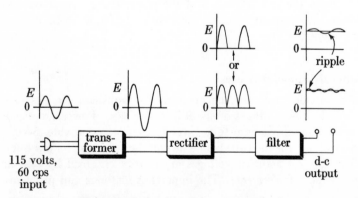

Figure 2-1   Block diagram showing conversion of a-c input to d-c output voltage.

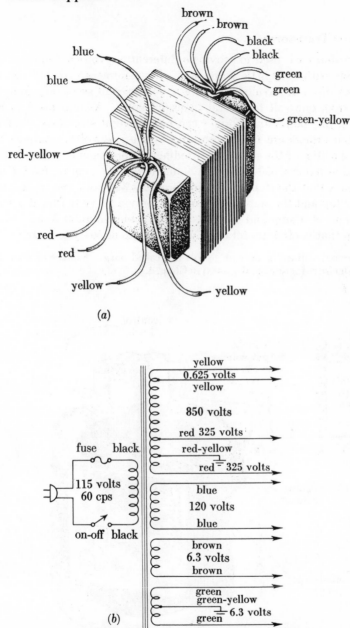

Figure 2-2 Power transformer with multiple secondary windings (for an oscilloscope): (a) pictorial; (b) schematic.

2-3   Power Transformers

A transformer is used to provide a different a-c voltage from the 115-volt a-c line with very little power loss. Transformers with 115-volt a-c primary windings are available with a wide choice of secondary (output) voltages, from one volt to several thousand volts. As illustrated in Fig. 2-2*a* and *b*, one power transformer can have several secondary windings. Power transformers are rated according to the rms voltage outputs and current capacities of the secondary windings. For example, a transformer designated as follows, 350-0-350 @ 100 ma, 5 volts @ 6 amps, 6.3 CT @ 3 amps, means that the step-up winding provides 350 volts rms each side of the center tap and the step-down windings provide 5 volts rms at a maximum current of 6 amp and 6.3 volts rms at a maximum of 3 amp with a center tap that is often useful in reducing pickup of 60-cycle *noise*.[4]

[4] Undesired voltage or current signals are called *noise*. Sources of noise and methods of noise reduction are discussed in Chap. 4.

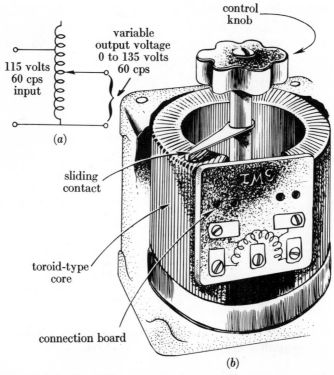

Figure 2-3   Variable autotransformer: (a) circuit representation; (b) construction.

Transformers have the feature of *isolating* the power supplied to the load from the power supplied by the 115-volt line. If isolation is not necessary, an autotransformer which has primary and secondary windings in common may save space and money. The variable autotransformer, or Variac, which is found associated with many laboratory devices, provides a continuously variable output and is illustrated in Fig. 2-3a and b. A sliding contact moves over a portion of the windings to provide a variable a-c output voltage. The output voltages of either the transformer or the autotransformer are reasonably independent of the current drawn by the load. It is also possible to obtain so-called "constant-voltage" transformers, which are useful in stabilizing many laboratory instruments against line-voltage fluctuations. Such transformers give a constant output within 1 to 2 per cent for wide variations of input line voltage (95 to 130 volts) or output current.

2-4 Rectifiers

The Ideal Rectifier. A rectifier is a device whose resistance depends on the sign of the potential applied to it. This is illustrated in Fig. 2-4. R_f is the "forward resistance" and is always less than R_b, the "backward resistance." In an a-c circuit, a rectifier has a greater resistance to current in one direction than to current in the other direction. From Fig. 2-4 it is seen that $I_f = E/R_f$ and $I_b = E/R_b$ and therefore that, if $R_f < R_b$, then $I_f > I_b$ or, quantitatively, that $R_b/R_f = I_f/I_b$. The ideal rectifier would be a perfect conductor for forward current and a perfect insulator for reverse current; so R_b/R_f approaches ∞ as the rectifier approaches the ideal. The ratio R_b/R_f is used as a figure of merit for rectification devices.

There are many types of rectifiers now in use, and a discussion follows of the most important types.

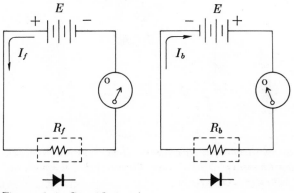

Figure 2-4 Rectifier action.

The Vacuum Diode. The schematic of a diode is shown in Fig. 2-5. One element of the diode, the cathode, is heated, either by an a-c or a d-c current (direct heating) or by being near a hot filament (indirect heating), to the temperature of thermionic emission of electrons. The other element, the anode, attracts and absorbs the emitted electrons when it is positive with respect to the cathode, and thus a current is passed through the diode. When the anode (sometimes called the plate) is negative with respect to the cathode, no charge will flow through the tube because the negative anode repels the emitted electrons, as illustrated in Fig. 2-6. The anode itself does not emit electrons because it is maintained below emission temperature.

For a typical vacuum diode, the current increases nonlinearly as the voltage between anode and cathode increases; or, in other words, R_f is not

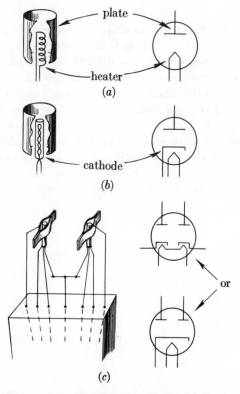

Figure 2-5   *The vacuum diode: (a) diode—direct heater; (b) diode—in-direct heater; (c) duodiode. Pictorial diagrams on the left, schematic on the right.*

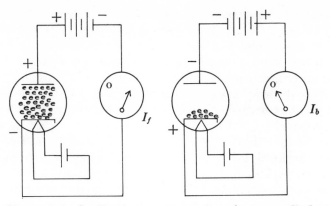

Figure 2-6 Qualitative representation of vacuum diode operation.

a constant. There is not a sharp break between the conducting and non-conducting regions of the curve. This is in contrast to the ideal diode, as illustrated in Fig. 2-7. The potential at which the current is reduced to zero is determined by two effects. First, the kinetic energy of the emitted electrons aids the flow of electrons to the anode. Second, the difference in work function of the cathode and anode material usually opposes the flow of electrons to the anode. The first effect is generally the greater, so that often a negative plate voltage of the order of 2 to 3 volts is required to prevent the passage of electrons from the cathode to the plate. In addition to these deviations from the ideal rectifier, there is some interelectrode capacity (3 to 4 pf)[5] which acts like a capacitor in parallel with the diode

[5] *Picofarad*, or 10^{-12} farad, is abbreviated pf. Until recently micromicrofarad, $\mu\mu$f or mmf, was used to designate this unit.

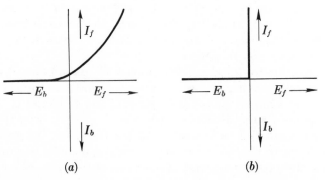

(a)   (b)

Figure 2-7 Current-voltage characteristics of (a) vacuum vs. (b) ideal diode.

and causes the diode's impedance (both directions) to decrease at higher frequencies. Typically, the forward resistance is between 100 and 1000 ohms, while the reverse resistance is of the order of 10 megohms.

Vacuum diodes are used for all purposes from low-voltage signal rectification to fairly high current power rectification. The current-carrying capacity of the diode is usually limited by the ability of the anode to dissipate heat. The plate dissipation in watts is obtained by multiplying i_b, the plate current, by e_b, the plate-to-cathode voltage. There is the possibility that *field emission*[6] of electrons from cold surfaces will occur if a sufficiently large electric field is applied. Therefore, there is a maximum peak inverse voltage rating above which the tube breaks down and electrons flow from anode to cathode. This rating must be considered in circuit design. It is also important not to exceed the maximum heater-to-cathode voltage, above which there is breakdown between heater and cathode.

The Gas-Filled Thermionic Diode. When the vacuum diode is conducting, the electrons which are in transit from the cathode to the anode, being negative, tend to limit the attractive force of the anode. This effect can be reduced in the following way to allow larger rates of electron flow for a given applied voltage: Enough metallic mercury is put in a vacuum-diode tube envelope to saturate the space with mercury vapor. If the cathode-to-anode voltage exceeds 10.39 volts (the ionization potential of mercury), the emitted electrons have enough energy to ionize the mercury atoms. The liberated electrons are attracted to the anode, while the positive mercury ions move more slowly toward the cathode. While the positive mercury ions exist between the cathode and the anode, they neutralize the charge effects of the electrons.

Even for very large currents, the voltage drop across the diode will not be much greater than the ionization potential. If too large a voltage is applied to such a tube and no provision is made to limit the current to a safe value, the tube will be destroyed. It is also necessary to warm the filament before voltage is applied to the anode. Cold-cathode gas-filled diodes are also available and are described in Sec. 2-7 for use as voltage-regulator tubes. The neon tube is a cold-cathode diode.

The Semiconductor Diode. Diodes made of semiconductors have become increasingly popular in recent years. Before considering the diode, however, it is important to review some of the properties of semiconductors, especially since an understanding of these same properties is essential for understanding the operation of the transistor, discussed in Chap. 3. As the name implies, a pure semiconductor material is neither a good conductor nor a good insulator, but is somewhere between. There are

---

[6] In *field emission*, an electric field instead of heat is used to provide escape energy to electrons at the metal surface.

charge carriers in a semiconductor that conduct a current when voltage is applied across it, but, since the number is small, the resistance is relatively high. Most of the electrons are strongly attached to the parent atoms and are not free to move about and conduct a current.

There are many types of semiconductors, including elements, intermetallic compounds, and even organic compounds, but at present the elements silicon and germanium are the most commercially important. These well-known Group IV elements have four electrons in their outer orbits that are available to form bonds with other atoms. Assume now that an absolutely pure germanium metal bar is melted and a small portion is withdrawn and allowed to cool in such a way that each atom in the solidified material is equidistant from four adjoining atoms. The four covalent bonds that join each atom to four others are difficult to disrupt, and the crystalline germanium is a semiconductor that exhibits a high resistance. In fact, it takes 0.75 ev to disrupt the bonds for pure germanium, and it takes even more energy, 1.12 ev, to break the valence bond for pure silicon. Since this amount of energy must be applied over lengths of about an atomic distance, the applied field strength necessary to break a bond for a germanium crystal is very high. At absolute zero the pure germanium crystal is an insulator, but at room temperature there are some free charge carriers that can conduct current because pairs of electrons will occasionally gain sufficient energy to break their bonds and become free. The free electrons can move randomly through the crystal lattice, in much the same way as molecules in a gas. When the electrons break away, they leave vacancies, or "holes." These holes, in turn, can be filled by electrons. As electrons move in to fill the holes, other holes are created and there is an apparent random movement of holes, as well as electrons, throughout the crystal.

As the temperature of a crystal increases, the rates of producing free electrons and holes increase, and some of the carriers have thermal velocities of more than 8 million cm/sec. Note that the crystal is electrically neutral and that an equilibrium is reached wherein the number of holes and electrons being formed is equal to their recombination rate. The "lifetime" of an individual electron or hole before recombination can vary over a range of less than a microsecond to more than a millisecond. Now, if a voltage is applied across the germanium lattice, there will be a net drift of the electrons toward the plus terminal and holes toward the negative terminal. The average velocity of each type of carrier is known as its "drift velocity," v_n for electrons, and v_p for holes. The current i_n that is carried by the electrons is

$$i_n = nqv_n$$

and the current carried by the holes is

$$i_p = pqv_p$$

where n and p are the number of electrons and holes, respectively, per cubic centimeter, and q is the charge of the electron. The total current is the sum of the individual currents, so that

$$I = i_n + i_p = q(nv_n + pv_p) \qquad (2\text{-}1)$$

and since the velocities of electrons and holes are proportional to the applied field E (that is, $v_n = \mu_n E$, and $v_p = \mu_p E$), then

$$I = q(n\mu_n + p\mu_p)E \qquad (2\text{-}2)$$

From Ohm's law it is apparent that $q(n\mu_n + p\mu_p)$ is the "conductivity" σ of the semiconductor (that is, σ is the reciprocal of the resistivity ρ).

In terms of energy bands, the valence band is nearly full of electrons, but a few electrons have moved up into the conduction band. The inherent ability of a pure semiconductor to conduct current is known as its "intrinsic conductivity." It is dependent on the number of electrons in the conduction band, and this number is a function of temperature, as given by the expression

$$np = n_i{}^2 = AT^3 e^{E_g/kT} \qquad (2\text{-}3)$$

where n_i is the "intrinsic carrier concentration," A and k are constants, E_g is the energy of the forbidden gap between valence and conduction bands, and T is the absolute temperature. For germanium $n_i \cong 2.5 \times 10^{13}$ carriers per cubic centimeter at room temperature, and for silicon $n_i \cong 1.5 \times 10^{10}$ carriers per cubic centimeter.

Although the intrinsic properties of a pure semiconductor are important considerations, the desirable characteristics of semiconductors for use in diode rectifiers and transistors are obtained by purposely adding small amounts of selected impurities. Assume that a small amount of a Group V element, such as antimony, is added to germanium, so that the ratio of antimony to germanium is about 1 ppm.[7] Each antimony atom is therefore completely surrounded by germanium atoms, and four of its five valence electrons form covalent bonds, as the antimony atom becomes part of the crystal lattice. The extra electron is now only loosely bound to the atom, and an energy of only about 0.01 ev is required to free it.

The antimony atoms are called "donors" because they contribute an excess electron concentration n which greatly increases the conductivity of the germanium semiconductor. A semiconductor doped with donor atoms is referred to as an "n-type" semiconductor. It is likewise possible to dope germanium with a Group III element, such as indium, so as to produce an

[7] Parts per million, by weight, is abbreviated ppm.

excess hole concentration p. The resulting impure crystal is known as a "p-type" semiconductor, and the impurity is called an "acceptor."

Note that when donor atoms contribute excess electrons to the semiconductor there is a greater probability of the intrinsic holes recombining with electrons. The concentration of holes, therefore, is reduced considerably below the intrinsic number present at room temperature for a pure semiconductor. Since the electrons are now, by far, the "majority carrier," the application of a voltage to the n-type semiconductor results in a current carried primarily by electrons and Eq. (2-2) reduces to

$$I_n = qn\mu_n E \tag{2-4a}$$

In an analogous way,

$$I_p = qp\mu_p E \tag{2-4b}$$

when a voltage is applied across a p-type semiconductor. Note that in a p-type semiconductor the holes move in the semiconductor but electrons flow in the connecting wires.

Now consider what happens when p-type and n-type semiconductors are joined together at a junction. As might be expected, the electrons and holes combine, but only for a very narrow region right at the junction. The reason for the narrow region of recombination is that the n type becomes positively charged as electrons move into the p type, and the p type becomes negatively charged as the holes move into the n type. The result is a "barrier field," or "built-in potential," ϕ_0, of about 0.3 volt which repels most of the majority carriers of each type from approaching the junction. The movement of the intrinsic minority carriers, however, is aided by the barrier field. The resulting current from the minority carriers is exactly balanced by the few majority carriers that do gain sufficient energy to cross the barrier, so that equilibrium and a net current of zero is maintained for the unbiased diode, which is represented in Fig. 2-8a. The narrow region at the junction is called the "depletion layer" because it contains very few mobile charge carriers. The electric field within the depletion layer is a result of the ionized acceptors and donors that exist there. Outside this narrow region the electric field is essentially zero, so that the net charge within the depletion region must be zero.

If a voltage V is applied across the p-n diode, so that the p-type semiconductor is made positive with respect to the n-type, it opposes the built-in potential ϕ_0, as shown in Fig. 2-8b. In effect, then, the electrons of the n type and the holes of the p type are forced closer together. Therefore, the probability of majority carriers passing across the barrier is increased, and a "forward current" I_f is obtained. If the forward current is small,

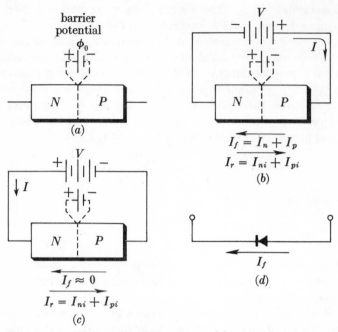

Figure 2-8   *The p-n junction diode: (a) unbiased; (b) forward-biased;
(c) reverse-biased; (d) schematic symbol.*

so that the voltage drops in the semiconductor material are small, the potential drop across the depletion layer is $\phi_0 - V$. There is still a reverse current I_r due to minority carriers, but it is small compared with I_f, and the net current is in the forward direction.

If the diode is now reverse-biased, as shown in Fig. 2-8c, the potential barrier at the junction is increased to $\phi_0 + V$ and the width of the depletion layer is increased. The effect is to reduce the probability of majority carriers crossing the barrier. The reverse current, due to minority carriers, remains the same as before, assuming the same temperature. Therefore, as the reverse voltage is applied, the forward current becomes insignificant and the reverse current remains constant at the small value I_r, even though the reverse voltage V is changed over a wide range. It is thus apparent that the p-n diode is a good rectifier, as illustrated by the current-voltage curve in Fig. 2-9. The current is high when the applied voltage is in one direction, and the current is very low when the applied voltage is reversed.

Although the reverse current is very small over a wide range of reverse voltage, it is observed in Fig. 2-9 that it suddenly increases to a large value

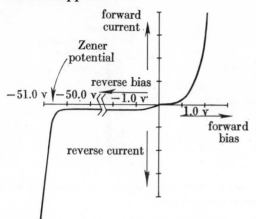

Figure 2-9   Current-voltage characteristics of a p-n-junction diode.

at a high reverse bias. The sudden increase in current has been attributed to two effects, the "Zener breakdown" and the "avalanche breakdown." In the former, the large reverse bias produces an electric field that is sufficient to break the covalent bonds and produce free electron-hole pairs. In the avalanche effect, the electrons drifting through the depletion layer pick up sufficient kinetic energy to ionize other atoms with which they collide. The process is cumulative, so as to produce the sudden large reverse current illustrated in Fig. 2-9. For rectifier applications, the reverse breakdown voltage is the peak inverse voltage rating of the diode and should not be exceeded. In some other circuits, the reverse breakdown region is used to advantage (Sec. 2-7).

The *p-n* semiconductor diode is a better rectifier in many respects than the vacuum diode. For one thing, the interelectrode capacitance of the junction diode is only about 1 pf. It should be noted, of course, that the reverse current is a function of thermally generated electron-hole pairs. For germanium diodes, this current becomes high enough to impair the rectification at 75°C. Silicon diodes, however, are usable up to about 200°C. In either case, heating is to be avoided since the reverse current almost doubles for each 10°C rise in temperature.

Metallic Rectifiers. Selenium and copper oxide rectifiers were known for some time before the discovery of the *p-n* junction. Because they are not formed of single crystals, their behavior is not so readily characterized as that of the *p-n* junction. Their construction is shown in Fig. 2-10. Their main characteristics, along with those of silicon and germanium *p-n*-junction diodes, are summarized in Table 2-1.

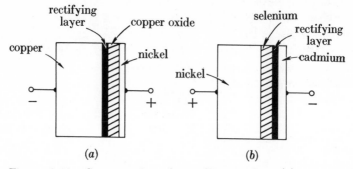

Figure 2-10   Construction of metallic rectifiers: (a) copper oxide recti-
fier; (b) selenium rectifier.

Table 2-1   *Characteristics of rectifiers* *

Characteristic	Copper oxide	Selenium	Germa-nium	Silicon
Back-front resistance ratio	10^3	5×10^3	4×10^5	10^6
Maximum current density, amp/in.^{2}	0.25	0.32	300	1000
Maximum operating temperature, °C	60	100	65	150
Maximum back voltage per cell, volts	5	52	200	600

* Adapted from K. R. Spangenberg, "Fundamentals of Electron Devices," McGraw-Hill, New York, 1957, p. 177.

2-5   Rectifier Circuits

Since a rectifier conducts current in only one direction, the current in a circuit which is in series with a diode must necessarily be d-c. The simplest rectifier circuit is shown in Fig. 2-11. On the positive half cycle of the a-c voltage, the diode can conduct, allowing current to pass through R_L. R_L is the "load," or the circuit which is to be supplied with direct current. On the negative half cycle, the diode is reverse-biased and therefore nonconducting. This rectifier circuit is called a half-wave rectifier because only half of the a-c current wave is present in the load circuit.

In considering rectifier circuits, it is important to consider the ratings of the rectifiers, which have the following specifications: *The peak forward-current rating*, which is the peak voltage divided by R_L. In the case of Fig. 2-11, 200 volts rms $\times$ 1.4 = 280 volts peak. I_{peak} = 280 volts/R_L. *The maximum average forward-current rating*, which is $\frac{1}{2} \times E_{\text{av}}/R_L$, because the diode conducts only half the time. *The peak inverse voltage*, which is the maximum voltage of the reverse or nonconduction polarity which should be applied to the rectifier. The diode of Fig. 2-11 has to withstand a peak inverse voltage of 200 $\times$ 1.4 = 280 volts. *The forward resistance* R_f: The effective resistance of a conducting diode is not constant but depends on the current. However, an approximate knowledge of the forward resistance allows one to calculate the power loss in the rectifier $(I^2 R_f)$ and the voltage drop in the rectifier (IR_f). *The reverse resistance R_b*: For a diode to be an effective rectifier, R_b must be much greater than R_f.

For many applications it is desirable to have a rectifier circuit which supplies current during both half cycles of the a-c power and thus provides a more continuous current to the load. A "full-wave" rectifier circuit is shown in Fig. 2-12. This circuit is essentially two half-wave rectifiers in parallel whose inputs have a phase difference of 180°. The voltage output of the full-wave rectifier is equal to the voltage developed by each half of the transformer secondary. For a 300-volt output from a full-wave rectifier, one would use about a 650-volt center-tapped transformer. The extra 50 volts is to compensate for the drop in the rectifiers and transformer. Note that the rectifiers must withstand an inverse voltage of two times the peak value of the source. For the case above, the peak inverse voltage would be 1.4 $\times$ 650 = 920 volts. Vacuum-tube diodes are most often used in the full-wave rectifier because they can withstand much higher inverse voltages than semiconductor diodes. Also, such high-voltage supplies often

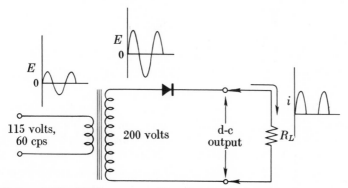

Figure 2-11   Half-wave rectifier circuit.

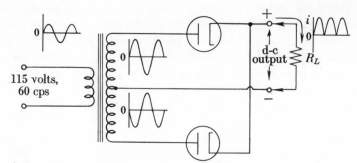

Figure 2-12   Full-wave rectifier circuit.

need to supply only a few hundred milliamperes, which is well within the capability of common and inexpensive tubes.

A way to obtain full-wave rectification which does not require a center-tapped transformer is shown in Fig. 2-13. This circuit is called the bridge rectifier. Trace the current path through the rectifiers. On the positive half cycle, D_2 and D_4 conduct. On the negative half cycle, D_1 and D_3 conduct. In each case, the direction of electron flow through the load R_L is the same. The bridge rectifier has two disadvantages. One is that there are two rectifiers in series with the load. The other disadvantage is that the cathodes of the rectifiers D_1 and D_4 experience such extremes in potential that, in order to avoid breakdown between the heater and cathode, separate filament supplies are required for each tube. For this last reason, the bridge-rectifier circuit is most often found with semiconductor recti-

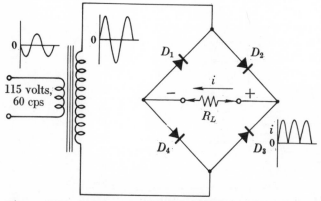

Figure 2-13   Bridge-rectifier circuit.

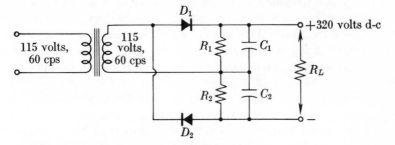

Figure 2-14   Voltage-doubler rectifier circuit.

fiers. On the other hand, the transformer supplying power to the bridge rectifier can be smaller, because it has only one secondary winding, and the current in that winding is always sinusoidal. Having two rectifiers in series with the load drops the peak inverse voltage that each rectifier must withstand to the peak value of the supply voltage. This is an advantage for semiconductor rectifiers, which have rather low peak inverse voltage ratings.

Two rectifiers can be connected to a single a-c source and wired so that their outputs are in series as in Fig. 2-14. The output voltage available from such a circuit is twice that which is available from the a-c source with a half-wave or bridge rectifier. For this reason, this kind of circuit is called a voltage-doubler rectifier. On the positive half cycle, capacitor C_1 is charged to the peak value of the supply voltage (in this case 115 × 1.4 = 160 volts). On the negative half cycle, C_2 is charged to the same potential. Since C_1 and C_2 are in series across the load, the output voltage is twice the *peak* voltage of the a-c source. The capacitors are essential to the operation of the circuit, because they maintain the potential developed during one half cycle so that the potential developed during the next half cycle can be added to it. The capacitors C_1 and C_2 have a filtering action which is described in the next section. Since current is supplied to the load during both half cycles, this voltage-doubler circuit is considered to be full wave. The peak inverse voltage applied to each rectifier is twice the peak value of the supply voltage, in this case 320 volts. As in the case of the bridge rectifier, the cathodes are operated at such different potentials that they cannot be heated with a single filament supply. Semiconductor diodes are most often used with this circuit. Where the peak inverse voltage rating of the diode is insufficient, two diodes may be put in series so that their peak inverse voltage ratings are additive. In this case, except for the doubling effect, the circuit has no advantage over the bridge rectifier.

The power dissipated by an alternating current in a load R_L is equal to $(I_{\text{rms}})^2 R_L$. When the alternating current is passed through a rectifier, the waveshape is changed. Half- and full-wave rectifiers supply current to the load during half the cycle and over the entire cycle, respectively. In both cases the current through the load varies between zero and some peak value. Often the rectified current is passed through a filter to reduce the current variation through the load. With an effective filter, the current through the load is the current supplied by the rectifier averaged over at least one cycle. The power dissipated in the load is thus $(I_{\text{av}})^2 R_L$. The average value of alternating current is commonly less than the rms value.[8] This results in a loss in the effectiveness of the current through the process of filtering. If a half-wave rectifier supplies current to a filter and load over the entire half cycle, the rms current is $I_{\text{peak}}/2$, but the average current is only I_{peak}/π. Thus the power dissipated in the load by the filtered current is only $(2/\pi)^2 \times 100 = 40.6$ per cent of the power dissipated by the same current unfiltered. The evaluation of this loss in effectiveness is complicated by the fact that the filter also affects the fraction of a cycle the rectifier conducts, as shown in Fig. 2-16. However, the loss is generally less for full-wave than for half-wave rectifiers.

[8] The relationship between rms and average values for sine and other waveforms will be found in Supplement 3.

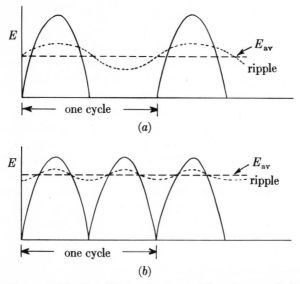

Figure 2-15   Rectified voltage and fundamental ripple frequency: (a) half-wave and (b) full-wave rectifier outputs.

2-6 Filtering the Rectified Voltage

The output voltages of the rectifier circuits discussed in the previous section vary with time as shown in Fig. 2-15. The output can be considered as a voltage which varies about the average d-c potential. The average d-c potential is called the d-c component of the output. For the half-wave rectifier output, the lowest and most predominant frequency of the a-c component is the frequency of the a-c line as shown by the dotted line in Fig. 2-15a. From Fig. 2-15b, it can be seen that the lowest and most predominant frequency of the output from a full-wave rectifier is twice the a-c supply frequency. For most applications, it is necessary to reduce the magnitude of the a-c component of the rectifier output to a value which is very small compared with the average d-c potential. The electrical device which accomplishes this task is called a filter. The effectiveness of the filter is the ripple factor, which is defined as the rms value of the a-c component, or "ripple," divided by the average d-c potential.

A rather effective filter is simply a large capacitance in parallel with the load R_L. The capacitor may be thought of as storing charge when the a-c component is positive and as discharging through the load when the a-c component is negative. Another way to put this is that the impedance of the large capacitor for the ripple frequency is low compared with R_L and thus diverts most of the alternating current away from the load circuit.

A more detailed picture of the action of a capacitor filter is presented in Fig. 2-16. The capacitor charges to the peak value of the input voltage. If R_L were infinite, the voltage across the capacitor would quickly reach a constant value equal to the peak value of the alternating current supplying the rectifier. In the practical case where R_L is not infinite, the capacitor begins to discharge through R_L as soon as the input voltage reaches that voltage to which the capacitor has discharged. This results in the output waveshapes shown in Fig. 2-16.

It can be seen from Fig. 2-16 that the magnitude of the ripple voltage will be decreased if R_L, C, or the frequency is increased. The expression for the ripple factor, $r = 1/(2\sqrt{3}fCR_L$, bears this out. f is the frequency of the main a-c component, equal to the line frequency for half-wave rectifiers and twice the line frequency for full-wave rectifiers. It can also be seen that, as the ripple increases in magnitude, the average d-c output will decrease. $E_{dc} = 1.4E_{rms} - I_{dc}/2fC$, where E_{rms} is the rms value of the rectifier supply voltage and I_{dc} is the average d-c current through R_L. The regulation of the capacitor filter improves also with larger values of C and f.

All the above equations, and in fact all the equations in the rest of this section, have been derived on the assumption that the components used are more or less ideal. Some simplifying assumptions have also been made with regard to waveshape. While the equations may be accurate only to

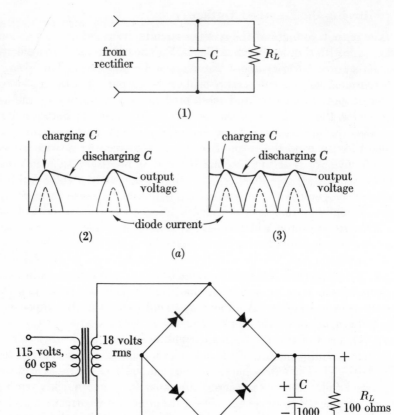

Figure 2-16   *(a)* *Capacitor filter: (1) circuit; (2) half-wave input; (3) full-wave input.*   *(b)* *Low-voltage, capacitor-filtered power supply.*

about 10 per cent, they are very useful in determining the effectiveness and general characteristics of the several filters in common use.

The output voltage and ripple voltage are determined here for the low-voltage power source of Fig. 2-16b. Note that, since this is a full-wave rectifier, $f = 2 \times$ line frequency $= 120$ cps. The output voltage is $E_{dc} = 1.4 \times 18$ volts $- I_{dc}/2fC$. $I_{dc} = E_{dc}/R_L$.   Substituting for I_{dc}, $E_{dc} = (1.4 \times 18)/(1 + 1/2fCR_L)$. $E_{dc} = (1.4 \times 18)/[1 + 1/(2 \times 120 \times 1000 \times 10^{-6} \times 100)] = 24$ volts.   The ripple factor $r = 1/(2\sqrt{3} \times f \times C \times R_L)$

$= 1/(3.5 \times 120 \times 1000 \times 10^{-6} \times 100) = 0.024$. The rms ripple voltage $= r \times E_{dc} = 0.60$ volt (1.7 volts peak-to-peak).

Another filter device is simply an *inductance*[9] in series with the load. The inductance, by opposing the changes in current through it, tends to maintain a more constant current through the load. This necessarily results in a more constant output voltage. The *inductor*, or *choke*, does not store charge the way a capacitor does; it merely reacts against a change in the current passing through it. The current tends toward the average value under the influence of the inductance. The voltage across the load then becomes the average voltage output of the rectifier. For a full-wave rectifier and a choke filter, $E_{dc} = 0.90E_{rms}$. This expression assumes that the d-c resistances of the transformer, rectifier, and choke are negligible compared with R_L. Notice that the output voltage is then virtually independent of the load, making the choke-filtered supply very well regulated. The output voltage, however, is considerably lower than that with the capacitor filter.

To be effective with a half-wave rectifier, the inductance value must be rather large. The sharp increase in current which occurs at the beginning of the conduction cycle in a half-wave rectifier causes such a large voltage to be induced in the coil that a severe strain is put on the insulation of the windings. For this reason, it is not practical to use chokes to filter the output of a half-wave rectifier.

Obviously, the larger the value of the inductance, the more effective the filter will be. For the full-wave rectifier, the only case we shall consider, the ripple factor is given by the expression

$$r = \frac{1}{3\sqrt{2}} \frac{R_L}{2\pi f L}$$

Notice that the ripple factor decreases with decreasing R_L (increasing load current). This is contrary to the behavior of the capacitor filter. The ripple output from the choke filter is generally much larger than that of the capacitor filter. The main advantages of the choke filter are improved regulation and better filtering for high-output currents.

Various combinations of chokes and capacitors are used as filters. The first is the *L*-section filter shown in Fig. 2-17. This filter takes advantage of the good regulating characteristics of the inductor. When the rectifier output is filtered first by the choke, it is called a choke-input filter. Choke-input filters are not used with half-wave rectifiers for the reason mentioned above.

The output voltage for the *L*-section filter is the same as that for the

[9] *Inductance* and inductive circuits are discussed in Supplement 3.

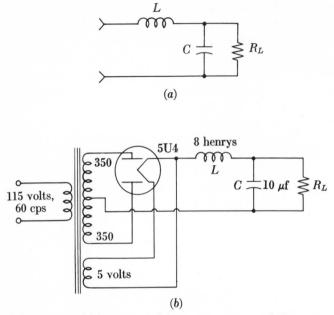

Figure 2-17   *(a) L section; (b) power supply with L-section filter.*

choke filter.   That is, $E_{dc} = 0.90E_{rms}$.   It can be seen from Fig. 2-17 that, if the load current is zero, the inductance has no effect and the circuit behaves like the capacitor filter.   In this case the output voltage would be equal to the peak value of the input voltage.   As the load current increases, the output voltage drops rather quickly to the average value and then remains constant.   The minimum load current for good regulation depends on the value of the inductance.   For good regulation, it can be shown that L must be equal to or greater than $R_L/1100$ (for a 60-cycle a-c supply).

The power supply of Fig. 2-17b is called upon to supply 310 volts to a variable load.   The current through the load varies from 50 to 150 ma. The effective value of R_L thus varies within the range of about 6 to 2 kilohms.   In order to maintain good regulation, it was said that $L \geq R_L/$ 1100, so that in this case L must be at least 6 henrys.   An 8-henry 200-ma choke was chosen for the supply.

The ripple factor of the choke filter decreases with increasing current. The ripple factor of the capacitor filter increases with increasing current. When both filters are used together, these opposite effects cancel each other and the ripple factor is essentially independent of the load current.   The formula for the ripple factor is $r = (\sqrt{2}/3)(X_C/X_L)$.   In the case of the power supply of Fig. 2-17b, the ripple factor is calculated as follows:

$$r = \frac{\sqrt{2}}{3} \frac{1}{2\pi fC} \frac{1}{2\pi fL}$$

$$= 0.47 \frac{1}{2\pi \times 120 \times 10 \times 10^{-6}} \frac{1}{2\pi \times 120 \times 8}$$

$$= 0.47 \frac{1}{7.5 \times 10^{-3}} \frac{1}{6 \times 10^{3}} = 0.01 \tag{2-5}$$

Additional L sections may be added to the L-section filter as shown in Fig. 2-18. This has the effect of reducing the ripple factor by the factor X_C/X_L for every additional section. In the above case, an additional identical L section would reduce the ripple by a factor of 45, making $r = 0.01/45 = 0.0002$. The regulation is somewhat decreased, owing to the resistance of the additional chokes.

Variations on the capacitance filter are very common, because they provide good filtering at low cost and small size and weight and can be used with half-wave rectifiers. They also provide a higher output voltage, but at the expense of regulation. The most popular is the π-section filter illustrated in Fig. 2-19. The output voltage is essentially the same as that of the capacitance filter. The ripple factor is nearly that of the capacitance filter multiplied by the L-section factor given above,

$$r = \sqrt{2} \frac{X_{C1}X_{C2}}{R_L X_L} \tag{2-6}$$

The voltage-doubler rectifier circuit requires a capacitor input filter, as explained in the previous section. Figure 2-19b is the rectifier of Fig. 2-14, with an additional L section making a π-section filter. Capacitor C_1 of the π-section filter (Fig. 2-19a) is actually C_1' and C_1'' in series (Fig. 2-19b). The actual value of C_1 as far as the filter is concerned would thus be given by $1/C_1 = 1/C_1' + 1/C_1''$, or in this case 10 μf. The ripple factor

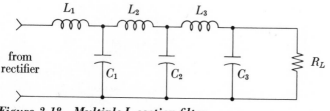

Figure 2-18   Multiple L-section filter.

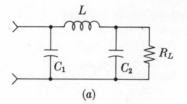

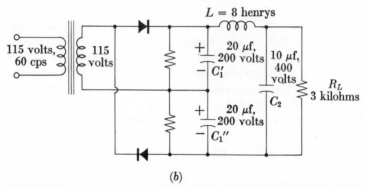

(b)

Figure 2-19   (a) π-section filter; (b) power supply with π-section filter.

is calculated as follows:

$$r = \sqrt{2} \frac{(1/2\pi f C_1)(1/2\pi f C_2)}{R_L \times 2\pi f L}$$

$$= \frac{\sqrt{2}}{(7.5 \times 10^{-3})^2 (6 \times 10^3)(3 \times 10^3)}$$

$$= \frac{1.4}{1000} = 0.0014 \tag{2-7}$$

Additional L sections may be added to the π-section filter. The equations for the output voltage are the same. The ripple factor would be that of the π-section filter times $(X_C/X_L)^n$, where n is the number of additional L sections.

In some cases, the choke of the π-section filter can be replaced with a resistor. To provide the same ripple factor, the value of the resistance

Table 2-2   Peak-to-peak ripple voltages

	Peak-to-peak ripple voltage	
Filter type	Full-wave rectifier	Half-wave rectifier
L	63 volts	
C	6 volts	12 volts
L section	1.1 volts	
2 L sections	3.5 mv	
π section	18 mv	120 mv
π section plus one L section	62 μv	1.7 mv
R-C, π section	0.10 volt	0.4 volt

should equal X_L. The reactance X_L of a 10-henry choke at 60 cycles (half-wave rectifier) = 3.8 kilohms. The regulation suffers greatly from the substitution of that size of resistance for a choke which may have a resistance of about 200 ohms. In fact, if the load draws 50 ma, the voltage drop across the filter is 190 volts. In the typical application of this circuit, R is between 100 and 1000 ohms, the capacitors are of the order of 10 to 100 μf each, and the load-current demands are small.

Table 2-2 lists the peak-to-peak ripple voltages of a power supply which has a 250-volt rms 60-cycle source and a filter as described and which provides 50 ma under full load. All capacitors are 50 μf, all chokes are 10 henrys, and all resistors are 1 kilohm. The output voltages vary from 225 to 300 volts.

From the discussion in this section, it is clear that each filter type has its particular area of application. For large current requirements and/or very good regulation, one of the choke-input types is used. Where smaller currents are required and where regulation is less important, the π-section filter should be used. The resistor π-section filter may be perfectly adequate for very low current requirements.

Table 2-3 is a summary of the expressions discussed in this section, evaluated for a 60-cycle supply frequency. E_{rms} refers to the rms value of the input voltage to the filter. The reduction of the output voltage due to the average IR drops in the transformer, rectifying element, and filter chokes has been neglected. For most common components the voltage drop in these elements would be within the 10 per cent accuracy ascribed to the expressions.

Table 2-3 Power-supply expressions

Filter type	Full-wave rectifier		Half-wave rectifier	
	Output voltage	Ripple factor	Output voltage	Ripple factor
L	$0.90E_{rms}$	$R_L/1600L$	Do not use	Do not use
C	$1.4E_{rms} - I_{dc}/240C$	$1/420CR_L$	$1.4E_{rms} - I_{dc}/120C$	$1/210CR_L$
L section	$0.90E_{rms}$	$8.3 \times 10^{-7}/CL$	Do not use	Do not use
n L sections	$0.90E_{rms}$	$0.47 \times \left(\dfrac{1.76 \times 10^{-6}}{LC} \right)^n$	Do not use	Do not use

Circuit				
	$1.4E_{rms} - I_{dc}/240C_1$	$3.3 \times 10^{-9}/C_1C_2L_1R_L$	$1.4E_{rms} - I_{dc}/120C_1$	$2.6 \times 10^{-8}/C_1C_2L_1R_L$
π section plus n L sections	$1.4E_{rms} - I_{dc}/240C_1$	$\dfrac{3.3 \times 10^{-9}}{C_1C_2L_1R_L} \times \left(\dfrac{1.76 \times 10^{-6}}{LC}\right)^n$	$1.4E_{rms} - I_{dc}/120C_1$	$\dfrac{2.6 \times 10^{-8}}{C_1C_2L_1R_L} \times \left(\dfrac{7 \times 10^{-6}}{LC}\right)^n$
π-section RC	$1.4E_{rms} - I_{dc}\left(\dfrac{1}{240C_1} + R\right)$	$2.5 \times 10^{-6}/C_1C_2RR_L$	$1.4E_{rms} - I_{dc}\left(\dfrac{1}{120C_1} + R\right)$	$10^{-5}/C_1C_2RR_L$
π-section RC plus n RC sections	$1.4E_{rms} - I_{dc} \times \left(\dfrac{1}{240C_1} + R_1 + nR\right)$	$\dfrac{2.5 \times 10^{-6}}{C_1C_2R_1R_L} \times \left(\dfrac{1.3 \times 10^{-3}}{RC}\right)^n$	$1.4E_{rms} - I_{dc} \times \left(\dfrac{1}{120C_1} + R_1 + nR\right)$	$\dfrac{10^{-5}}{C_1C_2RR_L} \times \left(\dfrac{2.6 \times 10^{-3}}{RC}\right)^n$

73

2-7   Regulation of the Output D-C Voltage

In the preceding section, regulation was defined as the quality of maintaining a constant output voltage despite variations in load current. If a perfectly constant output voltage is to be maintained, it should be added that this should be in spite of variations in input voltage, temperature, and age as well. This kind of regulation is beyond the ability of the choke-input filter. A well-regulated voltage for low currents can be obtained through the use of a Zener diode or glow-discharge voltage-regulator tube.

The Glow-Discharge Tube. A gas at low pressure, such as neon, is placed in a glass envelope with two electrodes. If the potential between these two electrodes is high enough, an ion and electron caused by a chance ionization will be accelerated sufficiently to cause further ionization. If the current between the two electrodes in the ionized gas is limited by a resistor, a controlled discharge will result. The potential between the electrodes is nearly independent of the current through the tube, owing to the constant potential of the neutralization reactions at each electrode. These tubes are available for voltage-regulator service with maintaining potentials of 90 to 150 volts. A circuit employing a glow-discharge tube is shown in Fig. 2-20. The voltage-regulator tube is rated according to the firing voltage, the voltage drop which will be maintained across it, and the current range over which the voltage will remain essentially constant. The d-c supply voltage must be greater than the firing voltage of the VR tube. The difference between the supply voltage and the maintaining voltage of the VR tube will be developed across R_s. The choice of the proper value for the resistance R_s will depend on the changes expected in the supply voltage and the load resistance, as well as on the VR-tube characteristics. The method for determining the correct value of R_s is illustrated for the following case:

A constant voltage of 150 volts is desired. There are two voltage-regulator tubes with an operating potential of 150 volts: the miniature type OA2, which operates at 5 to 30 ma, and the octal-base type OD3/VR 150, which operates at 5 to 40 ma. For the purposes of this illustration,

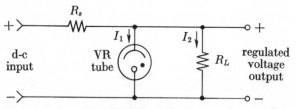

Figure 2-20   Circuit with a voltage-regulator tube.

the OD3 will be chosen because it has the widest operating range. The firing potential of the OD3 is 185 volts. Assume an average load resistance of 5 kilohms. The average current through the load, I_2, will be 30 ma. Assume a d-c supply voltage of 225 volts. If the OD3 is to be operated in the middle of its range, $I_1 = 22$ ma. $I_1 + I_2 = 52$ ma. The voltage across R_s will be $225 - 150 = 75$ volts. Therefore $R_s = 75/0.052 = 1.44$ kilohms. To determine the maximum d-c supply-voltage range, assume that R_L is constant at 5 kilohms (I_2 constant at 30 ma).

Minimum supply voltage

$$= 150 + (5 \text{ ma} + 30 \text{ ma}) \times 1.44 \text{ kilohms} = 200 \text{ volts}$$

Maximum supply voltage

$$= 150 + (40 \text{ ma} + 30 \text{ ma}) \times 1.44 \text{ kilohms} = 250 \text{ volts}$$

It is obvious that, the greater the load current, the smaller the permissible range of supply voltages.

To determine the range of R_L over which the output voltage will remain constant, assume that the supply voltage is constant at 225 volts. The voltage across R_s is then constant at 75 volts, and $I_1 + I_2$ is constant at 52 ma.

$$\text{Maximum load resistance} = \frac{150 \text{ volts}}{52 \text{ ma} - 40 \text{ ma}} = 12.5 \text{ kilohms}$$

$$\text{Minimum load resistance} = \frac{150 \text{ volts}}{52 \text{ ma} - 5 \text{ ma}} = 3.2 \text{ kilohms}$$

Of course, if both the supply voltage and the load resistance vary, the range of each variable in which regulation is maintained will be diminished correspondingly. Voltage-regulator tubes may be used in series and their control voltages added for control at larger voltages. The operating current limits of the series group are the smallest of the maximum currents and the largest of the minimum currents.

The Zener Diode. The reverse-bias current-voltage characteristic of the p-n junction diode is shown in Fig. 2-9. At a particular reverse-bias voltage the reverse current increases sharply. This "breakdown" of the high reverse resistance of the p-n junction may be due to either the "avalanche" or "Zener" effects, as described in Sec. 2-4. In either case, when the current is limited to a value which will not dangerously heat the diode, it is found that the voltage across the diode is virtually independent of the reverse current through the diode. Diodes designed to operate under reverse bias for regulation purposes are called Zener diodes. They are rated according to their breakdown voltage (2 volts to several hundred volts) and their maximum operating current. The use of Zener diodes in regulat-

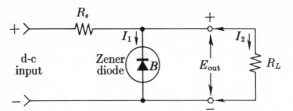

Figure 2-21   Zener diode voltage-regulator circuit.

ing circuits and the analysis of the circuit (Fig. 2-21) are the same as for the VR tube, except that the breakdown voltage of the Zener diode is the same as its control voltage.   Zener diodes may be used in series to provide higher control voltages.   Neither Zener diodes nor VR tubes should be used in parallel.   Only the regulator element with the lowest control voltage would carry any current.

Voltage regulators with better regulation and much greater current capability have been devised.   These involve an electronic or electromechanical control system and are discussed in Chap. 8.

2-8   Batteries as Sources of D-C Voltage

Despite the availability of high-quality units for the conversion of line-voltage alternating current to direct current in all voltage and current ranges, batteries find a widespread application in modern scientific instruments.   The use of batteries as power sources for instruments is essential in remote places, such as outer space, underseas, and in mines, where a central line voltage is not available.   Batteries are called for when mobility, portability, and extremely high reliability are required.   For some applications, a battery is less expensive and simpler than a power supply which would have the equivalent stability or freedom from line frequency noise.

A battery consists of several electrochemical "cells" which are connected to provide the necessary voltage and current capacity.   However, it is not unusual to hear the term "battery" used in reference to a single cell.   Only a decade ago, there were only two kinds of batteries readily available which were suitable for light- or moderate-duty applications. These were the familiar carbon-zinc dry cell and the lead-acid storage battery.   Today the designer or user of batteries has a choice of half a dozen different kinds of batteries, all commercially available in a wide variety of sizes and voltages.   Each of these battery types has characteristics which make it particularly valuable for certain uses.   Some new kinds of batteries come in the same case sizes and voltage ratings as the familiar carbon-zinc dry cell, thus forcing the user to choose the best type for his particular application. In this section, the construction, characteristics, and general areas of usefulness in instruments will be discussed for each of the common battery types.

The Carbon-Zinc Dry Cell. This is still the most generally used of all the so-called dry cells. The structure is shown in Fig. 2-22. During discharge, the zinc (Zn) metal of the can goes into the electrolyte as zinc chloride, hydroxide, ammine, or oxychloride, leaving two electrons in the zinc can for every atom of zinc dissolved. The MnO_2 in contact with the carbon (C) electrode changes to $Mn_2O_3 \cdot H_2O$, requiring one electron from the carbon for every molecule of MnO_2 converted.

This chemical action establishes a voltage between the two electrodes of about 1.5 to 1.6 volts. The carbon electrode is positive, and electrons flow in an external circuit from the zinc can to the carbon rod. Thirty individual cylindrical cells could be connected in series to provide a standard 45-volt battery, but this causes waste space. Therefore, dry batteries are generally made by stacking a carbon plate, a layer of electrolyte paste, and a zinc plate, alternately, as many times as necessary to give the desired voltage. The most common dry batteries have voltages of $1\frac{1}{2}$, 3, 6, $7\frac{1}{2}$, $22\frac{1}{2}$, 45, $67\frac{1}{2}$, and 90 volts.

The C-Zn dry cell is one of several kinds of *primary* batteries, that is, nonrechargeable, "one-shot" batteries. A primary battery is often classi-

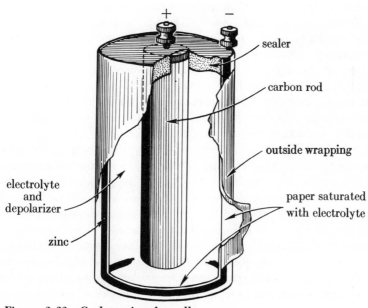

Figure 2-22   Carbon-zinc dry cell.

fied according to its usual application. An A battery is of low voltage and high current capability and is used to heat filaments of electron tubes, operate flashlights, and provide a constant current in potentiometer circuits and in many other laboratory applications. The B battery is capable of providing a low continuous current at a relatively high voltage and is useful as a plate and screen supply for certain electron tubes or as a stable high voltage for operating a photomultiplier tube. The C battery is a small, compact unit with very low current capability and is useful primarily in providing grid-bias voltages, as a reference voltage, or in similar applications where extremely low currents are used.

The service life of a battery is the number of operating hours during which a fresh battery will satisfactorily operate the actual circuit under normal operating conditions. The service life of a battery can vary manyfold depending on the following factors: the quality of the battery, the length of time it has been stored before use, its temperature during the storage period, the rate at which it is being discharged, the number and duration of the off periods, its temperature during the discharge, and the lowest potential for satisfactory operation of the circuit. All batteries discharge at some rate internally. This limits the time a dry cell can be stored before use. At room temperature a dry cell could be stored for about a year, but increasing temperature shortens the shelf life considerably.

It is very important to use a battery which is physically large enough to handle the current drain comfortably. The discharge rate is commonly measured by the number of operating hours necessary to wear out the battery, that is, the service life. For a C-Zn cell, a service life of less than 10 hr is considered a heavy drain. In addition to the nuisance of frequent battery changing, the number of milliampere-hours (the capacity) of the battery falls off severely as the rate of discharge increases. Furthermore, the voltage of a battery under heavy drain is low because of the IR drop in the cell and the polarization at the electrodes. If a C-Zn dry cell must be used under conditions of heavy drain, periodic rest periods will definitely extend the capacity and thus the service life of the battery.

Carbon-zinc dry cells do not work very effectively at temperatures below freezing. Even at temperatures where the cell can still supply a current, the service life may be very low. The potential of the carbon-zinc cell falls off continuously during use. This is due partly to the formation of compounds which interfere with the operation of the battery and partly to the fact that substances in the electrolyte are involved, to some extent, in the electrode reaction. When this is true, the change in electrolyte composition during discharge has a direct effect on the electrode potentials.

The dissolution of the zinc tends to weaken the structure of the cell. Furthermore, during discharge or storage a pressure of evolved hydrogen gas builds up. This can lead to a rupture of the zinc and the leakage of the corrosive electrolyte into the instrument. Instruments using these dry cells should therefore not be stored with the batteries installed.

The Alkaline-Manganese Battery. Commonly called the alkaline battery, the alkaline-manganese battery is quite similar in mechanism to the carbon-zinc dry cell. The electrode reactions are basically the same. The arrangement of the electrodes is different, and the electrolyte is strongly basic. The structure is shown in Fig. 2-23. The changes have resulted in quite a number of improvements over the ordinary C-Zn cell. The capacity has roughly doubled. The shelf life has increased. The capacity does not fall off under heavy drain. The internal impedance is lower, and the available current is higher. The low-temperature operating limit has been reduced to $-40°F$. At roughly four times the price, the alkaline battery will not replace the C-Zn cell completely. It does have obvious advantages for heavy drain applications, where the capacity of the conventional cell is greatly decreased. Its longer shelf life and lower operating temperature make it a much better choice for an emergency power source. Its low internal impedance would give it an advantage for circuits where large fluctuations in the current demand occur.

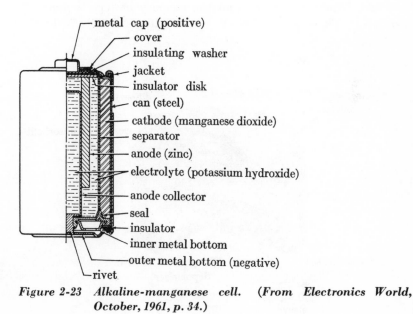

Figure 2-23 Alkaline-manganese cell. (From Electronics World,
October, 1961, p. 34.)

The Mercury Battery. This is the third kind of primary cell. It has a zinc amalgam for one electrode and mercuric oxide–carbon for the other. During discharge the zinc oxidizes to zinc oxide, yielding two electrons per atom, while the mercuric oxide is reduced to mercury by accepting two electrons per molecule from the carbon electrode. The structure is shown in Fig. 2-24. The potential developed by this cell is 1.35 volts and is remarkably reproducible from one cell to the next. The capacity of this cell is somewhat greater than even that of the alkaline cell, but this capacity is not maintained under heavy drain. The internal impedance is very low, as with the alkaline battery. In addition to the reproducibility of cell voltages, the great virtue of the mercury battery is its virtually constant voltage during discharge. This is achieved because of the electrode structure and composition and because the electrolyte does not change composition during discharge. The voltage-discharge curve (Fig. 2-25) is so flat that the mercury battery is used in many instruments as a secondary voltage standard. No gas is evolved in the mercury battery, and its structure is not deteriorated; so it is safe to use and keep in instruments. Because of its high price (about five times that of the alkaline battery for a comparable size), the mercury battery is likely to be used only where a constant potential during discharge is important. In many applications, notably transistor circuits, the circuit will not operate satisfactorily at reduced voltages. This requirement shortens the service life of the less expensive batteries so much that the mercury battery is practical economically. They are available in many voltages from 1.35 to 42 volts.

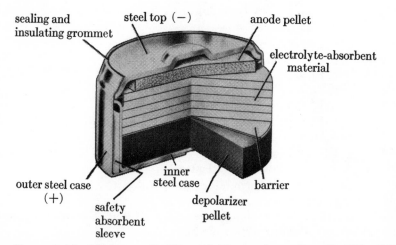

Figure 2-24   Mercury cell. (From J. Electrochem. Soc., 99, 197c, 1952.)

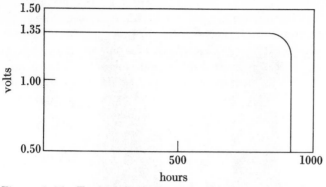

Figure 2-25 Typical discharge curve for a mercury cell.

The Lead-Acid Storage Battery. The familiar car battery, this is a series combination of several $Pb/H_2SO_4/PbO_2$ cells. A common structural arrangement for this battery is shown in Fig. 2-26. Under discharge the lead (Pb) in the lead electrode is converted to insoluble lead sulfate, releasing two electrons to the lead electrode per molecule of lead sulfate created. The lead dioxide in the PbO_2-Pb electrode is reduced to lead sulfate by accepting two electrons per molecule of lead sulfate formed. The chemical reaction which provides the electrical energy is

$$Pb + PbO_2 + 2H_2SO_4 \longrightarrow 2PbSO_4 + 2H_2O$$

When fully charged, the potential of each cell is 2.06 to 2.14 volts. The lead-acid battery is a *secondary* cell; i.e., it can be recharged. When a reverse or charging current is forced through the cell, the $PbSO_4$ is converted to Pb and PbO_2, respectively, so that the cell is returned to very nearly its original state.

The reaction shows that sulfuric acid is converted to water on discharge. This dilution of the sulfuric acid causes the cell voltage to decrease during discharge. The decrease in voltage is slow at first but becomes quite rapid during the last one-third of the service life. The output voltage as a function of time for various discharge rates is shown in Fig. 2-27. From this figure it can be seen that, for light to moderate drains, the voltage is quite constant for the first one-third to one-half of the service life. The internal resistance of the lead-acid battery is so low that it can be ignored at normal discharge rates. The high current free from a-c ripple makes it the most economical power source for certain applications. However, the lead-acid battery is bulky and heavy and requires a considerable amount of care if it is to give proper service. For this reason the very much more

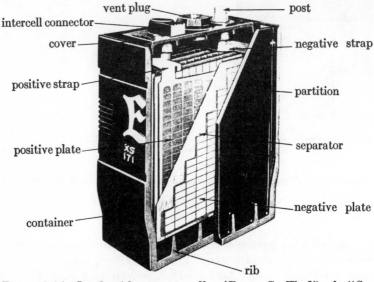

Figure 2-26   Lead-acid storage cell.   (From   G.   W.   Vinal, "Storage Batteries," Wiley, 1955, p. 72.)

expensive high-current, carefully regulated d-c supplies which operate from the a-c line are often preferred.   The lead-acid storage battery is, of course, the basic source of electrical power for electronic equipment in airplanes, automobiles, and the like.   In these cases the 6-, 12-, or 24-volt batteries can be used in combination with various d-c to a-c converters and conventional rectifier circuits to provide the high d-c voltages required by most vacuum-tube circuits.   Direct-current to alternating-current converters are discussed in Sec. 2-9.

If a lead-acid battery is to provide good service, it must be kept charged, and it must be charged properly.   Its self-discharge rate is such that a charge is required every few months even if the battery has not been used.   There are several common methods of charging batteries.   All these methods are attempts to charge at an efficient rate, but not at the excessive rate which causes gas evolution and electrode deterioration.   The safe rate of charge for a discharged battery is very much higher than the "finishing rate" at which the battery can be brought up to its peak charge.   The constant-current method of charging simply applies the finishing rate of charge until the battery is charged.   The state of charge of the battery is determined by measuring the density of the electrolyte, which is actually

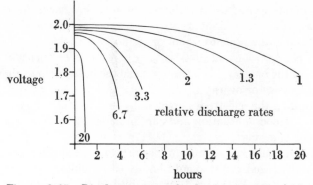

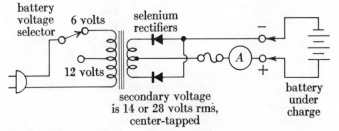

hours

*Figure 2-27   Discharge curve for lead-acid cell. (Adapted from W. D.
Cockrell (ed.), "Industrial Electronics Handbook," Mc-
Graw-Hill, 1958.)*

a measure of the sulfuric acid concentration. A faster method of charging
is to apply a higher current until the battery is about 85 per cent charged
and then apply the finishing rate. With the constant-potential method, a
constant potential of 2.35 volts per cell is applied. The charging current
is extremely high at first but decreases as the battery becomes charged.
The method charges the battery in the minimum safe time, but it requires
an unusually heavy source for the charging current. Most battery chargers
on the market today which are used to charge a single 6- or 12-volt battery
are a modified constant-voltage design. With these chargers, the initial
rate of charge is limited, and as the battery voltage increases, the charging
rate tapers off to a safe and reasonable finishing rate. A circuit for this
type of battery charger is shown in Fig. 2-28. When the transformer voltage exceeds the battery voltage, charging current will flow through the
rectifier. If the battery voltage is very low, charging current will flow dur-

Figure 2-28   Modified constant-voltage battery charger.

ing a considerable fraction of the a-c cycle. As the battery voltage increases, the time of charge and the driving potential of the charge decrease. The maximum rate of charge is limited by the resistance of the transformer, the rectifier, and sometimes an additional resistance. A trickle charge is a very low current charge which actually is only enough to compensate for the self-discharge of the battery. It is used to keep the battery up to charge during periods of storage or disuse.

During charging, the electrodes evolve hydrogen and oxygen—an explosive mixture. Good ventilation and careful handling to avoid sparks are required during charging.

Electrolysis and evaporation cause a loss of water from the lead-acid cell. Distilled or deionized water should be used to maintain the proper level of electrolyte in the cell. It has been established that concentrations of iron or chloride (common elements in tap water) in excess of 5 ppm in the electrolyte will decrease the performance and service life of the battery.

The Nickel-Cadmium Battery. The nickel-cadmium battery, which has long been popular in Europe, is just coming into widespread use in America. One reason for its rapid growth in popularity has been the development of the sealed nickel-cadmium cell. This is a completely sealed unit which requires no attention other than charging. Two forms

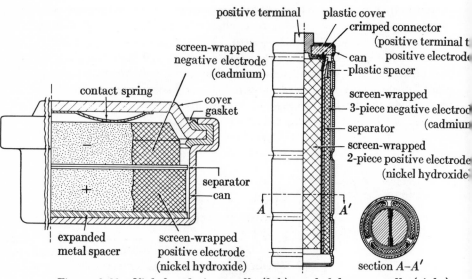

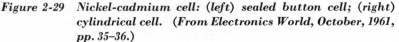

Figure 2-29 Nickel-cadmium cell: (left) sealed button cell; (right) cylindrical cell. (From Electronics World, October, 1961, pp. 35–36.)

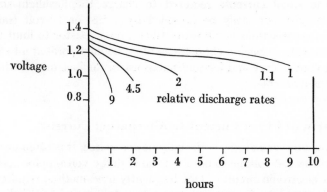

Figure 2-30   *Discharge curve for nickel-cadmium cell.* (*Adapted from W. D. Cockrell (ed.), "Industrial Electronics Handbook," McGraw-Hill, 1958.*)

of this cell are shown in Fig. 2-29. Under discharge the cadmium (Cd) is oxidized, supplying electrons, while, at the positive electrode, nickel oxide is reduced to a lower oxidation state by accepting electrons. The open-circuit potential of this cell is 1.3 volts. The electrolyte is not involved in the electrode reaction, and thus the potential is fairly constant over the service life. This is shown in Fig. 2-30. The capacity of the Ni-Cd battery is reduced very little even at very high discharge rates. The batteries can be stored charged or discharged without harm. The sealed units will not leak. They have the lowest self-discharge rate of any secondary cell. Sealed Ni-Cd batteries are made in many sizes and voltages which make them interchangeable with the primary batteries. To all the areas of the application of conventional batteries, Ni-Cd batteries offer the advantages of high current capability, long service life, reasonably constant potential, and the possibility of recharge. These characteristics are particularly suited to instruments where heavy drain and frequent use would require frequent battery replacement. The price is about twenty-five times that of a similar-sized C-Zn dry cell.

During the charging process, the nickel oxide is reoxidized to its higher oxidation state and the cadmium oxide is reduced. The cell is constructed with some oxidized cadmium so that the nickel electrode is the first electrode to reach full charge. If the cell is overcharged, the oxygen gas produced at the nickel electrode diffuses to the cadmium electrode, where it is reduced. This provides a "chemical short circuit" for excess charge and prevents the build-up of a large gas pressure. Nickel-cadmium cells can be charged by the same methods as described for the lead-acid cells. The finishing rate of charge should not exceed the ampere-hour rating divided by 10 hr. The small currents required to charge the flashlight-sized nickel-cadmium cells can easily be provided by a 6.3- or 10-volt transformer, a half-wave selenium or silicon rectifier, and a resistor to limit the current to a safe value. Such a charger can often be incorporated into the instrument for convenience and for continuous use of the instrument where the a-c supply is available.

2-9   Conversion of Direct Current to Alternating Current

When a low-voltage battery is the only power source, it is often necessary to convert low d-c voltage to both a-c and high d-c voltages for operation of various electronic circuits. One frequently used method requires a mechanical vibrator. A vibrating contact alternately switches the direct current in such a way as to provide an a-c output. The low a-c voltage can then be stepped up to a higher a-c voltage with a transformer, and a rectifier-filter circuit can be used to obtain a high d-c voltage. One possible circuit is shown in Fig. 2-31a. The vibrating-reed contact is set so that its normal position is against a fixed contact. When the d-c supply is turned on, current passes through the magnet coil of the vibrator and the transformer primary. The magnetic field of the coil pulls the reed away from

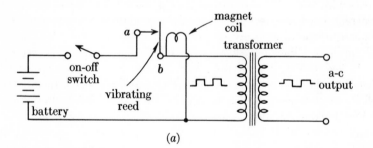

(a)

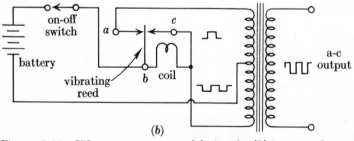

(b)

Figure 2-31   Vibrator convertors: (a) simple; (b) improved.

the fixed contact, thereby stopping the flow of current through the transformer. The reed is then released, springs back to its normal position, and the cycle repeats itself. The resulting square-wave d-c pulses in the primary of the transformer induce an a-c voltage in the secondary.

Another type of vibrator has the reed normally midway between two fixed contacts, as shown in Fig. 2-31b. By connecting the battery the magnet coil is activated and pulls the reed against fixed contact c. This short-circuits the magnet coil, and the reed breaks away from contact c. However, inertia of the reed causes it to move past its normal position and against contact a, causing current to flow in the other half of the transformer winding. Meanwhile the magnet coil has been reenergized, and the cycle repeats itself. This vibrator circuit has the advantage, over that shown in Fig. 2-31a, that it keeps the battery under continuous load so the peak-to-peak primary voltage can be twice the d-c supply voltage. The magnitude of the a-c output depends on the d-c supply voltage and the turns ratio of the transformer. The fundamental frequency of the a-c voltage depends on the mechanical design of the vibrator.

Until recently the vibrator and the motor-generator, sometimes called a dynamotor, were the commonly accepted means for converting from direct current to alternating current. Transistor circuits, however, are now possible that have certain advantages, especially in efficiency and length of uninterrupted service. Two transistors replace the vibrator and act as an alternating switch so as to convert the d-c to an a-c voltage.

References

The following books contain additional information:

"The Radio Amateur's Handbook," published annually by the American Radio Relay League, West Hartford, Conn., contains a wealth of very practical information on the design and construction of power supplies.

Lurch, E. N., "Fundamentals of Electronics," Wiley, New York, 1960. For supplementary reading; written on a moderate level.

Seely, S., "Electron-Tube Circuits," 2d ed., McGraw-Hill, New York, 1958.

Angelo, E. J., "Electronic Circuits," McGraw-Hill, New York, 1958. This and the preceding entry contain rigorous, advanced treatments of rectifiers and filtering circuits.

Problems

2-1 By what factor will the secondary voltage of a transformer be reduced if the line voltage decreases from 115 volts a-c to 95 volts a-c?

Ans.: 17 per cent

2-2 A particular junction diode has an interelectrode capacitance of 100 pf and an average forward resistance of 10 ohms. At about what frequency would the rectifying efficiency drop 10 per cent due to the capacitance?

Ans.: roughly 16 mc

2-3 Various rectifier circuits are being considered for use with a 100–0–100-volt power transformer secondary. The load may be considered negligible, and the rectifiers and transformers considered ideal. What is the maximum output voltage obtainable for the following rectifier circuits with a capacitor input filter: (a) half-wave; (b) full-wave; (c) full-wave bridge; (d) full-wave doubler?

Ans.: (a) 280 volts; (b) 140 volts; (c) 280 volts; (d) 560 volts

2-4 What is the minimum acceptable peak inverse voltage rating for the rectifiers used in each of the circuits of Prob. 2-3?

Ans.: (a) 560 volts; (b) 280 volts; (c) 280 volts; (d) 560 volts

2-5 If the voltage-doubler rectifier of Fig. 2-14 were to be wired using vacuum diodes, what is the minimum acceptable heater-to-cathode voltage rating? That is, what is the maximum potential of each cathode with respect to the connection between C_1 and C_2?   *Ans.:* D_1, +160 volts; D_2, −160 volts

2-6 Consider the rectifier and transformer of the power supply shown Fig. P2-6 to be ideal. Calculate: (a) output voltage; (b) current through the 5-kilohm load; (c) rms ripple voltage; (d) output voltage if the effective diode and transformer resistance were 500 ohms.

Ans.: (a) 240 volts; (b) 48 ma; (c) 24 volts; (d) 216 volts

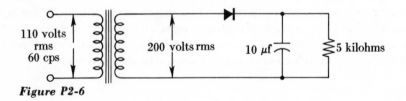

Figure P2-6

2-7 In aircraft and missile applications, 400-cps line voltages are used to reduce the size of transformers and filter components. The filter of the power supply of Fig. 2-17b has an LC product of 80 henry-microfarads. What LC product would result in the same ripple voltage from a 400-cps supply?

Ans.: LC = 1.8 henry-microfarads

2-8 A Zener diode is used in a low-voltage source as shown in Fig. P2-8. The IN751 is rated at 5.1 volts and can dissipate a maximum of 400 mw. Calculate the value of R_s for R_L = 200 ohms and a dissipation of 100 mw in the IN751 diode.

Ans.: R_s = about 65 ohms

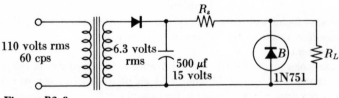

Figure P2-8

EXPERIMENTS

This set of experiments is designed to familiarize the reader with the characteristics of the various types of rectifier and filter systems used in voltage power supplies. The experiments described are performed on a power-supply unit which has been designed for general laboratory use. In addition, it has been designed with the special connectors described in Supplement 1 and laid out in such a way that the many different rectifier and filter circuits may be rapidly wired and studied. Specifically studied in this experiment are the half-wave, full-wave, bridge, and doubler rectifier circuits, as well as several *LC* and *RC* filter networks, and the effect of *loading* on the output voltage. At the conclusion of the experiments, the experimental power supply is left wired to be used as the basic power supply throughout the remaining experiments. A complete description of the power-supply unit is given in Supplement 1. This power-supply unit also contains a voltage regulator circuit which is studied in Chap. 8. The regulator section is essential, not only to provide a unit for the study of regulation but also because a well-regulated power source of this quality is required to power critical circuits in many instrumental applications.

Expt. 2-1 Familiarization with the Power-Supply Unit

The following steps and observations will acquaint the experimenter with the location of the main components, the design of the power supply, and the scheme for connecting the various rectifier and filter circuits.

Unplug the power supply. Remove the top and bottom covers. With the power supply inverted and the front panel to the right, follow the line cord into the chassis, through the fuse, and to the on-off switch on the front panel. Tip the chassis up and locate the power transformer. Looking again on the underside of the chassis, observe how the two red high-voltage windings come to the HV posts and how the red-yellow high-voltage center tap comes to the CT post. Now locate the four diodes. Note that these four diodes are between posts so that they may be connected in the various rectifier configurations. Locate the filter capacitors, the filter choke atop the chassis, and locate their connections to the posts under the chassis. Note that C_3 is actually two capacitors in series. This arrangement is used to obtain the required voltage rating. A voltage divider is provided to allow taking a fraction of the full power-supply voltage. The divider consists of 5 power resistors in series, mounted near the rear panel. The circuit diagram is shown in Fig. 2-32. Note that the metal back plate helps dissipate the heat from the power resistors. Trace the wires that connect the power resistors to the divider switch on the front panel. Referring to Fig. 2-33, note how the divider is connected to the posts P_1, P_2, and P_3. Trace the lead from the rotor contact of the divider switch through the fuse to post P_1. Note from Fig. 2-33 that the positive d-c voltage from the rectifiers and filter would be connected to P_3 and would go through the DIV-REG switch on the front panel to the divider. When P_1 and P_2 are connected, the output from the divider goes through another pole of the DIV-REG switch, through the HV switch, and to the d-c+ front-panel output jack. In the REG position, the positive d-c voltage is connected to the regulator and the regulator output is connected to the d-c+ output jack through a fuse and the HV switch. The octal

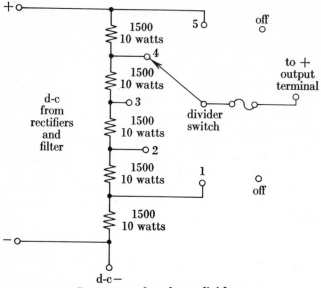

Figure 2-32   *Power-supply voltage divider.*

power sockets on the front panel provide a convenient means for connecting experimental and laboratory circuits to the power supply. In Fig. 2-33, the banana jack to the right of the d-c+ terminal connects to pin 3 of the octal power sockets on the front panel. Therefore, to connect the d-c + to pin 3, it is necessary to connect a current meter of appropriate range or a jumper (short banana patch cord) between the d-c+ banana jack and the banana jack to its right. The d-c− output goes to pin 1 of the power sockets. A banana jack which is connected to the chassis ground is also provided on the front panel. Neither the d-c− nor d-c+ is connected to the chassis ground unless done so with a patch cord on the front panel. Pins 5 and 7 on the octal power sockets are connected to a 6.3-volt winding of the power transformer. Follow the green leads from the power transformer to the FILS terminals on the front panel. The center tap of the filament winding is connected to d-c−. The remainder of the power supply consists of the regulator section, which will be discussed in Chap. 8.

Expt. 2-2   Measurement of Transformer Voltages

Turn the power supply to reveal the underside of the chassis. Plug the power supply into a line socket. Make sure the POWER switch is OFF. DANGER—line voltages are now exposed in this chassis, even with the POWER switch OFF. A good rule to avoid serious shocks is always to keep one hand away from the circuit. Connect the VTVM common lead to the high-voltage winding center tap. Turn the POWER switch to ON. Measure the voltages on both sides of the high-voltage winding. Turn off the power supply and remove the VTVM common lead.

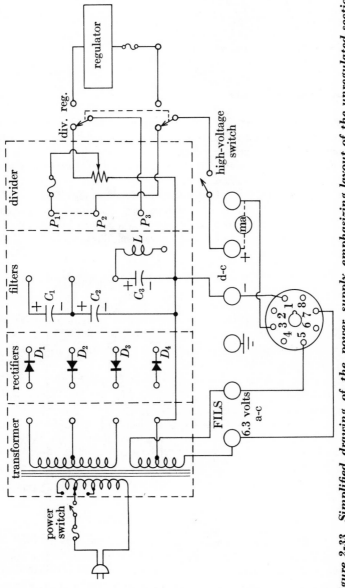

Figure 2-33 Simplified drawing of the power supply emphasizing layout of the unregulated section.

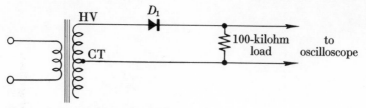

Figure 2-34   Half-wave rectifier.

Expt. 2-3   Rectifier Circuits

a. The Half-Wave Rectifier.   With the power supply OFF remove *all* spring-clip leads, except in the regulator circuit. (See Supplement 1 for information on power-supply and spring-clip connections.)   Wire the half-wave rectifier circuit shown in Fig. 2-34.   Observe the output waveform and magnitude on the oscilloscope.   Use the d-c input position.

Turn the power supply off.   Always turn the power supply off when working on the power-supply circuit.   Reverse the connections to the diode in the half-wave rectifier of Fig. 2-34.   This is most easily done by using diode D_2, which is oriented in the opposite direction.   Observe the waveform from this rectifier.   Note that the output is a negative potential.

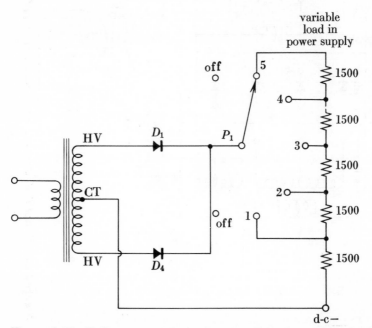

Figure 2-35   Full-wave rectifier and connection of a variable load.

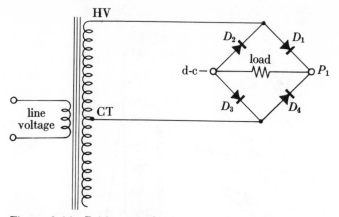

Figure 2-36   Bridge rectifier.

b. The Full-Wave Rectifier. Wire the full-wave rectifier circuit as shown in Fig. 2-35. The divider resistors may be used as a load by connecting the rectifier output between post P_1 and the d-c— post as shown. Be sure the divider voltage switch is in position 5. This is the maximum load resistance (minimum *load* current). Observe the full-wave rectifier output waveform. Note that the peak value of the rectified voltage is the same as the half-wave.

c. Bridge Rectifier. Wire the bridge rectifier as shown in Fig. 2-36. Again use the divider for the load as in the previous experiment. Observe the output waveform and magnitude.

Expt. 2-4   Filter Networks

Filter networks vary considerably in their filtering ability and the stability of the d-c output voltage. To characterize the main filter types, the *output voltage* and *ripple voltage* of each is noted as a function of the *output current*. The characteristics of the filter types can best be compared by plotting the ripple voltages for all types on the same graph. Suitable scale magnitudes for this plot are shown in Fig. 2-37*a*. It is recommended that the data be put on the graphs directly. The output voltages can also be plotted on a single graph, whose scales are shown in Fig. 2-37*b*.

a. Capacitor Input Filters. Capacitor input filters are studied by wiring the π-section filter for the measurements. The output voltage and ripple voltage of the capacitor filter are unaffected by the additional LC section. Thus the characteristics of both the capacitor and π-section filters can be taken at the same time. Both these filters are studied with the half-wave rectifier, then with the full-wave.

Disconnect the bridge rectifier. Wire a half-wave rectifier, but do not attach a load. Wire a π-section filter and connect to the load and half-wave rectifier as in Fig. 2-38. Use the VOM for the milliammeter shown. Turn the DIVIDER VOLT-

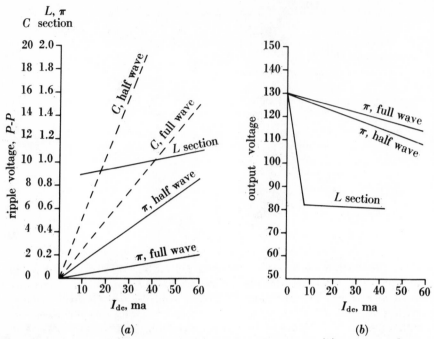

Figure 2-37   *Dependence of (a) ripple voltage and (b) output voltage
on filter type.*

AGE switch to position 5.   Measure the peak-to-peak a-c voltage across capacitors C_2 and C_3 with the oscilloscope.   Be sure to switch the oscilloscope to a-c input for this measurement.   Note the *load current*.   Plot these points on the graph.   Turn the DIVIDER VOLTAGE switch to OFF (no load).   Demonstrate that both filters are perfect with no load.   Plot these points.   Plot the values of the *ripple voltage* against *load current* for both filters at all other settings (4, 3, 2, 1) of the DIVIDER VOLTAGE switch.

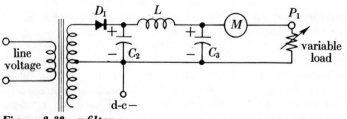

Figure 2-38   *π filter.*

Using the VTVM, measure the d-c voltage at C_3 for all positions of the DI-VIDER VOLTAGE switch. Plot these points against the load current indicated by the VOM.

Wire a full-wave rectifier to connect to the π-section filter. Repeat the above measurements of ripple voltage and output voltage. Note that the ripple frequency is twice that of the half-wave rectifier.

b. The Choke-Input Filter. Disconnect C_2 from the π-section filter of the previous experiment. *Keep the full-wave rectifier.* Measure the output voltage as a function of load current and plot. Also measure the ripple voltage as a function of current. These two measurements can be made simultaneously. Note that the output voltage of the choke-input filter is relatively constant above a certain critical load current.

Expt. 2-5   The Voltage Doubler

The voltage-doubler rectifier circuit necessarily includes the input-filter capacitance; therefore the rectifier and filter cannot be studied independently. Certain characteristics of the doubler circuit will be noted in this experiment. Since the doubler is the normal rectifier circuit for this power supply, the unit will be in normal operating order at the completion of this experiment.

Wire the voltage-doubler circuit as shown in Fig. 2-39. The diodes are wired in series to increase the peak inverse-voltage rating to the required value. Turn the DIVIDER VOLTAGE switch OFF. The output voltage of this circuit is great enough to burn out the divider resistors if the DIVIDER VOLTAGE switch is put in position 1, 2, or 3, while the resistors are still connected as a load.

Measure the output voltage with no load. Note that the doubler provides four times the voltage of the full-wave rectifier using the same transformer. Measure the output voltage as a function of load current at DIVIDER VOLTAGE positions 5 and 4. Since the output voltage has been shown to be a linear function of the current in previous experiments, the output voltage for higher loads can be estimated.

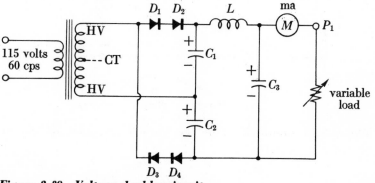

Figure 2-39   Voltage-doubler circuit.

Measure the ripple voltage at C_1 and C_3 with the DIVIDER VOLTAGE at positions 5 and 4. Note that the ripple frequency is twice the line frequency; therefore the doubler is a full-wave circuit.

Expt. 2-6   Restoration of the Power Supply

The power supply is now nearly wired in its normal operating state. Only the divider resistor bank must be rewired to perform its normal function as a *voltage divider*, rather than as a *variable load*. The required connections to P_1, P_2, and P_3 are shown in Fig. 2-40. When this is complete, check the wiring of the rectifiers and filter against Fig. 2-40. If all seems to be in order, turn the power supply right side up. Turn the DIVIDER-REGULATOR switch to DIVIDER, the DIVIDER VOLTAGE to position 5, and the ON-OFF switch to ON. Measure the voltage between the d-c+ and d-c− terminals with the VTVM. Measure the output voltage for each of the divider positions. Turn the DIVIDER-REGULATOR switch to REGULATOR, and measure the range of output voltages available when the REGULATED VOLTAGE control is rotated. For most of the experiments in subsequent chapters the power supply will be operated in the REGU-LATOR position at various specified voltages between 200 and 350 volts.

Replace the bottom and top covers.

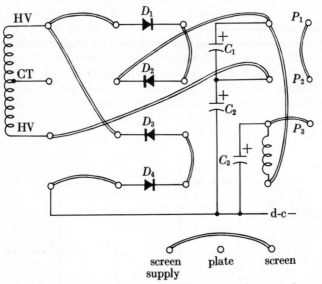

Figure 2-40   ***Connections for the normal operation of the power supply.***

chapter three

Amplification by Vacuum Tubes and Transistors

3-1 Amplification

Amplification is the most common operation that is performed on electrical signals, so a thorough understanding of the principles of amplification and amplifier circuits is obviously important. Amplification is accomplished by controlling a power supply with an element that is actuated by the input signal. This is shown in block form in Fig. 3-1. The triode vacuum tube, the pentode vacuum tube, and the transistor are the most common control elements used in amplifiers. The means by which each of these control elements amplifies (i.e., controls current in the power circuit in response to an input signal) are presented in this chapter.

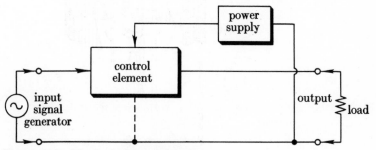

Figure 3-1   Method of amplification.

3-2   The Vacuum Triode

The cathode of the vacuum triode (Fig. 3-2) is heated to the temperature required for the thermionic emission of electrons.   During normal
operation the anode (plate) is positive with respect to the cathode, and
electrons flow from the cathode to the anode.   A control grid is placed
relatively close to the cathode.   Because of its proximity, a small negative
potential on the grid with respect to the cathode can counteract the attractive force of a relatively large positive potential of anode with respect
to cathode.   As the grid is made less negative (more positive), more electrons will be attracted to the anode; thus the grid-cathode voltage controls
the current from a power supply connected between cathode and anode.
In circuit diagrams, the heater or filament is often omitted.   It is under-

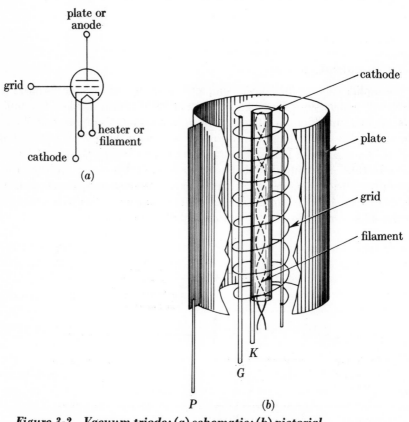

Figure 3-2   Vacuum triode: (a) schematic; (b) pictorial.

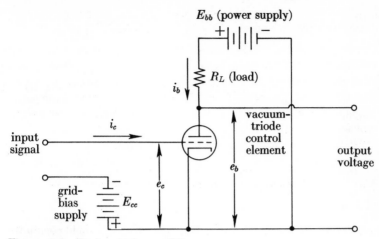

Figure 3-3   Basic triode amplifier.

stood that this element is present and connected to the proper power source.

A basic triode-amplifier circuit is shown in Fig. 3-3. The grid of the triode amplifier is normally operated at a negative potential with respect to the cathode. The voltage E_{cc} is introduced into the grid circuit so that the grid remains negative even when the input signal swings positive. The subscript c has become associated with the grid circuit, so that the grid-to-cathode voltage is referred to as e_c and the grid current as i_c. The power-supply voltage E_{bb} is necessary to the circuit to make the anode positive with respect to the cathode and to provide a source for the output current. The subscript b refers to the plate circuit, and thus the plate-to-cathode voltage and plate current are e_b and i_b, respectively. The resistance R_L is the load referred to in the block diagram of Fig. 3-1. The grid voltage of the triode controls the current through the tube and through the load resistor which is in series with the tube. The voltage across R_L ($i_b R_L$) and the voltage e_b will change equally and oppositely with changes of e_c since their sum is the constant E_{bb}, that is, $e_b + i_b R_L = E_{bb}$. Thus the amplified output voltage may equally well be taken across the load or across the tube, as shown. The latter is usually more convenient for connection to subsequent circuits.

Characteristic Curves. The interrelationships of e_c, i_c, e_b, and i_b are the triode's characteristics. They are slightly different for each individual tube and vary greatly from one type of triode to another. An understanding of these characteristics is essential for determining the relation of the input and output signals in an amplifier circuit. They can be deter-

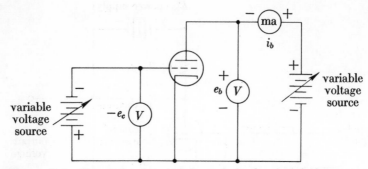

Figure 3-4   Circuit for determining triode characteristics.

mined by using the circuit shown in Fig. 3-4.   First e_c is held constant while i_b is measured for various values of e_b.   The relationship between i_b and e_b is then measured for other values of e_c.   A family of curves is obtained as shown in Fig. 3-5.   The plot of i_b vs. e_b is called the plate-characteristic curve.   If e_b is held constant and i_b measured as a function of e_c, a family of curves called the transfer characteristics (Fig. 3-6) results.   However, the plate characteristic contains all the necessary information and is particularly useful for determining the average values of e_c, i_b, and e_b in a particular circuit.   Note that the relationship between i_c and the other

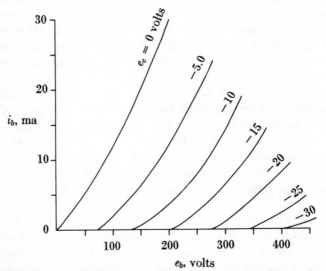

Figure 3-5   Average plate characteristics, 12AU7 triode.   (Courtesy of Sylvania.)

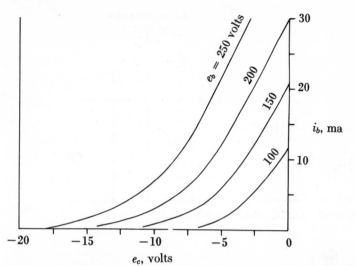

Figure 3-6 *Average transfer characteristics, 12AU7 triode. (Courtesy of Sylvania.)*

variables has not been determined. When the triode is in its normal operating region (e_c negative), i_c is of the order of 1 μa. In most circuits this is so small that the variation of i_c as a function of e_c, i_b, and e_b has no influence on the signal source and is ignored.

3-3 The Triode Common-Cathode Amplifier

For the typical triode amplifier (Fig. 3-7) the input voltage e_{in} is between grid and cathode and the output voltage e_{out} between plate and cathode. The cathode is common to both input and output. There are particular values for i_b, e_b, and e_c even when no signal is applied to the input. (It should be noted that "no signal" usually means a signal of zero volts, not an open grid circuit.) The no-signal values of i_b, e_b, and e_c are called the quiescent, or average, values and are given the symbols I_b, E_b, and E_c. The point defined by I_b, E_b, and E_c on the characteristic curve is called the quiescent point. The location of the quiescent point on the characteristic curve is an important part of the analysis of an amplifier circuit. The procedure is as follows: First a "load line" is determined for the values of supply voltage E_{bb} and load resistance R_L which are to be used in the amplifier circuit. Assume that e_c is so negative that the plate current $i_b = 0$. If this were true, the voltage drop across R_L would be zero and e_b would equal E_{bb}. This point 1 is plotted on the plate-characteristic

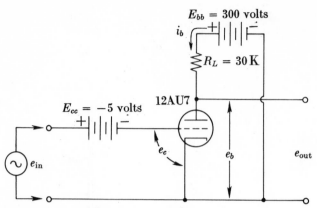

Figure 3-7   12AU7 triode amplifier.

curve (Fig. 3-8).   Then it is assumed that the grid is so positive that the triode becomes a perfect conductor so that the plate is in effect tied to the cathode ($e_b = 0$ and $i_b = E_{bb}/R_L$).   Plot this point 2 on the characteristic curve, and join points 1 and 2 with a straight line as in Fig. 3-8.   This line is called the load line because it is determined only by the values of the load and E_{bb}.

For the selected values of E_{bb} and R_L the resulting values of e_b and i_b must fall along the load line.   If the no-signal value E_c is now specified by choosing a value for the voltage E_{cc}, the no-signal values E_b and I_b are established.   Figure 3-8, point 3, shows the no-signal values for E_b and I_b as determined by the load line and the plate characteristic for the selected average grid voltage $E_c = -5$ volts.   These values are also called the quiescent, average, and operating-point values.   The instantaneous grid voltage e_c depends on the sum of grid bias and input signal, and, by moving along the load line, the instantaneous values of e_b and i_b can be read from the graph for any given value of e_c.

Practical Signal Limits.   There are two more points on the load line which are of interest because they define the limits of amplification.   They are the cutoff and saturation points.   When the grid voltage is very negative, the plate current is zero, the plate voltage is E_{bb}, and the tube is said to be cut off (point 4 on Fig. 3-8).   The minimum grid voltage necessary to produce a cutoff condition is called E_{co}.   When the grid is more negative than E_{co}, the plate voltage can no longer change with changing e_c; hence the amplification ceases.   On the other hand, the grid usually cannot go more positive than $E_c = 0$.   When e_{in} is more positive than the bias, the grid attracts electrons to cause electron flow in the grid

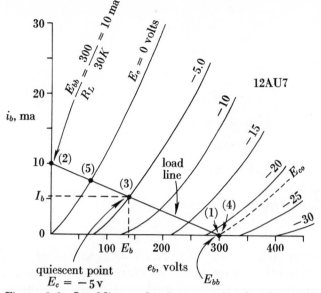

Figure 3-8   Load line and quiescent point for the amplifier of Fig. 3-7.

circuit.   Large resistances, usually present in the grid circuit or the signal source, will prevent appreciable grid current, and the low resistance between grid and cathode will prevent e_c from becoming significantly positive.   Therefore, the tube is said to be "saturated" because it is in its maximum conducting condition.   The saturation point is point 5 on the load line of Fig. 3-8.

Self-Biasing.   A grid-bias battery is rarely used in modern vacuum-tube circuits.   Instead, a resistance R_K (Fig. 3-9) is put in the cathode circuit.   Then electrons flowing from the negative terminal of the power supply E_{bb} through R_K, the tube, R_L, and to the positive terminal cause a voltage drop $i_b R_K$ across the cathode resistance.   The end of the resistor connected to the cathode is at a more positive potential than the other end connected to the common point for input and output circuits.   This in effect makes the grid negative with respect to the cathode.   The average grid voltage E_c will be $-I_b \times R_K$.   The quiescent values E_b, I_b are slightly more difficult to determine in this case because the grid-bias voltage depends on the plate current and the cathode resistor.   It can be done, however, by using the plate-characteristic curves.   Draw a load line as shown in Fig. 3-10.   Note that R_K must be added to R_L when calculating the current-axis intercept.   To find the operating point on the load line, the relationship $-e_c = i_b R_K$ is employed.   Mark the point $i_b = -e_c/R_K$ on

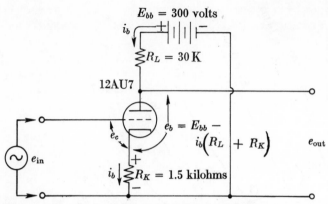

Figure 3-9   *Cathode-biased triode amplifier.*

every plate-characteristic curve.   Join these points with a curve.   The intersection of this line with the load line is the quiescent point.   The quiescent grid voltage E_c can be estimated by its position between two plate-characteristic curves.   The size of R_K is chosen for the particular value of E_c desired.

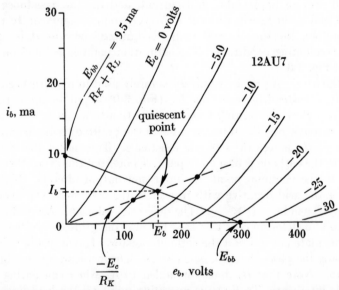

Figure 3-10   *Location of quiescent point for a self-biased amplifier.*

Small-Signal Parameters.   The change in e_b or i_b as a result of an input signal (a change in e_c) could be determined by a graphical analysis of the plate-characteristic curve as above for each value of e_c.   However, it is much more convenient to analyze the circuit mathematically after substituting an equivalent circuit for the triode.   It is not possible to derive a simple circuit which would replace the triode for its entire operating range.   This is because the characteristics of the triode are not linear, as shown in Figs. 3-5 and 3-6.   A linear equivalent circuit is only a valid approximation over small portions of the operating range.   In other words, the equivalent circuit will not describe the relationship of the total quantities i_b, e_b, and e_c, but it will describe the relationship of the small changes in the quantities i_b, e_b, and e_c.

The application of a signal to the grid of an amplifier causes i_b, e_b, and e_c to differ from their quiescent values.   The differences between the actual values and the quiescent values are called the signal values and are given the symbols i_p, e_p, and e_g.   In other words, $i_b - I_b = i_p$, where i_p is the change in the plate current due to the signal, $e_c - E_c = e_g$, etc.

Upon noting that the quantities i_b, e_b, and e_c are interdependent variables and choosing e_b as the dependent variable, the equation

$$e_b = f(e_c, i_b) \tag{3-1}$$

results.   The differential of e_b is thus*

$$de_b = \left(\frac{\partial e_b}{\partial e_c}\right)_{i_b} de_c + \left(\frac{\partial e_b}{\partial i_b}\right)_{e_c} di_b \tag{3-2}$$

The partial differential $(\partial e_b/\partial i_b)_{e_c}$ is the reciprocal slope of the plate-characteristic curve (Fig. 3-5), has the units ohms, and is called the plate resistance r_p.   It is customary to evaluate r_p at the quiescent point for the particular amplifier circuit involved.   The partial differential $-(\partial e_b/\partial e_c)_{i_b}$ is called the amplification factor μ.   It can be determined by drawing a constant-plate-current line through I_b on the plate-characteristic curve and noting the change in e_b for a given change in e_c.   The amplification factor has no units.   On the plate-characteristic curve (Fig. 3-11) μ and r_p are evaluated for the 12AU7 tube at the quiescent point found for the amplifier of Fig. 3-9.

Since the partial differentials have been assumed to be constant over

---

* A knowledge of differential equations is *not* necessary to understand this formula or the derivation.   Equation (3-2) reads simply: The change in e_b is equal to the change in e_b resulting from a change in e_c at constant i_b times the change in e_c, plus the change in e_b resulting from a change in i_b at constant e_c times the change in i_b.

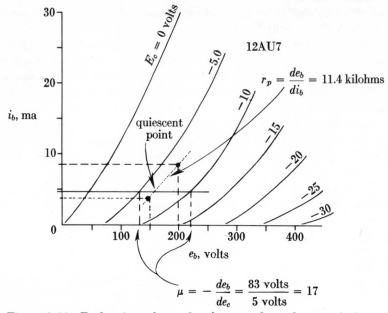

Figure 3-11   *Evaluation of μ and r_p from a plate-characteristic curve.*

a limited range, the expanded equation can now be written

$$\Delta e_b = -\mu \, \Delta e_c + r_p \, \Delta i_b \tag{3-3}$$

where Δe_b is equal to the signal voltage e_p at the plate.   Similarly, $\Delta e_c = e_g$, and $\Delta i_b = i_p$.   Now the expanded equation is

$$e_p = -\mu e_g + r_p i_p \tag{3-4}$$

This equation says that the signal voltage between the plate and the

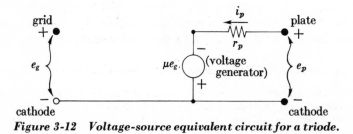

Figure 3-12   *Voltage-source equivalent circuit for a triode.*

cathode is equal to an opposing voltage source μe_g and the voltage drop across a resistance r_p caused by the plate-current signal i_p. This equivalent circuit is shown schematically in Fig. 3-12.

The use of the equivalent circuit for the a-c, or small-signal, analysis of an amplifier circuit is illustrated in Fig. 3-13. Consider the amplifier circuit of Fig. 3-13a. Figure 3-13b is the equivalent circuit. The equivalent circuit is simply a voltage source of $-\mu e_g$ volts in series with resistance r_p and R_L. Therefore

$$i_p = \frac{-\mu e_g}{R_L + r_p} \tag{3-5}$$

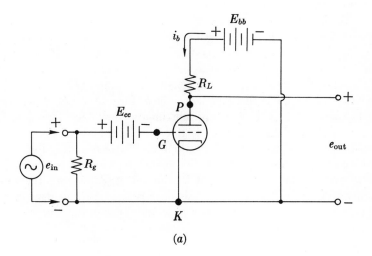

(a)

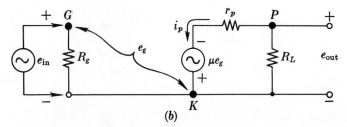

(b)

Figure 3-13   Triode amplifier: (a) actual circuit; (b) voltage-source equivalent circuit.

The output voltage e_{out}, with the polarity shown in Fig. 3-13b, is then

$$e_{\text{out}} = i_p R_L = \frac{-\mu e_g R_L}{R_L + r_p} \tag{3-6}$$

The gain of the amplifier, $e_{\text{out}}/e_{\text{in}}$, is

$$A = \text{gain} = \frac{-\mu R_L}{r_p + R_L} \tag{3-7}$$

since $e_g = e_{\text{in}}$. The minus sign in the gain formula indicates that the output-signal voltage is opposite in sign from the input-signal voltage. The output voltage decreases when the grid voltage increases (becomes more positive or less negative) so that the input and output signals are 180° out of phase. For the amplifier of Fig. 3-7 the gain is $(-21 \times 30K)/(12K + 30K) = -15$. In order to determine the effect of the amplifier on the input-signal source, the amplifier input resistance must be determined. According to Fig. 3-13 the input resistance is simply R_g. The resistor R_g is put in the circuit to provide a leakage path for the electrons which happen to strike the grid of the triode. Without R_g the grid would soon build up a negative charge and change the quiescent values of the circuit, and perhaps even cause the tube to cut off. The maximum allowable value for R_g (usually 500 kilohms to 10 megohms) is given in the tube manuals.

The effect of drawing current from the amplifier output terminals can be determined by considering the amplifier equivalent circuit as a voltage source with an internal resistance. With the aid of Thévenin's theorem (see Supplement 2) we see that the resistance is r_p and R_L in parallel or $(R_L \times r_p)/(R_L + r_p)$. Thus the output resistance of the amplifier is

$$R_{\text{out}} = \frac{R_L r_p}{R_L + r_p} \tag{3-8}$$

For the amplifier of Fig. 3-7, the output impedance is $(30K \times 12K)/(30K + 12K) = 8.6K$.

When the cathode bias circuit of Fig. 3-9 is used, an analysis of the equivalent circuit shows that the voltage gain A is

$$A = \frac{-21 \times 30K}{22 \times 1.5K + 30K + 12K} = -8.4 \tag{3-9}$$

The gain of the amplifier in Fig. 3-9 is thus

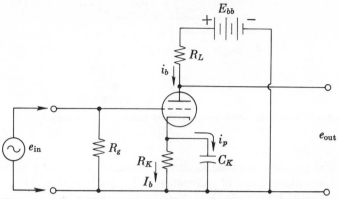

Figure 3-14 *Self-biased amplifier with a bypass capacitor.*

Notice that in the process of eliminating the C battery the voltage gain has been reduced because of the term $(1 + \mu)R_K$ in the denominator of Eq. (3-9). This disadvantage can be nullified for a-c signals by introducing a cathode capacitor C_K as in Fig. 3-14. In this case, a grid bias equal to $I_b R_K$ is maintained, where I_b is the average plate current. The capacitor C_K normally has a very large capacitance value so that its a-c impedance for signals of 100 cps or over is negligible. Thus the signal current is effectively bypassed around R_K so that it does not affect the bias voltage. When the equivalent circuit is drawn for a-c signals, R_K is omitted, giving the equivalent circuit of Fig. 3-13b. The analysis of the circuit is the same as that of Fig. 3-13b, except for the restriction that the signal must be a-c. The method for the determination of the quiescent point (Fig. 3-10) is not affected by C_K.

Current-Source Equivalent Circuit. Out of the three variables for the triode (i_b, e_b, and e_c), e_b was chosen somewhat arbitrarily to be the dependent variable [Eq. (3-1)]. It would be equally valid to choose either one of the other variables as the dependent one. If i_b is chosen as the dependent variable,

$$i_b = f(e_c, e_b)$$

and taking the differential,

$$di_b = \left(\frac{\partial i_b}{\partial e_c}\right)_{e_b} de_c + \left(\frac{\partial i_b}{\partial e_b}\right)_{e_c} de_b \qquad (3\text{-}10)$$

Note that $(\partial i_b / \partial e_b)_{e_c} = 1/r_p$. The partial differential $(\partial i_b / \partial e_c)_{e_b}$ is the slope of the transfer characteristic (Fig. 3-6). This slope has the units 1/ohms, or mhos, and is called the mutual conductance, or transconduct-

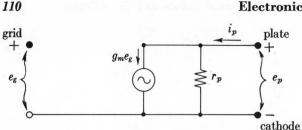

Figure 3-15   Current-source equivalent circuit for a triode.

ance, g_m. The transconductance g_m can be evaluated from the plate-characteristic curves along a line of constant e_b. Assuming that r_p and g_m are
constant for a limited range of values, Eq. (3-10) can be written

$$i_p = g_m e_g + \frac{e_p}{r_p} \qquad (3\text{-}11)$$

This equation suggests that the signal plate current is the sum of the currents in two current paths between the cathode and plate. One is the current source $g_m e_g$, and the other is the current through r_p as a result of the
potential e_p, that is, e_p/r_p. This equivalent circuit is shown schematically
in Fig. 3-15. It is called the current-source equivalent circuit because the
signal results in a current $g_m e_g$ generated in the output circuit. The current-
source equivalent circuit of the amplifier of Fig. 3-13a is shown in Fig. 3-16.
With the current-source equivalent circuit the current $g_m e_g$ is divided between r_p and R_L. The voltage across R_L and r_p is the output voltage e_{out},

$$e_{out} = -g_m e_g \frac{r_p R_L}{r_p + R_L} \qquad (3\text{-}12)$$

Notice that, since $\mu = g_m r_p$, Eq. (3-12) is the same as Eq. (3-6), which was
derived for the voltage-source equivalent circuit. The same results will be
obtained from analysis by either equivalent circuit. However, one equivalent circuit is sometimes more convenient to use than another. It will be

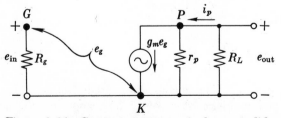

Figure 3-16   Current-source equivalent amplifier circuit.

seen in Sec. 3-5 that the current-source equivalent circuit is particularly useful for pentode-amplifier circuit analysis.

3-4   The Vacuum Pentode

The addition of two more grids besides cathode, anode, and control grid produces a five-element tube that has certain advantages over the triode.   The schematic representation of the pentode tube is shown in Fig. 3-17.   The function of the heater, cathode, control grid, and plate are identical with those elements of the triode.   The screen grid is operated with a potential of the order of the plate-supply voltage.   The screen grid acts as an attractive force to the electrons, but it has a small enough cross section so that relatively few electrons are captured by it.   The electrons pass through the screen grid to the plate.   The screen-grid potential has much more influence over the plate current than has the plate voltage because it is so much closer to the cathode than the plate.

Occasionally an electron striking the plate will rebound or cause other electrons to be emitted.   The suppressor grid is introduced in order to prevent these electrons from being attracted to the screen grid.   The suppressor grid is normally connected to the cathode and is thus negative with respect to the plate.   The negative potential repels the plate electrons back to the plate.

In the case of the tetrode, which does not have a suppressor grid, the useful operating range of the tube is reduced.   This is because considerable screen-grid current will flow if the screen-grid potential is greater than that of the plate.   Thus the plate current drops off even at a relatively high plate voltage.   Tetrodes, except for some special types, are virtually obsolete.

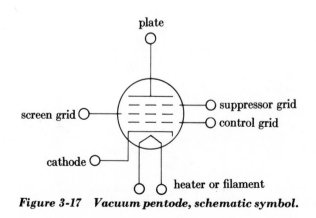

Figure 3-17   Vacuum pentode, schematic symbol.

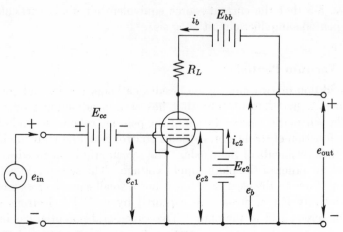

Figure 3-18   Basic pentode amplifier.

A basic pentode-amplifier circuit illustrating the grid connections is shown in Fig. 3-18. The characteristics of the vacuum pentode can be determined just as they are for the triode except that there are two more variables, the screen-grid voltage, e_{c2}, and the suppressor-grid voltage e_{c3}. In the customary use of the pentode, the suppressor is connected to the cathode and is thus at zero potential. The screen-grid voltage is normally held constant; i.e., it is not a function of e_c or i_b. If the screen-grid potential is set at a constant value as with the circuit of Fig. 3-19, the plate characteristics can be determined just as they were for the triode in Sec. 3-2. A typical pentode plate-characteristic curve is shown in Fig. 3-20. Notice that the plate current is relatively independent of the plate voltage. This gives the pentode an extremely high value of plate resistance ($\partial e_b/\partial i_b$). If

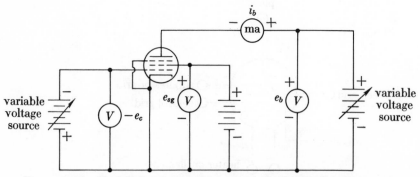

Figure 3-19   Circuit for determining pentode characteristics.

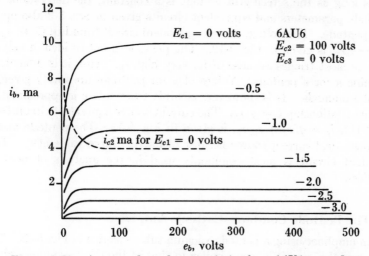

Figure 3-20   Average plate characteristics for a 6AU6 pentode.

the screen-grid voltage is changed, the entire plate-characteristic curve is changed, as shown in Fig. 3-21. The transfer characteristic of the pentode is very similar to that of the triode except that the family of curves resulting from different plate voltages will be practically superimposed.

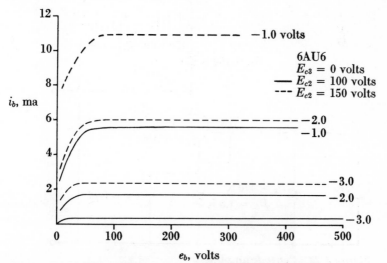

Figure 3-21   Effect of E_{c2} on pentode plate characteristics.

As long as the screen-grid voltage is a constant, the derivations for the triode parameters and equivalent circuits given in Sec. 3-2 also apply to the pentode. The voltage-source equivalent circuit from Eq. (3-4), $e_p = -\mu e_g + i_p r_p$, is given in Fig. 3-12. The pentode is not so ideal a voltage source as most triodes because of its very high r_p. Also, it is difficult to determine μ for a pentode. Values of μ for pentodes are rarely given in the tube manuals. It is, however, possible to calculate μ approximately from the relationship $\mu = g_m r_p$. The current-source equivalent circuit from Eq. (3-11), $i_p = g_m e_g + e_p/r_p$, is given in Fig. 3-15. The pentode makes an almost ideal current source because of its very large value of r_p. This equivalent circuit is most commonly used in the analysis of pentode amplifiers.

3-5   The Pentode Common-Cathode Amplifier

An amplifier using a pentode vacuum tube is shown in Fig. 3-22. The analysis of this circuit is very similar to that of the triode amplifier given in Sec. 3-3. The determination of the load line and the quiescent point is demonstrated in Fig. 3-23. The determination of the quiescent grid voltage E_{c1} is less exact than for the triode. Substituting $-e_{c1} = 2.0$, 2.25, and 2.5 volts in the equation $-e_{c1}/R_K = i_b$ shows that 2.25 volts is the only reason-

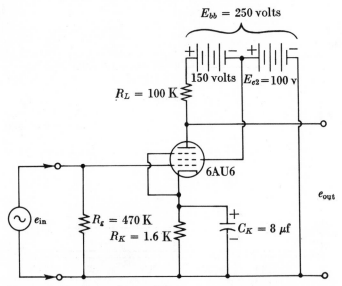

Figure 3-22   Pentode amplifier.

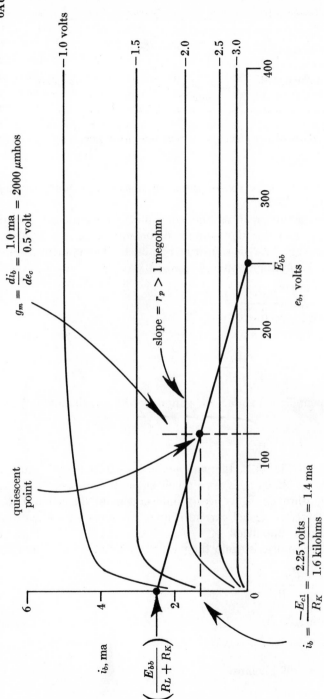

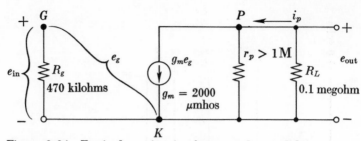

Figure 3-24   Equivalent circuit of a pentode amplifier.

able value. Thus without very exact graphical analysis it can only be said that E_{c1} is close to -2.25 volts.

For the a-c circuit analysis the current-source equivalent circuit (Fig. 3-15) will be used for the pentode. The equivalent circuit of the pentode amplifier (Fig. 3-22) is shown in Fig. 3-24. The input resistance is, of course, R_g. From the formula [Eq. (3-12)],

$$e_{\text{out}} = -g_m e_g \frac{r_p R_L}{r_p + R_L}$$

so that the gain

$$A = \frac{e_{\text{out}}}{e_g} = -g_m \frac{r_p R_L}{r_p + R_L} \tag{3-13}$$

Since r_p for the pentode is so large, the gain may be approximated in many cases as

$$A \approx -g_m R_L \tag{3-14}$$

For the amplifier of Fig. 3-22, the gain would be -1100×10^{-6} mho $\times$ 10^5 ohms $= -110$. When r_p is very much larger than R_L, $i_p \approx -g_m e_g$. Thus the current through R_L is nearly independent of the value of R_L. The pentode is therefore a good current source, and advantage is taken of this characteristic for amplifiers.

The output resistance is again the parallel combination of r_p and R_L,

$$R_{\text{out}} = \frac{r_p R_L}{r_p + R_L}$$

And again because $r_p \gg R_L$,

$$R_{\text{out}} \approx R_L$$

In this case $R_{\text{out}} \approx 100$ kilohms.

In general it can be said that the pentode amplifier has higher gain, higher output impedance, and a smaller acceptable range of signal voltages than the triode amplifier.

3-6   The Transistor

The transistor is formed by making two p-n junctions to a single p- or n-type semiconductor. The resulting device may be represented as in Fig. 3-25. The principle of operation of the transistor is illustrated for the n-p-n transistor. The distribution of free charge carriers in the n-p-n transistor under no applied electric field is shown in Fig. 3-26a. There are mostly holes in the base region and mostly electrons in the emitter and collector regions. If the emitter-base junction is reverse-biased, the majority of the charge carriers will be attracted away from the junction and very little current will flow in the emitter-base circuit, as shown in Fig. 3-26b. When the emitter-base junction is forward-biased, the charge carriers are attracted to and cross the junction, allowing a current to flow in the emitter-base circuit as in Fig. 3-26c. This phenomenon is the usual p-n-junction diode behavior described in Sec. 2-4.

Notice in Fig. 3-26c that the holes and electrons which cross the boundary may travel some distance before they are neutralized. If the p layer is made very thin, under the forward-bias conditions of Fig. 3-26c some electrons may completely traverse the p section without being neutralized. These electrons can be collected, and a current will flow between E and C when a positive potential is applied to terminal C. This is illustrated in Fig. 3-26d. In practical n-p-n transistors the p region, or base, is extremely thin so that under the conditions of Fig. 3-26d more than 90 per cent of the electrons crossing the boundary between E and B are collected at C. The potential applied between the emitter and the base controls the number of electrons which enter the p region and thus controls the collector current.

The operation of the p-n-p transistor (Fig. 3-25b) is essentially the

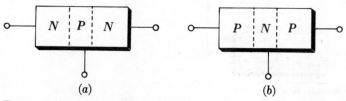

(a)   (b)

Figure 3-25   Basic transistor types: (a) n-p-n transistor; (b) p-n-p transistor.

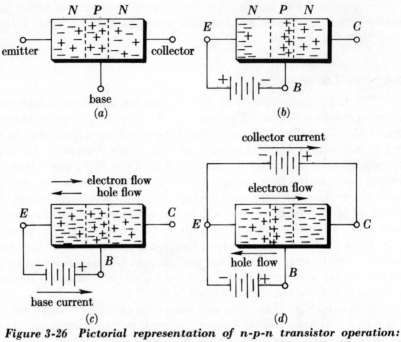

*Figure 3-26 Pictorial representation of n-p-n transistor operation:
(a) no applied potential; (b) reverse base bias; (c) forward
base bias; (d) collector voltage applied. (−, electrons; +,
holes.)*

same as that of the *n-p-n* transistor described above. In the case of the
p-n-p transistor, the polarities of the potentials applied to the base and the
collector are reversed, and the holes transfer the charge across the *n* region,
or base. A properly biased *p-n-p* transistor is shown in Fig. 3-27.

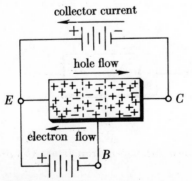

Figure 3-27 Forward-biased p-n-p transistor.

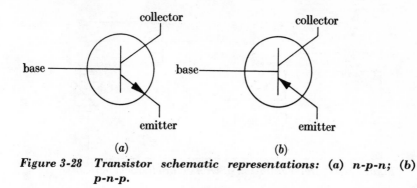

(a)   (b)

Figure 3-28   *Transistor schematic representations: (a) n-p-n; (b) p-n-p.*

Transistor-Characteristic Curves. The schematic representations of the *n-p-n* and *p-n-p* transistors are shown in Fig. 3-28. Notice that the arrow on the emitter lead points in the direction of the flow of positive charges. A basic transistor-amplifier circuit is shown in Fig. 3-29. The functions of the emitter, base, and collector in the transistor are roughly analogous to the cathode, grid, and plate, respectively, in a triode. One great difference between the transistor and the triode is that in the transistor there is an appreciable current in the base circuit. This is because the emitter-base junction is forward-biased for control of the emitter-collector current. In a triode the cathode grid is reverse-biased, and virtually no current flows in the grid circuit. In many ways the base of the

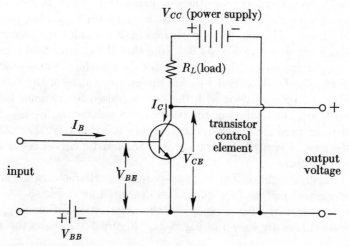

Figure 3-29   *Transistor amplifier.*

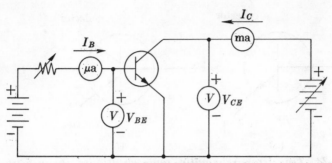

Figure 3-30   Determination of transistor characteristics.

transistor is more analogous to the screen grid of a pentode than the control grid of a triode. The screen grid is forward-biased with respect to the cathode and does carry some current. In fact, the characteristic curves of the transistor are much more like those of the pentode than those of the triode.

The input signal, I_B and V_{BE}, helps to determine the charge distribution and thus the operating characteristics of the transistor. Hence the characteristics of the output circuit (emitter to collector) are dependent on certain parameters of the input circuit. Similarly, conditions in the output circuit will affect the characteristics of the input circuit. The interdependence of the input and output circuits of the transistor is one of the main differences between the vacuum tube and the transistor and is a complicating factor in the analysis of transistor-amplifier circuits.

The characteristic curves of the transistor may be measured by use of the circuit of Fig. 3-30. One of the variables is held constant while the relationship between two of the others is measured. Then the value of the controlled variable is changed and the measurement repeated to give a family of curves. The quantities measured in determining the transistor characteristics are shown in Fig. 3-30. Note that the emitter lead is common to the input and output signals. This is known as the common-emitter configuration. I_B, I_C, V_{BE}, and V_{CE} are the *average* values of the voltage and current. To be consistent with the notation used for vacuum tubes, the total instantaneous values of the current and voltage, i_B, i_C, v_{BE}, and v_{CE}, ought to be used for the characteristic curves. However, the custom of using the capital symbols for transistor-characteristic curves is too well established to ignore.

Theoretically, eight different three-parameter characteristic curves can be determined for the four quantities measured as in Fig. 3-30. At least two are necessary for a complete characterization. Some typical characteristic curves are shown in Fig. 3-31. Figure 3-31a shows the similarity between the transistor and the pentode. Note, however, that I_B is the constant parameter. The forward-biased diode of the emitter base presents such a low impedance to the signal source that a normally high impedance signal source acts as a constant-current source. Thus the input current is the controlled variable rather than the input voltage. Figure 3-31a, then, is analogous to the plate characteristic of the vacuum tube, and Fig. 3-31d is analogous to the transfer characteristic of the vacuum tube, except that input current has replaced input voltage.

Transistor Equivalent Circuit. To derive an equivalent circuit for the transistor, one must consider all four variables, I_B, V_{BE}, I_C, and V_{CE}. The symbols for instantaneous values, i_B, v_{BE}, i_C, and v_{CE}, are used because changing values are considered in the discussion. Two variables are chosen as independent. It is most logical to choose the two most easy to control, which are i_B and v_{CE}. The other two variables are dependent. Thus we have the equations

$$v_{BE} = f_1(i_B, v_{CE}) \tag{3-15}$$

$$i_C = f_2(i_B, v_{CE}) \tag{3-16}$$

The differentiation of the first will yield the input equivalent circuit, and the differentiation of the second the output equivalent circuit. From the first equation,

$$dv_{BE} = \left(\frac{\partial v_{BE}}{\partial i_B}\right)_{v_{CE}} di_B + \left(\frac{\partial v_{BE}}{\partial v_{CE}}\right)_{i_B} dv_{CE} \tag{3-17}$$

The partial differential $(\partial v_{BE}/\partial i_B)_{v_{CE}}$ is the slope of the V_{BE} vs. I_B characteristic curve (Fig. 3-31c) and is defined as h_{ie}. The symbol h is for hybrid, since the parameters developed by these equations are called hybrid parameters. The i indicates input, and e is for the common-emitter configuration. Note that h_{ie} has the units of resistance and is sometimes referred to as the input resistance. The partial differential $(\partial v_{BE}/\partial v_{CE})_{i_B}$ is the slope of the V_{BE} vs. V_{CE} characteristic curve (Fig. 3-31b) and is defined as μ_{re}. This parameter indicates the effect of the output voltage on the input voltage and hence is a sort of amplification factor in reverse. μ is for amplification factor, r is for reverse, and e is the common-emitter configuration.

With the substituted parameters, the input-circuit equation is

$$v_{be} = h_{ie}i_b + \mu_{re}v_{ce} \tag{3-18}$$

where v_{be}, i_b, v_{ce}, and other symbols with lower-case subscripts are defined as the signal values. This equation suggests a resistance h_{ie} in the base lead which develops an iR drop of $i_b h_{ie}$ in series with a voltage source $\mu_{re}v_{ee}$. The schematic representation of the transistor input equivalent

circuit is shown as part of Fig. 3-32. The term $\mu_{re}v_{ce}$ in Eq. (3-18) shows
the dependence of the input circuit on the conditions existing in the output
circuit (v_{ce}). The reverse amplification factor μ_{re} is a measure of the degree
of interaction between the input and output voltages.

Differentiating the output equation, Eq. (3-16),

$$di_C = \left(\frac{\partial i_C}{\partial i_B}\right)_{v_{CE}} di_B + \left(\frac{\partial i_C}{\partial v_{CE}}\right)_{i_B} dv_{CE} \tag{3-19a}$$

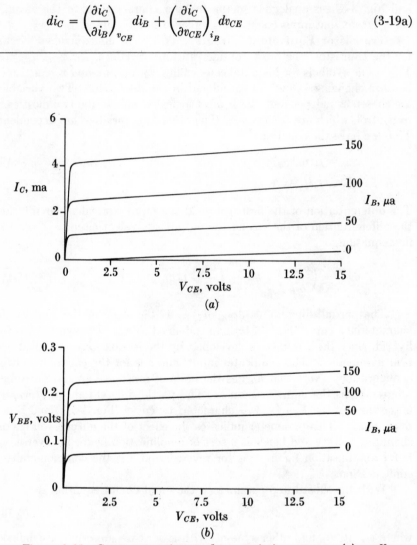

Figure 3-31   *Common-emitter characteristic curves: (a) collector
characteristic curves; (b) reverse-transfer characteristic
curves; (c, right) input characteristic curves; (d, right)
forward-transfer characteristic curves.*

The partial differential $(\partial i_C/\partial i_B)_{v_{CE}}$ is the slope of the I_C vs. I_B characteristic curve (Fig. 3-31d). It is the current amplification factor symbolized by α_{fe}, the α for amplification factor, f for forward, and e for the common-emitter configuration. The partial differential $(\partial i_C/\partial v_{CE})_{i_B}$ is the slope of the I_C vs. v_{CE} characteristic curve (Fig. 3-31a). It is a conductance, has the units of mhos, and is symbolized by h_{oe}. Again h is for hybrid, and the o indicates output and e the common-emitter configuration. Therefore,

$$i_c = \alpha_{fe}i_b + h_{oe}v_{ce} \qquad\qquad (3\text{-}19b)$$

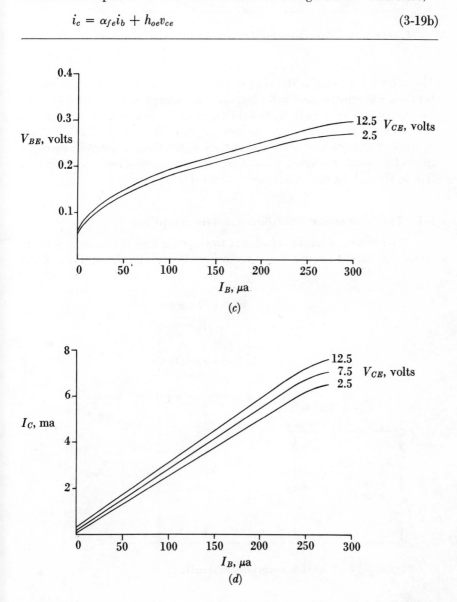

(c)

(d)

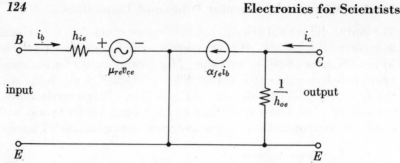

Figure 3-32   Transistor equivalent circuit, hybrid parameters.

The collector current is the sum of two current paths, a conductance h_{oe} between the emitter and collector, and the amplified input current $\alpha_{fe}i_b$. In the equivalent circuit the conductance h_{oe} is shown as a resistance of $1/h_{oe}$ ohms. The resulting equivalent circuit is shown in Fig. 3-32. Other equivalent circuits and other parameters result from a different choice of the independent variables. The more common parameters and their relation to the hybrid parameters are explained in Appendix A.

3-7   The Transistor Common-Emitter Amplifier

A transistor amplifier which has the emitter lead in common with the input and output circuits is shown in Fig. 3-33. The d-c analysis of this

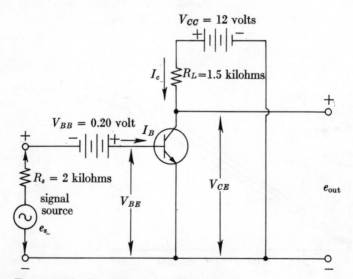

Figure 3-33   Transistor-amplifier circuit.

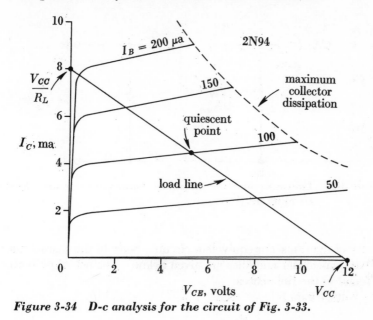

Figure 3-34   D-c analysis for the circuit of Fig. 3-33.

circuit is very similar to that of the vacuum tube. First the load line is determined by connecting V_{CC} on the voltage axis with V_{CC}/R_L on the current axis of the collector-characteristic curve for the transistor used (Fig. 3-34). Note that the load line should fall well within the maximum collector-dissipation line. The maximum collector dissipation $P_{\max}$ is a characteristic of the transistor and is usually given in the transistor manuals or catalogue descriptions. The maximum collector-dissipation line is drawn by connecting all the points which satisfy the equation $I_C \cdot V_{CE} = P_{\max}$. The quiescent base current can be estimated by considering the input circuit of Fig. 3-33. Assume that the base-to-emitter junction is simply the transistor input resistance h_{ie}. If $e_s = 0$ (quiescent state), $I_B = V_{BB}/(R_s + h_{ie})$. Often R_s will be very much greater than h_{ie} so that $I_B \approx V_{BB}/R_s$. In this case, then, $I_B \approx 0.20$ volt/2 kilohms $= 100$ μa. Thus the choice of bias voltage will depend on the nature of the signal source. Other methods of biasing will be explained later, but none of them is independent of the input-signal circuit to the extent that the vacuum tube is.

Transistor-Amplifier Characteristics. The common-emitter amplifier equivalent circuit is shown in Fig. 3-35. Equations for the various amplifier characteristics may be derived from the equivalent circuit and the mathematical relations used to obtain that circuit. The derivations are more involved than those of the triode amplifier because of the greater

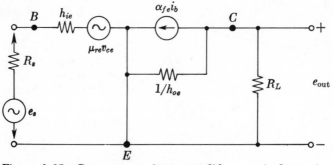

Figure 3-35   Common emitter–amplifier equivalent circuit, hybrid parameters.

complexity of the transistor equivalent circuit. Some of the characteristics of the common-emitter amplifier are given below. The actual derivations can be found in the References.

The voltage gain is

$$A_e = \frac{-\alpha_{fe}R_L}{(h_{ie}h_{oe} - \alpha_{fe}\mu_{re})R_L + h_{ie}} \tag{3-20}$$

For the transistor and amplifier circuit shown in Fig. 3-33, the gain can be calculated if the parameters for the transistor are known. Assume that

$$\alpha_{fe} = 55$$

$$h_{ie} = 2720 \text{ ohms}$$

$$h_{oe} = 14 \times 10^{-6} \text{ mho}$$

$$\mu_{re} = 3.23 \times 10^{-4}$$

Then,

$$A_e = \frac{-55 \times 1500}{(2720 \times 14 \times 10^{-6} - 55 \times 3.23 \times 10^{-4})1500 + 2720}$$

$$= \frac{-8.3 \times 10^4}{(3.8 \times 10^{-2} - 1.8 \times 10^{-2})1500 + 2720}$$

$$= \frac{-8.3 \times 10^4}{30 + 2720} = -30$$

The term $h_{ie}h_{oe} - \alpha_{fe}\mu_{re}$ is found so often in transistor equations that it is given a special symbol, Δh_e. For this transistor, $\Delta h_e = 0.02$. It can be seen from the above equation that the term $\Delta h_e R_L$ in the denominator does not influence the result significantly. Thus the voltage gain could be approximated by the equation

$$A_e \approx \frac{-\alpha_{fe}R_L}{h_{ie}} \tag{3-21}$$

unless Δh_e or R_L is unusually large. The minus sign indicates that the output voltage is 180° out of phase from the input voltage. Recall that phase inversion is also a characteristic of the analogous vacuum-tube circuit (the common-cathode amplifier). Assume that R_L of Fig. 3-35 is a much better conductor than $1/h_{oe}$, that is, $R_L \ll 1/h_{oe}$. Assume also that the generator voltage $\mu_{re}v_{ce}$ is small compared with the voltage $i_b h_{ie}$. Now the equivalent circuit could be drawn as in Fig. 3-36. From this circuit it can be seen that $e_{\text{in}} = i_b h_{ie}$ and that $e_{\text{out}} = -\alpha_{fe}i_b R_L$, so that the gain $A_e = e_{\text{out}}/e_{\text{in}} = -\alpha_{fe}i_b R_L/i_b h_{ie} = \alpha_{fe}R_L/h_{ie}$, which is Eq. (3-21). Thus the assumptions leading to Eq. (3-21), which were not obvious previously, actually are $R_L \ll 1/h_{oe}$ and $\mu_{re}v_{ce} \ll i_b h_{ie}$.

The current gain A_i is given by the formula

$$A_i = \frac{-\alpha_{fe}}{h_{oe}R_L + 1} \tag{3-22}$$

The current gain for the amplifier of Fig. 3-33 is then

$$A_i = \frac{-55}{14 \times 10^{-6} \times 1500 + 1} = \frac{-55}{2.1 \times 10^{-2} + 1} = -55$$

The term $h_{oe}R_L$ is generally so small compared with 1 that it can be neglected. Thus

$$A_i \approx -\alpha_{fe} \tag{3-23}$$

Again the minus sign is an indication of the phase reversal between the input and output signals. The assumption made in Eq. (3-23), that is, $h_{oe}R_L \ll 1$, is the same as saying $R_L \ll 1/h_{oe}$, the previous assumption. In calculating this current gain, the output current is defined as the current through R_L, not the current which can be drawn from the terminals e_{out}. If additional load is connected to the output terminals of the amplifier, the output current will be split between the two loads and the effective value of R_L in the above equations will be reduced to the resistance of the parallel loads.

The power gain A_p is simply the product of the current and voltage gains. When the assumptions made in Eqs. (3-21) and (3-23) are valid,

$$A_p \approx \frac{(\alpha_{fe})^2 R_L}{h_{ie}} \tag{3-24}$$

For the amplifier under analysis,

$$A_p \approx (-30)(-55) \qquad \text{or} \qquad \frac{(-55)^2(1500)}{2720} = 1660$$

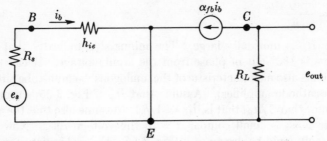

Figure 3-36   Transistor-amplifier simplified equivalent circuit.

The power gain does not include power losses in the signal source or in transferring the output signal to a load other than R_L. It is simply the ratio of the signal power dissipated in R_L to the signal power dissipated in h_{ie}. Equation (3-24) verifies this definition.

The input resistance R_{in} is found from the formula

$$R_{\text{in}} = \frac{h_{ie} + (h_{oe}h_{ie} - \alpha_{fe}\mu_{re})R_L}{1 + h_{oe}R_L} = \frac{h_{ie} + \Delta h_e R_L}{1 + h_{oe}R_L} \tag{3-25}$$

Substitution of the parameters shows R_{in}, in this case, to be

$$R_{\text{in}} = \frac{2720 + 0.02 \times 1500}{1 + (14 \times 10^{-6}) \times 1500} = \frac{2720 + 30}{1 + 2.1 \times 10^{-2}} = 2700 \text{ ohms}$$

Since $\Delta h_e R_L \ll h_{ie}$ and $h_{oe}R_L \ll 1$,

$$R_{\text{in}} \approx h_{ie} \tag{3-26}$$

It is obvious that the assumption that $\mu_{re}v_{ce} \ll i_b h_{ie}$ made in Fig. 3-36 leads to this same conclusion. Note also that $R_{\text{in}} = R_L(A_i/A_e)$.

The output resistance R_{out} can be calculated from

$$R_{\text{out}} = \frac{h_{ie} + R}{h_{oe}h_{ie} - \mu_{re}\alpha_{fe} + h_{oe}R_s} = \frac{h_{ie} + R_s}{\Delta h_e + h_{oe}R_s} \tag{3-27}$$

For the circuit of Fig. 3-33,

$$R_{\text{out}} = \frac{2720 + 2000}{0.02 + 14 \times 10^{-6} \times 2000} = \frac{4720}{0.048} = 10^5 \text{ ohms}$$

In this case both terms in the numerator and the denominator are of the same order of magnitude. It can be seen that, if R_s were small compared with h_{ie},

$$R_{\text{out}} \approx \frac{h_{ie}}{\Delta h_e} \tag{3-28}$$

or that, if R_s were much larger than h_{ie},

$$R_{\text{out}} \approx \frac{1}{h_{oe}} \tag{3-29}$$

As Eq. (3-29) indicates, the output resistance R_{out} is in this case the resistance that the transistor as a power source presents to the load R_L. R_{out} actually corresponds to r_p of the vacuum tube. The output resistance of the entire amplifier circuit as seen by a device attached to the terminals e_{out} would actually be R_{out} in parallel with R_L, just as in the case of the vacuum-tube circuit.

The common-emitter amplifier is thus shown to possess the properties of voltage gain, current gain, phase reversal of the input signal, low input resistance, and high output resistance.

Transistor Biasing. The use of a separate power source for the input and output circuits of the transistor amplifier is costly and inconvenient. Methods of providing the proper bias voltages from a single power source have, therefore, been devised. To understand and design transistor-bias circuits, it is necessary to take a more critical look at the current flow in the transistor. Consider the *n-p-n* transistor shown in Fig. 3-37. The total current for each element is the sum of the currents to each of the other two elements. The emitter current is the sum of the emitter-base current I_{EB} and the emitter-collector current $\alpha_{fe}I_{EB}$. Despite the reverse bias, there is a collector-base current I_{co}. Minority carriers, thermally generated in the collector and base regions, drift toward the collector-base junction under the influence of the electric field and give rise to the collector leakage current I_{co}. The collector current is then given by the following equation:

$$I_C = \alpha_{fe}I_{EB} + I_{co} \tag{3-30}$$

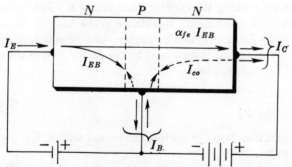

Figure 3-37   *Current flow in an n-p-n transistor.* (*Solid arrow, electron current; dashed arrow, hole current.*)

Because I_{co} is due to the thermal generation of minority carriers, the value of I_{co} increases very sharply with temperature.

The current I_{co} tends to develop a bias on the base which increases the emitter-to-collector current in the transistor. Consider the circuit of Fig. 3-37 with the base lead disconnected. With an open base circuit, there can be no net base current. In other words, $I_{EB} = I_{co}$. From Eq. (3-30), if I_{co} is 100 μa and $\alpha_{fe} = 50$, $I_C = 5.1$ ma. This collector current may warm the transistor somewhat, increasing I_{co}, which increases I_C even more. This phenomenon is called thermal runaway and can easily lead to the destruction of the transistor or its associated circuitry. The methods used to counteract this self-destructive tendency are to keep the base-circuit resistance low so that excessive bias cannot build up and to put resistors in the emitter or collector circuits to prevent excessive current flow.

The primary problem in transistor biasing is to provide a bias which is stable despite variations in the collector leakage currents. It is also very desirable to be able to do this without using a separate bias battery. Three bias circuits are shown in Fig. 3-38 for n-p-n transistors. Figure 3-38a is called the fixed bias circuit. The quiescent base current $I_B = V_{CC}/R_B$. A measure of an amplifier's stability against temperature changes and thermal runaway is the ratio of the change in I_C for a given change in I_{co}, in other words, dI_C/dI_{co}. This ratio should, of course, be as small as possible. Figure 3-38a, by applying a constant base bias current does nothing to stabilize the amplifier against changes in I_{co}. According to Eq. (3-30) the stability ratio would be simply α_{fe}. The higher α_{fe} is, the less stable the circuit. The circuit is quite unstable in any case.

The bias of Fig. 3-38b is obtained by adjusting the value of R_B so that the collector leakage current gives the right bias. This circuit would be no more stable than Fig. 3-38a except for the emitter resistor R_E. In addition to limiting the emitter current, R_E helps stabilize the bias. If the emitter current starts to increase in response to a change in I_{co}, the iR drop across R_E increases, making the emitter more positive. This reduces the effect of the change in bias current. Resistance in the emitter circuit is thus more effective in stabilizing the circuit than is resistance in the collector lead. The stability of this circuit is increased by the factor F over the unstabilized amplifier of Fig. 3-38a, where

$$F = 1 + \frac{\alpha_{fe}}{1 + R_B/R_E} \tag{3-31}$$

The stability ratio would then be α_{fe}/F. Since the second term of Eq. (3-31) is generally larger than 1,

$$\text{Stability ratio} = \frac{\alpha_{fe}}{F} \approx 1 + \frac{R_B}{R_E} \tag{3-32}$$

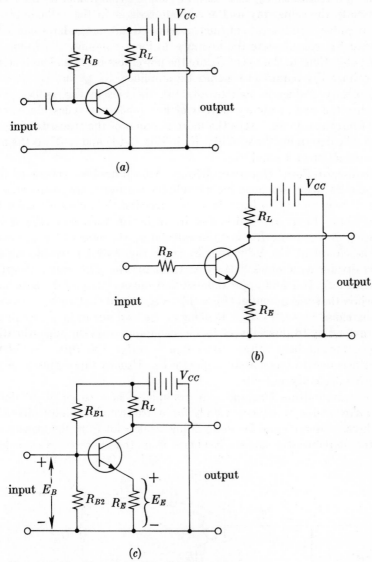

Figure 3-38   Transistor-biasing circuits.

This bears out the previous statement that decreasing R_B and increasing R_E increases the stability.   However, it is not practical to make the ratio of R_B to R_E less than about 5.   For good stability with transistors having moderately high α_{fe} (50 or more), it is necessary to approach the limiting value of R_B/R_E of 5.   Whenever possible the stability ratio should be less than 8. The resistance R_E decreases the gain of the amplifier by the factor F in exactly the same way as the cathode resistor in the cathode-biased triode amplifier. In the case of the transistor circuit, too, a large capacitor bypassing R_E will alleviate the loss in gain for a-c signals. The only remaining objections to the use of R_E are the power lost in R_E and an increase in the voltage V_{CC} required to operate the amplifier.

A voltage divider is used to establish the bias in Fig. 3-38c. This circuit has the same stability as that of Fig. 3-38b but is less dependent on the source resistance. It is the most common of the transistor-biasing circuits. To determine the stability, R_B in Eqs. (3-31) and (3-32) is the parallel combination of R_{B1} and R_{B2}.

Quiescent-Point Determination. After it has been concluded that most practical transistor amplifiers would have a resistance in the emitter circuit, it is necessary to learn how to determine the quiescent point for such circuits. First, the load line is drawn in the usual way (Fig. 3-34), care being taken to use $R_E + R_L$ in calculating the current for $V_{CE} = 0$. Now the circuit of Fig. 3-38c is redrawn as Fig. 3-39 by considering the voltage divider as a series battery and resistor R_B (Thévenin's theorem, Supplement 2). It is first approximated that the emitter and the base have very nearly the same potential ($E_E = E_B \approx E_{BB}$) and that I_E is very nearly I_C. Therefore, $I_C \approx E_{BB}/R_E$. Looking at the load line to find the value of I_B corresponding to this value of I_C, one can improve on the approximation by correcting the base voltage to $= E_{BB} - I_B R_B$. Use this value of the base voltage to calculate a better value for I_C. Usually this second approximation is sufficiently accurate.

Transistor-Bias Design. An example of how to go about determining reasonable resistance values for a transistor-amplifier circuit is given here. First, choose the desired quiescent point from the transistor's collector-characteristic curve. Evaluate from the characteristics or look

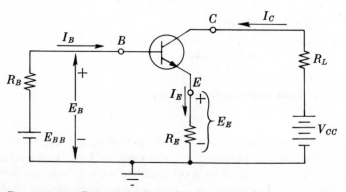

Figure 3-39   Determination of quiescent values.

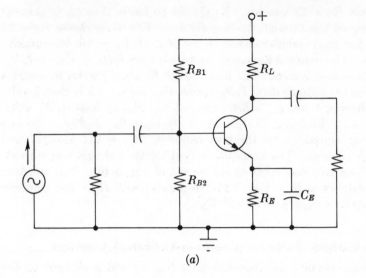

(a)

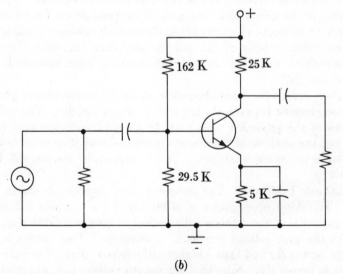

(b)

Figure 3-40   Transistor-amplifier bias design.

up values for α_{fe}, h_{ie}, and h_{oe}.   The amplifier circuit is to look like Fig. 3-40a.   Assume that, at the desired quiescent point, $I_C = 1$ ma, $V_{CE} = 5$ volts, $\alpha_{fe} = 55$, $h_{ie} = 2720$ ohms, and $h_{oe} = 14\,\mu$mhos.   Choose R_L according to gain requirements and impedance matching, high values for current gain, moderate values for voltage gain with moderate output impedance.   For this example $R_L = 25$ kilohms. R_B should be larger than h_{ie} to prevent excessive signal loss through the bias divider. Therefore, choose $R_B = 25$ kilohms. For good stability choose $R_E = \frac{1}{5}R_B$. If $R_E = 5K$, the stability ratio ≈ 6. The required d-c supply voltage is then $I_C R_L + V_{CE} + I_E R_E$, which is $25 + 5 + 5$ volts. The bias voltage E_B should equal the emitter voltage plus the voltage drop $I_B R_B$ (recall Fig. 3-39). E_B is thus 5 volts $+ 25$ kilohms $\times 1$ ma$/\alpha_{fe} = 5.4$ volts $= [R_{B2}/(R_{B1} + R_{B2})] \times 35$ volts. Since $R_B = 25$ kilohms, 25 kilohms $= R_{B1}R_{B2}/(R_{B1} + R_{B2})$. Solving simultaneous equations for the bias resistors, $R_{B1} = 162$ kilohms and $R_{B2} = 29.5$ kilohms. The formulas derived for the voltage- and current-gain transistor amplifier apply to the circuit of Fig. 3-40b. The amplifier output resistance is R_{out} [Eq. (3-27)] in parallel with R_L. The amplifier input resistance is h_{ie} in parallel with R_B.

3-8   The Cathode-Follower (Common-Collector) Amplifier

Amplifier circuits are classified according to which element of the amplification device is common to the input and output circuits. There are, in the case of the triode and transistor, three possible configurations, each having very different characteristics. The most common configuration is the grounded cathode circuit and the analogous transistor circuit, the common-emitter amplifier. These circuits have been discussed in Secs. 3-3, 3-5, and 3-7.

This section deals with the configuration in which the collector or plate is the common element between the input and output circuits. The main characteristics of the grounded plate and the common-collector amplifier are similar, but the analysis of the circuits differs somewhat as in all cases of vacuum-tube–transistor analogies. The vacuum-tube circuit will be discussed first.

The Cathode Follower.   The grounded-plate amplifier is shown in Fig. 3-41a. This kind of amplifier is often called the cathode follower because the potential of the cathode with respect to ground follows that of the grid. As the grid voltage increases, i_b increases. This results in a higher voltage across R_K and thus a higher cathode potential. The output voltage is taken across R_K. Note that the output voltage is *in phase* with the input voltage. From the equivalent circuit (Fig. 3-41b), $i_p = \mu e_g/(R_K + r_p)$, and $e_g = e_{\text{in}} - i_p R_K$. Solving for i_p,

$$i_p = \frac{\mu e_{\text{in}}}{(1 + \mu)R_K + r_p} \tag{3-33}$$

For the equivalent circuit to show more clearly the relationship between e_{in} and e_{out}, it is helpful to derive an equivalent circuit from the above

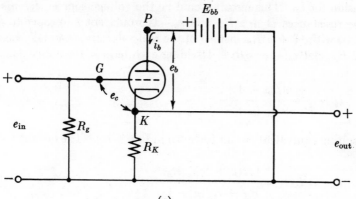

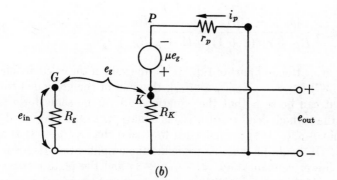

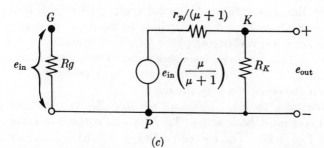

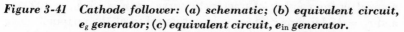

Figure 3-41   *Cathode follower: (a) schematic; (b) equivalent circuit,*
e_g generator; (c) equivalent circuit, e_{in} generator.

relationship for i_p. This circuit would be the voltage source μe_{in} in series with the resistances $(1 + \mu)R_K$ and r_p. It would not be proper to draw the circuit with $(1 + \mu)R_K$ instead of the real value R_K, especially because $e_{out} = i_p R_K$, not $i_p(1 + \mu)R_K$. Dividing each term in the above equation by $\mu + 1$,

$$i_p = \frac{e_{in}[\mu/(\mu + 1)]}{R_K + r_p/(\mu + 1)} \tag{3-34}$$

The resulting equivalent circuit is shown in Fig. 3-41c. The output voltage is

$$e_{out} = i_p R_K = \frac{[\mu/(\mu + 1)]e_{in}R_K}{R_K + r_p/(\mu + 1)} \tag{3-35}$$

The voltage gain $A = e_{out}/e_{in}$ is

$$A = \frac{[\mu/(\mu + 1)]R_K}{R_K + r_p/(\mu + 1)} = \frac{\mu R_K}{(1 + \mu)R_K + r_p} \tag{3-36}$$

Comparing the first part of Eq. (3-36), the gain of the cathode follower, with Eq. (3-7) $[A = -\mu R_L/(r_p + R_L)]$, the gain of the grounded cathode amplifier, it can be seen that the equations are of the same form. It is seen that the cathode-load resistor R_K is analogous to the plate-load resistor R_L, that $-\mu/(\mu + 1)$ is analogous to μ, and that $r_p/(\mu + 1)$ is analogous to r_p. It would be possible to define the amplification factor for the cathode-follower configuration as $-\mu/(\mu + 1)$ and the plate resistance as $r_p/(\mu + 1)$. If this were done, the gain, output resistance, other formulas, and the equivalent circuit would be the same as for the grounded cathode amplifier but the constants would be different. Although this approach may have some advantages, it is customary to use the μ, g_m, and r_p as defined for the grounded cathode amplifier for all configurations. As will be shown in this section, however, transistor parameters are redefined for each configuration, so that the constants change from configuration to configuration but the equations stay the same.

Referring back to Eq. (3-36), we see that the voltage gain of the cathode follower must be less than 1. A typical cathode-follower circuit is shown in Fig. 3-42. The characteristics of a 12AU7 found in a tube manual, or from a plate-characteristic curve, are $\mu = 15$, $g_m = 1000$ μmhos, and $r_p = 15$ kilohms. These values were taken at the midpoint along the load line drawn on the plate-characteristic curve. The gain of this amplifier is thus

$$A = \frac{15 \times 50K}{(15 + 1)50K + 15K} = \frac{750K}{815K} = 0.92$$

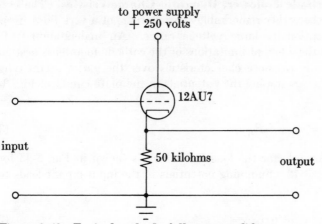

to power supply
+ 250 volts

12AU7

input

50 kilohms   output

Figure 3-42   Typical cathode-follower amplifier.

The r_p term in the denominator of the above expression is seen to be relatively unimportant. For tubes with a small r_p the gain of a cathode follower can be approximated as

$$A \approx \frac{\mu}{\mu + 1} \tag{3-37}$$

Using Eq. (3-37) to calculate the gain in the above example, $A \approx 15/16 = 0.94$.

From Fig. 3-41c the output impedance (for a load connected parallel to R_K) is seen to be R_K in parallel with $r_p/(\mu + 1)$, or

$$R_\text{out} = \frac{R_K[r_p/(\mu + 1)]}{R_K + r_p/(\mu + 1)} = \frac{R_K r_p}{r_p + R_K(\mu + 1)}$$

The output impedance of the circuit of Fig. 3-42 is thus

$$R_\text{out} = \frac{50K \times 15K}{15K + 50K(15 + 1)} = \frac{750K}{815} = 920 \text{ ohms}$$

This very low output impedance is one of the great virtues of the cathode-follower amplifier. Again, the term r_p in the denominator is of little consequence, so that $R_\text{out} \approx r_p/(\mu + 1) \approx r_p/\mu$. Since $\mu = g_m r_p$, $r_p/\mu = 1/g_m$, and

$$R_\text{out} \approx \frac{r_p}{\mu} = \frac{1}{g_m} \tag{3-38}$$

The Cathode Follower, Dynamic Characteristics. The cathode follower has the rather remarkable characteristic of a very linear response over an exceptionally large voltage range. An understanding of this property and the inherent limitations of the cathode follower is best gained by studying the response characteristics over the entire useful range of input voltages. Summing the potentials in the plate circuit of Fig. 3-41a, we see that

$$E_{bb} = e_b + i_b R_K \tag{3-39}$$

This is the formula for the load line which is shown in Fig. 3-43 for the circuit of Fig. 3-42. Summing potentials in the input circuit leads to the equation

$$e_{\text{in}} = e_c + i_b R_K \tag{3-40}$$

From Eq. (3-39) it is seen that the output voltage e_o is $E_{bb} - e_b$. The maximum output voltage then would correspond to the minimum e_b, that is, where the load line crosses the characteristic for $e_c = 0$. Figure 3-43 shows the maximum e_o to be $250 - 40 = 210$ volts. Since e_c is zero for this output voltage, Eq. (3-40) shows e_{in} to equal e_o. The minimum output voltage would be zero, i.e., at cutoff when $e_b = E_{bb}$ and $i_b = 0$. At this point $e_{\text{in}} = e_c$. In the case illustrated by Figs. 3-42 and 3-43, the minimum input voltage is -18 volts. Thus the input has a useful range of 228 volts, over nine-tenths the value of E_{bb}!

The determination of the exact relationship between the input and output voltages as well as the determination of the quiescent-point values is done graphically. At the intersection of the load line and each of the

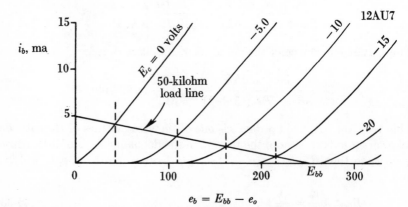

$$e_b = E_{bb} - e_o$$

Figure 3-43   Load line for a cathode follower, $R_K = 50$ kilohms.

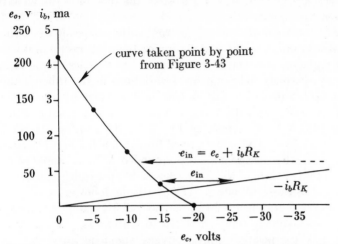

e_o, v i_b, ma

curve taken point by point from Figure 3-43

$e_{in} = e_c + i_b R_K$

e_{in}

$-i_b R_K$

e_c, volts

Figure 3-44   *Dynamic characteristics and quiescent-point determination for a cathode follower.*

characteristic curves, i_b is noted and plotted against e_c as shown in Fig. 3-44.* This is called the dynamic-response characteristic. Note that the ordinate can be labeled e_o or i_b because these quantities differ only by the scale factor R_K. To determine the input voltage, the line $-e_o = -i_b R_K$ is plotted on the graph with the dynamic-characteristic curve. The input voltage for any given i_b or e_o is the potential difference between e_c and $-e_o$ and along a line of constant i_b. This is because the input voltage is always less than the output voltage by the amount of the grid bias, as stated in Eq. (3-40). The input voltage is zero at the intersection of the two curves in Fig. 3-44. This, then, must be the quiescent point. The value of e_c is seen to be about -16 volts in this case, which means that $e_o = 16$ volts when $e_{in} = 0$.

Several interesting observations can be made from Fig. 3-44. It is impressive that the dynamic characteristic is essentially linear over the whole region where i_b is greater than the quiescent value. However, if the abscissa and the ordinate had the same voltage scale so that e_o and e_{in} had the same scale factor, the nonlinearity of the dynamic curve would be completely insignificant. The amazing linearity of the cathode follower is thus explained. The nonlinearity occurring as cutoff is approached is worth noting. The curvature is such that a cathode follower approaching cutoff has decreased gain and consequently increased output resistance. When

---

* When the slope of the load line is small, as in the example chosen, it is easier to read e_b for each characteristic and calculate $i_b = (E_{bb} - e_b)/R_K$.

the tube is actually cut off, $R_{\text{out}} = R_K$, since the tube has been effectively removed from the circuit.

Since Fig. 3-44 demonstrates that the actual shape of the dynamic curve is relatively unimportant in determining the relationship of the input and output voltages, one would expect the characteristics of the cathode follower to be relatively independent of variations in the tube characteristics. The extent to which this is true is illustrated by the following example: If someone accidently put a 12AT7 ($\mu = 55$, $r_p = 20$ kilohms) in place of the 12AU7 in the circuit of Fig. 3-42, the gain of the amplifier would be $A \approx 55/56 = 0.98$. The gain of the cathode follower has changed about 4 per cent, whereas the gain of a grounded cathode amplifier would have changed by the ratio of the μ's, or nearly 400 per cent!

Cathode-Follower Biasing. The cathode follower of Fig. 3-42, which was analyzed graphically in Figs. 3-43 and 3-44, was shown to have a maximum input-voltage range of $+210$ to -18 volts. It was also observed that only the positive input voltages would be truly undistorted in the output. It is not always convenient for the input signal to be limited to positive voltages. One way to avoid this limitation is shown in Fig. 3-45. The cathode resistor R_K is connected to a minus supply voltage (a separate power supply whose positive terminal is grounded). With this circuit the input signal could be -50 volts and still be in the linear operating region of the amplifier circuit. The quiescent point of Fig. 3-45 can be determined roughly by assuming that the output voltage is about zero when the input is grounded. i_b would then be 75 volts/20 kilohms = 3.75 ma. From the load line and plate characteristics, determine what

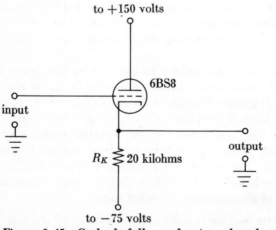

to -75 volts
Figure 3-45   Cathode follower for $+$ and $-$ d-c signals.

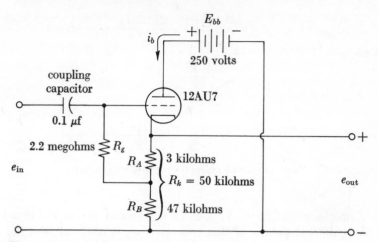

Figure 3-46 Self-biased cathode follower.

value of e_c corresponds to an i_b of 3.75 ma. In this case it is -4 volts. From this, one may conclude that the output voltage is actually $+4$ volts. The calculation of i_b based on the original assumption was off by only 5 per cent.

For a-c signals, a cathode follower can be biased as shown in Fig. 3-46. With no input signal, the grid is positive by the amount I_bR_B, and thus a moderate negative-going signal will not cut the tube off. When the optimum values for R_A and R_B are chosen, the maximum positive and negative undistorted input voltages are equal. The load line for the amplifier in Fig. 3-46 is shown in Fig. 3-43. The maximum linear range of e_b was shown to be from about 40 to 230 volts. To be biased in the middle of this range ($e_b = 135$ volts) the grid bias should be about -7 volts. For $e_b = 135$ volts, $i_b = (250 - 135)/50$ kilohms $= 2.3$ ma. The bias e_c is equal to the potential across R_A, that is, i_bR_A. Therefore, for a 7-volt bias, $R_A = 7$ volts/2.3 ma $= 3$ kilohms. R_B must then be 47 kilohms, since $R_A + R_B$ was chosen to be 50 kilohms.

Common–Collector Amplifier. The basic common-collector amplifier is shown in Fig. 3-47. This circuit is analogous to the cathode-follower amplifier and is sometimes referred to as the emitter-follower amplifier. If V_{EC} is less positive than V_{BC}, the base-emitter junction is forward-biased, causing a higher current through R_L and thus raising V_{BC}. In this way V_{EC} tends to follow V_{BC}. The common-collector amplifier is capable of current gain, but, like the cathode follower, the voltage gain is somewhat less than 1. It has the highest input impedance and the lowest output impedance of all the transistor configurations.

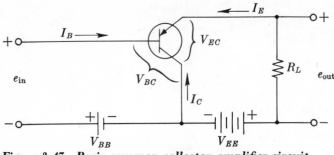

Figure 3-47   Basic common collector–amplifier circuit.

A characteristic of I_E vs. V_{CE}, at I_B = constant, is required to determine the quiescent point. If this characteristic is not available, the I_C vs. V_{CE} curves (Fig. 3-31a) could be used for an estimate. This assumes that $I_E \approx I_C$, which must be true for small I_B. Construct the load line. The quiescent point is the intersection of the load line with the quiescent I_B value.

Adapting the common-emitter parameters to other transistor-amplifier configurations results in very complex formulas and equivalent circuits. It is easier to derive a separate set of parameters for each configuration. In a manner exactly parallel to the derivation of the common-emitter equivalent circuit, the equivalent circuit using the hybrid parameters is derived from the formulas

$$v_{BC} = f_1(i_B, v_{EC}) \tag{3-41}$$

and $\qquad i_E = f_2(i_B, v_{EC}) \tag{3-42}$

(Note that the potentials are measured with respect to a common element.) When these equations are expanded, they yield

$$v_{bc} = h_{ic}i_b + \mu_{rc}v_{ec} \tag{3-43}$$

and $\qquad i_e = \alpha_{fc}i_b + h_{oc}v_{ec} \tag{3-44}$

where $h_{ic} = (\partial v_{BC}/\partial i_B)_{v_{EC}}$, $\mu_{rc} = (\partial v_{BC}/\partial v_{EC})_{i_B}$, $\alpha_{fc} = (\partial i_E/\partial i_B)_{v_{EC}}$, and $h_{oc} = (\partial i_E/\partial v_{ec})_{i_B}$. The resulting common collector–amplifier equivalent circuit is shown in Fig. 3-48. Except for the substitution of the subscript c denoting the common-collector configuration, this equivalent circuit is identical to that of the common-emitter amplifier (Fig. 3-32). Therefore, all the exact gain and resistance formulas derived for the common-emitter amplifier apply as well to the common-collector amplifier. It is necessary only to use the common-collector parameters instead of the common-emitter. These equations are repeated here with the common-collector parameters substituted.

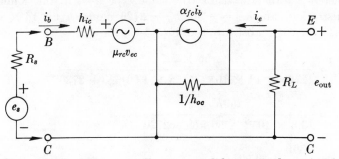

Figure 3-48   Common collector-amplifier equivalent circuit.

$$A_e = \frac{-\alpha_{fc}R_L}{(h_{ic}h_{oc} - \alpha_{fc}\mu_{rc})R_L + h_{ic}} = \frac{-\alpha_{fc}R_L}{\Delta h_c \, R_L + h_{ic}} \tag{3-45}$$

$$A_i = \frac{-\alpha_{fc}}{h_{oc}R_L + 1} \tag{3-46}$$

$$A_p = A_e \times A_i \tag{3-47}$$

$$R_{in} = \frac{h_{ic} + (h_{oc}h_{ic} - \alpha_{fc}\mu_{rc})R_L}{1 + h_{oc}R_L} = \frac{h_{ic} + \Delta h_c \, R_L}{1 + h_{oc}R_L} \tag{3-48}$$

$$R_{out} = \frac{h_{ic} + R_s}{h_{oc}h_{ic} - \mu_{rc}\alpha_{fc} + h_{oc}R_s} = \frac{h_{ic} + R_s}{\Delta h_c + h_{oc}R_s} \tag{3-49}$$

The approximations of these equations made for the common-emitter configuration may not be valid when common-collector parameters are used. If common-collector parameters are not known for the particular transistor, they can be calculated from the parameters for other configurations by using the table of conversion expressions in Appendix A.

A common-collector amplifier with typical values is shown in Fig. 3-49.

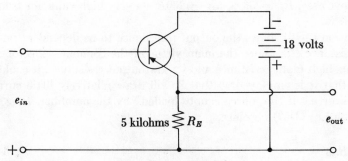

Figure 3-49   Common-collector amplifier.

The parameters for the transistor (the same type used in the common-emitter illustration) are $\alpha_{fc} = -56$, $h_{ic} = 2720$ ohms, $h_{oc} = 14 \times 10^{-6}$ mho, and $\mu_{rc} = 1.00$. Substituting in Eq. (3-45) for A_e,

$$A_e = \frac{56 \times 5K}{(2720 \times 14 \times 10^{-6} + 56 \times 1.00)5K + 2720}$$

$$= \frac{280K}{(3.8 \times 10^{-3} + 56)5K + 2720}$$

$$= \frac{280K}{283K} = 0.99$$

The above calculation demonstrates that $h_{ic}h_{oc} \ll \alpha_{fc}\mu_{rc}$ and can be ignored in the calculation. Since μ_{rc} is always very close to 1 and since $h_{ic} \ll \alpha_{fc}R_L$,

$$A_e \approx \frac{\alpha_{fc}R_L}{\alpha_{fc}R_L + h_{ic}} \approx 1 \tag{3-50}$$

Substituting in Eq. (3-46) for A_i,

$$A_i = \frac{56}{14 \times 10^{-6} \times 5K + 1} = \frac{56}{1 + 0.07} = 52$$

Since $h_{oe}R_L \ll 1$ for most values of R_L,

$$A_i \approx \alpha_{fc} \tag{3-51}$$

In this case,

$$A_p \approx \alpha_{fc} \tag{3-52}$$

When the assumptions made for Eqs. (3-50) and (3-51) are applied to Eq. (3-48),

$$R_{\text{in}} \approx \frac{\alpha_{fc}R_L}{1} \tag{3-53}$$

In the above case, $R_{\text{in}} = 56 \times 5K = 280K$—a very high value for transistor amplifiers.

Equation (3-49) shows the output impedance to be dependent on the source resistance R_s. Since the main virtue of the common-collector amplifier is its high input resistance and its low output resistance, it could be assumed that it is employed so that it will draw relatively little current from the source. If the source is not "loaded" by the amplifier, $R_s \ll h_{ic}$. In this case Eq. (3-49) becomes

$$R_{\text{out}} = \frac{h_{ic}}{-\alpha_{fc}} \tag{3-54}$$

'or the above example, $R_{out} = 2720/56 = 49$ ohms, which is very low
ndeed.

Comparing Figs. 3-49 and 3-38 (b) and (c) shows the difference be-
ween the common-collector amplifier and the practical common-emitter
mplifiers to be the presence of R_L. The biasing and stability considera-
ions for the common-collector amplifier will thus be the same as those
liscussed in Sec. 3-7. Recall that stability improves as the ratio of the
mitter resistance to the base lead resistance increases. Since the emitter
esistance can be larger in the emitter follower than in the common-emitter
mplifier, the maximum practical input impedance is increased corre-
pondingly.

The common-collector amplifier, then, exhibits the characteristics of
oninversion, high input resistance, low output resistance, unity voltage
;ain, and, like the cathode follower, low distortion for a wide range of
ignal voltages.

-9 The Common-Base (Grounded-Grid) Amplifier

The third amplifier configuration is that in which the grid, or base, is
he common element. The grounded-grid amplifier is used only in very
igh frequency circuits, where the grounded grid is used to shield the input
ircuit from the output circuit. This application is considered too special-
zed to make an analysis of this amplifier worthwhile.

The common-base amplifier, however, is not at all unusual. The basic
ommon-base amplifier circuit is shown in Fig. 3-50. The emitter-base
potential controls the resistance between the input and output terminals.
This amplifier is capable of high voltage gains, but the current gain must
be less than 1. It has a very low input impedance and a very high output
mpedance.

To determine the quiescent point, a characteristic of I_C vs. V_{CB} at I_E
onstant is required. I_E is virtually independent of V_{CB} and is normally

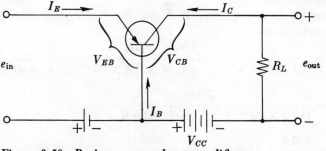

Figure 3-50 Basic common-base amplifier.

just a bit larger than I_C because the emitter supplies most of the base current I_B as well as the collector current I_C. If this curve is not available, it can be estimated. The load line is constructed in the usual way. The quiescent point is the intersection of the load line and the emitter current.

The equivalent circuit is derived in the same way as the common-emitter equivalent circuit was derived. The input current and the output voltage are considered the independent variables. Thus

$$v_{EB} = f_1(i_E, v_{CB}) \tag{3-55}$$

and $\quad i_C = f_2(i_E, v_{CB}) \tag{3-56}$

When these equations are differentiated, they yield

$$v_{eb} = h_{ib}i_e + \mu_{rb}v_{cb} \tag{3-57}$$

and $\quad i_c = \alpha_{fb}i_e + h_{ob}v_{cb} \tag{3-58}$

where $h_{ib} = (\partial v_{EB}/\partial i_B)_{v_{CB}}$, $\mu_{rb} = (\partial v_{EB}/\partial v_{CB})_{i_E}$, and $\alpha_{fb} = (\partial i_C/\partial v_{CB})_{i_E}$. The terms have the same significance as the equivalent terms derived for the common-emitter configuration. They are designated for the common-base configuration by the subscript b. The equivalent circuit for the common-base amplifier is identical to that of the common-emitter and common-collector configurations. The equations derived for the voltage gain, current gain, input resistance, and output resistance also apply to the common-base amplifier. It is necessary only to substitute the subscript b for e in each of the parameters.

For the same transistor that has been used to illustrate the other configurations, $\alpha_{fb} = -0.98$, $h_{ib} = 49$ ohms, $h_{ob} = 0.25 \times 10^{-6}$, and $\mu_{rb} = 6.8 \times 10^{-4}$. Assume that R_L in Fig. 3-50 is 300 kilohms. This is an unusually high load resistance for a transistor amplifier, but since $I_E \approx I_C$, the voltage gain is achieved by having R_L very much higher than the source resistance. The fact that the transistor can maintain the input current through such a high load resistance demonstrates the transistor's qualities as a constant current source. The transistor is a good constant current source (as is the pentode) because the collector current is essentially independent of the collector voltage.

The voltage gain is calculated by using Eq. (3-20) with the above parameters substituted.

$$A_e = \frac{0.98 \times 300K}{(49 \times 0.25 \times 10^{-6} + 0.98 \times 6.8 \times 10^{-4})300K + 49}$$

$$= \frac{294K}{(12.2 \times 10^{-6} + 6.7 \times 10^{-4})300K + 49}$$

$$= \frac{294K}{250} = 1160$$

Note that the amplifier does not invert and that the voltage gain is indeed very high. Since $\alpha_{fb} \approx 1$ and $h_{ib}h_{ob} \ll \alpha_{fb}\mu_{rb}$, Eq. (3-20) may be simplified for the common-base amplifier.

$$A_e \approx \frac{R_L}{\mu_{rc}R_L + h_{ib}} \tag{3-59}$$

Substituting in Eq. (3-22) for the current gain,

$$A_i = \frac{0.98}{0.25 \times 10^{-6} \times 300K + 1} = \frac{0.98}{1.07} = 0.92$$

For the common-base amplifier the current gain is approximately equal to $-\alpha_{fb}$, which is nearly 1.

$$A_i \approx -\alpha_{fb} \approx 1 \tag{3-60}$$

The input resistance is found by substituting the parameters into Eq. (3-25).

$$R_{\text{in}} = \frac{49 + (0.25 \times 10^{-6} \times 49 + 0.98 \times 6.8 \times 10^{-4})300K}{1 + 0.25 \times 10^{-6}R_L}$$

$$= \frac{253}{1.07} = 236 \text{ ohms}$$

From the above it can be seen that

$$R_{\text{in}} \approx h_{ib} + \mu_{rb}R_L \tag{3-61}$$

The output resistance of the grounded-base amplifier is very high—as it should be for a constant current source. Substituting the parameters in Eq. (3-27), and assuming that $R_s = 1$ kilohm,

$$R_{\text{out}} = \frac{49 + 1K}{(0.25 \times 10^{-6} \times 49 + 0.98 \times 6.8 \\ \times 10^{-4} + 0.25 \times 10^{-6} \times 1K)}$$

$$= \frac{49K}{7.5 \times 10^{-2}} = 650K$$

$$\approx \frac{h_{ib}R_s}{\mu_{rb}} \tag{3-62}$$

While the grounded-base amplifier has achieved a very high voltage gain, only a grounded-collector amplifier or vacuum-tube amplifier could be connected to the output without greatly attenuating the output signal.

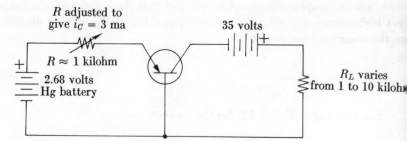

Figure 3-51   Transistor constant current source.

The capabilities of the grounded-base amplifier as a constant current source are illustrated by Fig. 3-51.   By using the same transistor as for the above calculations, the variation of R_{in} as R_L goes from 1 to 10 kilohms is 49.7 to 55.8 ohms, or 6.1 ohms change.   The current gain will vary imperceptibly from $-\alpha_{fb}$ (-0.98) for these values of R_L.   For $i_C = 3$ ma, $i_E = 3$ ma/$0.98 = 3.06$ ma.   The emitter-circuit resistance should then be 2.68 volts/3.06 ma $= 872$ ohms.   Since the input resistance changes 6.1 ohms, the emitter current will change $(6.1/872) \times 100 = 0.7$ per cent for a load variation of 1 to 10 kilohms.   This application would be more common if it were not for the relatively large temperature dependence of α_{fb}.

3-10   The Unipolar Field-Effect Transistor (FET)

One of the disadvantages of bipolar transistors (as discussed in Sec. 3-6) is the low input impedance which prevents their application in many electronic circuits.   Therefore, the recent development of the unipolar transistor with its inherent high input impedance should be very significant.   By combining desirable features found in both vacuum tubes and transistors, the unipolar FET could be a superior substitute for either in the design of many electronic circuits.   The designation "unipolar" indicates that it is a device which essertially contains only one type of current carrier, either holes or electrons, but not both as for the bipolar p-n-p and n-p-n transistors.   Whether holes or electrons are the current carriers will depend on the type of unipolar material chosen.

The basis of operation of a unipolar FET is intuitively easy to understand.   A semiconductor provides a current path whose resistance R to the flow of a specific carrier (electrons or holes, depending on the material) is varied by applying a transverse electric field.   As an example, a bar of silicon containing excess n impurity will be used as shown in Fig. 3-52.   It

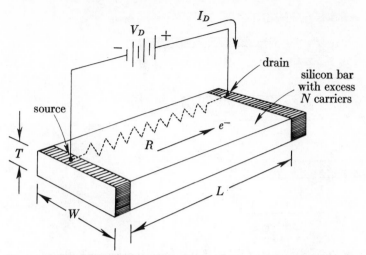

Figure 3-52   *Unipolar semiconductor bar.*

has a length L, width W, and thickness T. The resistance of the bar is directly proportional to its length L and is inversely dependent on the width W, thickness T, and conductivity σ, as expressed in Eq. (3-63).

$$R = \frac{L}{WT\sigma} \tag{3-63}$$

The conductivity σ depends on the number, mobility, and charge of each type of carrier; so

$$\sigma = q(nu_n + pu_p)$$

where q is the electron charge, n the electron density, p the hole density, and u_n and u_p the mobilities of electrons and holes, respectively. If it is assumed that the electron density n is much greater than hole density p ($n \gg p$), then $\sigma \approx qnu_n$ and the *conductance* G is

$$G = \frac{1}{R} = \frac{\sigma WT}{L} \approx \frac{(qu)nWT}{L} \tag{3-64}$$

From Eq. (3-64) it is obvious that with q, u, W, and L constant, the conductance G could be varied only by changing n or T. The operation of the unipolar FET as a variable resistance depends on the formation of a

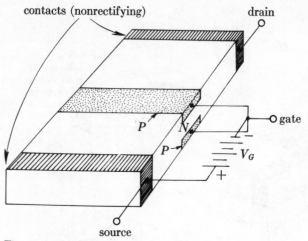

Figure 3-53   Unipolar FET with p-n junctions reverse-biased.

"channel" of variable thickness through which the electrons must pass. The channel is formed by introducing p-type impurities into opposite sides of the bar, as illustrated in Fig. 3-53. A space charge is developed at the two p-type "gate" regions which provides a certain effective channel thickness through which electrons can flow. Now, by applying a reverse bias between the source and the gate diodes, the space charge is increased, and the effective channel thickness for electron flow is decreased, as illustrated in Fig. 3-54.

When the switch is closed to apply V_D, the drain is made positive with respect to the source and electrons flow from the source through the channel to the drain. The gate voltage V_G controls the current by controlling the effective channel thickness. As would be expected, there is a critical drain voltage above which there is no increase in drain current. This is called the "pinch-off voltage" V_p and is dependent on the mobility of the electrons in the silicon bar. As shown in Fig. 3-55 a plot of drain current vs. drain voltage provides a family of curves similar to the plate characteristics of a pentode vacuum tube. Note that when the drain voltage becomes too large there is a sudden upsurge of current, indicating ionization breakdown of the semiconductor crystal. Transfer-characteristic curves would also be quite similar for both the vacuum-tube and unipolar FET.

The Unipolar FET Amplifier. From the characteristic curves and the inherent high input impedance of the unipolar FET, it would be expected that its use as an amplifier would be analogous to vacuum tubes

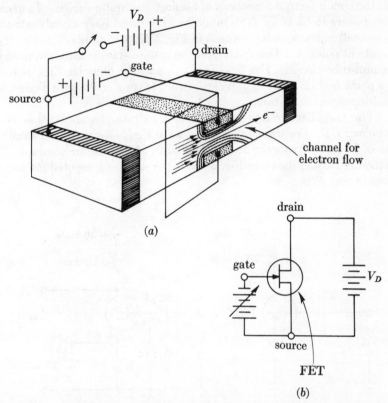

(a)

(b)

Figure 3-54   Control of electron flow through the channel gate for a unipolar FET: (a) pictorial; (b) schematic.

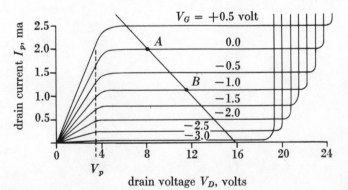

Figure 3-55   Unipolar FET characteristics. (From Texas Instruments Information Bulletin.)

and the circuit analysis, methods of biasing, etc., quite similar. In general, this appears to be true. The unipolar FET could have an advantage for very small input signals. As seen in Fig. 3-55 no gate bias is necessary to operate at point A. This eliminates the cathode-bias resistor required in a vacuum-tube circuit. For large input signals the unipolar FET is biased to a point B (Fig. 3-55) to prevent forward biasing of the gate diodes, with resulting signal distortion.

The amplifier circuits in Fig. 3-56 illustrate the application of the unipolar FET. For the small-signal case in Fig. 3-56a a voltage amplification of 20 and a frequency response of 20 to 30,000 cps are common. The method of biasing shown in Fig. 3-56b is the same as presented for vacuum tubes in Sec. 3-3.

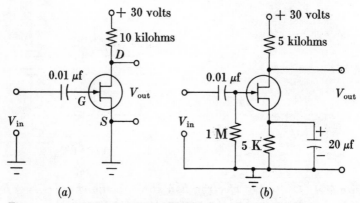

(a)   (b)

Figure 3-56   Unipolar FET amplifiers.   (From Texas Instruments Information Bulletin.)

References

The following books contain additional related information:

Angelo, E. J., "Electronic Circuits," McGraw-Hill, New York, 1958. An intensive discussion of amplification devices and their application. Theoretical and practical.

Lurch, E. N., "Fundamentals of Electronics," Wiley, New York, 1960. A thorough and solid presentation of vacuum tube and transistor amplification. Less mathematical than Angelo.

"Radar Electronic Fundamentals," NAVSHIPS 900,016, U.S. Government Printing Office, Washington, D.C., 1944. A very basic approach to vacuum tube amplifiers.

"Basic Theory and Application of Transistors," Army Technical Manual TM 11-690, U.S. Government Printing Office, Washington, D.C., 1959. A great deal of information on transistor characteristics and common applications.

Both of the following manuals have fine discussions of the types of devices available, their characteristics, and their application. Practical circuits are included, as well as many specific device characteristics.

"RCA Receiving Tube Manual," Radio Corporation of America, Harrison, N.J., latest edition.

"General Electric Transistor Manual," General Electric Company, Semiconductor Products Department, Syracuse, N.Y., latest edition.

Problems

3-1 Draw the dynamic response characteristic for the amplifier of Fig. 3-7. This is done by plotting output voltage e_b as a function of input voltage e_c from the load line and characteristic curves (Fig. 3-8). Determine the amplifier gain from the slope of the dynamic response characteristic. Compare this value with the gain of -15 calculated from Eq. (3-7). Determine also the maximum input signal that will be amplified without distortion.

3-2 It is necessary to design a self-biased triode amplifier similar to that of Fig. 3-9. The triode is to be a 12AU7 and the desired values for I_b and E_c are 5 ma and -5.0 volts, respectively. The power-supply voltage available is 200 volts. (*a*) Calculate the required value for $R_K + R_L$; a load line is required. (*b*) Calculate the required values for R_K and R_L. (*c*) If an amplifier were designed with the same quiescent point but for a power source of 250 volts, would its gain be higher or lower than that of the above amplifier? (*d*) Obtain graphically the values of μ and r_p at the quiescent point. (*e*) Calculate the gain of the amplifier with R_K bypassed. (*f*) Calculate the gain without R_K bypassed.

Ans.: (*a*) 13 kilohms; (*b*) $R_K = 1$ kilohm, $R_L = 12$ kilohms; (*c*) higher; (*d*) $\mu \approx 18$, $r_p \approx 10$ kilohms; (*e*) 9.8; (*f*) 7.0

3-3 Using Fig. 3-21, determine the g_m of a 6AU6 pentode for $E_{c2} = 100$ volts and for $E_{c2} = 150$ volts. Use $e_b = 200$ volts and e_{c1} from -1.0 to -2.0 volts. Which screen grid voltage gives the higher g_m?

Ans.: 3900 μmhos at $e_{c2} = 100$ volts, and 4900 μmhos at $e_{c2} = 150$ volts

3-4   The screen voltage supply for a pentode is usually obtained from the plate power supply.   A dropping resistor R_{sg} is used to reduce the voltage to the desired screen voltage value as shown in Fig. P3-4.   A large filter capacitor C_{sg} is used to maintain a constant screen voltage despite signal fluctuations.   (a) Calculate the proper value for R_{sg} so that $E_{c2} = 100$ volts when $E_{c1} = -2.0$ volts.   Use the characteristics given in Fig. 3-20 and assume that the change in screen current for a given change in grid voltage is proportional to that for the plate current.   (b) Calculate the value of R_K required to bias the control grid at -2.0 volts.   Remember that $I_{\text{cathode}} = I_b + I_{c2}$.   *Ans.:* (a) $I_{c2} = 0.6$ ma, $R_{sg} = 250$ kilohms; (b) 770 ohms

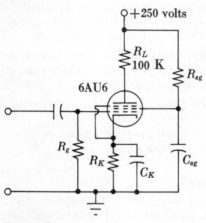

$\bigcirc +250$ volts

R_L
100 K

R_{sg}

6AU6

R_g

R_K

C_K

C_{sg}

Figure P3-4

3-5   A 6BH6 pentode has a transconductance of 3400 μmhos and a plate resistance of 0.7 megohm when the plate supply and screen voltages are both $+100$ volts.   A suitable quiescent point is obtained with $R_L = 27$ kilohms and $R_K = 200$ ohms.   (a) Calculate the gain of the 6BH6 amplifier described when R_K is bypassed. (b) Calculate the gain when R_K is not bypassed.   Assume that E_{c2} will remain constant at 100 volts.   *Ans.:* (a) 92; (b) 54

3-6   Determine α_{fe}, h_{ie}, μ_{re}, and h_{oe} from the transistor characteristic curves in Fig. 3-31a to d.

Ans.: $\alpha_{fe} \approx 25$, $h_{ie} \approx 700$ ohms, $\mu_{re} \approx 6 \times 10^{-4}$, $h_{oe} \approx 50$ μmhos

3-7   Consider the common-emitter amplifier of Fig. 3-38c to have the following parameters: $V_{CC} = 15$ volts, $R_{B1} = 180$ kilohms, $R_{B2} = 10$ kilohms, $R_E = 1$ kilohm, $R_L = 10$ kilohms, $\alpha_{fe} = 50$.   (a) Is the amplifier properly biased for stability?   (b) If not, suggest a better value for R_E.

Ans.: (a) No, stability ratio ≈ 11; (b) $R_E \approx 2.0$ kilohms, stability ratio ≈ 6

3-8 From the collector-characteristic curve of Fig. 3-31a, a quiescent point of $I_b = 100$ μa and $V_{CE} = 5$ volts is chosen for an amplifier. The circuit of Fig. 3-40a is to be used. The available supply voltage is 15 volts. R_B is chosen to be 5 kilohms so that it is larger than h_{ie} (700 ohms, as determined in Prob. 3-7). (*a*) Calculate the required value of $R_L + R_E$ from the load line. (*b*) Calculate the value of R_E required for good bias stability. (*c*) Calculate the value of R_L. (*d*) Calculate the values of R_{B1} and R_{B2}. (*e*) Calculate the voltage gain of the amplifier. (*f*) Calculate the amplifier output resistance. (*g*) Calculate the amplifier input resistance.

Ans.: (*a*) 3.6 kilohms; (*b*) 750 ohms for a stability ratio of 6; (*c*) 2.8 kilohms; (*d*) $E_B = 2.5$ volts, $R_{B1} = 30$ kilohms, $R_{B2} = 6$ kilohms; (*e*) $A_e \approx 100$; (*f*) $\approx$ 2.5 kilohms; (*g*) $\approx$ 600 ohms

3-9 The cathode-follower amplifier shown in Fig. P3-9 might be used as the final amplifier in an operational amplifier where the output voltage may have to be either positive or negative with respect to ground. For this amplifier: (*a*) Calculate the gain; for the 12AX7, $\mu = 100$, $r_p = 62$ kilohms, and $g_m = 1600$ μmhos; plate characteristics are given in Appendix B. (*b*) Calculate the maximum and minimum input voltages. (*c*) Graphically locate the quiescent point. (*d*) What is the output voltage e_o at the quiescent point? (*e*) What is the output resistance?

Ans.: (*a*) 0.99; (*b*) $E_{\max} \approx 260$ volts, $E_{\min} \approx -310$ volts; (*c*) $E_c = -3.0$ volts, $I_b \approx 0.6$ ma; (*d*) $+3.0$ volts; (*e*) $R_{\text{out}} \approx 625$ ohms

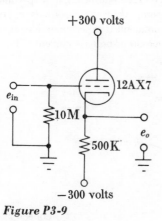

Figure P3-9

3-10 (*a*) Calculate the output resistance of a common-collector amplifier made from the transistor whose characteristics were found in Prob. 3-6. (*b*) What would the voltage gain of this amplifier be if R_L were 5 kilohms? (*c*) The input resistance? (*d*) Which affects a common-collector amplifier input resistance more, the transistor input resistance h_{ic} or α_{fc}?

Ans.: (*a*) $R_{\text{out}} = 27$ ohms; (*b*) $A_e = 0.995$; (*c*) $R_{\text{in}} = 130$ kilohms; (*d*) α_{fc}

EXPERIMENTS

The determination of amplification-element characteristic curves is illustrated for the transistor in the common-emitter configuration. From these characteristic curves, it is possible to determine the d-c operating point (quiescent point) of the amplification element in any circuit. The procedure for this analysis is illustrated for two common vacuum triodes. The d-c analysis of the cathode-follower amplifier and the measurement of some of its special characteristics are performed. The emitter-follower power amplifier in the transistor power supply is also studied. The procedures outlined in the experiment are illustrative of the techniques used to measure amplification-element characteristics. Devices other than those specifically used may be characterized by using the same general approach.

Expt. 3-1 Determination of Common-Emitter Characteristics for a *p-n-p* Transistor

The collector characteristics and the reverse-transfer characteristics (Fig. 3-31*b*) are measured for a typical inexpensive, low-power *p-n-p* transistor. The characteristics of ordinary transistors vary so much from unit to unit that the specification of a particular transistor for these experiments is almost meaningless. Any germanium *p-n-p* 150-mw transistor with α_{fe} of about 100 is suitable.

a. Connections to the Transistor. Three common configurations for transistor connecting leads are shown in Fig. 3-57. Locate the base, emitter, and collector leads of the transistor. Wire the circuit of Fig. 3-58, using an experimental chassis for the connection of the transistor and components. Suggestions on layout and the arrangement of components for the recommended experimental system are given in Supplement 1. The VOM is used to measure the base current. The col-

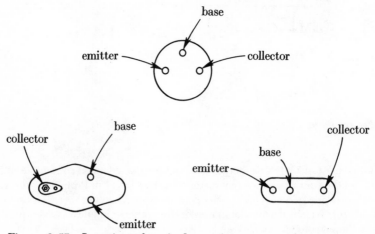

Figure 3-57 Location of typical transistor connections.

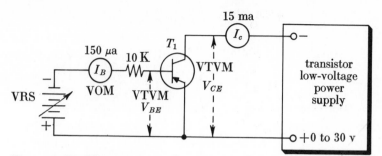

Figure 3-58   Measurement of transistor characteristics.

lector current is measured by making a 15-ma meter from the basic meter movement. The absolute accuracy of this measurement is not critical. A shunt for 15 ma may be quickly made as described in Experiment 1-2e.

b. Plotting the Characteristic Curves. Prepare the graph paper. Use the scale ranges of Fig. 3-31a and b. Plot the 150-mw maximum collector dissipation line on the collector-characteristic curve. Do not exceed this line when measuring the transistor characteristics. The VTVM probe is transferred from base to collector to measure V_{BE} and V_{CE} for a given I_B. Measure the characteristics for $I_B =$ 20 μa, 30 μa, and 40 μa. Do not exceed the maximum collector voltage rating for the transistor (25 volts for the 2N1274). At high base currents and collector voltages, the readings should be made rapidly and immediately returned to a low collector voltage to avoid heating the transistor. The heating is observed as a drifting increase in collector current.

An identifying mark should be put on this transistor because the same transistor will be used in an amplifier for an experiment in Chap. 4. The gain and quiescent point of that amplifier will be checked against the values predicted by the characteristics just measured.

Use the characteristic curves to determine the four hybrid parameters.

Expt. 3-2   Determination of Quiescent Operating Point of a Triode Amplifier

In this experiment the quiescent point of a self-biased triode amplifier is determined. Both the 12AX7 and the 12AU7 triodes are used. The proper value of the cathode resistor is calculated, and the predicted quiescent point checked experimentally. The effect of the cathode bypass capacitor on the a-c gain is noted.

a. Graphical Determination of R_K and Quiescent Point. Draw the load line for $R_L = 10$ kilohms and $E_{bb} = 250$ volts on the plate-characteristic curve of a 12AU7. (Characteristic curves and base diagrams are given in Appendix B.) Select a point on the load line halfway between cutoff and saturation. Note E_c and I_b at this point. Calculate R_K from $R_K = -E_c/I_b$. Wire the circuit of Fig. 3-59, using the above values for R_L and R_K. Use one section of the duotriode tube. (Don't forget to connect the filaments.) The 12-volt filament between pins 4 and 5

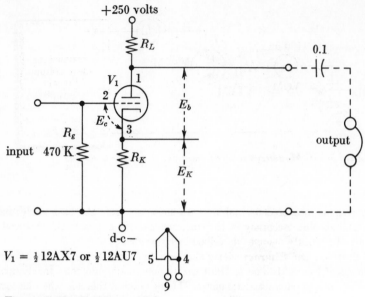

Figure 3-59   Triode amplifier.

is split for connection to a 6-volt filament source. Connect pins 4 and 5 together and connect pins 4 and 9 to the 6.3-volt a-c supply.

b. Experimental Determination of Quiescent Point. Turn on the power for the above circuit and, after waiting a minute for filament warm-up, measure the quiescent values E_c, E_b, and I_b with the VTVM. I_b may be measured by noting the iR drop across R_L or R_K, or by putting a milliammeter across the meter terminals of the universal power supply.

Adjust the frequency of the signal generator to about 1 kc. Connect the sine-wave output to the amplifier input. Connect the earphone across the amplifier input, and adjust the output of the signal generator so that the tone is just loud enough to be heard plainly. Connect the earphone to the amplifier output, using a capacitor as shown in Fig. 3-59. Note the increase in volume. Connect a 20-μf 150-volt bypass capacitor across R_K, and note the increase in the gain of the amplifier. Observe the polarity marks on the electrolytic capacitor. Arrange a touch contact for one capacitor lead so that the gain change is more apparent.

c. Quiescent Point of a High-μ Triode. Repeat parts a and b above for a 12AX7. Use $R_L = 100$ kilohms. The tube-base connections are the same for the 12AX7 and the 12AU7. Only the values of R_L and R_K need to be changed. Note especially the greater gain of the 12AX7.

Expt. 3-3   Cathode-Follower Characteristics

In this experiment a cathode follower is constructed, and its gain and maximum undistorted output voltage are measured.

Wire the cathode-follower amplifier shown in Fig. 3-60.   Connect an a-c signal source of about 75 volts by using the multitapped signal transformer (Supplement 1).   Observe the output voltage as a function of time.   Note the distortion of the sine wave.   Calibrate both the vertical and horizontal deflections of the oscilloscope at 40 volts/div.   Now connect the scope as shown in Fig. 3-60 to observe the *output voltage* as a function of the *input voltage*.   When the scope is connected in this way, it is being used as an *x-y* plotter.   The signal source varies the instantaneous input voltage, and the output voltage of the amplifier varies accordingly.   If the amplifier is perfectly linear, a straight line will be observed on the *x-y* plot.   If the signal-source voltage is less than about 35 volts rms (obtained with the sine generator), a linear relationship between input and output voltages will be observed.   When the 75-volt signal source from the tapped transformer is used, the cutoff and saturation regions are observed.   Measure the maximum undistorted output signal. From the measured slope of the linear portion of the *x-y* plot, calculate the cathode-follower gain.

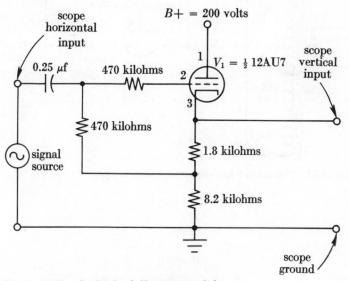

Figure 3-60   Cathode-follower amplifier.

Expt. 3-4   Emitter-Follower Power Amplifier

The circuit of the low-voltage power supply is given in Fig. 3-61. The voltage at the base of the transistor is obtained from a voltage divider and filter and is set by the voltage control knob. The emitter, in following this voltage, establishes the control voltage across the load; thus the transistor controls the power in the load in response to a low-power input signal. The emitter follower is known to have a low output resistance, which is certainly a desirable characteristic for a voltage source. The output resistance of the power source may be determined by measuring the no-load output voltage at a particular voltage setting, and then remeasuring the voltage after connecting a 1-kilohm power resistor to the output for a load. Include a milliammeter to measure the load current. Considering the power source as a Thévenin equivalent circuit (Supplement 2), calculate its output resistance.

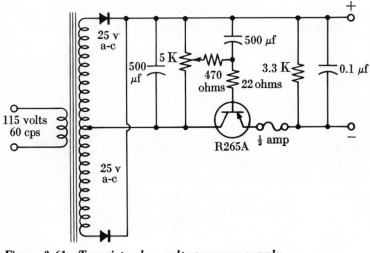

Figure 3-61   Transistor low-voltage power supply.

chapter four

Amplifier Circuits

In the following sections, various practical amplifier circuits are discussed according to their general characteristics and area of application. There are three common methods of combining (cascading) several amplifier stages to increase the over-all gain: *RC* coupling, transformer coupling, and direct coupling. These methods of coupling are each presented in the context of the amplifier types for which they are best suited. A discussion of noise and distortion in amplifier circuits is given, and the important topic of "feedback" is introduced.

4-1 Audio Preamplifiers

An audio preamplifier is a voltage amplifier designed to amplify, with very little distortion, a-c signals in the frequency range from 20 cps to 20 kc. Both vacuum tubes and transistors are suitable amplification elements. The preamplifier is usually followed by a power amplifier (Sec. 4-2), which is used to drive a load requiring current, such as a motor or a loudspeaker coil. The methods of amplifier coupling for a-c signals, the determination of amplifier gain, the various forms of signal distortion (including the frequency limitations of the amplifier), and the development of practical preamplifier circuits are described in this section.

A single stage of amplification is often insufficient to bring a small signal up to a useful level, and it is necessary to feed the output signal from

161

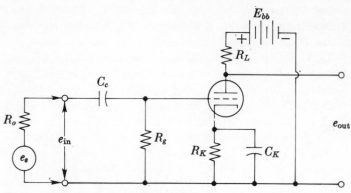

Figure 4-1   Typical triode amplifier.

one stage into another to increase the total amplifier gain.   For example, an a-c signal of 2 mv might be amplified to 60 mv by a single stage with voltage gain 30.   This 60-mv signal could then be fed into another stage with gain 30 to provide an output 60 × 30 = 1800 mv.   The over-all gain is the product of individual gains for each stage (gain = 30 × 30 = 900 for two stages of 30 each).   For an a-c amplifier, the problem arises of how to connect the output of one stage to the input of the next and yet eliminate the d-c voltage from the output of the first stage, which would interfere with the operation of the second stage.   The same holds true for subsequent stages.   The simplest and most common method of isolating the a-c signal from the d-c component is by *"RC* coupling."   *RC* coupling is likewise effective in separating the a-c signal information from a transducer which contains a large d-c voltage component.

Let us consider again the single-stage triode amplifier as shown in Fig. 4-1.   This is the same as the self-biased amplifier of Fig. 3-14, except that a "coupling" capacitor C_c has been added.   This capacitor ensures that the *average* grid-to-ground potential is zero regardless of any d-c component in the input-signal source.   In other words, the capacitor C_c blocks any d-c input voltage, and only an a-c voltage appears across the grid resistor R_g. The gain of this amplifier is given by Eq. (3-7) derived in Sec. 3-3,

$$A_e = \frac{-\mu R_L}{r_p + R_L}$$

Unfortunately, however, the gain A_e is not constant for all frequencies; i.e., the frequency response of the amplifier is limited.

Low-Frequency Response.   The *RC*-coupled amplifier has a certain "bandwidth" over which the gain is relatively constant.   In a mid-frequency range the gain can be expressed by the above equation.   As the frequency becomes too low or too high, the gain decreases. There are two effects which reduce the gain for low frequencies. The coupling capacitor C_c and grid resistor R_g act as a voltage divider (a high-pass network). The reactance $X_{Cc} = 1/(2\pi f C_c)$ increases as the frequency decreases, and an increasing fraction of the input voltage appears across C_c rather than between the grid and cathode of the tube. The cathode capacitor C_K is also responsible for a drop-off in gain at lower frequencies. The capacitor C_K should provide a path of negligible impedance $X_{CK} = 1/(2\pi f C_K)$ to shunt the signal around R_K. However, as the frequency decreases, the impedance of C_K increases, and the cathode voltage follows the grid to some extent, so that the gain of the amplifier is decreased. The effect of the cathode circuit on the low-frequency response is normally much less than that of the input or coupling network. There are two reasons for this—C_K is usually chosen to be of a very large capacitance (ca. 50 μf electrolytic capacitor) so that X_C is quite small for all except very low frequencies, and even if C_K were not present, the gain of the amplifier would be reduced only to that of the unbypassed amplifier.

By convention, the lower frequency-response limit f_1 of an amplifier is defined as that point at which the low-frequency gain $A_{e,\mathrm{LF}}$ is 0.707 times the mid-frequency gain A_e. This corresponds to a reduction in gain of 3 db. [Power or voltage ratios are often given in units of decibels; db = 20 log $(E_{\mathrm{out}}/E_{\mathrm{in}}) = 10 \log (P_{\mathrm{out}}/P_{\mathrm{in}})$.] In a high-pass network, a signal is attenuated to 0.707 of its value when $R = X_c$. If the low-frequency attenuation is due entirely to the input network, at the frequency f_1,

$$X_{Cc} = \frac{1}{2\pi f_1 C_c} = R_o + R_g$$

The resistance in the network is $R_o + R_g$ because, when C_c charges or discharges, it must be through the series combination of R_o and R_g. Solving for f_1 in the above equation,

$$f_1 = \frac{1}{2\pi C_c(R_o + R_g)} \tag{4-1}$$

Thus, for extended low-frequency response, R_g and C_c are made as large as necessary. It is not desirable for R_o to be large, as then too much signal voltage is lost in the source. The relative gain of the amplifier at any low frequency f can be determined from the formula

$$k_{\mathrm{LF}} = \frac{1}{\sqrt{1 + (f_1/f)^2}} \tag{4-2}$$

where $k_{\mathrm{LF}} = A_{e,\mathrm{LF}}/A_e$.

High-Frequency Response.   The high-frequency limitations of the amplifier of Fig. 4-1 are not so apparent.   They arise from shunt capacitances that are not intentionally part of the circuit and effectively short-circuit the a-c signal to ground.   Figure 4-2 shows the most important of these capacitances. C_o is the output capacitance of the signal source plus the capacitance of the wire connecting the signal source to the amplifier. C_i is the capacitance between the grid wire and the chassis, the tube socket capacitance, and the grid-to-cathode capacitance of the tube.   The effect of the grid-to-plate potential changes μ times as much as the grid potential and in the opposite direction, because of the amplification in the tube. C_{gp} would thus charge toward the potential $(\mu + 1)e_g$.   This is called the "Miller effect." C_o, C_i, and $(\mu + 1)C_{gp}$ all shunt the signal and can be considered to act in parallel.   The parallel combination of these shunt capacitances will be called C_s.   Thus the input-signal voltage is developed across C_s, which is charged through the parallel combination of R_o and R_g.   The value of R_o and R_g in parallel will be called R_s.   Thus R_s and C_s form a low-pass filter.   In the low-pass filter, too, a signal is attenuated to 0.707 of its value when $R = X_c$.   The upper frequency-response limit f_2 therefore is

$$f_2 = \frac{1}{2\pi C_s R_s} \tag{4-3}$$

The bandwidth of an amplifier is defined as $f_2 - f_1$.   The relative gain at any high frequency may be found by the formula

$$k_{\mathrm{HF}} = \frac{1}{\sqrt{1 + (f/f_2)^2}} \tag{4-4}$$

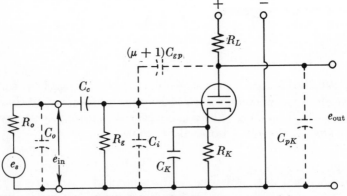

Figure 4-2   Amplifier circuit showing stray capacities.

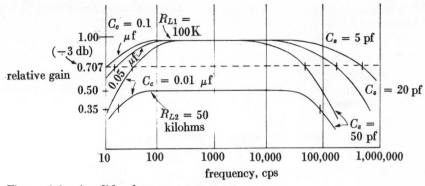

Figure 4-3 Amplifier frequency response.

where $k_{\mathrm{HF}} = A_{e,\mathrm{HF}}/A_e$. From Eq. (4-3) it can be seen that in order to extend the high-frequency response it is necessary to decrease C_s and R_s. As was shown before, R_g must be very large in order to maintain the low-frequency response. R_s can be kept small by using a low-impedance signal source (small R_o). C_s can be reduced to some extent by care in wiring, but the large effect of $(\mu + 1)C_{gp}$ will remain. Two means are used to minimize the effects of C_{gp}. One is to use a cathode-follower amplifier where C_{gp} is not multiplied by the factor $\mu + 1$. The other way is to use a pentode. The screen and suppressor grids isolate the control grid from the plate so that the effects of C_{gp} are much reduced. Typical frequency-response curves for an amplifier are shown in Fig. 4-3. These curves show the effects of C_c, C_s, and R_L on the bandwidth of an RC-coupled amplifier.

Phase Distortion. Phase distortion occurs when the signal suffers a phase change in passing through a high-pass or low-pass network. The extent of the phase change depends on the frequency. A complex waveform can be severely distorted in shape by phase distortion. The phase change in a high- or low-pass network is significant only in regions of attenuation. Therefore, as the gain of the amplifier falls off, the phase distortion increases. Figure 4-4 shows the gain and the phase shift as a function of f/f_1 or f_2/f. This graph shows that the frequency must be nearly ten times f_1 or $\frac{1}{10}f_2$ before the mid-frequency gain is reached. The phase shift between the input and output signals for a high-pass network can be expressed in terms of f_1 or f_2. The exact relationship is that ϕ, the phase shift, is the angle whose tangent is f_1/f or f/f_2. Thus the phase distortion is small within the region of good frequency response (f_1/f and f/f_2 much less than 1). For virtually undistorted amplification of nonsinusoidal signals, it may be necessary for f_1 to be 100 times greater than the signal frequency in order to

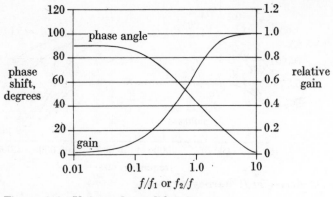

Figure 4-4   Universal amplification curve.

avoid phase distortion. Note that at the 3-db point the phase shift is 45°.
At f_1 the output leads the input signal; at f_2 it lags.

Amplifier Coupling. If the amplifier of Fig. 4-2 were the signal
source for another stage of amplification, its values R_o and C_o would have
to be known to calculate its effect on the frequency response of the next
stage. As derived in Sec. 3-3, the output resistance R_o is simply R_i in
parallel with r_p. The output capacitance C_o is simply the plate-to-cathode
capacitance C_{pK} plus the wiring capacitance. Recall that, to reduce the
effects of a capacitive load, it is best to have R_o as small as practical. When
a resistive load which is not very much larger than R_L is connected to the
amplifier, the effect of this load in parallel with R_L must be considered in
the amplifier voltage-gain calculation.

Bandwidth of Cascaded Amplifiers. It is quite common to amplify a signal successively through several tubes, or "stages of amplification." Such an amplifier is shown in Fig. 4-5. Any practical number of
stages can be used. The gain of the resulting amplifier is the product of the
gains of each stage. The bandwidth of the whole amplifier can be no better
than the bandwidth of the worst stage.

In fact, if all the stages of the amplifier have the same bandwidth, the
bandwidth of the resulting amplifier is somewhat worse than that of each
stage. This is because each stage imposes its frequency-range limitations
on a signal which has already been suppressed in the same frequency range.
The bandwidth decreases as the number of identical stages increases, as
shown by the formula

$$\frac{f_1}{f_{1n}} = \frac{f_{2n}}{f_2} = \sqrt{2^{1/n} - 1} \tag{4-5}$$

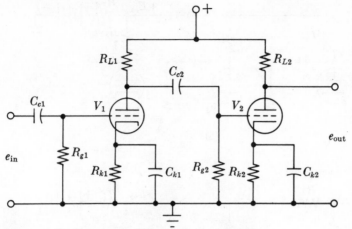

Figure 4-5   Two-stage RC-coupled amplifier.

where n is the number of identical stages and f_{1n} and f_{2n} are the 3-db points for the amplifier of n stages. f_1 and f_2 are the 3-db points of each stage.

Decoupling.   When three or more stages of amplification using the same high-voltage source are cascaded, unintentional interstage coupling may occur which would cause severe distortion and perhaps instability. Suppose that somehow a fraction of the output voltage of the two-stage amplifier of Fig. 4-5 were coupled to the amplifier input terminal of the grid of V_1. Since the signal is inverted twice in the amplifier, the output signal coupled back to the input would augment and enhance the size of the input signal. The output signal would be increased still further, causing an even greater enhancement of the signal. This phenomenon is called "feedback." If the amplifier has sufficient gain to maintain the output signal by amplifying the fraction of the output signal which is "fed back" to the input, the signal source is no longer required to produce the output signal! Whatever purpose such a circuit may have, it is not a desirable characteristic of an amplifier.

A common power supply is the usual cause of unwanted coupling of signals between the various stages of an amplifier. The way in which this happens is shown for a three-stage amplifier in Fig. 4-6. The three amplification stages are connected to a power source having a resistance R_{ps}. The signal voltage drop across R_{ps} is the sum of the three signal currents $i_1 + i_2 + i_3$ times R_{ps}. The signal current i_3 is many times larger than either of the other currents because of the amplification. Thus the voltage $+E_{bb}$ will have superimposed on it a signal voltage of about $i_3 R_{ps}$. This variation in the supply voltage applied to the amplifiers will cause a variation in the

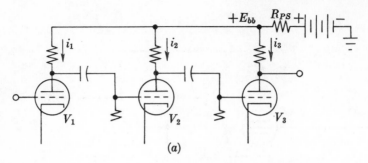

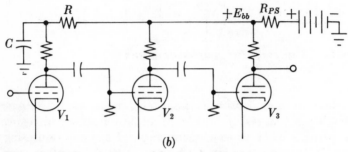

Figure 4-6 *Decoupling: (a) three stages with a common power supply; (b) stage 1 decoupled.*

plate voltage of V_1, which is, in turn, passed directly on to the grid of V_2. This results in the undesirable feedback condition described above.

The obvious cure for this condition is to prevent the signal of V_3 from entering the plate circuit of V_1. This is done by putting a low-pass filter in the power-supply lead of V_1 so that the signal frequencies will be filtered out of the supply voltage to V_1. This technique, called "decoupling," is illustrated in Fig. 4-6b. For the greatest effectiveness the product RC must be large. Since a large R introduces a voltage and power loss in the circuit of V_1, a large electrolytic capacitor is used for C and R is kept as small as practical. Unless the power source has exceptionally low impedance, it is necessary to use decoupling circuits in every amplifier with more than two stages of amplification.

Transistor-Amplifier Coupling. A transistor-amplifier circuit is shown in Fig. 4-7. The limitations on the frequency response of this amplifier are essentially the same as those of the vacuum tube. The high-pass network is C_c charging through the series combination of R_o and the resistance between the base and ground. The latter is the parallel combination of R_B and R_{in} for the transistor. If this parallel combination is substituted for R_g, then Eq. (4-1) would apply equally well for determining f_1 of the transistor circuit. It is obviously advantageous to make C_c, R_B, and R_{in} as large as practical for good low-frequency response. However, R_B cannot be very large, for the reasons of stability discussed in Sec. 3-7. Therefore, in order to have an RC-input-time constant high enough to pass the equivalent low frequencies of vacuum-tube circuits, one must use capacitors of the order of 10 μf. This can reduce the transistor's advantage of compact circuitry. Special electrolytic capacitors have been developed for transistor circuits. They are of physically small size and have low voltage ratings because these circuits need only relatively low voltages. The bandwidth of vacuum-tube circuits cannot be improved above a certain point because the size of coupling capacitors causes a considerable shunt capacitance. This reduces the high-frequency response while improving low-frequency response. The small electrolytics cannot be used for vacuum-tube coupling because their voltage rating is too low for the high voltages encountered in vacuum-tube circuits.

The high-frequency response of the transistor amplifier cannot be determined as simply as that of the triode amplifier. In most transistors, the transit time of the charges from one element to another becomes an important factor at only moderately high frequencies (not far above the audio range). This causes the interelectrode capacitances shown in Fig. 4-7 and the other transistor parameters to be very frequency-dependent. Often the bandwidth-limiting factor is the frequency dependence of α_{fb}. The 3-db point of a grounded-emitter amplifier is given by the formula

$$f_2 = (1 - \alpha_{fb})f_\alpha \tag{4-6}$$

where f_α is the α-cutoff frequency—a characteristic often given in the

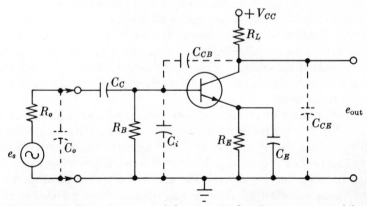

Figure 4-7   Transistor-amplifier circuit showing stray capacities.

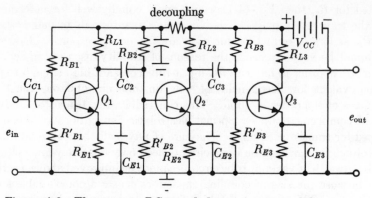

Figure 4-8   Three-stage RC-coupled transistor amplifier.

manuals.   Recall that α_{fb} is usually a number between 0.95 and 0.99, so that f_α must be very large for a reasonable bandwidth.

The impedance of any circuit connected to the output of the transistor amplifier acts as an impedance in parallel with R_L.   In the case of the transistor the impedance of the load affects not only the gain and frequency response but also the input impedance.   A three-stage RC-coupled amplifier is shown in Fig. 4-8.   In order to calculate the gain of this amplifier, it is necessary to calculate the gain and R_{in} of the third stage, considering the output load, then to calculate the gain of stage 2, considering the load of R_{in} of stage 3, and so on.   The vacuum tube is a voltage-actuated device, and the relatively low output resistance and very high input resistance provide the ideal conditions for voltage transfer from one stage to another. The transistor, however, is primarily a current-actuated device, having a low input resistance, and thus requiring current from the signal source. To connect from a high-impedance output to a low-impedance input without excessive loss in the signal voltage, it is often necessary to employ some impedance-matching device to couple the two stages.   In this case an appropriate impedance-matching device would have a high input impedance and a low output impedance.   Commonly used in this application would be a common-collector amplifier or a transformer with a high primary-to-secondary turns ratio.

Transformer Coupling.   In a transformer-coupled amplifier, such as that of Fig. 4-9, the transformer replaces the load resistance and the RC-coupling network to the next stage.   The separate transformer windings serve to isolate the d-c potentials between the two stages while providing a coupling path for the a-c signal.   Transformer coupling provides a more efficient signal transfer than RC coupling because there is little power loss in the transformer windings.   Also the problem of impedance matching be-

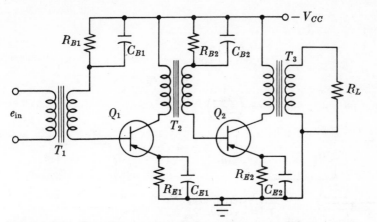

Figure 4-9   Transformer-coupled transistor amplifier.

tween circuits is solved by choosing the appropriate turns ratio between the primary and secondary windings.   On the other hand, the transformer is bulky and expensive and has a limited frequency response.

4-2   Audio Power Amplifier

A power amplifier is an amplifier whose output is considered more in terms of its power capability than its voltage or current limitations.   Relatively high output power is required when the amplifier is used to operate a motor, drive a loudspeaker, or perform some similar task.   Not only must the amplifier be capable of generating sufficient power, but some means must be found to transfer the power in the amplifier circuit effectively to the load.   The latter point will be considered first.

Impedance Matching.   Consider a generator of resistance R_s to which a load R_L is connected (Fig. 4-10).   The generator voltage will be

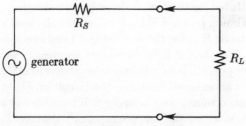

Figure 4-10   Impedance matching.

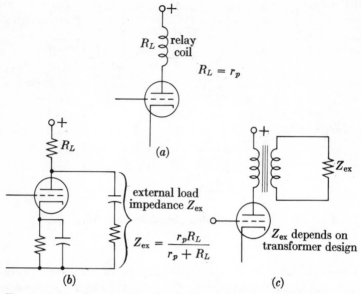

Figure 4-11   *Connecting the load to the power amplifier: (a) direct connection; (b) RC-coupled; (c) transformer-coupled.*

transferred to R_L most effectively when the voltage drop across R_s is minimized, i.e., when R_L is much greater than R_s. For the maximum generator current in R_L, R_L should be much less than R_s. These are the same conditions set forth in Chap. 1 for accurate measurements of voltage and current when the measuring device is the load R_L.

The substitution of a few values for R_s and R_L will quickly show that $I^2 R_L$ (the power dissipated in the load) is a maximum when $R_L = R_s$. This means that the maximum efficiency of power transfer is 50 per cent. Even when the output impedance of one stage is matched to the input impedance of the next, the efficiency of the RC-coupled amplifier is low because of the power wasted in R_L and R_B. The purpose of impedance matching, then, is to optimize power transfer.

When the load is substituted for the load resistor R_L in a simple amplifier circuit (Fig. 4-11a), maximum power will be developed in the load when $R_L = r_p$ for the vacuum tube or R_{out} for the transistor. Loads such as relays may be driven in this way, but it is inconvenient to operate motors and speakers at the elevated potentials of vacuum-tube plate circuits. To connect the power output to an external load Z_{ex}, the circuit of Fig. 4-11b may be used. In this case maximum power transfer will be achieved when Z_{ex} equals the output impedance of the amplifier circuit, that is, $Z_{ex} = r_p R_L/(r_p + R_L)$. The efficiency for this circuit will be substantially less than 50 per cent. Transformer coupling to the load as in Fig. 4-11c is often employed. The transformer transfers power from the plate circuit of the amplifier to the load Z_{ex}, isolates Z_{ex} from the amplifier d-c output potentials, and matches the impedance between r_p and Z_{ex}. The efficiency of this circuit is the same as that of Fig. 4-11a, 50 per cent. With so many advantages, transformer coupling to the load is a very common practice in power amplification.

Push-Pull Amplifier. Sometimes the power required by the load is more than can be handled by convenient amplification elements. There are two common ways to connect more than one amplification element to a load. These are illustrated in Fig. 4-12. The first (a) is called the parallel

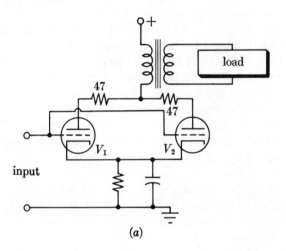

(a)

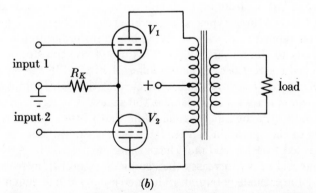

(b)

Figure 4-12   Multitube power amplifiers: (a) parallel connection; (b) push-pull connection.

connection. Small resistors are often put in series with each plate to help equalize the current distribution between the tubes and to suppress oscillation. When n identical tubes are put in parallel, the resultant amplification factor is unaffected, the plate resistance of a one-tube amplifier is divided by n, and the single-tube transconductance is increased n-fold.

Figure 4-12b illustrates the push-pull amplifier. In this circuit inputs 1 and 2 are 180° out of phase; so one tube is "pushing" the signal through the output transformer, while the other tube is "pulling." The power developed in the load will be twice the power developed in each half of the transformer primary. For high-powered amplifiers, the push-pull circuit is generally considered to be worth the trouble of obtaining out-of-phase input signals. This is because certain distortions developed by operating the tubes in their nonlinear regions for greater power are largely canceled in the output. This is explained more completely in Sec. 4-6.

When the deflection of the electron beam in a cathode-ray tube (CRT) was explained in Chap. 1, it was simply mentioned that a potential difference was applied to the deflection plates. If one plate of a pair of deflection plates were grounded and the signal applied to the other, the average voltage would vary with the signal strength. This would cause a variation in the focus of the beam and the deflection sensitivity of the CRT. In actual practice, equal but opposite signal voltages are applied to each pair of deflection plates, so that the acceleration of the electron beam is not a function of the deflection signal. For this application, an amplifier which has two equal outputs 180° out of phase with each other is required. Here again, the push-pull amplifier is called for. To make the circuit of Fig. 4-12b suitable for supplying a signal to a pair of CRT deflection plates, simply replace each half of the transformer primary with a resistor and connect the CRT deflection plates to the plates of the output tubes.

Phase Inverter. The amplifier which provides the push-pull output stage with the equal but opposite input signals is the phase-inverter amplifier. Figure 4-13 shows three types of phase-inverter amplifiers. Figure 4-13a uses a center-tapped secondary on a coupling transformer to provide out-of-phase signals to the output stage. This use of the transformer is similar to the full-wave rectifier. The amplifier of Fig. 4-13b has equal-valued plate and cathode resistors. Since the current through R_L and R_K is the same, the signal across each resistor is the same. The signal at the plate is out of phase with the input signal, while that of the cathode is in phase. The clue to the operation of Fig. 4-13c is that the cathodes of V_1 and V_2 are connected together and must have the same potential. A positive signal on the grid of V_1 increases the conductance of V_1, decreasing e_{o1} and increasing the cathode potential. The increase in cathode potential causes V_2 to conduct more poorly, increasing e_{o2}. Since the changes in grid-to-cathode voltage of V_1 and V_2 are necessarily equal and opposite, the output voltages will be equal in magnitude but 180° out of phase.

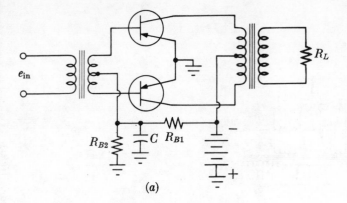

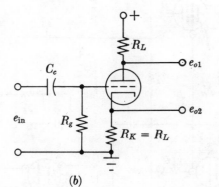

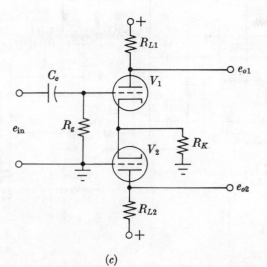

(c)

Figure 4-13   Three-phase inverter amplifiers: (a) transformer phase inverter with transistor push-pull amplifier; (b) cathode-resistor phase inverter; (c) difference-amplifier phase inverter.

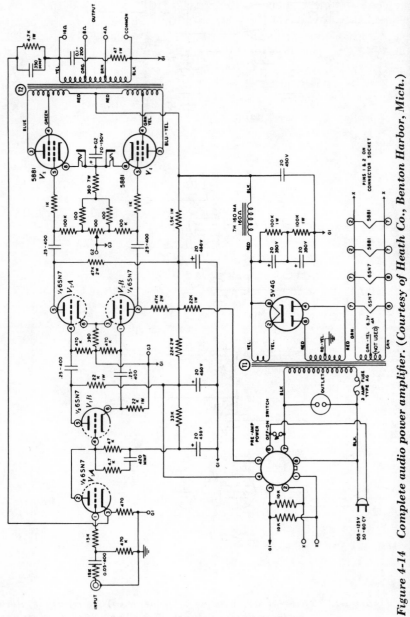

Figure 4-14 Complete audio power amplifier. (Courtesy of Heath Co., Benton Harbor, Mich.)

The phase inverter of Fig. 4-13*b* is called an unbalanced phase inverter because the output impedances of the two outputs are not identical. This becomes serious at low and high frequencies because the phase difference of e_{o1} and e_{o2} at these frequencies is not exactly 180°. Since the outputs of the balanced phase inverter of Fig. 4-13*c* are at the plates of identical tubes with identical load resistors, the phase of both of the outputs will remain at 180° independent of frequency, even if both the outputs differ from the input phase by some amount other than 0 or 180°.

A Power Amplifier. A complete power amplifier is shown in Fig. 4-14. Note that the first stage of the amplifier does not use a cathode by-pass capacitor. The second stage (V_1B) is the phase inverter of Fig. 4-13*b*. The inverted signal is again amplified in the third stage (V_2). Connecting the cathodes of V_2A and V_2B keeps the outputs equal but opposite as in the phase inverter of Fig. 4-13*c*. V_3 and V_4 form the push-pull output amplifier. An adjustment is provided to equalize the output current of each tube. The voltmeter will read zero when the amplifiers are balanced. The output transformer secondary has several taps for obtaining the proper impedance match for various load impedances. The connection between the output transformer secondary and the cathode of the input stage feeds about one-eleventh of the output voltage back to the input. It has already been shown that feedback tending to enhance the input signal leads to a potentially unstable amplifier. However, in this amplifier the feedback is out of phase with the input signal, so that the effect is a *reduction* in the effectiveness of the input signal. This type of feedback actually increases the stability and linearity of the amplifier, with some sacrifice in gain. Feedback will be explained much more thoroughly in Sec. 4-7 and in Chaps. 5, 7, and 8.

4-3 The Direct-Coupled Amplifier

The output of a thermocouple, an electrolytic cell, and many other transducers is a d-c voltage. Capacitor- or transformer-coupled amplifiers block d-c voltages so that some type of direct coupling is required to amplify a d-c signal. Two examples of direct-coupled amplifiers are shown in Fig. 4-15. One of the problems of direct coupling is to bring the signal at the output of the first stage to the proper d-c level for the next amplifier stage. In Fig. 4-15*a* this is accomplished by operating the second stage at an elevated potential. The output will also be at a high potential. The number of separate supply voltages and the magnitude of the quiescent output increase with each additional stage. The circuit of Fig. 4-15*b* drops the d-c level at the output of each stage with a voltage divider connected to a negative supply voltage. Assume that the quiescent plate voltage of V_1 is $+100$ volts and that the negative supply voltage is -200 volts. The quiescent

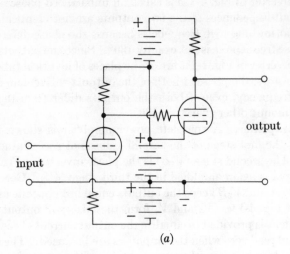

(a)

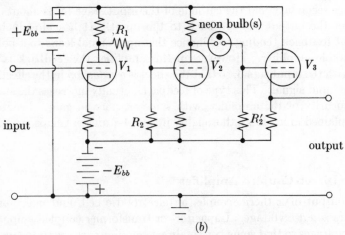

(b)

*Figure 4-15   Direct-coupled amplifiers: (a) battery-coupled, (b) re-
sistance-coupled and glow-tube-coupled.*

d-c voltage at the grid of V_2 will be restored to 0 volts if $R_1 = \frac{1}{2}R_2$. Typical
values for R_1 and R_2 would be 500 kilohms and 1 megohm. Note that the
signal is also divided across R_1 and R_2 so that the signal reaches the grid of
V_2 attenuated by the factor $R_2/(R_1 + R_2)$. In the case cited, one-third
of the signal is lost.

In the coupling between V_2 and V_3, a neon bulb replaces R_1. Recall
that the potential across a neon bulb is nearly independent of the current
through it, within the proper current range (Sec. 2-7). The potential

across a neon bulb is about 50 to 55 volts. Therefore, to drop the d-c level about 100 volts between the plate of V_2 and the grid of V_3, two neon bulbs would be used in series. R_2' would be chosen to give the proper operating current through the neon bulbs. Since the plate of V_2 and the grid of V_3 are always different in potential by a constant value, the signal is transferred unattenuated from the second to the third stage. A Zener diode may be used in place of the neon bulbs, giving the same effect. Zener diodes have the advantage of being available in a wide assortment of voltages and operating currents.

When it is desired to extend the range of the amplifier for negative input voltages, the amplifier cathodes are returned to the negative power-supply voltage. Thus direct-coupled amplifiers often require both positive and negative supply voltages. The output stage is a cathode follower, so that the output d-c level will not be greatly elevated. In fact, if the dividers are properly adjusted, it is possible to have a zero output voltage when the input voltage is zero.

Stability is another problem in the direct-coupled amplifier. Every change in a component value, tube characteristic, or supply voltage will appear amplified and indistinguishable from the signal at the output. Obviously the components must be well stabilized, the power-supply voltages very well regulated, and the zero level must be watched and adjusted fairly often (as with the VTVM, which has a direct-coupled amplifier).

Another way to amplify a d-c voltage is by the chopper amplifier, which converts the d-c signal to alternating current, amplifies, then reconverts to direct current. These amplifiers are known for their high stability. They are discussed in Chaps. 6 and 8.

Not too long ago the direct-coupled amplifier was considered to be notoriously unreliable and unstable. Recent advances in the design of components and stable, well-regulated power supplies have brought d-c amplifiers into wide application. In addition to being able to amplify d-c signals, the bandwidth of a direct-coupled amplifier is often very much larger than its RC-coupled equivalent. Obviously, the elimination of RC coupling removes the low-frequency limitation of the amplifier altogether. (Cathode and emitter bypass capacitors must also be eliminated.) The elimination of the bulky coupling capacitor reduces the shunt capacitance of the coupling network and can, therefore, improve the high-frequency response as well. Whereas an oscilloscope with a d-c amplifier was a very expensive and unusual instrument ten years ago, today nearly all good-quality oscilloscopes employ direct-coupled amplifiers for both vertical- and horizontal-deflection amplification.

Oscilloscope Amplifier. A wide-band vertical-deflection amplifier for an oscilloscope is shown in Fig. 4-16. This circuit has a large bandpass of d-c ($f = 0$) to 3.6 Mc. The input stage is a cathode follower. The pentode second stage amplifies the signal and is connected to a phase-

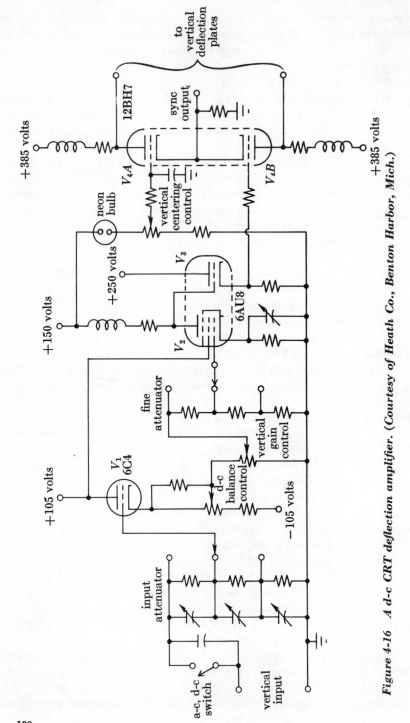

Figure 4-16 A d-c CRT deflection amplifier. (Courtesy of Heath Co., Benton Harbor, Mich.)

inverter amplifier (V_4) through another cathode follower (V_3). The outputs of the phase inverter are "push-pull" in the sense that they are out of phase by 180°. Since virtually no current is required to drive the CRT deflection plates, a push-pull power-amplifier stage is unnecessary. If more voltage gain were required, or if the deflection system were electromagnetic instead of electrostatic, another push-pull stage would be added.

In addition to the techniques of direct coupling, the circuit of Fig. 4-16 is of great interest because it uses several common techniques for obtaining extended high-frequency response. Consequently it is worthwhile to analyze the design of this amplifier, beginning with the first stage (V_1). The first stage was chosen to be a cathode follower so that the amplifier would have the cathode follower's characteristics of high input resistance and low input capacitance. (Recall that the input capacitance of the common cathode amplifier is high because of the Miller effect—Sec. 4-1.) The cathode resistor is returned to a negative supply voltage to bias the tube in its linear operating region. This is the only method for biasing a direct-coupled cathode follower.

Attenuator Compensation. An attenuator is provided at the input for signals which are too large for the sensitive amplifier to handle. The

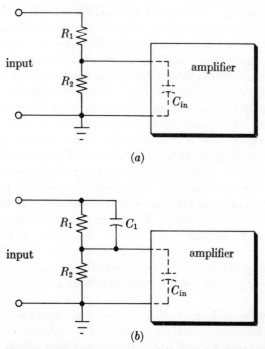

Figure 4-17   Attenuators: (a) uncompensated; (b) compensated.

presence of the adjustable capacitors across the attenuator resistors can be explained as follows: An ordinary attenuator is shown in Fig. 4-17a. The amplifier input capacitance provides a shunt at high frequencies around resistor R_2. Thus the high frequencies will be attenuated more than the mid- and low frequencies. If a capacitance C_1 is added to shunt the resistance R_1 as in Fig. 4-17b, the impedance of R_1 and C_1 will decrease at high frequencies just as that of R_2C_{in}. To provide constant attenuation over all frequencies, $C_1 = C_{in}(R_2/R_1)$. The capacitors in the attenuator of Fig. 4-16 are then simply compensating capacitors. They are adjustable because the amplifier input capacitance may change as the tube ages or is replaced.

D-C Balance. The d-c balance control is simply a bias voltage adjustment on the cathode follower. It is adjusted so that there is no output signal when the input is grounded. The vertical centering control can also be used to adjust the point of zero deflection for zero input and could thus compensate for a misadjustment of the bias of V_1. If this is done, the trace will move when the vertical gain control is turned because the fraction of the d-c output voltage of V_1 which is sent on through the deflection amplifiers will change. When the d-c balance control is adjusted properly, the zero deflection point on the CRT will be independent of the settings of the gain and attenuator controls.

High-Frequency Peaking. The gain of an amplifier falls off at high frequencies owing to the shunt capacitances, which must charge through the output impedance of the previous stage. This effect has been minimized for the amplifier V_2 through the use of a pentode which has low shunt capacities and through the use of the cathode follower in the previous stage, which has a low output impedance. Still another technique to improve the high-frequency response is to increase the gain of the amplification circuit for those frequencies being attenuated by the shunt capacitances. The peaking coil in the plate circuit is a small inductance which increases the plate-load impedance at high frequencies but which has no effect at the low frequencies. The high-frequency gain can also be increased by bypassing the cathode resistor with a small capacitor. This reduces the loss in gain due to cathode biasing, but only at the high frequencies, where greater gain is needed to compensate for the losses. High-frequency peaking cannot extend the response of an amplifier indefinitely. When the peaking coil or capacitor is too large, this causes uneven response in the mid-frequencies, which would otherwise have been smooth. Typical high-frequency-response curves of peaked and unpeaked amplifiers are compared in Fig. 4-18.

Because of the high value of R_2 used with V_2, the input capacitance of an ordinary stage of amplification would have ruined the high-frequency response. The cathode follower V_3 acts to isolate the amplifier circuit of

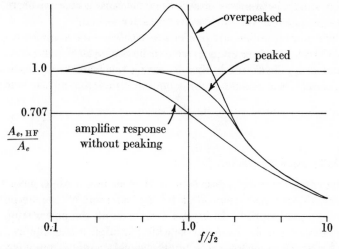

Figure 4-18   Response of a peaked amplifier.

V_2 from the load of the phase-inverter circuit. Notice that the phase-inverter circuit also employs peaking coils in the plate circuits.

The Electrometer Amplifier. If an ordinary VTVM (input resistance about 10 megohms) is connected across a charged capacitor, the capacitor is discharged through the input resistance and the voltage across the capacitor can be significantly changed before the measurement is completed. To measure the voltage across the capacitor without significantly affecting the charge on it, it is necessary to have an amplifier with extremely high input impedance. Likewise, a high input impedance is necessary if the resistance of an input source is very high, say, 1000 megohms (typical of a glass pH electrode), because otherwise only a fraction of the input voltage appears across the input of the measuring device.

As described in Sec. 3-8, a cathode follower can increase the input impedance, but this increase is insufficient for certain applications. Therefore, special tubes with very low grid currents (and consequently high input impedance) have been designed for critical measurements of charge, current, and voltage. These tubes are known as *electrometer tubes*, and several factors are carefully controlled in their construction and use to ensure a low grid current. A very good vacuum is provided in the manufacture of the tube; the tube is operated in darkness to minimize photoemission from the grid; the glass envelope is kept scrupulously clean and dry (with desiccant) and is often coated to keep its resistance high; the plate potential is kept low (a few volts) to minimize gas ionization in the tube; and cathode emission is maintained at a low value with a low filament current. With sufficient care some electrometer circuits can measure a current of 10^{-17} amp. This represents only about 64 electrons per second.

One of the most familiar applications of electrometer amplifiers is in pH meters, and a typical circuit is presented in Sec. 6-2 (Fig. 6-14). Another widespread application is in direct-reading spectrometers, wherein a capacitor integrates the current from a photomultiplier, and the voltage $(E = \dfrac{1}{C} \int i \, dt)$ is measured with the electrometer circuit.

4-4 The Difference Amplifier

All of the amplifier circuits discussed in the previous sections have had one of the input terminals connected to the common of the amplifier output and the power supply. In most instruments all the power supplies and amplifiers have a point in common which is often called the system ground. It is sometimes necessary to amplify signals coming from a circuit which has neither output terminal connected to ground. In other words, one may wish to amplify the potential difference between two points in a circuit when neither of these points is ground. This might be done with an amplifier and power supply which are not connected to the common ground. A power supply or circuit which is not connected to the common ground of the system, and whose potentials therefore are not fixed with respect to the ground, is said to be "floating." It is very difficult electrically to isolate a circuit from its surroundings, especially when all the circuits within the instrument must operate from the same a-c power line. Floating circuits are usually prone to noise, shock hazard, and imperfect isolation from the associated circuitry.

An amplifier whose output is a function of the potential difference between two input signal voltages is shown in Fig. 4-19. The output voltage is simply the difference in the output voltage of two amplifiers, Amp 1 and Amp 2. If A_1 is the gain of Amp 1, and A_2 the gain of Amp 2,

$$e_{\text{out}} = A_1 e_1 - A_2 e_2 \tag{4-7}$$

If $A_1 = A_2 = A$,

$$e_{\text{out}} = A(e_1 - e_2) \tag{4-8}$$

where $A = -\mu R_L/(R_L + r_p)$. For A_2 to equal A_1, the two halves of the circuit must be electrically identical. The characteristics of V_1 and V_2 are likely to be very similar if they are in the same glass envelope. Minor adjustments in gain can be made with the trimmer on the plate-load resistors. A less obvious assumption of Eq. (4-8) is that A is independent of e_1 and e_2. This will be true only over that portion of the load line for which μ and r_p are constants.

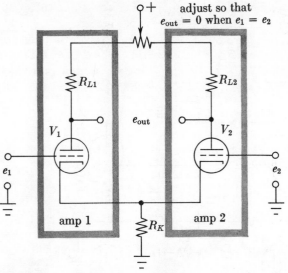

Figure 4-19   *Difference amplifier.*

The circuit of Fig. 4-19 can be recognized as the phase-inverter amplifier of Fig. 4-13c. The only differences between these two circuits are that, with the phase inverter, the output at each plate was considered separately and one of the amplifier grids was grounded. Following the same argument for Fig. 4-19 which was advanced for the circuit of Fig. 4-13c, when e_1 goes positive, the plate of V_1 goes negative, the cathodes of V_1 and V_2 go positive, and the plate of V_2 goes positive. Thus the output signal voltages on the two plates will be equal and opposite regardless of the direction of the change *or of which input voltage changed*. If both input voltages change equally, the output voltages would also change equally but their difference would remain zero. This circuit then provides a phase inverter or push-pull output in response to the difference between the input signal potentials.

Oscilloscope Difference Amplifier. The circuit of Fig. 4-19 is the push-pull stage in the oscilloscope amplifier of Fig. 4-16. The push-pull output corresponds to the difference between the amplified signal voltage and the adjustable vertical centering voltage. Thus "zero" volts could be set at any desired deflection angle. To obtain a deflection on a CRT which is proportional to the difference between two input voltages, one would need only a succession of amplifiers like those of Fig. 4-19, leading to the deflection plates. The circuit of such an amplifier is shown in Fig. 4-20.

A much greater linear operating region and a greatly decreased effect of differences in the tubes can be achieved by using a cathode-follower dif-

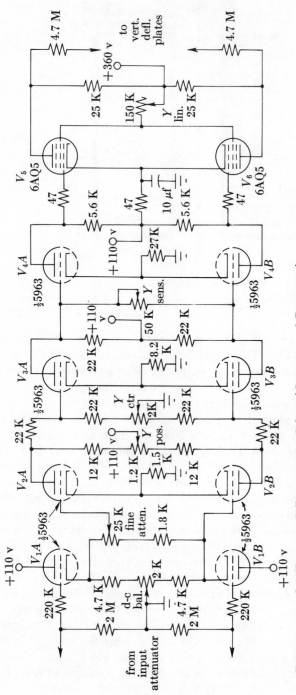

Figure 4-20 Oscilloscope difference amplifier. (Courtesy of Dumont.)

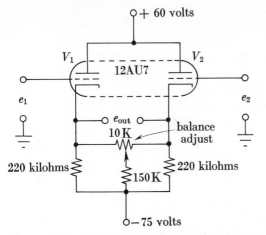

Figure 4-21   Cathode-follower difference amplifier.

ference amplifier. This circuit is shown in Fig. 4-21. Of course, the voltage gain is less than 1, but the input impedance is very high, and the output impedance is very low. This circuit is often used in the vacuum-tube volt-meter. The meter is connected directly to the output terminals.

The difference amplifier is a very stable amplifier because changes in supply voltages, component aging, temperature, noise from magnetic or electromagnetic fields, etc., tend to affect both tubes equally and hence do not appear in the output signal. For this reason, the difference amplifier is often found with one grid connected to a conventional grounded signal source and the other grid connected to ground or some stable reference voltage.

The Vacuum-Tube Voltmeter. A vacuum-tube voltmeter (VTVM) circuit is shown in Fig. 4-22. The basic amplifier circuit is that of Fig. 4-21. One input is grounded; the other is connected to the attenuated input signal. The meter, in series with a calibrating resistor selected for each measure-ment function, is connected between the cathodes of V_1 and V_2. On the ohms scale, the amplifier measures the voltage across a resistor in series with the unknown resistor and a battery. Alternating-current voltages are rectified, filtered, attenuated, and then measured with the same d-c difference-amplifier circuit.

Neither output terminal of the above difference amplifiers, shown in Figs. 4-19 and 4-21, is connected to ground. Further amplification would thus involve more difference amplifiers. A difference-amplifier circuit has been devised which has a "single-ended" output. (One output terminal is

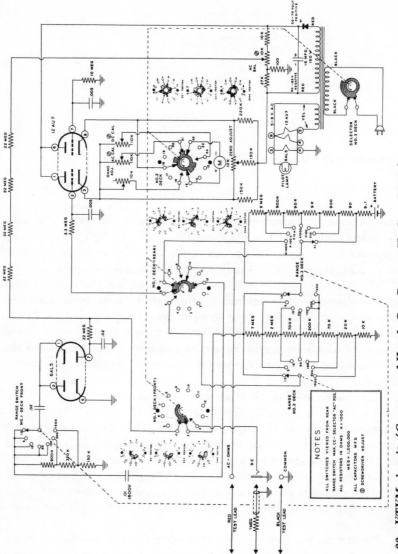

Figure 4-22 VTVM circuit. (*Courtesy of Heath Co., Benton Harbor, Mich.*)

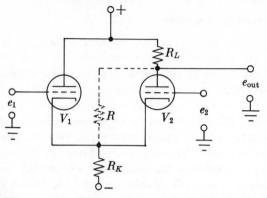

Figure 4-23 Difference amplifier with single-ended output.

ground.) This circuit is shown in Fig. 4-23. The output is a function of the grid-to-cathode potential of V_2. One signal is connected to the grid of V_2, and the other signal is connected to the cathode of V_2 through the cathode follower of V_1. If the cathode-follower amplifier had a gain of unity, the output signal voltage is given by the equation

$$e_{\text{out}} = \frac{\mu R_L}{R_L + 2r_p} (e_1 - e_2) \qquad (4\text{-}9)$$

when the resistance R is not in the circuit [see the References (Seely)]. However, the cathode follower does not have unity gain except when $R_K = \infty$, so that the gains for e_1 and e_2 are slightly different.

Ideally, no signal which is common to both e_1 and e_2 should appear in the output. That is, if the same signal were applied to both inputs, there should be no output signal. The ability of an amplifier to achieve this effect is called its "common-mode signal-rejection ratio." This is defined as

$$\text{CM}_{\text{rej}} = \frac{\text{gain of amplifier to difference signal}}{\text{gain of amplifier to common signal}}$$

The addition of the resistance $R = R_K$ to the circuit of Fig. 4-23 greatly improves its common-mode rejection ratio [see the References (Seely)], while reducing gain somewhat. Another technique for improving the common-mode rejection ratio is greatly to increase the effective value of R_K by substituting a vacuum tube for R_K [see the References ("Vacuum Tube Amplifiers," M.I.T.)].

Many oscilloscopes, amplifiers, and recorders have what are called "differential" or "balanced" inputs. It is important to know what the common-mode rejection ratio is before relying on this equipment to yield a true difference input when neither input is grounded.

4-5   Noise and Distortion in Amplifiers

In most amplifier applications a primary concern is that the input signal appear at the output changed only in magnitude. Any change in the waveshape of the signal is due to a distortion of the signal within the amplifier or to the addition of some sort of noise signal. Noise may be considered a form of distortion in that it is superimposed on, and therefore distorts, the output signal. Distortion may be considered noise in that a distorted output signal contains signal components which were not present at the input. The terms noise and distortion are used only to distinguish the causes for the discrepancy between the output waveshape and the input. The sources of noise in electronic circuitry will be considered first; then the various distortions due to nonlinear components and circuits will be discussed.

Noise.   Noise signals which appear in the amplifier circuitry are usually divided into two groups: those generated externally which enter the circuit by some connection or as electromagnetic radiation, and those which are generated within the amplifier components themselves. The sources of external noise and the general remedies will be discussed first.

Electromagnetic Radiation.   Any electrical conductor acts as an antenna for the reception of electromagnetic radiation in the radio-frequency range. The radio waves thus received are added to any signal present in the wire. The efficiency of the wire as an antenna depends on the nature of the radiation and the physical dimensions of the wire. Electromagnetic radiation of various frequencies and intensities is ever with us. Some sources of radiation produce a very narrow band of frequencies. These include radio transmitters, exposed oscillators in radios and instruments, and the 60-cps power lines, cables, and connections. Other radiation sources produce a wide spectrum of frequencies. Examples of this type are ionospheric phenomena and electrical discharges (lightning, ignition systems, spectrographic power units, X-ray tubes, motors with brushes, etc.).

The reception of radio waves by wire or circuit elements can be greatly reduced by proper shielding. This consists of enclosing the circuit or critical wires with a conducting material which is grounded to earth or to a system ground. The shield then intercepts the radiation, and the ground connection short-circuits the radiation signal harmlessly to ground. Metal chassis and cabinets are used for the construction of electronic equipment, and the metal parts are connected to the circuit ground. Shielded wires are used for external signal connections to the circuit. Occasionally shielded wire is used for critical internal connections because of the presence of 60-cps or other frequency radiated within the instrument cabinet. The appearance and construction of typical shielded wire are shown in

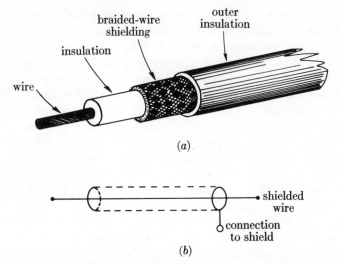

(a)

(b)

Figure 4-24   Shielded cable: (a) construction; (b) schematic.

Fig. 4-24. The schematic representation of a shielded grid lead is also shown. The sensitivity of a wire or component to radiation is roughly proportional to its physical length and cross section, the impedance to ground at that point of the circuit, and the voltage amplification in subsequent stages of the circuit. In high-gain amplifiers, some care must be taken to ground all shields to a common point without introducing "ground loops," which are closed paths in the chassis-shield system that may induce noise signals in nearby components.

Magnetic Fields. A signal voltage may be induced in a wire which is within a changing magnetic field. The changing magnetic field can result from the flow of alternating current through any coil such as a choke, transformer, or motor, or even through a straight wire such as a filament connection or a-c power cord. A ferromagnetic material must be used to shield circuits or components from magnetic fields. When necessary, either the source of the magnetic field or an especially critical component is shielded. A material of high magnetic permeability, such as Mumetal,* is best suited for this purpose. Since magnetic fields usually carry only a short distance, it is often possible to isolate the source of the magnetic field by placing it well away from sensitive circuitry. In general, it is good practice to keep critical wires and components away from transformer and power connectors, and perpendicular to any nearby wires carrying over a few milliamperes of alternating current.

* Allegheny Ludlum Steel Corp., Pittsburgh, Pa.

Associated Circuitry. Often noise is introduced into a circuit via connections to external equipment or power sources. Of course the proper shielding of associated equipment is essential. The connection to the power source is often the most troublesome. Heavy-duty electrical equipment in a laboratory building can cause pulses or fluctuations in the power-line voltage which are imposed on the signal in many parts of the circuit. The power-supply voltage itself, if not well filtered, can introduce 60- or 120-cps noise into the circuits it is powering. The remedies for these problems are: power-line filters to reduce pulses in the a-c power line, better filtering in the power supply, and in extreme cases battery-operated equipment.

Microphonics. Mechanical vibration of most parts of an electronic circuit has no electrical effect. However, vacuum tubes and many signal sources are sensitive to vibration. In the case of the vacuum tube the greatest effect comes from a movement of the control grid which changes the characteristics of the tube. In this way the mechanical movement is converted to an electrical signal in an instrument. This effect has been given the name microphonics. Some tube types are more microphonic than others, and tubes may become microphonic with age. A new type of tube with a rigid grid structure called a "frame grid" is used in modern circuits to avoid microphonics. Microphonic noise is a very low level signal, and so only amplifiers in low-level portions of the circuit will be affected. A soft shock mounting of the tubes in these sections will help considerably. Transistors and other components having a rigid structure are not much affected by vibration.

Inherent Component Noise. Low-signal-level electronic circuits are also troubled by noise signals which occur within the amplifier elements themselves and are quite apart from any external fields or forces. The major contributors of these noise signals are: thermal noise due to the random movement of charged particles, and shot noise due to the discrete nature of charges in a nonmetallic medium.

Thermal Noise. Charged particles in a medium undergo a continuous random motion which is thermally agitated at all temperatures above $0°K$. Owing to this motion, currents flow through the medium, giving rise to a difference in potential across the medium. This potential difference undergoes changes in sign and magnitude. The average d-c potential is zero (in the absence of an electric field). The potential variations are called thermal noise. They are completely random in frequency; i.e., the noise signal is generated at all frequencies equally. Because it is due to thermal agitation, thermal noise increases with temperature and is completely eliminated only at a temperature of absolute zero. The magnitude of the thermal noise increases as the resistance of the component increases. Finally, since the noise is generated at all frequencies, the total noise energy will depend on the range of frequencies allowed in the circuit. These relationships are given quantitatively by the expression

$$\bar{E}_{rms} = (4RkT\ \Delta F)^{1/2} \qquad (4\text{-}10)$$

where $\bar{E}_{rms}$ is the rms value of the noise voltage, R is the resistance of the element, k is the Boltzmann constant $= 1.38 \times 10^{-23}$ joule/°K, T is the absolute temperature in degrees Kelvin, and ΔF is the bandwidth of the circuit. Equation (4-10) gives the lower theoretical limit for thermal noise. Real components approach this value only with careful design. As with all other forms of noise, the low-level input stages of the amplifier are the most susceptible.

The methods for reducing thermal noise are all suggested by Eq. (4-10): (1) Keep the resistance of the elements in the critical circuits low. This will force a compromise between high input resistance and low noise. Use special low-noise resistors. (2) Keep the circuit temperature down. Here the transistor has an obvious advantage over the vacuum tube, since the latter must operate with a heated cathode. (3) Reduce the bandwidth to just that which is necessary for the application.

Shot Noise. The passage of current through vacuum tubes and transistors is accomplished by the movement of discrete charges. Thus the total current is the sum of all the separate pulses or units of charge which traverse the electric field and is therefore not continuous. The magnitude of the discontinuities depends on the charge q on each charge carrier, on the total current I through the tube or transistor, on the value of the load resistor R_L used in the circuit, and on the bandwidth ΔF. The formula for the maximum shot-effect noise is

$$\bar{E}_{rms} = (2qIR_L^2\ \Delta F)^{1/2}$$

$$= (3.2 \times 10^{-19} I R_L^2\ \Delta F)^{1/2} \qquad (4\text{-}11)$$

Actual transistors and vacuum tubes usually have shot-effect values which are only a fraction of that predicted by Eq. (4-11), because of averaging effects of the space charge. The shot-effect noise is calculated for the output of an amplifier stage. To compare this with the thermal noise generated in a resistor in the input circuit, the value of Eq. (4-11) should be divided by the amplifier gain. Because the total noise is the sum of the thermal and shot noise, it does no good to reduce the thermal noise much below the minimum value for the shot noise. The optimum input impedance for a vacuum-tube circuit is of the order of 1 megohm or more, while for a transistor it is 500 to 1000 ohms. When the input impedances are properly chosen, the noise for a given signal level is a comparable value for vacuum-tube and transistor amplifiers. Clearly the vacuum tube is better for high-impedance signal sources. Again, the bandwidth is an important factor.

Signal-to-Noise Ratio. The signal-to-noise ratio is the figure of merit which describes the purity of the signal waveform. Both noise and distortion signals are considered noise in calculating this ratio. The signal-to-noise ratio is usually given as a power ratio in decibels,

$$\frac{S}{N} \text{ (db power)} = 10 \log \frac{\text{signal power}}{\text{noise power}} \qquad (4\text{-}12)$$

or as a voltage ratio in decibels,

$$\frac{S}{N} \text{ (db voltage)} = 20 \log \frac{\text{signal voltage}}{\text{noise voltage}} \qquad (4\text{-}13)$$

While the signal-to-noise ratio is very useful in considering how difficult it will be to obtain the signal information in the presence of the noise, it does not tell how much noise was added to the signal by a specific unit such as the amplifier. For this purpose the noise factor (NF or F) is used. It is defined as

$$F = \frac{S/N \text{ (input)}}{S/N \text{ (output)}} \qquad (4\text{-}14)$$

Note that, for an amplifier which contributes no noise, $F = 1$.

Measurements on Noisy Signals. A very large area in modern communications research is concerned with how to sort the intended signal

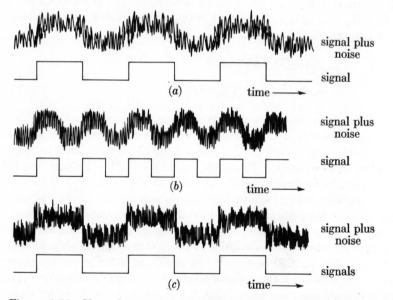

Figure 4-25 *Use of repetitive measurements to distinguish signal from noise: (a) 3 cycles—single sweep; (b) 6 cycles— single sweep; (c) 3 cycles—10 sweeps superimposed. (From E. J. Bair, Introduction to Chemical Instrumentation, McGraw-Hill, New York, 1962.)*

from noise and thus maintain an accurate transmittal of information. When the noise in a circuit has been reduced to a minimum but is still objectionable, a means must be devised to measure the signal in the presence of the noise.

One of the general approaches used is readily applicable to common instrumental measurements. It is based on the assumption that the noise component is random but that the signal is reproducible. If the measurement of signal plus noise is repeated many times and averaged, the average noise component will be zero and only the signal will remain. The effectiveness of the repetitive-signal measurement is shown in Fig. 4-25. Even the repetitive signal must be averaged further by the experiments. These fluctuations could not have been smoothed out electrically without ruining the bandwidth for the passage of the signal; thus the net effect is to decrease the effective bandwidth of the circuit, decreasing the noise in accordance with Eqs. (4-10) and (4-11). This method is applicable only to random noise; it will not work with distortion where the signal waveform is reproducibly distorted by the amplifier.

Frequency and Phase Distortion. In the first four sections of this chapter, particular attention was paid to the problems of frequency response and phase shift in amplifiers. Since a nonsinusoidal waveform is a composite signal of many frequencies, an unequal amplification of these fre-

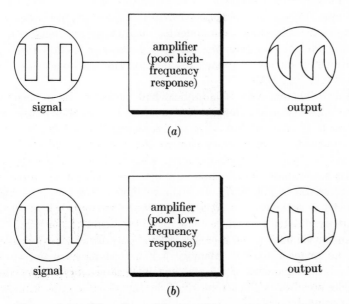

Figure 4-26 *The effect of frequency response on a square-wave signal: (a) poor high-frequency response; (b) poor low-frequency response.*

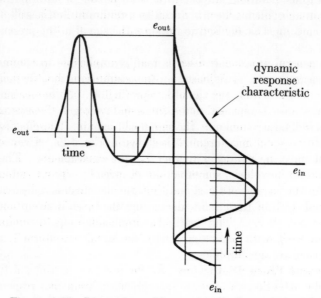

Figure 4-27   Distortion of large signals (harmonic distortion).

quencies or an uneven phase shift will distort the waveform. According to Fourier analysis, the rapidly changing parts of the waveform are composed mostly of the highest-frequency components. A square-wave signal amplified by an amplifier having poor high-frequency response is shown in Fig. 4-26a. However, poor low-frequency response causes the square wave to droop as shown in Fig. 4-26b.

Harmonic Distortion. If amplifiers had perfectly linear response curves, amplitude distortion (uneven frequency response) and phase distortion (unequal phase shift for different frequencies) would be the only distortions observed. Amplification-element characteristic curves are not linear, nor are the dynamic response characteristics. The amplifier output waveform for a sinusoidal input signal is plotted by using a dynamic response characteristic in Fig. 4-27. It is shown that at large input signals the nonlinearity is so severe that it is noticeable to the eye. Obviously a smaller input signal would result in a less distorted output waveform.

The nonsinusoidal character of the output waveform indicates that the signal is no longer a single frequency. A Fourier analysis of the waveform would show frequencies of integral multiples of the input-signal frequencies. The creation of "harmonics" of the signal within the amplifier is called harmonic distortion.

The remedy for harmonic distortion is to optimize the linear-response region of the amplifier and use as small a signal as possible. It is very inefficient, however, to operate an amplifier over such a small portion of its useful operating range.

When two amplifiers operating over their full operating range are arranged in the push-pull configuration, the even harmonics cancel in the output. Since the second harmonic (twice the fundamental frequency) has the greatest magnitude ordinarily, the harmonic distortion is greatly reduced.

Intermodulation Distortion. Many signals to be amplified are nonsinusoidal and thus are a composite of many frequencies. In a linear amplifier circuit there would be no interaction of these frequencies. In a nonlinear circuit, however, the signals of different frequencies will intermodulate to produce the sum-and-difference frequencies or "beat" frequencies. Since this introduces new signals, it is a form of distortion. Modulation and the production of the beat note are often used to great advantage, as explained in the next two chapters, but intermodulation is not a desirable characteristic of signal amplifiers.

When signals from separate sources are to be amplified together, it is

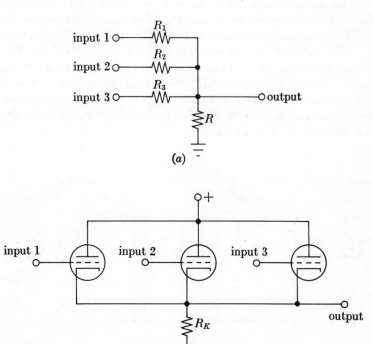

Figure 4-28   Methods of summing: (a) passive network; (b) cathode-follower network.

important to make their connection to the amplifier in such a way that the signals will not interact on each other. Two common methods are shown in Fig. 4-28. In Fig. 4-28a the signals are summed across R. If R_1, R_2, and R_3 are all much larger than the output resistances of the sources, the signals will not intermodulate. The cathode-follower chain of Fig. 4-28 provides complete isolation of each input circuit into a very linear amplifier.

4-6 The Radio-Frequency Amplifier

In Sec. 4-5 the importance of bandwidth in the determination of the signal-to-noise ratio was emphasized. In earlier sections, the importance of a wide bandpass was stressed for the undistorted amplification of signals. These are conflicting requirements. There are, in fact, many applications where the signal to be amplified is a single frequency or is a narrow band of frequencies. Great reductions in noise can be made by restricting the bandwidth of the amplifier in such a case. Radio communications have relied on this principle for a long time. There are now several good methods for putting information in the form of a narrow band of frequencies (see Sec. 5-6 on modulation). Many modern instruments take advantage of this technique and amplify the information with restricted-bandpass amplifiers. The frequencies are chosen to be well away from the usual ambient noises. The amplified signal is then detected and the information obtained.

Tuned amplifiers are generally divided into two types: radio frequency, and audio. This is because the LC tuned circuit works very well at radio frequencies but is awkward below about $1/\sqrt{LC}$. Tuned amplifiers in the audio range use an RC network and feedback; a discussion of these devices will be found in Sec. 4-7 on feedback.

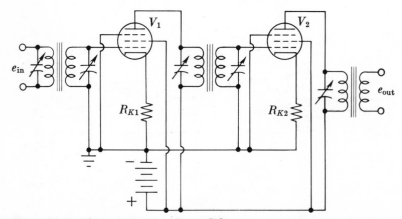

Figure 4-29   Two-stage tuned amplifier.

The tuned r-f amplifier is basically a transformer-coupled amplifier, as shown in Fig. 4-29. When a capacitor is put in parallel with the transformer winding, a parallel resonant circuit results (see Supplement 3). The impedance of the parallel resonant circuit is a maximum at the resonant frequency. Thus the gain of the amplifier will have a maximum at this frequency, and the amplifier is then referred to as a "tuned amplifier." A two-stage tuned amplifier is shown. In this circuit, each inductance is tuned (resonant). The values of the capacitors are each adjusted to give the desired resonant frequency. This type of amplifier can give extremely high gains with low noise for a signal of one frequency or a narrow band of frequencies.

When both the primary and secondary of the coupling transformer are tuned as in Fig. 4-29, the circuit is called a double-tuned transformer-coupled amplifier.

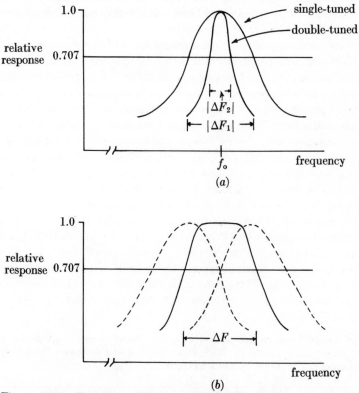

Figure 4-30 *Tuned-amplifier frequency-response curves: (a) single-and double-tuned amplifiers; (b) stagger-tuned amplifier. (Dashed lines are the response of each stage.)*

It is frequently difficult to tune both windings to have the same resonant frequency. However, a much sharper response curve results from double tuning as compared with single tuning where the primary capacitor is removed. The effect of double and single tuning is illustrated in Fig. 4-30a. Note that the bandwidth ΔF_2 of the double-tuned circuit is smaller than ΔF_1 for the single-tuned circuit.* In many cases, a narrow bandwidth is required because a single or very narrow band of frequencies is to be amplified with a minimum of noise.

Frequently, as in the case of frequency-modulation (FM) receivers, a larger band of frequencies must be passed than even single tuning can accomplish. To pass larger bands with tuned amplifiers, "stagger tuning" is used. Single-tuned stages are tuned to different resonant frequencies such that the response curves intersect at their 3-db points. The result of this operation is shown in Fig. 4-30b.

The bands under consideration are relatively narrow; e.g., the bandwidth of an FM signal may be 100 kc, but the resonant frequency may be the intermediate amplifier frequency of an FM receiver, which is 10.7 Mc. At this frequency, the entire signal bandwidth is only one hundredth of the intermediate frequency.

The narrow bandpass of a tuned amplifier reduces distortion as well as noise. Of course, amplitude and phase distortion apply equally well to the frequencies within the bandpass of the amplifier. The distortions due to nonlinearity which introduced harmonic and beat frequencies are virtually eliminated, because these frequencies are probably outside the bandpass of the amplifier. There is no longer a restriction to stay in the linear region of amplification. In r-f power amplifiers, where efficiency is important, the tuned amplifiers are often run with the grids biased to cutoff. The input and output waveforms are shown in Fig. 3-31b. The plate-current signal is extremely distorted—in fact it is rectified, but it supplies power to the tank circuit every cycle, which is enough to keep the tank oscillating evenly at its resonant frequency. Amplification with the tube biased at cutoff is called Class B operation. Class A operation (Fig. 4-31a) is the conventional linear amplification, avoiding cutoff and saturation.

It is not necessary to supply power to the tank circuit during the entire half cycle as in Class B. If the tube is biased well below cutoff, the fraction of time the tank is powered decreases. This is called Class C operation and is shown in Fig. 4-31c.

* For narrow-band coupling, the coupling transformer windings must be "loosely" coupled magnetically. High magnetic coupling increases the bandpass. [See References ("The Radio Amateur's Handbook").]

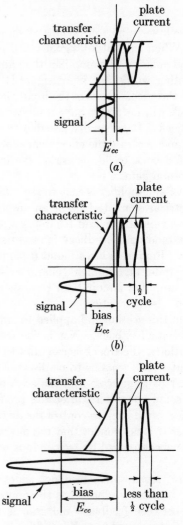

Figure 4-31 Amplifier classification according to grid bias: (a) Class A operation; (b) Class B operation; (c) Class C operation. (From Walter Richter, "Fundamentals of Industrial Electronic Circuits," McGraw-Hill, New York, 1947.)

4-7   Amplifiers with Feedback

An amplifier is said to have feedback when part of its output signal is added to the signal being amplified. When the output signal is fed back in such a way that the input signal is augmented, the amplifier then amplifies the augmented input signal. In other words, the input signal is "regenerated" by the amplifier to enhance the effectiveness of the input signal. An amplifier with regenerative feedback will naturally have a higher gain than the same amplifier with no feedback. It is equally possible to feed back the output signal so as to oppose and decrease the effectiveness of the input signal. The amplifier which is fed back to "degenerate" the input signal will suffer a decrease from its normal gain.

The effect of feedback on the gain of an amplifier is easy to see. However, feedback affects every other electrical characteristic of an amplifier as well. Feedback can be used to improve stability and bandpass and to reduce noise and distortion. An understanding of feedback is essential to an understanding of modern amplifiers. Engineers have found it simpler, and in many cases more satisfactory, to tailor an amplifier's characteristics by adding feedback to a conventional amplifier circuit than to design an unfedback amplifier with the required characteristics.

The effects of feedback developed in this section and applied to amplifiers apply equally well to all systems with feedback. Nor is the use of feedback restricted to amplifier applications. Feedback is essential to the operation of virtually every basic circuit which remains to be discussed in this text. Feedback can also be a part of large-scale systems such as a process-control system. In this case some characteristic of the product (output) is measured and this information is fed back to control the quantities or processes on the input materials. It is no wonder that the development of the theory of feedback has been accompanied by tremendous technological advancement.

Gain. It has been mentioned that regenerative feedback increases the net gain of an amplifier, while degenerative feedback has the opposite effect. The quantitative relationship between feedback and gain is not difficult to find by use of the relationships developed from Fig. 4-32, a block diagram of an amplifier with feedback. A fraction β of the output signal is fed back and added to the input signal as shown. The voltage input to the amplifier e_{in} is thus the sum of the signal voltage e_{sig} and the feedback voltage βe_{out},

$$e_{in} = e_{sig} + \beta e_{out} \qquad (4\text{-}15)$$

And from the gain of the amplifier A,

$$e_{out} = A e_{in} \qquad (4\text{-}16)$$

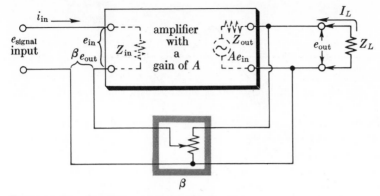

Figure 4-32   Amplifier with feedback.

Substituting for e_{in} and solving for the resultant gain, A',

$$A' = \frac{e_{out}}{e_{sig}} = \frac{A}{1 - \beta A} \qquad (4\text{-}17)$$

When the signal feedback enhances the input signal, βA is positive, $1 - \beta A$ is less than 1, and the gain is greater than A. This is called "positive," or "regenerative," feedback. Despite the increase in gain, positive feedback is not widely used in amplifiers because of the concurrent decrease in other desirable characteristics.

When the output voltage is fed back so as to decrease the input signal, βA is negative, $1 - \beta A$ is greater than 1, and the resulting amplifier gain is less than A. This is called "negative," or "degenerative" feedback. Although the gain is reduced, degenerative feedback is often used for its improvement of other amplifier characteristics. One of the improved characteristics is stability and accuracy of the gain. If $-\beta A \gg 1$, the gain of the amplifier will be very nearly $1/\beta$. Thus the gain is virtually independent of the amplifier's characteristics.

Noise and Distortion.   It was shown above that, as the amount of negative feedback is increased, the gain of the amplifier becomes less dependent on the amplifier and more a function of the feedback network. If the impedance of the feedback network is nonreactive, so that the fraction β is independent of frequency, the gain A' of the fedback amplifier will be virtually independent of frequency. The frequency response is not extended indefinitely by negative feedback, because as the unfedback gain of the amplifier A decreases, $-\beta A$ approaches 1, resulting in a decrease in A'. Remember that the improvement in bandwidth is accompanied by a decrease in amplifier gain. It also follows from Eq. (4-17) that positive feed-

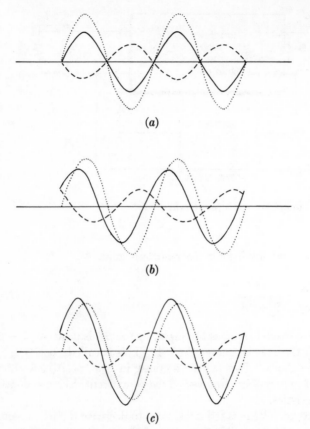

(a)

(b)

(c)

Figure 4-33   Sum of signals of different phase angle: (a) φ = 180°;
(b) φ = 225°; (c) φ = 270°. (Dotted line, input signal;
dashed line, feedback signal; solid line, resulting input
signal.)

back would tend to augment the frequency limitations of the amplifier and
that a decreased bandpass would result.

The phase relationship between a sine-wave signal and the feedback
signal is shown for negative feedback in Fig. 4-33a. Note that the voltage
at the amplifier input is the same phase as the signal voltage, but reduced in
magnitude. Suppose that the signal is delayed in the amplifier high-pass
RC networks by 45°. The feedback signal would thus have a phase angle
of 180° + 45° with respect to the input signal. The resultant amplifier
input signal for this case is shown in Fig. 4-33b. Note that the resultant
input signal is advanced in phase, which tends to compensate for the delay
in the amplifier. Thus negative feedback decreases phase distortion. The

same corrective action could be shown had the phase angle of the feedback signal been less than 180° instead of greater. The effect of a phase shift in the amplifier of greater than 45° is shown in Fig. 4-33c. Here a phase angle of 180° + 90° is shown to correct the phase less than the 45° phase shift. Note too that the amplitude of the input signal is actually augmented. In this case the combined phase shift of the amplifier (90°) and the feedback network (180°) results in regenerative feedback. Thus it is shown that negative feedback can reduce moderate amounts of phase distortion, but a larger phase distortion can actually result in positive feedback and an enhancement of the distortion. In this way signals well outside the normal bandpass of the amplifier, which are attenuated and shifted in phase in the amplifier, can be regenerated by the feedback loop and appear in the output signal. In general, the presence of these distorted and augmented signals is undesirable. Increasing the negative feedback only increases the regeneration of these unwanted signal components. They can be eliminated only by a better rejection of the unwanted frequencies, either in the amplifier or in the feedback network.

Nonlinearity of amplification and noise signals from the amplifier are also reduced by negative feedback. A noise signal at the amplifier output which is fed back (attenuated) to the input out of phase causes the amplifier to counteract the spurious signal at the output. Suppose that a noise signal N is generated in the amplifier. Because of the feedback, the actual noise signal at the output will be different from N. The output noise will be designated N'. A signal $\beta N'$ will be fed back to the amplifier input. The actual output noise N' will then be the sum of N, the noise generated in the amplifier, and $A\beta N'$, the amplified noise fed back to the input. Solving for N',

$$N' = N + A\beta N' \tag{4-18}$$

$$N' = \frac{N}{1 - A\beta} \tag{4-19}$$

It is seen that noise is reduced by the same factor as the gain. Just how negative feedback might be used to increase the signal-to-noise ratio depends on the source of the noise. Three causes will be considered: (1) Suppose that the noise generated in the amplifier (N) is independent of the size of the signal. Examples of this would be thermal noise in the components and 60-cycle noise from the tube filaments. In this case negative feedback will reduce the output signal and the noise by the same amount, and the signal-to-noise ratio will not be improved. Improvements in the signal-to-noise ratio could be gained only by increasing the size of the input signal (output signal increases proportionately, but noise remains constant), using less noisy components, or increasing the ratio of the signal gain to noise value of the amplifier. (2) Suppose that the noise is actually distortion due to the nonlinearity of the amplifier. Negative feedback reduces this distortion by two effects. The input signal is reduced, which helps to keep the signal within more linear regions of amplification. The remaining distortion component in the output is further reduced by the factor $1 - \beta A$. If the size of the input signal had been increased to compensate for the reduction in gain, the output signal would be the same magnitude as with the unfedback amplifier but the distortion component would be reduced by the factor $1 - \beta A$. Thus increasing the input-signal magnitude and introducing negative feedback will increase the signal-to-noise ratio for both sources of noise considered thus far. (3) If the noise is present in the signal to be amplified, there must be some means for distinguishing signal and noise if the signal-to-noise ratio is to be improved. Some sort of circuit which rejects the nonsignal frequencies is ordinarily used. Except for imposing a narrow bandpass, there is no way by which amplification, with or without feedback, can improve the signal-to-noise ratio of a noisy input signal. Negative feedback reduces only that noise which is generated in the amplifier or the feedback circuit.

Input Impedance. The input impedance of an amplifier can be defined by using the quantities shown in Fig. 4-32 as

$$Z_{\text{in}} = \frac{e_{\text{in}}}{i_{\text{in}}} \tag{4-20}$$

For an amplifier without feedback, e_{in} and e_{sig} are identical and interchangeable in Eq. (4-20). With feedback, however, e_{in} is not the same as e_{sig}. From Eqs. (4-15) and (4-16), e_{in} is seen to be

$$e_{\text{in}} = e_{\text{sig}} + \beta A e_{\text{in}} \tag{4-21}$$

Solving for e_{in},

$$e_{\text{in}} = \frac{e_{\text{sig}}}{1 - \beta A} \tag{4-22}$$

The input impedance Z'_{in} of the feedback amplifier is $e_{\text{sig}}/i_{\text{in}}$. Substituting for e_{sig} from Eq. (4-22), and noting that $e_{\text{in}}/i_{\text{in}} = Z_{\text{in}}$ from Eq. (4-20),

$$Z'_{\text{in}} = \frac{e_{\text{sig}}}{i_{\text{in}}} = \frac{e_{\text{in}}(1 - \beta A)}{i_{\text{in}}} = Z_{\text{in}}(1 - \beta A) \tag{4-23}$$

The input impedance is seen to be increased by negative feedback.

Consider the cathode-follower amplifier of Fig. 3-46. Note that the fraction e_{out} which is across R_B is in series with the input circuit. The cathode follower is thus an amplifier with negative feedback. Because R_K is common to the input and output circuit, it is not possible to differentiate e_{sig} from e_{in} in the same way as was done for Fig. 4-32. The considerations used to derive Eq. (4-23) can be used to find the actual input impedance of the cathode follower. The fraction of the output voltage fed back in series with e_{in} is $R_B(R_A + R_B) = 47K/50K = 0.94$. The gain of the cathode follower is about $\mu/(\mu + 1) = 15/16 = 0.94$ [Eq. (3-34)]. The fraction of the total *input* voltage across R_B is thus $0.94 \times 0.94 = 0.88$. The fraction of the input voltage across R_g is thus $1 - 0.88 = 0.12$. R_g must therefore be 0.12 of the total input resistance, which is then $2.2M$ [1]$/0.12 = 18.4M$. Thus the high input impedance of the cathode follower is explained by negative feedback.

Output Impedance. When a fraction of the output voltage is fed back to the input as in Fig. 4-32, the output impedance is affected. Consider the case of an amplifier with negative feedback. If Z_L decreases, I_L increases and e_{out} would have a tendency to decrease because of the increase in current through Z_{out}. However, if e_{out} decreases, the negative-feedback voltage decreases, allowing a larger value of signal voltage at the amplifier input. Thus negative-voltage feedback tends to stabilize the output voltage, in other words, to reduce the output impedance of the amplifier.

The amplifier output voltage will be Ae_{in} reduced by the IR drop in Z_{out}.

$$e_{out} = Ae_{in} - I_L Z_{out} \tag{4-24}$$

Recall from Eq. (4-15) that $e_{in} = e_{sig} + \beta e_{out}$. Substituting for e_{in} in Eq. (4-24) and solving for e_{out},

$$e_{out} = \frac{A}{1 - \beta A} e_{sig} - I_L \frac{Z_{out}}{1 - \beta A} \tag{4-25}$$

This equation is exactly the same form as Eq. (4-24), that is, a voltage source $A'e_{sig}$ in series with an impedance $Z_{out}/(1 - \beta A)$ and supplying a current I_L. The effective output impedance Z'_{out} of the fedback amplifier is thus

$$Z'_{out} = \frac{Z_{out}}{1 - \beta A} \tag{4-26}$$

Negative-voltage feedback reduces the output impedance, making the amplifier a better voltage source. Positive feedback, of course, has the opposite effect.

Current Feedback. The feedback amplifiers discussed above employ "voltage feedback" in that a fraction of the output *voltage* is fed back to the input. An amplifier is said to have current feedback when the signal fed back is proportional to the output current rather than the output

---

[1] M is sometimes used for megohms in calculations.

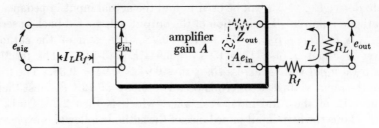

Figure 4-34 Amplifier with current feedback.

voltage. A block diagram of an amplifier with this kind of feedback is shown in Fig. 4-34. Consider the case of negative-current feedback. If I_L increases because of a change in R_L, the feedback voltage $I_L R_f$ will increase, e_{in} will decrease, and the output voltage will decrease to cause a drop in I_L. In this case it is the output *current* which is stabilized by the feedback. As a good, stable current source, the negative-current feedback amplifier should have a high output impedance. This can be shown quite easily.

From Fig. 4-34, note that

$$e_{out} = Ae_{in} - I_L(Z_{out} + R_f)$$
(4-27)

and $e_{in} = e_{sig} + I_L R_f$
(4-28)

Solving Eqs. (4-27) and (4-28) for e_{out},

$$e_{out} = Ae_{sig} - I_L[Z_{out} + R_f(1 - A)]$$
(4-29)

Equation (4-29) shows the no-load output voltage to be A times the signal voltage. Thus current feedback has no effect on the voltage gain of the amplifier. The effective output impedance, however, is shown to be $Z_{out} + R_f(1 - A)$, a change of $-R_f A$ from the unfedback amplifier. Negative feedback results in a positive value for $R_f A$ and thus increases the output impedance.

In every respect other than output impedance the effect of current feedback is similar to that of voltage feedback. That is, negative-current feedback increases input resistance and reduces noise and distortion in the output *current* signal. Equation (4-29) may be solved for I_L by noting that $e_{out} = I_L R_L$ in Fig. 4-34.

$$I_L = \frac{Ae_{sig}}{R_L + Z_{out} + R_f - R_f A} \approx -\frac{e_{sig}}{R_f}$$
(4-30)

R_f and A are large and A is negative, I_L is virtually independent of the amplifier gain and the characteristics of the load and is a simple function of the signal voltage.

The Possibility of Oscillation. The gain of the voltage-feedback amplifier was given in Eq. (4-17).

$$A' = \frac{A}{1 - \beta A}$$

When βA is positive, the quantity $1 - \beta A$ is less than 1 and A' is greater than A. In other words there is positive, or regenerative, feedback. As βA approaches 1, the gain A' approaches infinity. Another way of saying this is that the signal voltage e_{sig} required for a given output voltage decreases to 0 as βA approaches 1. When βA equals 1, the feedback voltage is sufficient to maintain an output signal even though the input-signal voltage is 0. Such an amplifier would satisfy the definition of an oscillator as given at the beginning of Chap. 5. All frequencies for which the condition $\beta A = 1$ is fulfilled will be present in the output. When a feedback path exists in an amplifier, it is essential that the conditions necessary for oscillation do not exist.

Even when the feedback is negative at normal frequencies, the possibility of positive feedback at frequencies on the fringe of the bandpass exists. A set of curves showing the effect of negative feedback on frequency response is shown in Fig. 4-35. A moderate amount of feedback flattens the response curve a great deal. Frequencies at the extremes of the response curve are shifted in phase through the amplifier so that the feedback for them is actually positive. This is shown by the fact that the gain at these

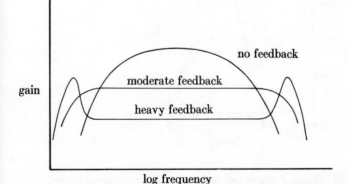

Figure 4-35   Effect of negative feedback on frequency response.

frequencies is greater than for unfedback amplifier. When a larger amount of feedback is applied, a greater regeneration of the extreme frequencies occurs, as shown. The response shown is sufficient to cause definite distortion of the input waveform. Were the feedback to be increased still further, the condition of oscillation might well be fulfilled for either the very low or the very high frequency.

If heavy negative feedback is required, the possibility of oscillation can be eliminated by putting filters in the feedback loop to eliminate regeneration of the offending frequency or by deliberately limiting the bandwidth of one of the amplifier stages. The resistor and capacitor in the feedback path of the Williamson amplifier (Fig. 4-14) was introduced to eliminate the possibility of a high-frequency oscillation.

Selective Feedback. The discussion thus far has almost entirely dealt with feedback networks which are frequency-independent. It has

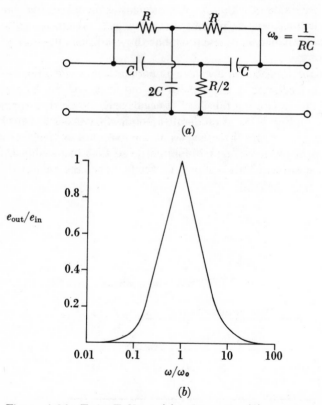

(a)

(b)

Figure 4-36   Twin T filter: (a) schematic; (b) response curve.

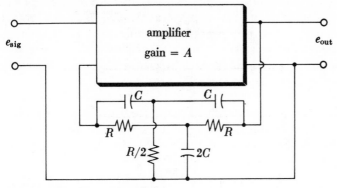

Figure 4-37   Tuned amplifier.

just been mentioned that a filter might be used to restrict the feedback signal to a certain frequency range. If the bandpass of the feedback network is very narrow, a frequency-selective, or tuned, amplifier will result.

A frequency-selective network made up of resistors and capacitors is shown in Fig. 4-36a. It is called the twin T, or parallel T, network, from the shape of its schematic. It is a combination of a low-pass filter (R, R, and $2C$) and a high-pass filter (C, C, and $\frac{1}{2}R$). The response curve is shown in Fig. 4-36b. The phase shift through the network is zero at the rejection frequency ω_o and at frequencies different from the rejection frequency by more than a decade or two. For frequencies just lower than ω_o, the phase shift is lagging, while the phase shift is leading at frequencies higher than ω_o.

If the twin T network is used in the negative-feedback loop of an amplifier as shown in Fig. 4-37, an amplifier of very narrow bandpass would result. β would be large (low gain) for all frequencies except ω_o. At ω_o, $\beta = 0$, and $A' = A$, the full amplifier gain. Since even a small negative feedback reduces the gain by quite a bit, the sharpness of the rejection by the filter is increased by the feedback action. The higher the amplifier gain, the better the rejection. The application of this kind of tuned amplifier is in the audio-frequency range, where the LC tuned circuit is large and costly and has poor rejection (Q) because of the resistance in the coil.

The bridged T network shown in Fig. 4-38a is simpler than the twin T but does not afford as complete or as sharp a rejection. It is often used in less critical applications and has the advantage that the precision of the component values is much less critical than in the case of the twin T filter.

An actual tuned-amplifier circuit is shown in Fig. 4-38b. The circuit is basically the cathode-coupled difference amplifier, with the feedback circuit

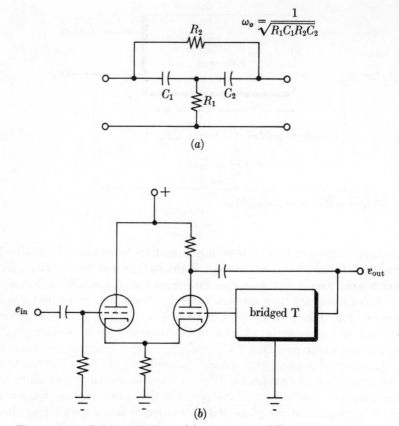

Figure 4-38   Bridged T filter: (a) schematic; (b) tuned amplifier.

using one input and the input signal the other.   The output of the rejection filter must be connected to a high impedance, because the selectivity of the filter falls off as the load resistance is decreased.

References
The following books contain additional related information:

Bair, E. J., "Introduction to Chemical Instrumentation," McGraw-Hill, New York, 1962. Contains a discussion of the sources of electrical noise.

"Basic Theory and Application of Transistors," Army Technical Manual TM 11-690, U.S. Government Printing Office, Washington, D.C., 1959. A thorough discussion of transistor-amplifier applications.

Cannon, C. G., "Electronics for Spectroscopists," Hilger and Watts, Bristol, England, 1960. Contains a chapter on low-frequency tuned amplifiers.

Partridge, G. R., "Principles of Electronic Instruments," Prentice-Hall, Englewood Cliffs, N.J., 1958. Includes 18 pages on electrometer tubes and circuits.

"The Radio Amateur's Handbook," published annually by the American Radio Relay League, West Hartford, Conn. Basic and practical information on power amplifiers and high-frequency tuned amplifiers.

Seely, S., "Electron-Tube Circuits," 2d ed., McGraw-Hill, New York, 1958. Contains analyses of many amplifier circuits, including several difference amplifiers.

"Vacuum Tube Amplifiers," M.I.T. Radiation Laboratory Series, Vol. 18, L. N. Ridenoux (ed.), McGraw-Hill, New York, 1948. An extensive treatment of d-c amplifiers and difference amplifiers.

Problems

4-1 For amplifier circuits such as Fig. 4-1 in which $R_g \gg R_o$, Eq. (4-1) can be reduced to $f_1 = 1/(2\pi R_g C_c)$. (a) Calculate the lower frequency cutoff f_1, when $R_g = 1$ megohm and $C_c = 0.01$ μf. (b) What value of C_c is necessary to achieve the same f_1 in a transistor amplifier with $R_{in} = 2$ kilohms?

Ans.: (a) 16 cps; (b) 5 μf

4-2 Typical values for a triode audio-amplifier stage as shown in Fig. 4-2 are: $C_{pK} = 1$ pf, $C_{in} = 3$ pf, $C_{gp} = 4$ pf, $\mu = 20$, $r_p = 8$ kilohms, $R_g = 1$ megohm, $R_L = 10$ kilohms, $C_c = 0.01$ μf, $R_o = 5$ kilohms, $C_K \cong \infty$, and $C_o = 5$ pf. Using these values: (a) Calculate the midfrequency gain. (b) Calculate f_1 and the gain at f_1. (c) Calculate f_2. (d) Calculate the gain at 1 Mc.

Ans.: (a) 11; (b) 16 cps, 8; (c) 350 kc; (d) 4

4-3 A figure of merit for pentodes for high-frequency amplifiers is the gain-bandwidth product $A_e \times f_2$. (a) Show that the gain-bandwidth product is approximately equal to $g_m/2\pi C_s$, where C_s is C_{in} and $C_o(C_{pK})$ of the previous stage in parallel. (b) What is the gain-bandwidth product of a 6AK5 amplifier, assuming the previous stage is an identical 6AK5 amplifier? ($g_m = 5000$ μmhos, $C_{gK} = 4.0$ pf, $C_{pK} = 2.8$ pf. Since the gain-bandwidth product is the maximum theoretically obtainable, wiring and socket capacitances are assumed negligible.) (c) How does the possible gain of the 6AK5 amplifier at 1 Mc compare with that of the triode amplifier of Prob. 4-2? *Ans.:* (b) 116 Mc; (c) 6AK5 gain is 30 times greater

4-4 Calculate f_2 for a single-stage transistor amplifier. Assume $f_\alpha = 1$ Mc and $\alpha_{fe} = 20$. *Ans.:* 50 kc

4-5 Calculate the power dissipated in R_L of Fig. 4-10 for R_L having values of 1, 10, and 100 ohms, assuming the generator is a 10-volt battery and R_s is a 10-ohm resistor. *Ans.:* 0.8 watts, 2.5 watts, 1 watt

4-6 What fraction of a 1-kc signal output from stage 1 is applied to the base of stage 2 in the transistor amplifier of Fig. 4-8? For all 3 stages, $R_{B_1} = 150$ kilohms, $R_{B_2} = 27$ kilohms, $R_L = 22$ kilohms, $R_E = 5$ kilohms, $C_c = 2$ μf, $R_{out} = 50$ kilohms, $R_{in} = 2.5$ kilohms. Also calculate f_1 for this three-stage amplifier.

Ans.: Output resistance of stage 1 = 15.3 kilohms, input resistance of stage 2 = 2.25 kilohms; 0.128 $\cong$ 1/8 of the output signal is applied to the input; $f_1 = 5$ cps for one stage and $f_1 = 9$ cps for all three stages.

4-7 The input capacitance of the oscilloscope amplifier of Fig. 4-20 is probably about 10.0 pf. (a) What size compensating capacitor would be required for a

$\times 10$ attenuator? (b) What would be the resulting input resistance of the oscilloscope? (c) What would the input impedance be at 500 kc?

Ans.: (a) 1.1 pf; (b) 20 megohms; (c) 320 kilohms

4-8 Using the differential input of an oscilloscope, it is desired to measure a 300-mv signal to within 1 per cent. If the common-mode signal-rejection ratio for the oscilloscope amplifier is 1000:1, what is the maximum allowable common-mode signal? *Ans.:* 3 volts

4-9 A 12AU7 triode is used for the phase-inverter circuit shown in Fig. 4-13b ($R_L = R_K = 20$ kilohms; $r_p = 7500$ ohms; $\mu = 17$). (a) What is the gain of this stage of amplification? (b) What would the gain of the difference amplifier phase inverter of Fig. 4-13c be if $R_L = 20$ kilohms and a 12AU7 were used?

Ans.: (a) 0.88; (b) 9.7

4-10 (a) Calculate the maximum mid-frequency voltage gain of the amplifier of Fig. 4-43. For the 12AX7, $\mu = 100$, $r_p = 65$ kilohms; for the 6BQ5, $g_m = 11,300$ μmhos; the primary-to-secondary turns ratio for the output transformer is 40. A feedback loop may be introduced into this amplifier by connecting a resistance R_f from the ungrounded output terminal to the cathode of the 12AX7. (b) If the feedback is positive, what value of R_f will just cause oscillation if the gain control is on full? (c) With negative feedback and $R_f = 15$ kilohms, calculate the over-all maximum voltage gain. (d) With the feedback of part (c) and the gain control at 1/2, what is the gain?

Ans.: (a) $A_e = 71$; (b) R_f for oscillation ≈ 100 kilohms; (c) $A_e = 9.6$; (d) $A_e = 8.4$.

4-11 If the cathode-follower amplifier did not employ feedback (i.e., if the signal were connected from grid to cathode instead of from grid to ground), its gain would be $\mu R_K/(r_p + R_K)$. Using Eq. (4-17) for the gain of a feedback amplifier, derive Eq. (3-36) for the gain of the cathode follower. In the same way, the formula for the gain of an amplifier with unbypassed cathode resistor [Eq. (3-9)] can be derived if the unfedback gain is considered to be $\mu R_L/(r_p + R_L + R_K)$.

EXPERIMENTS

These experiments continue the study of amplification and amplifiers begun in Chap. 3. Particular emphasis is placed on the a-c signal response and the nonlinearities and distortions common to amplifiers. RC coupling is studied for both vacuum-tube and transistor amplifiers. A power amplifier is constructed on a standard chassis using soldered connections. Practice is thereby gained in soldering technique, and the amplifier thus built is useful in several later experiments. The changes in amplifier characteristics resulting from positive and negative feedback are observed. The cathode-coupled phase-inverter and difference-amplifier circuits are studied in some detail.

Expt. 4-1   The RC-Coupled Triode Amplifier

The single-stage RC-coupled amplifier of Fig. 4-39 is wired. When the oscilloscope is connected to the output and input terminals as shown, the output signal voltage is plotted against the input signal voltage. Nonlinearity in the amplifier

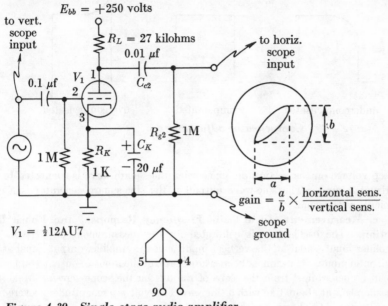

Figure 4-39 Single-stage audio amplifier.

response is indicated by a curved line. The gain can be determined from the slope of the linear portion of the line. Phase distortion is indicated by an elliptical pattern. The following procedure is recommended for these tests.

a. Wiring of the Circuit. Turn on the signal generator and the scope so that they can warm up. Wire the amplifier of Fig. 4-39, taking care to bring the input and output points to convenient terminals for the connection of the scope and generator.

b. Adjusting the Scope Response for Minimum Distortion. In order to make phase and amplitude comparisons of two signals using the scope as an *x-y* plotter, it is important that the phase difference does not occur in, and that the response is not limited by, the scope horizontal and vertical amplifiers. A scope designed for *x-y* plotting has identical vertical and horizontal amplifiers, a condition which eliminates most of the problems of measuring frequency and phase distortion; however, it is very important that no distortions occur in the input attenuators of the scope amplifiers. For this reason the adjustment of the compensating capacitors on the input attenuator must be checked now.

Connect the square-wave output of the signal generator to the scope vertical input. Observe the waveshape of a 1-kc square wave. Adjust the compensating capacitor until the step of the wave has minimum rise time without peaking. This is illustrated in Fig. 4-40. Consult your instruction manual for the location of the compensating capacitors and the order of their adjustment.

A similar adjustment of the horizontal attenuator compensators will require a

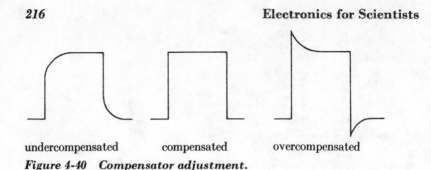

undercompensated   compensated   overcompensated

Figure 4-40   Compensator adjustment.

sweep voltage on the vertical amplifier when the square wave is connected to the horizontal input. The sine-wave output of the sine-square generator is a convenient sweep signal.

c. Measurement of the Gain, Frequency Response, and Phase Distortion. The oscilloscope is calibrated for the measurement of a 1-volt *p-p* amplifier input signal at the vertical input, and the amplifier output signal at the horizontal input. The gain is the measured ratio of the input to output voltages, or it can be determined from the slope of the line on the scope screen. Make this measurement at about 1 kc with a sine wave of 1-volt *p-p* magnitude. Severe nonlinearity would be observed with an input signal much over 2 volts.

The phase angle ϕ between the two signals is given as $\sin\phi = c/b$, where c and b are measurements on the ellipse, as shown in Fig. 4-41. This follows if it is assumed that one signal is of the form

$$e_1 = E_1 \sin \omega t$$

and the other is

$$e_2 = E_2 \sin (\omega t + \phi)$$

If the signal e_1 is put on the X axis, and the signal e_2 on the Y axis of an oscilloscope, the figure will be an ellipse, or one of its degenerate forms (circle or straight line). Note that when $\omega t = 0$, $e_2 = E_2 \sin \phi$, and this value corresponds to the height $c/2$. The maximum amplitude of e_2 is obviously $b/2$, and thus $b/2 = E_2$. The ratio

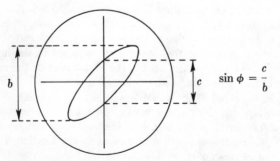

$$\sin \phi = \frac{c}{b}$$

Figure 4-41   Measurement of phase angle ϕ.

of c/b is therefore

$$\frac{c}{b} = \frac{E_2 \sin \phi}{E_2} = \sin \phi$$

or

$$\phi = \arcsin \frac{c}{b}$$

Note that it is not necessary to have the amplitudes of E_1 and E_2 equal to make the phase measurement.

Measure the *gain* and *phase shift* as a function of frequency at frequencies of 20, 30, 100, 300, 1 kc, 3 kc, 10 kc, 30 kc, 100 kc, and 200 kc. Make these measurements with and without C_K in the circuit. Plot the results on 4-cycle semilog graph paper. Note the frequencies at which the gain is 0.707 of the gain at 1 kc. These points are f_1 and f_2. Calculate the theoretical values of the gain at 1 kc with and without C_K in the circuit and calculate the expected values of f_1 and f_2 assuming $C_K = \infty$.

Change the plate load resistor to 10 kilohms, add the capacitor C_K, and measure the gain of the resulting amplifier at 1 kc.

Expt. 4-2 *RC*-Coupled Transistor Amplifier

The gain and phase shift of a transistor amplifier as functions of frequency are determined in the same way as in the previous experiment.

Wire the amplifier shown in Fig. 4-42. Use the same transistor whose characteristics were determined in Expt. 3-1. Calculate the theoretical voltage gain for this amplifier using the hybrid parameters measured in Expt. 3-1. Measure the gain and phase shift as a function of frequency, using the oscilloscope as an *x-y* plotter

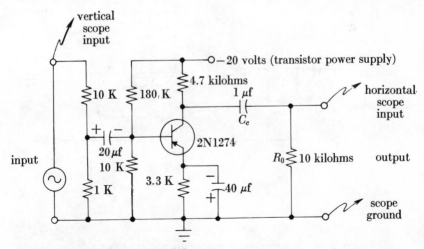

Figure 4-42 Transistor amplifier.

as in the previous experiment. Note that the 10 kilohms–1 kilohm input divider reduces the actual input about eleven times. This is necessary because of the low resistivity of most oscilloscopes, which otherwise precludes measurement of the input signal. Use a *p-p* signal input voltage of less than 500 mv. If the amplifier is overdriven (too large a signal to remain in linear amplification region), erroneous results will be obtained.

Expt. 4-3   Construction and Testing of a Two-Stage Power Amplifier

a. Wiring the Amplifier. The two-stage amplifier of Fig. 4-43 is to be wired permanently on a conventional chassis. The construction details and the chassis layout are shown in Fig. 4-44. The amplifier is powered from the universal power-supply unit through the regular four-conductor power cable. A typical layout and connection of the parts within the power amplifier chassis are shown in Fig. 4-44, but the experimenter is encouraged to wire from the wiring diagram as much as possible, using Fig. 4-44 only as a guide and final check.

b. Testing the Amplifier. Plug the amplifier power cable into the power-supply unit. Turn the POWER switch ON and see that the amplifier filaments light. Connect the microphone and speaker to the input and output terminals, respectively. Turn the gain control to the minimum position. Turn the

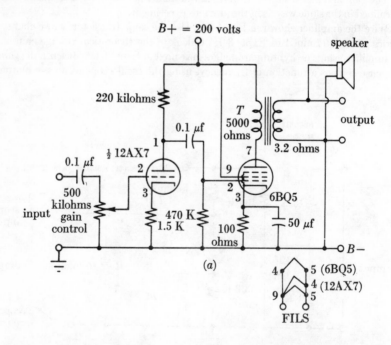

Figure 4-43   Experimental power amplifier schematic.

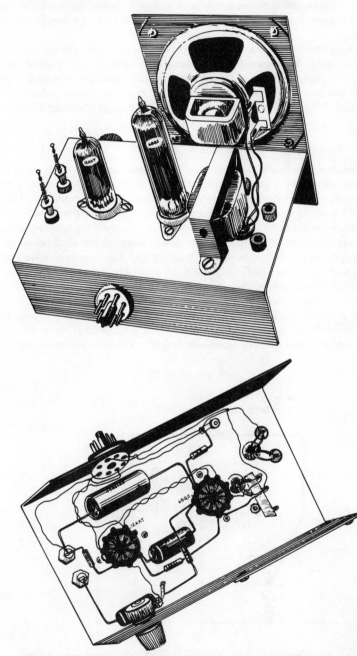

*Figure 4-44 Chassis layout and wiring pict>rial of the power ampli-
fier.*

HIGH VOLTAGE switch to ON (assuming that the d-c voltage has been properly adjusted). Tap the microphone gently as the gain is turned up until the tap is heard from the speaker. Note the quality of the amplifier and speaker for amplifying speech.

Turn the gain control to the minimum, remove the microphone connections, and connect the square-wave output of the signal generator to the amplifier input. Connect the oscilloscope input to the amplifier output terminals (leave the speaker connected) and note the response of the amplifier to a 1-kc square wave. Adjust the gain control and the generator output so that the amplifier is not overdriven.

Expt. 4-4   Experiments with Feedback

   a. Positive Feedback. Disconnect the ground lead from the grounded output terminal of the power amplifier. Use a banana-patch lead to temporarily connect one of the output terminals to the ground terminal. Connect the feedback path R_f from the ungrounded output terminal to the cathode of the 12AX7 as shown in Fig. 4-45. Set R_f at 330 kilohms. Connect the square-wave output of the signal generator to the amplifier input. Connect the oscilloscope across the output terminals. (Keep the speaker connected.) Turn the gain of the amplifier on full and use a very small signal from the signal generator. Turn the amplifier on, and by means of a touch contact in the feedback loop, determine whether the feedback is negative or positive (output signal decreases or increases, respectively). If it is negative feedback, reverse the connection to the output terminals. Now the signal should become louder when the feedback loop is connected. Decrease the size of R_f and note the increase in output. Note also the increased distor-

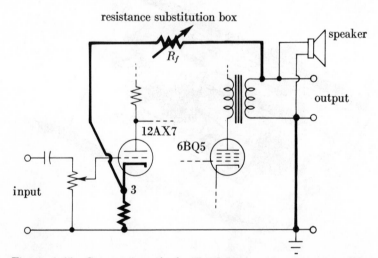

Figure 4-45   Connection of a feedback loop to the power amplifier.

tion of the signal. At what value of R_f do you have an oscillator? Note the effect of the gain control during oscillation.

b. Negative Feedback. Now reverse the connections to the output terminals so that an amplifier with negative feedback results. Decrease the value of R_f and note the decrease in gain and the decrease in the distortion of the square wave. Satisfy yourself that a simple attenuation of the signal does not achieve the same effect. Note that, for certain values of R_f, very low and/or very high frequency oscillation might occur. Remove the signal generator and attach the microphone to the input. Note the audible increase in fidelity over the unfedback amplifier. Resolder the ground lead to one of the output terminals, and set the amplifier aside for use in later experiments.

Expt. 4-5 Cathode-Coupled Amplifier

This amplifier configuration is used widely as a phase inverter and a difference amplifier. Its characteristics are therefore of great interest to people working with scientific instruments. First the phase-inverter or paraphase amplifier is studied. Then the difference amplifier is investigated. The common-mode–signal-rejection ratio is measured.

a. Phase-Inverter Amplifier. Wire the circuit shown in Fig. 4-46. Connect one of the inputs to ground and connect the other to a signal source of about 0.5 volt *p-p*. Measure the output signal between one plate and ground and calculate the gain. Compare the magnitudes and phase of the two output signals at the two plates.

b. Difference Amplifier. Short out one of the plate-load resistors in the circuit of Fig. 4-46 to make a difference amplifier as in Fig. 4-23. With one in-

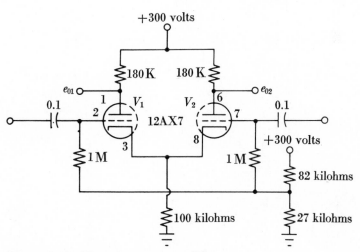

Figure 4-46   Phase-inverter amplifier.

put grounded and the signal into the other, measure the gain of the amplifier. (The output terminal is at the triode plate, which still has the 180-kilohm load resistor.) Connect the same signal into both inputs at once and measure the output voltage. Calculate the common-mode gain. Calculate the common-mode signal-rejection ratio. Put a 510-kilohm resistor between the output terminal and the cathodes (as in Fig. 4-23). Measure the common-mode signal gain. Remeasure the difference signal gain and calculate the common-mode signal-rejection ratio for the modified difference amplifier.

chapter five

Oscillators

An electronic oscillator is a device that produces an output signal which continuously repeats the same pattern of current and voltage variations with respect to time. Oscillator circuits can produce sine waves, square waves, sawtooth waves, or other a-c signals with only a d-c power source connected to the circuit. In this sense, an oscillator may be considered a d-c to a-c converter.

There are many applications for oscillators. Sine-wave oscillators are basic to modern communications because they provide the *carriers* for transmission of sound and picture information, and they play an important part in radio and television receivers for retrieving the transmitted information. Also, sine-wave oscillators are widely used in industry for induction and dielectric heating. Sine, square, and sawtooth oscillators are used for timing, triggering, and gating of events in instruments, including computers, oscilloscopes, and radar. Oscillators provide the necessary signals for testing equipment, energizing bridge networks, changing frequencies, and a host of other applications.

5-1 General Considerations

An oscillator is designed with a wave-forming network that produces the desired signal. To maintain oscillation, it is necessary that any signal losses within the wave-forming network be counteracted by the operation

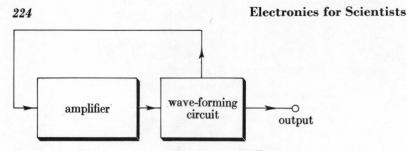

Figure 5-1   Block diagram of feedback oscillator.

of the other parts of the oscillator circuit. There are two general methods of overcoming the losses in wave-forming circuits. One is to neutralize the losses by amplification. This kind of oscillator is shown in block form in Fig. 5-1. The wave-forming stimulus is amplified sufficiently to sustain oscillation. The general form of this circuit will be recognized as that of the feedback amplifier discussed in Sec. 4-7. The special conditions for feedback oscillation and specific examples of this type of oscillator are given in Sec. 5-2. The other method is to use some circuit element which has a negative-resistance characteristic at least equal to the positive resistance in the wave-forming circuit. An element is said to have negative resistance when its current-voltage curve has a negative slope. Two current-voltage curves with regions of negative resistance are shown in Fig. 5-2. A block diagram of a negative-resistance oscillator is shown in Fig. 5-3. Specific circuit elements which exhibit negative-resistance characteristics and their application to oscillator circuits are discussed in Secs. 5-3 and 5-4.

Section 5-5 deals with some methods of stabilizing the frequency of oscillators. Methods for superimposing information on a carrier frequency from an oscillator and some methods of retrieving the transmitted information are presented in Sec. 5-6.

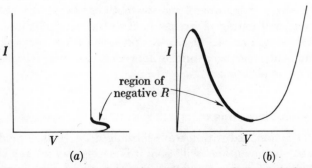

(a)   *(b)*

Figure 5-2   Typical negative-resistance characteristics.

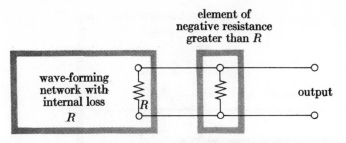

Figure 5-3   Block diagram of negative-resistance oscillator.

5-2   Feedback Oscillators

The basic form of the feedback oscillator is shown in Fig. 5-1. The wave-forming circuit is in the feedback loop of a feedback amplifier. To sustain oscillation, as has been stated, the amplifier must counteract the losses in the wave-forming circuit. The fraction of the amplifier output signal which is transferred in the feedback loop is β, following the convention established in Sec. 4-7. The amplifier gain A must then be at least $1/\beta$; in other words, $A\beta \geq 1$. The formula for the gain of the feedback amplifier [Eq. (4-17)] is $A/(1 - A\beta)$. Notice that, when $A\beta = 1$, the resulting gain is infinite. In other words, the feedback is regenerative. As the amount of positive feedback is increased in a regenerative amplifier, the gain approaches infinity. When the gain of the amplifier is infinite, it no longer needs an external signal source to amplify. Thermal noise within the amplifier is sufficient to start the regeneration process at all frequencies. If it were not for the wave-forming circuit, which restricts the signals which can be regenerated, the feedback oscillator would oscillate at all frequencies for which $A\beta \geq 1$. It is now apparent that two conditions must be met for this system to operate properly as an oscillator. One is that $A\beta$ must be equal to or greater than 1. The other is that the first condition be satisfied only by the particular waveform which is to be generated. Specific examples of feedback oscillators are discussed in the remainder of this section. It should be pointed out that the particular sequence of blocks shown in Fig. 5-1 is not sacred. The wave-forming circuit may be in the amplifier, the feedback loop, or both, and the output may be taken wherever it is convenient.

Phase-Shift Oscillator. A simple feedback oscillator is shown in Fig. 5-4. The amplifier is a common-emitter amplifier biased by a voltage divider involving the 180- and 10-kilohm resistors. With the common-emitter configuration the signal at the collector is 180° out of phase with the signal at the base. The feedback network that couples the collector and the emitter must shift the phase an additional 180° in order to have

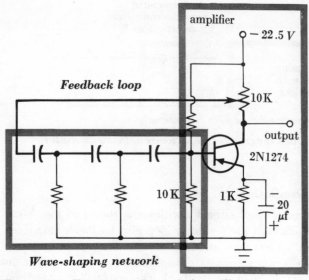

Figure 5-4   Transistor phase-shift oscillator.

regenerative feedback, and it must do this for only one frequency.   The network shown is a series of high-pass filters each of which shifts the phase of the feedback signal approximately an equal amount.   The degree of phase shift depends on the frequency, and the total phase shift will be the required 180°.   The phase-shift network thus fulfills the oscillation condition of regenerative feedback for only one frequency.   For a 60° phase shift, each high-pass filter attenuates the signal to about one-third. The output of the feedback network of Fig. 5-4 is one twenty-ninth of the input. The amplifier must have a voltage gain of at least 29 to fulfill the other condition of oscillation.   When R and C are the same for all three high-pass filters, the frequency of oscillation f_o is

$$f_o = \frac{1}{2\pi\sqrt{6}\,RC} \qquad\qquad (5\text{-}1)$$

This type of oscillator is called the phase-shift oscillator.   Other networks which provide a 180° phase shift for only one frequency could be used equally well.

   The Bridged T Oscillator.   The twin T, or bridged T, networks which were used in negative-feedback loops to make a frequency-selective amplifier (Sec. 4-7) can also be used with positive feedback to make a sine-wave oscillator.   The network cannot be used in a positive-feedback loop, because such a circuit would provide regeneration at all frequencies except the rejection frequency of the filter. The method of using these filters for limiting and selecting the oscillation frequency is actually a combination of negative and positive feedback.

Positive feedback is provided such that $A\beta$ is just equal to 1 for all the frequencies within the bandpass of the amplifier. The conditions for oscillation are thus fulfilled for a broad band of frequencies. A negative-feedback path employing the twin T filter is then introduced, which greatly reduces the gain of the amplifier for all frequencies except the rejection frequency of the filter. For this frequency, the gain of the amplifier is still A, and the conditions for oscillation are fulfilled. A simplified circuit for such an oscillator is shown in Fig. 5-5. The positive-feedback path is from the plate to the cathode of the amplifier tube. A cathode-follower amplifier is required to drive the low impedances of the amplifier cathode circuit. The negative-feedback path is from the plate to the grid of the amplifier tube. The conditions of oscillation are fulfilled for such a very narrow band of frequencies that the output is a nearly pure sine wave. This type of oscil-

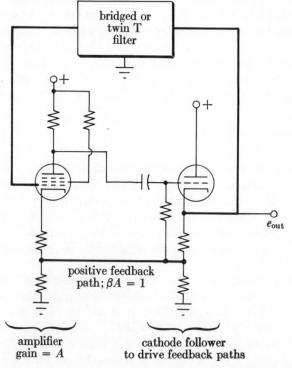

Figure 5-5   Simplified schematic of a bridged T oscillator.

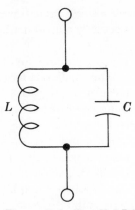

Figure 5-6   Parallel LC resonant circuit.

lator has become very popular in the audio-frequency range and up to several hundred kilocycles.

At higher frequencies, where chokes and capacitors are smaller and more efficient for a given reactance, LC circuits are more often used for oscillators. The parallel LC circuit of Fig. 5-6 has a tendency to oscillate at its resonant frequency when a pulse of energy is put into the circuit. The energy stored in the capacitor discharges into the inductance which builds up a counter emf and recharges the capacitor. This process will occur at only one frequency, where $X_L = X_C$; so $2\pi fL = 1/2\pi fC$, and solving for the frequency of oscillation f_o,

$$f_o = \frac{1}{2\pi\sqrt{LC}} \tag{5-2}$$

The resistive losses in the coil and wiring and the dielectric losses in the capacitor make this a damped oscillation. High-frequency oscillators can be made by using regenerative feedback to keep putting energy into the parallel resonant circuit in phase with its natural oscillations. The parallel LC circuit is often called the "tank" circuit when used in oscillators. Either the inductance or the capacitance may be adjusted to yield the desired resonant frequency.

The Armstrong Oscillator.   An Armstrong oscillator circuit is shown in Fig. 5-7. The tank circuit L_g-C is coupled to the grid of the amplifier tube through C_c and R_g. The amplifier output is fed back to the tank circuit through the mutual inductance of L_p and L_g. The feedback will be regenerative provided that the transformer, which is composed of L_p and L_g, is connected properly. The amplifier is biased by an arrangement called "grid-leak bias." When the tank circuit drives the grid in the posi-

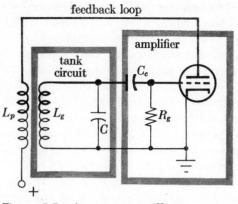

Figure 5-7   Armstrong oscillator.

tive direction through C_c, the grid will intercept some electrons and C_c will receive a negative charge on the grid side.. When the oscillation in the tank circuit then swings in the negative direction, the grid is even more negative and some of the charge on C_c leaks off through R_g.   The value of R_g must be small enough in relation to C_c so that the charge on C_c leaks off fast enough to prevent the tube from cutting itself off but not so fast that insufficient negative bias is established on the tube.   This bias arrangement is normally used only for fixed-frequency amplifiers and oscillators, because the bias and the choice of C_c and R_g depend on the signal frequency.

The output from the oscillator of Fig. 5-7 may be taken from (a) the

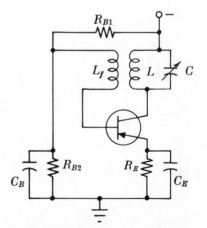

Figure 5-8   Transistor Armstrong oscillator.

plate of the tube, (b) a capacitive coupling to the tank circuit, or (c) a coil inductively coupled to L_g. The frequency of the oscillator should be $f_o = 1/2\pi\sqrt{L_gC}$, but a review of the high-frequency equivalent circuit of the amplifier will show why this is not precisely so. The input capacitance of the amplifier is in parallel with C and is part of the tuned circuit. In this way variations in the tube's characteristics, power supply, and load have an effect on the frequency of oscillation. The tuned circuit may be either in the grid circuit as shown or in the plate circuit. In the latter case the tuning capacitor C would be in parallel with L_p. A transistor Armstrong oscillator with a tuned-collector circuit is shown in Fig. 5-8. The resistance R_B imposes a self-bias on the transistor; C_B is the bypass. The coils L and L_f are inductively coupled. The Armstrong oscillator may also be constructed by using the common-base or common-collector configuration.

The Hartley Oscillator. One variation of the Hartley-oscillator circuit is shown in Fig. 5-9. The amplifier output is coupled to the grid circuit by the mutual inductance of parts L_p and L_g of coil L. In this case both L_p and L_g are parts of the tuned circuit. The capacitor C_b is to prevent a d-c short circuit from the plate to ground. The grid bias is the grid-leak arrangement discussed in connection with the Armstrong circuit. The radio-frequency choke (RFC) in the plate circuit takes the place of a load resistor. The a-c signal is developed across a coil as well as a resistor without the d-c $(i_b{}^2R_L)$ loss. Because of the frequency dependence of X_L, the RFC is used as a load in circuits where frequency changes by only about twofold.

The Colpitts oscillator shown in Fig. 5-28 is very similar to the Hartley except that the a-c voltage divider between the plate and grid portions of the tank circuit is the capacitor rather than the inductance.

There are several other possibilities for the arrangement of the tuned

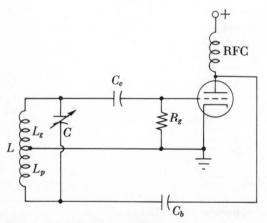

Figure 5-9   Hartley oscillator.

circuit, as well as many variations among the possible tube and transistor-amplifier configurations and feedback methods. The reader who needs design information for a radio-frequency oscillator or who is interested in the exact electrical analysis of the various feedback oscillator circuits is referred to the references at the end of the chapter.

5-3   Sinusoidal Negative-Resistance Oscillators

A block diagram of the negative-resistance oscillator was given in Fig. 5-3. In actual practice, the wave-forming circuit is usually the parallel resonant circuit of Fig. 5-6. If the coil and capacitor were a perfect inductance and capacitance, respectively, the impedance of the circuit at the resonant frequency would be infinite (see Supplement 3). The resistance R_c of the wire in the coil prevents the coil from being a perfect inductance. The "quality" of the inductor is defined as the ratio X_L/R_c and is given the symbol Q. It can be seen that Q depends on the frequency. The capacitor is usually so much more perfect than the inductor that its losses are neglected. Considering the resistance of the coil, the impedance of the tank circuit at resonance is $Z = QX_C$ when $Q \geq 10$. This impedance represents the resistance of the tank circuit at resonance. It follows then from Sec. 5-1 and Fig. 5-3 that, if an element of negative resistance equal to or greater than QX_C were placed in parallel with the tank circuit, the losses in the tank circuit would be offset. Under these circumstances an oscillation begun in the tank circuit could continue indefinitely. There are no "negative resistors" as such. There are, however, several components which exhibit a region of "negative resistance" in their current-voltage characteristics.

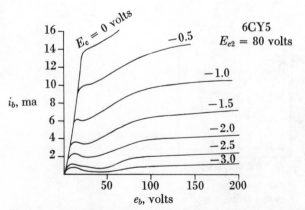

Figure 5-10   Plate characteristics of a 6CY5 tetrode. (Courtesy of RCA.)

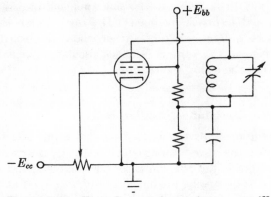

Figure 5-11   Tetrode negative-resistance oscillator.

The Tetrode Vacuum Tube.   The tetrode vacuum tube has a negative-resistance region in the plate characteristic as shown in Fig. 5-10.   The
tetrode (four elements, i.e., two grids, a plate, and a cathode) does not have
a suppressor grid to suppress the secondary emission of electrons from the
plate.   The rate of secondary emission increases as the plate voltage increases, but if the plate is less positive than the screen grid, most of the
emitted electrons will go to the screen grid.   This results in a region where
the plate current decreases as the plate voltage increases.   Thus in this
region the plate resistance $de_p/di_p = r_p$ is negative.   This negative-resistance region is used in an oscillator, as shown in Fig. 5-11.   The tank circuit
is in parallel with the plate resistance of the tube.   The rest of the circuit is
a d-c voltage divider to bias the control grid, establish the screen-grid voltage more positive than the plate, and supply the plate and screen currents.

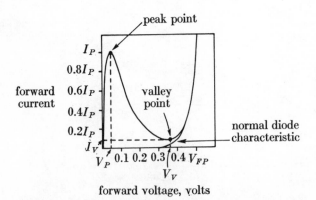

Figure 5-12   Tunnel-diode current-voltage curve.

The Tunnel Diode. The tunnel diode also has a region of negative resistance in its current-voltage characteristic (Fig. 5-12). The tunnel diode differs from the regular *p-n* junction diode (Sec. 2-4) in that the semiconductor used is much more heavily "doped" and has therefore a relatively large number of charge carriers. For small forward biases, the narrowness of the depletion layer allows charges to "tunnel" across the junction even though they do not have sufficient energy to overcome the counter emf of the junction. As the forward bias increases, the tunnel-conduction mechanism becomes less effective until eventually the potential at which the normal conduction process occurs is reached. When the diode is forward-biased about 150 mv, the negative-resistance characteristic can be utilized. The characteristics of various tunnel diodes will differ significantly only in the magnitude of the peak current I_P and the valley current I_V. The potentials are dependent on the semiconductor material and not the method of manufacture.

A 100-Mc tunnel-diode oscillator is shown in Fig. 5-13. The resistors R_{B1} and R_{B2} provide the forward bias for the tunnel diode. The capacitor C_B is a bypass for R_{B2} and puts the diode in parallel with the tank circuit as far as the 100-Mc signal is concerned. This circuit is actually part of a short-range FM transmitter [see the References (G.E., "Tunnel Diode Manual")].

The point-contact transistor also exhibits a negative-resistance characteristic similar to the tetrode's. This has caused it to be abandoned for amplifier applications, but some types are still manufactured for special purposes. The reader should consult the References (Lurch) for a discussion of the point-contact transistor and its use as an oscillator.

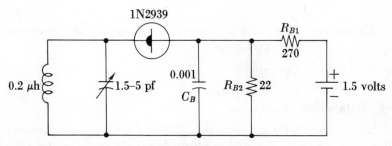

Figure 5-13   Tunnel-diode oscillator.

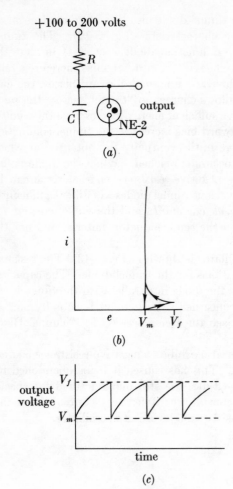

Figure 5-14   Neon-bulb oscillator: (a) schematic; (b) current-voltage curve; (c) output waveform.

5-4   Relaxation Oscillators

A negative-resistance element is also required for the relaxation oscillator. In principle, the relaxation oscillator differs from the negative-resistance oscillator only in that it is not confined to a linear portion of the negative-resistance region. The relaxation oscillator takes advantage of the double-valued current-voltage functions which occur because of the peaks in the current-voltage curves of negative-resistance devices (Fig. 5-2). This is illustrated for the neon-bulb oscillator of Fig. 5-14a.

The Neon Bulb. The neon bulb is a form of the glow-discharge tube described as a voltage-regulating element in Sec. 2-7. A higher potential is required to ionize the gas than is required to maintain conduction. This results in a negative-resistance region as shown in Fig. 5-14b. The operation of the oscillator of Fig. 5-14a may now be explained as follows: The voltage across capacitor C builds up as the capacitor charges through R. When the firing potential V_f is reached, the neon bulb conducts, dropping the potential across C to the maintaining potential V_m. The resistance R is too large to supply sufficient current for conduction, and so the neon bulb turns off, and the cycle begins again. The output waveform is shown in Fig. 5-14c.

The Thyratron. The thyratron is essentially a gas-filled diode (Sec. 2-4) with a grid placed between the cathode and the anode. The schematic symbol is shown in Fig. 5-15a. Gaseous conduction occurs in the gas-filled diode when the electrons accelerated from the cathode to the anode have sufficient energy to ionize the gas molecules in the tube. Since the potential on the thyratron grid affects the energy of the electrons accelerating to the

(a)

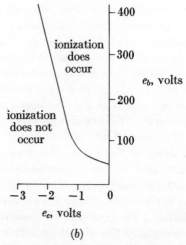

(b)

Figure 5-15 Thyratron: (a) schematic; (b) typical control characteristics.

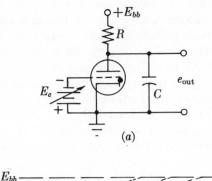

(a)

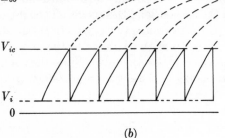

(b)

Figure 5-16   Thyratron relaxation oscillator: (a) schematic; (b) output waveform.

anode, the anode potential required for ionization is a function of the grid potential. The control of the grid voltage over the ionization potential is shown by the graph in Fig. 5-15b. Once ionization does occur, the negative grid becomes surrounded by positive ions and is thus neutralized. The potential across the tube drops to the ionization potential of the gas (about 10 volts for mercury). Ionization and current flow continue independent of the grid potential until the anode potential falls below the ionization potential of the gas. When ionization is stopped, the grid regains control and ionization cannot recur unless the conditions of Fig. 5-15b are met. Ionization is established in a few microseconds. To quench ionization, current must be stopped for a period of the order of 100 μsec.

A thyratron relaxation oscillator is shown in Fig. 5-16a. The capacitor charges through R. When the anode potential reaches the controlled ionization potential V_{ic}, the thyratron conducts, discharging C to the actual ionization potential V_i. The cycle is then repeated. The grid potential E_c controls the peak voltage of the oscillation. The period of the oscillation depends on E_{bb}, R, and E_c. The advantages of the thyratron relaxation oscillator over the neon bulb are a larger output voltage and a more complete control over the magnitude and period of the oscillation. Until recently the thyratron relaxation oscillator was the standard sweep generator used in oscilloscopes. The synchronizing signal was applied to the thyratron grid in addition to the d-c grid bias. As the plate voltage neared the firing potential, a positive signal on the grid would reduce the firing potential and discharge the capacitor. Thus the sweep frequency was synchronized to the signal frequency by means of the positive-going portions of the signal waveform.

The Unijunction Transistor. The unijunction transistor is actually a silicon *p-n* diode with two ohmic (nonrectifying) contacts to the *n*-type part of the diode. The construction and the schematic symbol are shown in Fig. 5-17. In the normal use of the device, a positive voltage V_{BB} is connected from $B2$ to $B1$. The resistance of the *n*-type silicon acts like a voltage divider to establish a potential ηV_{BB} at the emitter contact. If the externally applied emitter potential is less positive than ηV_{BB}, the emitter junction is reverse-biased and virtually no current will flow in the emitter circuit. If the emitter potential is made to be positive with respect to ηV_{BB}, the emitter junction is forward-biased, current begins to flow from the emitter to $B1$, and the emitter-$B1$ junction takes on the low-resistance characteristic of a forward-biased diode. As the emitter current increases, the junction resistance decreases and the emitter voltage decreases. The resulting negative-resistance characteristic is shown in Fig. 5-17c.

A relaxation oscillator using the unijunction transistor is shown in Fig. 5-17d. The operation of this circuit is very similar to that of the thyratron relaxation oscillator. The capacitor C charges through R until the emitter junction is forward-biased. At this potential the capacitor discharges through the emitter-$B2$ junction and R_1. When the emitter potential drops to about 2 volts, the junction no longer conducts and the cycle begins again. The period of oscillation is determined by the choice of R and C. The voltage waveforms at the emitter and $B1$ are shown in Fig. 5-17e.

The Tunnel Diode. The tunnel diode can also be used as a very stable relaxation oscillator. The circuit, operation path, and output waveform are shown in Fig. 5-18. When the voltage is first turned on, the bias voltage determined by the divider R_1 and R_2 is applied to the coil and diode in series. The current increases toward I_P at a rate determined by the inductance L. The voltage increases to V_P. When I_P is reached, the voltage instantly changes to V_{FP}. The voltage across the diode is now greater than the bias voltage, and so the current will decrease at a rate determined by L. When I_V is reached, the voltage instantly changes to practically zero and the process starts again. The operation of this circuit depends on the bias voltage being between V_P and V_V. The frequency and symmetry depend on L. For a given L, the frequency is a maximum and the oscillator most stable when $T_1 = T_2$.

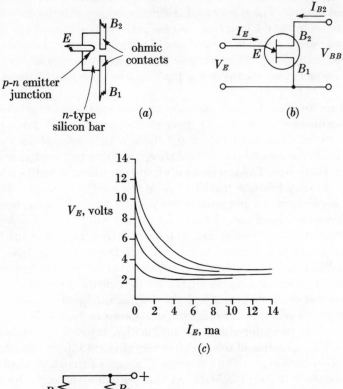

(a)

(b)

(c)

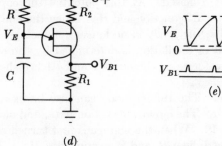

(d)

(e)

Figure 5-17   Unijunction transistor: (a) construction; (b) schematic; (c) emitter input characteristics; (d) oscillator schematic; (e) oscillator waveforms.

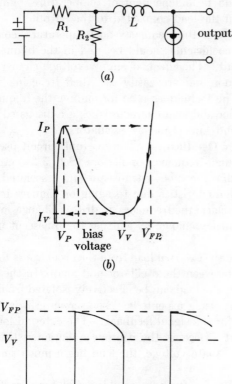

(a)

(b)

(c)

Figure 5-18 *Tunnel-diode relaxation oscillator: (a) schematic; (b) current-voltage curve and operating path; (c) output waveform.*

5-5 Oscillator Stabilization

An oscillator is often used to measure the frequency of another oscillator or to measure time intervals in the laboratory. If the oscillator frequency is known, the number of oscillations occurring during an elapsed interval can be a very accurate measurement of time. For this application it is essential that the oscillator frequency be known precisely and that its frequency of oscillation be stable from day to day. To be truly stable, the frequency of oscillation should be independent of temperature, aging of components, line voltage, and the load connected to the output.

To reduce the dependence of the frequency on temperature, components with low temperature coefficients should be used in the frequency-determining parts of the circuit. The effects of supply-voltage changes on oscillator frequency are minor and are easily remedied by using well-regulated power supplies. The techniques used for making the frequency less dependent on the amplifier and load characteristics are discussed separately for high-frequency and low-frequency oscillators.

Stable High-Frequency Oscillators. The LC tank circuit used to determine the frequency of high-frequency oscillators (Sec. 5-2) actually includes the capacitances within the tube or transistor and associated wiring. Changes in the tube characteristics due to aging or changes in the transistor temperature would cause the frequency to drift. Changes in the load would also cause a frequency change by shifting the quiescent point of the amplifier.

The easiest way to isolate the external load from the oscillator is to put a cathode-follower amplifier between the oscillator and load. In the case of the vacuum-tube oscillator, the load can be effectively isolated from the tank and feedback circuits by using a pentode. The screen grid is used, as the plate of the triode is, for the signal feedback. The external load is connected to the plate circuit. Because the pentode's characteristics are essentially independent of the plate voltage, the load has a much smaller effect on the feedback circuit.

Crystal Oscillators. By far the most stable oscillators are those which use a quartz crystal as the frequency-determining tuned circuit. A piece of quartz crystal sandwiched between metallic plates deforms mechanically when a potential is applied between the plates. When the external potential is removed, the relaxation of the crystal will induce a potential between the metal plates. There will be a natural vibration frequency of the crystal which depends on its cut and size. An a-c voltage of the resonant frequency of the crystal applied across it will maintain the resonant vibration in much the same way as oscillation is maintained in a tank circuit. The crystal is superior to the LC tank circuit because the frequency is virtually independent of external circuit parameters and because the resonance peak is very much sharper (Q much higher).

The circuit of a simple Pierce crystal oscillator is shown in Fig. 5-19a. The crystal is in the regenerative-feedback path. A practical crystal-oscillator circuit designed according to the Pierce circuit is shown in Fig. 5-19b. This circuit illustrates the use of the pentode for isolating the load. The plate-load impedance is a tuned circuit to eliminate any harmonic content from the oscillator output signal. The capacitor from screen to ground is adjusted so that there is just enough feedback to sustain oscillation.

The crystal oscillator has a fixed frequency. To change the frequency,

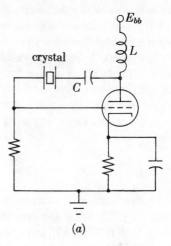

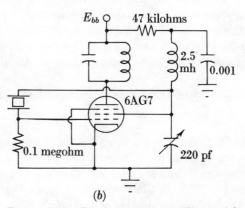

Figure 5-19   Pierce crystal oscillator: (a) simplified circuit; (b) practical circuit.

t is necessary to substitute another crystal of the appropriate dimensions. When the crystal temperature is controlled or when a zero-temperature-coefficient crystal is used, the crystal oscillator can be accurate and stable to better than 1 ppm.

Stable Low-Frequency Oscillators.   The frequency of an *RC* feedback oscillator such as the twin T oscillator of Fig. 5-5 is quite independent of the characteristics of the amplifier.   The load can be isolated with an additional cathode-follower stage.   If precision and low-temperature-coefficient components are used in the T network, the short-term stability of the oscillator can be of the order of 1 part in 10^4, or 0.01 per cent.   Greater stability and accuracy can be obtained with the crystal oscillator, as in the case of high frequencies. Crystals are available with frequencies as low as several kilocycles. The general form of the oscillator is the same as in Fig. 5-19a. When lower frequencies are required, a high-frequency crystal oscillator is used and its output frequency is divided by a sequence of one or more frequency-dividing circuits (Sec. 9-13). In this way low frequencies are obtained which have the same precision and stability as the high-frequency crystal oscillator. Another form of the audio oscillator which is very stable uses a special tuning fork in much the same way as the high-frequency oscillator uses the crystal.

5-6 Modulation and Demodulation

Conventional *modulation* consists in superimposing information on a *carrier* frequency from a sinusoidal oscillator. The most familiar examples are the modulation of medium-frequency (300 to 3000 kc), high-frequency (3 to 30 Mc), very-high-frequency (30 to 300 Mc), and ultra-high-frequency (300 to 3000 Mc) carriers with voice and picture information signals. These carriers are readily radiated through space, and a specific carrier frequency may be selectively *tuned in* by a receiver. The voice and picture information must then be extracted from the carrier by *demodulation*, or *detection*, within the receiver.

A sinusoidal carrier voltage at any time t may be expressed as

$$C_o = E_m \cos (2\pi f_o t + \phi)$$

where E_m is the peak amplitude, f_o the frequency, and ϕ the phase angle. *Amplitude modulation* (AM) is the variation of the carrier amplitude E_m as a function of the information signal (often called the "modulating frequency"). *Frequency modulation* (FM) is the variation of f_o, and *phase modulation* (PM) is the variation of ϕ as functions of the information signals. Another method of modulation consists in varying the starting points, or spacing, of pulses as a function of the information. This method is referred to as *pulse-position*, or *pulse-time*, *modulation*. The characteristics of only amplitude modulation and demodulation are considered in this section.

Amplitude Modulation. As noted above, in amplitude modulation the magnitude of the carrier is varied as a function of an information signal. This is illustrated in Fig. 5-20. In the modulation process two sideband frequencies are produced for each signal frequency. A carrier that is modulated with a signal frequency f_s will contain two frequencies, $f_o + f_s$ and $f_o - f_s$, in addition to the fundamental frequency f_o. For example, if $f_s = 5$ kc and $f_o = 1000$ kc, then the sidebands are 995 kc and 1005 kc. In other words, the total bandwidth is 10 kc, or *twice the modulating frequency*. In standard AM radio broadcasts a bandwidth of 10 kc is allocated for each station; so the maximum permissible modulating frequency is 5 kc.

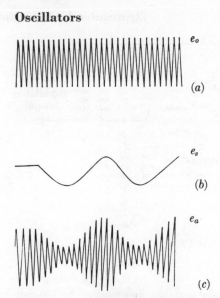

e_o

(a)

e_s

(b)

e_a

(c)

Figure 5-20 Amplitude modulation: (a) unmodulated carrier; (b) information signal; (c) amplitude-modulated wave.

The *degree of amplitude modulation* is determined by the ratio $\Delta E_m/E_m$, where ΔE_m is the maximum deviation from the magnitude E_m of the unmodulated carrier. Different degrees of modulation are illustrated in Fig. 5-21, and they are expressed as $100 \, \Delta E_m/E_m$, or per cent modulation. Note

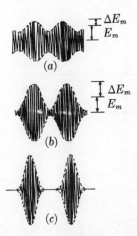

ΔE_m
E_m

(a)

ΔE_m
E_m

(b)

(c)

Figure 5-21 Degree of modulation: (a) 50 per cent; (b) 100 per cent; (c) greater than 100 per cent.

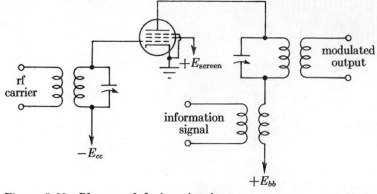

Figure 5-22   Plate modulation circuit.

that the magnitude of the modulated envelope increases up to 100 per cent
modulation, but distortion results when modulation exceeds 100 per cent.

There are various circuits for producing amplitude modulation. One
method, called plate modulation, is illustrated in Fig. 5-22. The information signal is fed to the plate of an r-f amplifier. This effectively varies the
plate supply, and consequently the gain of the tube, as a function of the
amplitude of the information signal. A cathode modulation circuit is
illustrated in Fig. 5-23, whereby the tube bias is varied as a function of the
signal amplitude. Other types of modulation circuits use grid or screen

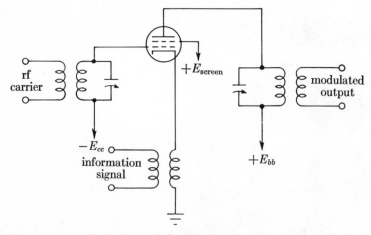

Figure 5-23   Cathode modulation circuit.

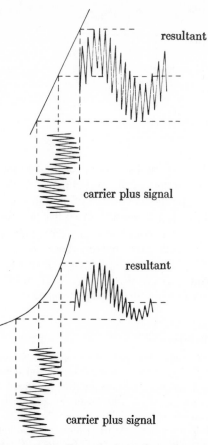

resultant

carrier plus signal

resultant

carrier plus signal

Figure 5-24   Summation of carrier and signal: (a) linear summation;
(b) nonlinear summation (modulation).

modulation, whereby the signal is fed to either the control or the screen
grids.   It is important to note that it is necessary for the tube to act as a
nonlinear element in order to produce a variation of carrier amplitude.   The
result of impressing two frequencies, carrier and signal, on a linear element
is shown in Fig. 5-24a.   The output waveshape contains the same frequencies as the carrier and signal.   The r-f amplifiers discriminate against the
signal, and only a carrier of constant amplitude is transmitted.   The result
of mixing carrier and signal frequencies in a nonlinear element is shown in
Fig. 5-24b.   In this case, the amplitude of the r-f carrier varies with the
modulating signal, and the information is now contained within its sidebands.

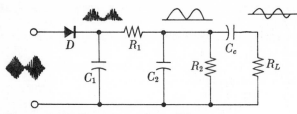

Figure 5-25   Detection of an AM wave.

Amplitude Detection.   The AM carrier may be easily demodulated within a receiver by simple diode detection, as illustrated in Fig. 5-25.   One half of the modulated wave passes the diode, and the other half is blocked by the diode.   A π-section filter is used to pass the rectified information envelope and eliminate the carrier.   The coupling capacitor C_c blocks the d-c component, and the pure a-c information signal appears across R_L.

The basic disadvantage of AM is, of course, well known to all AM radio listeners.   Atmospheric disturbances from storms, electrical machinery, and other sources can affect the carrier amplitude so as to mask the signal information.

References

Lurch, E. N., "Fundamentals of Electronics," Wiley, New York, 1960.   Contains a discussion of many types of oscillators as well as modulation and detection.

"The Radio Amateur's Handbook," published annually by the American Radio Relay League, West Hartford, Conn.   Basic discussion of practical high-frequency oscillator, modulator, and detector circuits.

"Basic Theory and Application of Transistors," Army Technical Manual TM 11-690, U.S. Government Printing Office, Washington, D.C., 1959.   Contains a section on transistor oscillators.

"Tunnel Diode Manual," General Electric Company, Semiconductor Products Department, Liverpool, N.Y., 1961.   Circuits, applications, and specifications of tunnel diodes.

Problems

5-1   Calculate the frequency of oscillation of the Hartley oscillator of Fig. 5-9 ($L_p = 1$ mh, $L_g = 9$ mh, and $C = 100$ pf).   *Ans.: f = 160 kc*

5-2   (a) Choose values of R and C in Fig. 5-16 to obtain an initial sweep rate of 50 volts/sec ($E_{bb} = 100$ volts).   [The initial charging rate of a capacitor may be found by expanding the charging equation, $E_c = E_{bb}(1 - e^{-t/RC})$, and taking the first two terms of the series

$$e^x = 1 + \frac{x}{1!} + \frac{x^2}{2!} + \frac{x^3}{3!} + \cdots + \frac{x^n}{n!}$$

(b) At what fraction of a time constant will the sweep voltage deviate from the linear equation assumed in part (a) by 1 per cent? (The third term in the expansion contributes the most error.)

Ans.: (a) $RC = 2$ sec; for convenience choose $C \approx 1$ μf and $R \approx 2$ megohms; (b) $0.02RC$

5-3 Assuming $E_c = -1$ volt, estimate the peak-to-peak output voltage for the circuit of Prob. 5-2, using the characteristics given in Fig. 5-15.

Ans.: Approximately 25 volts

5-4 (a) Calculate the frequency of oscillation for the bridged T oscillator of Fig. 5-5, with $R_1 = R_2 = 100$ kilohms, $C_1 = C_2 = 0.001$ μf. (Refer to Fig. 4-38.) (b) If R_g of the pentode is 1 megohm, what size blocking capacitor is necessary for efficient operation? *Ans.:* (a) 1.6 kc; (b) at least 5×100 pf

EXPERIMENTS

A sawtooth waveform is generated by a thyratron relaxation oscillator in the first experiment. A phase-shift oscillator using a transistor amplifier is then constructed and tested. A high-frequency signal is generated by a Colpitts oscillator circuit, and its output is then modulated with a low-frequency signal from the sine-wave generator. The modulated wave is demodulated with a diode detector, and the demodulated signal is observed on the oscilloscope and listened to with the earphone.

Expt. 5-1 Thyratron Sweep Generator

Wire the thyratron sweep generator of Fig. 5-26. Set E_{bb} initially at 300 volts; set E_c at -1.0 volt and C at 0.05 μf. Observe the output waveform on the oscilloscope. Note the effects on the magnitude and frequency of the sawtooth wave as

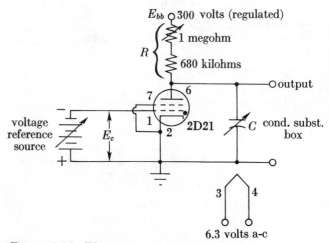

Figure 5-26   Thyratron sweep generator.

E_c is varied over the range 0 to -2.0 volts. Set E_c at -0.9 volt and measure the firing potential with the oscilloscope (d-c). Note the effect of variations in C, R, and E_{bb} on the frequency. With $C = 0.05$ μf and $E_{bb} = 300$ volts, measure the range of frequencies obtainable by adjusting resistance R with the 1-megohm potentiometer.

Expt. 5-2 Transistor Phase-Shift Oscillator

Wire the phase-shift oscillator as shown in Fig. 5-27. Adjust the transistor power-supply control to 22 volts. *Be sure that the polarity of the power supply and the emitter bypass capacitor are as indicated in the circuit diagram.* Rotate the feedback control so that the wiper is at the collector end of the potentiometer (maximum feedback signal). Observe the output waveform on the oscilloscope. If no oscillation is observed, increasing the power-supply voltage to a maximum value of 25 volts may increase the gain enough to sustain oscillation. If the circuit still does not oscillate, it may be that your transistor has insufficient gain. (Recall that a gain of 29 is necessary for $\beta A = 1$ with this circuit.)

Adjust the feedback control so that oscillation is just sustained. Measure the output voltage.

Now measure the voltage at points B, C, D, and E. Determine the attenuation of each RC section. Compare the loop gain between points B and E with the theoretical value. By using the oscilloscope as an x-y plotter, measure the 60°-phase shift of each RC section.

Measure the output frequency and compare it with the theoretical value $[f_o = 1/(2\pi \sqrt{6RC})]$.

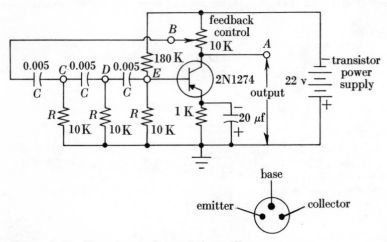

Figure 5-27   Transistor phase-shift oscillator.

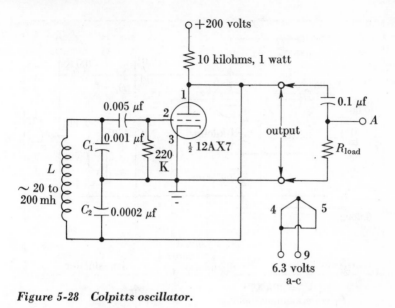

Figure 5-28 Colpitts oscillator.

Expt. 5-3 Colpitts Oscillator

Wire the Colpitts oscillator shown in Fig. 5-28. Adjust the regulated power supply to about 200 volts. Measure the peak voltage of the oscillations, using the calibrated d-c input of the oscilloscope; and using the sine-square generator as a frequency standard, measure the frequency. Compare the output frequency with the resonant frequency of the tank circuit. The tank circuit is made up of a coil of about 20 to 200 mh, with capacitors C_1 and C_2 in series.

Determine how loading the oscillator affects the frequency and output voltage. Loads of 1 megohm, 100 kilohms, and 10 kilohms are connected through a 0.1-μf blocking capacitor as shown in Fig. 5-28. *Do not disassemble your oscillator at this point, since it will be used in the next experiment.*

Expt. 5-4 Modulation and Demodulation

Wire the cathode-follower amplifier, using the second half of the 12AX7 as shown in Fig. 5-29. Connect the sine-wave output of the sine-square generator to the cathode-follower input. Disconnect the cathode lead and one end of the grid resistor of the Colpitts oscillator and reconnect to the cathode follower, as shown in Fig. 5-29. The modulating signal is thus introduced into the cathode circuit of the carrier oscillator. Set the frequency of the sine-square generator at about 500 cycles. Adjust the amplitude of the sine-wave output to about 1 volt, and observe the modulated carrier signal with the oscilloscope between point A and ground. Vary the amplitude and frequency of the modulating signal and observe the waveforms.

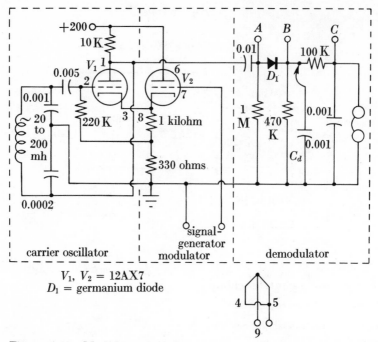

Figure 5-29   Modulator and demodulator.

Connect the demodulator as shown in Fig. 5-29, except do not yet connect the capacitor C_d to point B. Observe the rectified waveform at point B, and then connect capacitor C_d and again observe the waveform at point B. Now observe the waveform at point C after more filtering. Connect the earphone between point C and ground to hear the original modulating signal, which has been recovered by demodulating the carrier. The power amplifier with speaker constructed in Expt. 4-3 may be used instead of, or in addition to, the earphone.

chapter six

Comparison Measurements

6-1 The Principles of Comparison Methods

Measurements of high precision and accuracy are almost always the result of comparison methods. It is not surprising, therefore, that many scientific instruments operate on the basis of comparison procedures. For example, the accurate determination of the mass (weight) of an object is carried out by a comparison procedure, as illustrated in Fig. 6-1. An object of unknown mass is placed on one pan of a balance, and weights of standard mass are varied on the other pan until the pointer indicates a null point—the point at which the unknown and standard masses are equal. The analytical balance acts as the null detector. Its sensitivity depends on the design and construction of the analytical balance; the greater the sensitivity, the better the precision of measurement, and the smaller the difference in masses that can be detected. However, the accuracy [1] of determining the unknown mass not only depends on the sensitivity of the balance but also usually depends greatly on the accuracy of the standard masses. If a difference in mass of 0.0001 g can just be detected by a given balance, then the reproducibility of determining a mass of 0.1000 g will be 1 part/1000, or 0.1 per cent. However, it is possible for the standard weights to have an error of 1 per cent because of rough use or contamination. Then the value obtained for the unknown would be off from the true value by 1

---

[1] It is assumed that the buoyancy effect of air is negligible or corrected for.

251

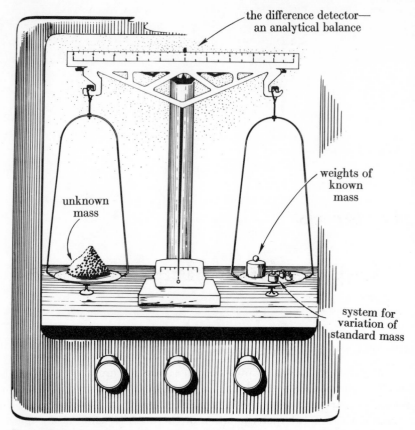

Figure 6-1   Determination of mass by a comparison measurement.

per cent, because of comparison with an erroneous standard, even though the null detector was operating perfectly within its design capability to show differences within 0.1 per cent for the 0.1-g mass.

This example illustrates the requirements inherent in all comparison measurements: (1) a selective detector which responds to small differences in mass or differences in current, resistance, potential, capacitance, frequency, or some other quantity to be measured; (2) known standards of the quantity to be determined; and (3) a system of varying the total amount of standard used for comparison, either continuously or by small increments. This can be generalized as shown in Fig. 6-2, where U and S_r are unknown and standard, respectively, and F and F' are fixed amounts (zero to some finite value) which are present when the initial null point is established.

For the example illustrated in Fig. 6-2, F and F' represent the masses of balance-arm–pan systems, U the unknown mass of the object to be measured, and S_r the standard weights necessary to return the pointer to the null point. The variation of mass in this case could be either by manipulation or by an automatic device for changing the amount of standard mass on the right pan. It is apparent that with an equal-arm balance and good technique $U = S_r \pm e$, where e is dependent on the smallest difference in mass that the specific balance can detect, the smallest increment to which the standard can be adjusted, and the error in the stated values for the standard weights.

Note that a large object of considerable weight and a counterweight could be included in F and F', respectively, at the initial null point. The mass W of the object itself might be of no concern: a small change ΔW in its weight is the significant information sought. If the mass of the object is about 100 g and the measured change is 0.0001 g, it is apparent that $\Delta W/W$ represents a relative mass change in the object of 1 ppm. It is a general characteristic of comparison methods that extremely small differences or changes can often be determined without regard for total magnitude of the quantity.

Another comparison procedure is illustrated by the block diagram of Fig. 6-3. In this case a standard S is included in the initial balancing to the null point so that $F + S = F''$. After including the unknown U with the standard, a known amount S_r of the standard S is removed in order to reestablish the null point, whereby $U = S_r$. This is the comparison procedure used with most of the modern automatic balances and is known as the "method of substitution." This method compensates for unequal balance

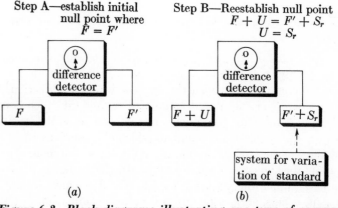

Step A—establish initial
null point where
$F = F'$

Step B—Reestablish null point
$F + U = F' + S_r$
$U = S_r$

difference detector

difference detector

F F' $F + U$ $F' + S_r$

system for varia-
tion of standard

(a)   (b)

Figure 6-2   Block diagrams illustrating one type of comparison procedure.

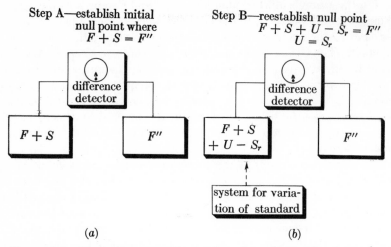

Step A—establish initial null point where $F + S = F''$

Step B—reestablish null point $F + S + U - S_r = F''$ $U = S_r$

(a)   (b)

Figure 6-3   *Block diagrams illustrating the substitution type of comparison procedure.*

arms in determining the mass of an object. Also, sensitivity is constant throughout the range of measurements because a constant load is applied at all times. In general, the method of substitution eliminates the problems of asymmetry in null systems. For extremely precise measurements it is the method of choice. This will be illustrated in Sec. 6-5.

In the following sections the null-point detectors, the standards, and their variation are described for the accurate comparison measurement of the various electrical quantities.

6-2   Accurate D-C Voltage Measurement by the Comparison Method

The measurement of voltage by a comparison procedure is represented schematically in Fig. 6-4. If the standard voltage is varied in a known way until the meter indicates no electron flow in either direction, then $E_u = E_s \pm e$, where E_s is the stated value of the standard which is in the circuit at the null point and e is again an error dependent on the sensitivity of the detector, the smallest increment to which the standard can be adjusted, and the accuracy of the standard. Obviously, the more sensitive the detector and the higher the accuracy of the standard voltage, the smaller the error in determining the unknown voltage E_u. Extremely small errors of 0.01 per cent, or less, are possible by this voltage-comparison technique. Comparison systems for measuring voltages have become known as "potentiometers." Therefore, *when potentiometer is used in this chapter, it will often refer to the entire voltage-comparison system.* It is also common practice to refer to a continuously variable voltage divider (a resistance with a continuously variable tap) as a potentiometer.

The Variable D-C Standard Voltage. In principle, a variable d-c standard voltage is obtained simply by connecting an accurate constant voltage across a variable-resistance voltage divider. In Fig. 6-5a the resistance is varied in discrete equal resistance steps so that R_v is a fraction of the total resistance R_p and $R_v/R_p = E_{\text{out}}/E_p$. If the applied voltage $E_p = 1.000$ volt and $R_v/R_p = 7.00/1000$ (limit of error of each resistance step is 0.1 per cent), then $E_{\text{out}} = 0.00700$ volt. In Fig. 6-5b a linear slidewire is used to vary the ratio R_v/R_p. The length L_v from one end of the wire to the sliding tap (slider or wiper) is a fraction of the total length L_p across which the accurate voltage E_p is applied. Therefore, $E_{\text{out}} = E_p L_v/L_p$. It is apparent from Fig. 6-5a and b that the accuracy of E_{out} is dependent on the accuracy of E_p, on the linearity of R_p, but not on the absolute value of R_p. In practice, however, R_p is usually made as an accurately known resistance. This is done so that accurate resistances can be added in series, and parallel, to change the voltage across the slide-wire by known amounts without changing the voltage supply.

It is useful to consider that in effect an *accurate constant current I* is provided through the resistance R_p to provide an accurate total applied voltage $IR_p = E_p$, as shown in Fig. 6-5c. Since the resistance R_v varies from 0 to R_p, the voltage varies from 0 to IR_p. If the current $= 10.00$ ma and $R_p = 10.00$ ohms, then E_{out} will vary from 0 to 100.0 mv and at any position will equal $100.0L_v/L_p$ mv.

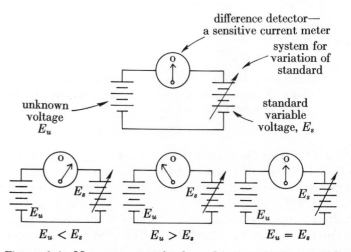

Figure 6-4 **Measurement of voltage by a comparison method.**

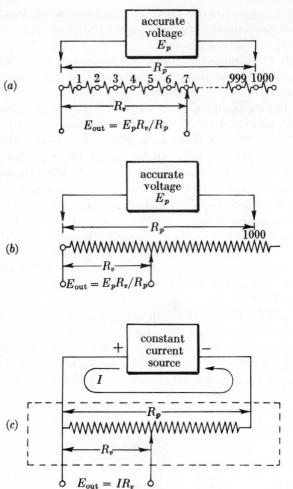

Figure 6-5 *Variable standard voltage: (a) resistance varied in equal steps; (b) resistance slidewire; (c) voltage proportional to preset constant current.*

A method of setting the current is illustrated in Fig. 6-6. The total resistance R_p of the slidewire is put in series with a standard resistance R_S and an adjustable resistance R_A, the sum of which determines the current through R_p [that is, $I = E/(R_A + R_p + R_S)$]. The value of R_S is chosen so that the voltage drop IR_S will equal a standard Weston-cell voltage for the desired current (that is, $R_S = 1.0183/I$). The resistance R_A is adjusted to give the selected value of current. A simple voltage comparison between IR_S and the standard cell voltage provides a precise and accurate way of adjusting the current I, assuming that the values of R_S and the Weston cell are accurate and the difference detector is sufficiently sensitive. The values for a practical single-dial potentiometer with a voltage span of 0 to 100.0 mv are shown in Fig. 6-7. To provide a standard constant current of 10.00 ma, the switch $S1$ is thrown to the left to connect contacts a–b; the resistance R_A is adjusted until the current meter reads zero, indicating that $IR_S = 1.018$ volts, and since $R_S = 101.8$ ohms, the current I must be 10.00 ma. Now, in order to measure an unknown voltage E_U, switch $S1$ is thrown to the right to make contacts b–c; the sliding tap is then varied until $IR_v = E_U$, as indicated again by no current through the difference detector. The voltage $IR_v = IR_pL_v/L_p = 100.0L_v/L_p$ mv for the example of Fig. 6-7, assuming perfect slidewire linearity.

The development and mass production of multiturn resistances have increased the availability of compact semiprecision potentiometers, both manual and automatic self-balancing. Helipot and Micropot are trade names (Beckman and Borg Company, respectively) for units with an integral number of turns of linear-resistance wire wound in a compact helical coil with a continuously variable tap that moves from one end to the other, as shown in Fig. 6-8. The coil is fixed in position in a cylindrical case made of a good insulator. Standard commercial units contain coils that require 3 turns, 10 turns, or 15 turns of the rotary contact. The rotation of the sliding contact follows the rotation of the rotor shaft but is free to move in a

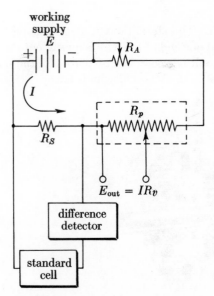

Figure 6-6 Method for setting an accurate constant current for potentiometers.

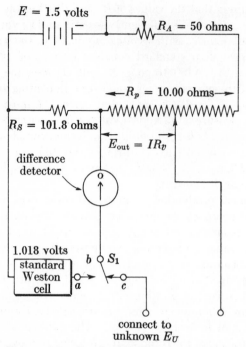

Figure 6-7   Single slidewire potentiometer with span of 0 to 100.0 mv.

groove along the length of the coil. Therefore, the variable resistance R_v between the sliding tap (wiper) and one end of the wire is dependent on the number of turns. With a 10-turn unit one complete revolution of the shaft represents one-tenth the total resistance, if the slidewire is linear.

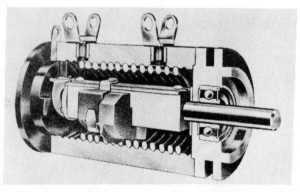

Figure 6-8   Cutaway view of multiturn potentiometer. (Courtesy of Helipot Corp., South Pasadena, Calif.)

The precision or repeatability of the variable resistance R_v for a given dial reading depends greatly on the mechanical stability of the wiper against the fixed slidewire. This can approach the readability of the dial in some cases. For a 10-turn potentiometer this might be about 0.02 per cent of full scale but is often less. If the repeatability of the setting L_v is 0.02 per cent of L_p, then $L_v = fL_p \pm 0.02$ per cent $L_p = L_p(f \pm 0.0002)$, where $f = L_v/L_p$. This indicates that the precision of L_v depends on the precision of the term $f \pm 0.0002$. When $f = 0.2$, the precision is 0.1 per cent. When $f = 0.02$ (20 divisions per 1000), the precision is only 1 per cent. The over-all accuracy of R_v is thus restricted by the repeatability when L_v/L_p is small and by the imperfect linearity of R_p as L_v/L_p increases.

To provide high accuracy for a wide range of R_v, combinations of highly accurate fixed resistances and a variable slidewire are connected in series as shown in Fig. 6-9. A switch selects the number of fixed resistances to be in series with the variable resistance R_{VS} of the slidewire. It is easily seen that, since the total variable resistance R_v is the sum of the fixed resistance R_F and slidewire resistance R_{VS}, the limit of error is the sum of two errors, one dependent on the error of the fixed resistances and the other amounting to a fixed percentage of the total slidewire resistance. Therefore, when all the fixed resistance is used as part of R_v, the error is at a minimum. As the fixed resistance decreases, the error increases slightly

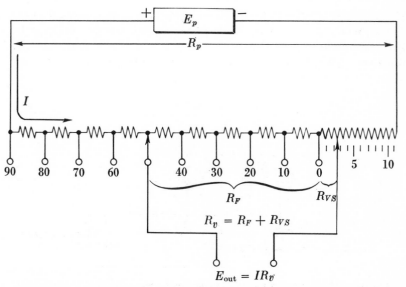

Figure 6-9   Combination of fixed resistances and slidewire for potentiometers.

until all fixed resistance is removed. Then, since R_v consists only of slide-wire resistance, the relative error increases considerably as R_v is decreased, as discussed above.

It should be noted that the dry cells which are commonly used for the working voltage supply E are not very constant and decrease in value quite rapidly. Therefore, frequent restandardization against the standard cell and readjustment of R_A are necessary to maintain the current I at the desired value. Note that "standardization" amounts to setting the current accurately through the slidewire. In order to overcome the problem of frequent standardization, there have been several recent developments. One method is to substitute mercury cells for the usual dry cells. As described in Sec. 2-8, the mercury cell maintains a very constant voltage over most of its life. Although this substitution can greatly reduce the number of standardizations, the circuit still requires occasional standardization for best accuracy. In some low-current circuits an accuracy of 0.3 per cent can be maintained for about 6 months without restandardizing. Therefore, the standard resistance R_S and Weston cell might be eliminated as a permanent part of the potentiometer circuit, although it should be checked occasionally by connecting a standard voltage in place of an unknown E_U.

Ideally, of course, it would be desirable to have an accurately known voltage of required current capacity that would remain highly stable throughout the life of the equipment. Also, it would be desirable to have an inexpensive, small, compact package that could fit easily within existing potentiometers. Recent developments of constant voltage Zener diode sources (see Sec. 2-7) make their use practical for supplying a constant voltage within 0.01 to 0.1 per cent across the linear slidewires of potentiometers. A useful circuit is shown in Fig. 6-10. A very stable and accurate supply can also be obtained by using an operational amplifier and standard cell as described in Chap. 8.

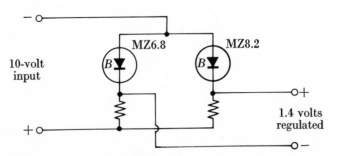

Figure 6-10   Zener constant voltage source.

Systems for Varying the Standard Voltage. As discussed above, when an unknown voltage E_U is measured, the slider is moved in a direction depending on the direction of electron flow through the detector. When $E_U = IR_v$, there is no detectable current through the detector and the movement of the sliding tap is stopped. Obviously the movement can be done manually while the detector is observed visually, or, as in the case of automatic potentiometers, the sliding tap can be rapidly driven to the null point by a motor. The direction of electron flow in the detector determines the direction of motor drive, and the motor stops when $IR_v = E_U$. The characteristics of an automatic potentiometer will be presented in Chap. 7.

It is, of course, very significant that at balance there is essentially no electron flow * to or from the unknown. Therefore, it is only during the period prior to balance that the potentiometer "loads" (causes significant electron flow to and from) the unknown. For unknown voltages whose values might be seriously affected by the loading prior to balance, it is necessary to use a system of balancing to the null point that causes a minimum of electron flow. The classical system consists of the well-known tapping key and the eye of the observer to note the direction of meter deflection and his hand to move the sliding tap—a sort of "hunt-and-peck" system for zeroing in on the null point. Fortunately, the modern motor-drive system operates rapidly and continuously to find and to maintain the null point, and some systems are capable of automatic balancing to the null point in 1 sec or less after the unknown is connected and of maintaining it within a few microvolts. Also, many of the new voltage-difference detectors have a high input resistance so that the maximum current is only a few microamperes, even with a 1-volt unbalance signal between E_U and IR_v.

The Null-Point Detector—Galvanometer. Several times in the preceding discussions it has been indicated that the accuracy of potentiometers (or any comparison system) depends greatly on the sensitivity of the null-point detector. The classical null-point detector for potential difference is the galvanometer. The usual galvanometer is a sensitive moving-coil meter similar in principle to the D'Arsonval current meters discussed in Sec. 1-2. In the galvanometer, however, the pivots are replaced by filamentary suspensions and the pointer by a mirror and light-beam system as shown in Fig. 6-11. A small rotation of the coil is amplified into a large horizontal displacement of the light beam reflected from a small mirror mounted on the coil. The light beam is projected on a scale usually divided into millimeter divisions that can be estimated to about 0.2 mm.

---

* Actually there can be some electron flow at apparent balance because of the small uncertainty in determining the perfect null point. If e represents the maximum error in volts and R_T the total resistance (dependent on detector, potentiometer, and source resistances) to the current i, then $i \leq e/R_T$.

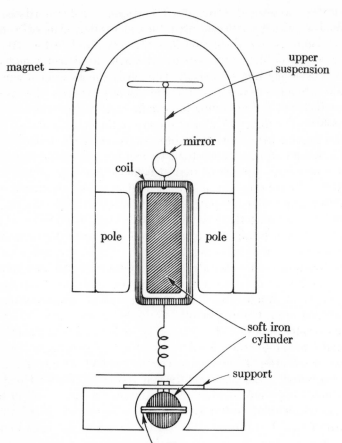

*Figure 6-11   Moving-coil galvanometer.   The upper suspension con-
sists of a gold wire about 0.001 in. in diameter, easily
damaged by excessive currents and jars.*

Sensitivity is often given as the microampere current necessary to give a
1-mm deflection (usually on a scale at a distance of 1 m).   In other cases
the "voltage sensitivity" is given.   This is the voltage in microvolts, across
the combination resistance of galvanometer coil and critical damping resistor, external (CDRX), required to give a 1-mm deflection.

Unless a galvanometer is damped, the coil will oscillate back and forth
across the balance point.   It is usually desirable, therefore, to damp the
meter critically by adjusting the resistance in the circuit external to the
galvanometer.   If the resistance is too small, it oscillates; if too large, the

meter approaches a balance point slowly: when critically damped, it reaches its final reading without oscillation and in the shortest possible time. Note that CDRX consists of any added circuit resistance, the source resistance R_u and the potentiometer resistance R_s, as seen from the galvanometer terminals. The resistance R_s varies with the position of the wiper contact on the slidewire so that optimum damping is not rigidly maintained. If $R_s + R_u$ is too large or too small, resistors may be used in series and/or parallel to produce the desired CDRX.

Box-type galvanometers are very common in scientific laboratories. In many of these the light beam traverses the box five times after reflection from the moving mirror, and this provides sensitivities of about 0.005 to 0.0005 $\mu a/mm$. Some laboratory galvanometers provide sensitivities of 10^{-10} amp/mm, or even 10^{-11} amp/mm in specially sensitive types. A comparison of important characteristics of a few types is given in Table 6-1. In general, the more sensitive the galvanometer, the more fragile, and the longer the period of oscillation.

The precision of determining the null point depends not only on the galvanometer sensitivity but also upon the resistance of the circuit in which it is placed. The circuit resistance often depends primarily on the unknown voltage source, as illustrated in Fig. 6-12, where the relatively small resistance from the galvanometer coil and potentiometer circuit are insignificant compared with the 10 or 100 kilohms from the source. Since the galvanometer requires 10^{-9} amp to give a detectable deflection (about 0.2 mm) of the light beam, the minimum detectable voltage is about 10^{-5} volt (10^{-9} amp $\times 10^4$ ohms). If the 10^{-5}-volt detection limit is compared with the 10^{-2} volt measured, it is apparent that the error is about 0.1 per

Table 6-1 Characteristics of a few d-c moving-coil galvanometers

Type	Sensitivity	CRDX *	Coil resistance	Period, sec
Box type	0.005 $\mu a/mm$	400	25	2.5
	0.005 $\mu a/mm$	25,000	550	3
	0.5 $\mu v/mm$	50	17	3
Pointer type	2 $\mu a/mm$	20	12	2.5
with taut	0.25 $\mu a/mm$	1,800	250	3
suspension				
Laboratory	0.0005 $\mu a/mm$	10,000	650	6
reflecting type	0.0001 $\mu a/mm$	22,000	500	14

* Critical damping resistance, external.

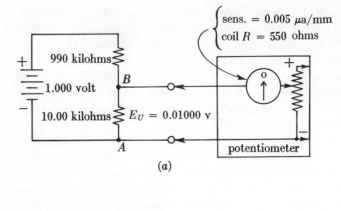

(a)

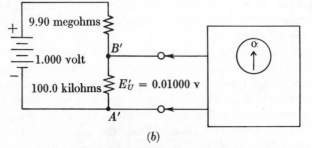

(b)

Figure 6-12   Effect of resistance on the accuracy of potentiometric measurement.

cent.   However, if the voltage E'_U of Fig. 6-12b is measured, the minimum detectable voltage is 10^{-4} volt (10^{-9} amp $\times 10^5$ ohms), and compared with the 10^{-2} volt measured, the possible error is about 1 per cent.   Also, the response would be sluggish because the largest common CDRX for available galvanometers is about 25,000 ohms.   In both cases the measured voltage is the same, 0.01 volt, but the error limit has increased from about 0.1 to 1 per cent with the same potentiometer.   This example illustrates the importance of circuit resistance in using a galvanometer as the null detector.   In some cases the resistance of E_U is so high (as with the glass-calomel cell for pH determination) that a galvanometer is useless as a null detector, and a high-input-impedance null detector must be used.

The Null-Point Detector—Electronic Amplifier.   From the summary in the previous section it is apparent that the galvanometer is not an ideal null detector.   Obviously it would be desirable to have a compact, rugged detector of high sensitivity, regardless of how high or low the resistance was from the unknown source, which would come to equilibrium within a fraction of a second, and which also would be insensitive to laboratory conditions. Although none of the electronic detectors to be discussed here can meet all these requirements, they do have several characteristics which make them ideal for many laboratory measurements.

To appreciate the general considerations, refer to Fig. 6-13a. This shows the resistance R_u for the voltage E_u which is to be measured, the resistance R_s of the standard voltage E_s, and the resistance R_d of the detector. When the detector is not connected (switch open), there is no current in the circuit and the voltage difference ΔE_o between the terminals a–b is equal to $E_u - E_s$. When the detector is connected (switch closed), the voltage difference ΔE_c across the detector (terminals a–b) is iR_d. Since $i = \Delta E_o/(R_u + R_s + R_d)$,

$$\Delta E_c = \frac{\Delta E_o R_d}{R_u + R_s + R_d} \tag{6-1}$$

It is obvious from Eq. (6-1) that, when $R_d \gg R_u + R_s$, then $\Delta E_c \approx \Delta E_o$, but when $R_u + R_s \gg R_d$, then ΔE_c is a small fraction of ΔE_o. This means that the detector sees only a small fraction of the unbalance voltage between E_u and E_s, with a corresponding decrease in sensitivity as a null detector. If R_u varies over a considerable range and moves up to rather

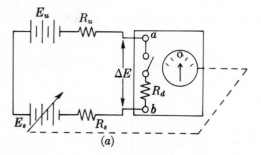

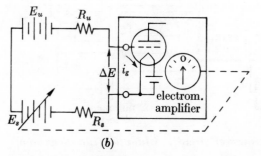

Figure 6-13 Potentiometer input to electronic null detector.

high values, then R_d should be made as large as possible so that the voltage $\Delta E_c \approx \Delta E_o$ at the detector input.

In Sec. 4-3, the direct-coupled amplifier and the electrometer were presented. These amplifiers, especially the latter, have very high input impedances and can be used to detect the d-c unbalance voltage ΔE_c. This is illustrated in Fig. 6-13b. A current i_g is indicated, which is the grid current caused by electrons from the cathode which are picked up by the grid, rather than passing through it. If the current i_g is appreciable and variable, the fluctuating voltage drop $i_g R_T$ across the total resistance in the circuit will swamp any small unbalance signal ΔE_o. However, $i_g \approx 10^{-14}$ to 10^{-17} amp for good electrometer tubes, so that, even if the circuit resistance were 10^8 ohms, it would result in less than 1 μv superimposed on the unbalance signal. Unfortunately, the plate current in the electrometer tube drifts slowly with time and also fluctuates even with a constant input signal between grid and cathode. In other words, there is a "noise signal" superimposed on the information signal (in this case ΔE_c). However, with very stable power supplies, long warm-up, and other precautions described in Sec. 4-4, it is possible to decrease the drift and to detect voltage changes of 0.1 mv or less. If this 0.1 mv can be detected for a case where $R_u = 1000$ megohms, it is apparent that the detector is equivalent to a galvanometer capable of detecting 10^{-4} volt/10^9 ohms $= 10^{-13}$ amp. Also, the indicator can be a rugged panel microammeter and the response time a fraction of a second. However, great care must be exercised in the amplifier design, layout of parts, and shielding of the input to prevent noise pickup.

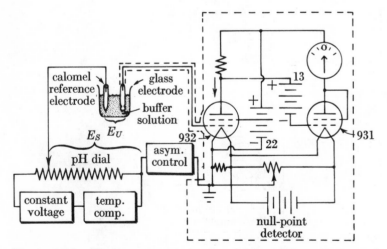

Figure 6-14   pH electrometer circuit.   (Adapted from Beckman.)

An electrometer null detector and potentiometer circuit for measurement of pH is shown in Fig. 6-14. The resistance R_u of the glass-calomel cell is usually 10^8 to 10^9 ohms, and yet an electrometer circuit of this type can detect changes of 0.002 pH unit (60 mv/pH unit), or approximately $2 \times 10^{-3} \times 60 = 0.12$ mv. Of course, the zero stability is not good and must be frequently checked. A system with high input impedance can also be provided by the operational amplifier, as described in Chap. 8.

The chopper-type d-c amplifier is the type of null detector found in potentiometer recorders and other self-balancing potentiometers (described in detail in Chap. 7). Also they are becoming increasingly popular as null detectors for manual potentiometers. There are many chopper-type circuits, but the principle is the same in all cases—to modulate the d-c off-balance voltage ΔE_o to convert it to an a-c signal, which is subsequently carried through an a-c amplifier. Since the a-c amplifier does not produce an output voltage signal for slow drifts or changes in the power supply or circuit components, the zero stability is excellent. This, of course, is a definite advantage compared with the direct-coupled amplifier, wherein all drifts appear at the output along with the information signal.

One method of modulating the d-c voltage ΔE_o is the simple mechanical chopper (switch), an example of which is shown in Fig. 6-15a. The switch is electrically opened and closed by the alternating magnetic field produced at the rate of 60 cps by a-c line current through a coil. The voltage across terminals a–b will be zero when the switch is closed and should equal ΔE_o when the switch is open. Therefore a 60-cps "square wave" will be produced across the grid resistor R_g with a peak-to-peak voltage of ΔE_c. As shown in Fig. 6-15b, when the off-balance signal of the potentiometer is large, the magnitude of the square wave is large, and when near the null point, it is small. When the polarity of ΔE_o across a–b reverses, the phase of the square wave changes by 180°. The droop in the square wave is due to the finite charging and discharging time for the RC network. Circuits of the type shown in Fig. 6-15a can be designed to be capable of detecting 0.01 mv with input resistances of 10^6 ohms, or more. In other words, for a case where $R_u \approx 1$ megohm this detector would be equivalent to a galvanometer with a sensitivity of at least $10^{-5}/10^6 = 10^{-11}$ amp. Once again the detector is rugged, is insensitive to vibrations, and gives almost an immediate indication of the off-balance signal. Once again, however, great care must go into the design, parts layout, input connections, and shielding to prevent interference by electrical noise.

The circuit of Fig. 6-15a is not a particularly efficient one, because current is drawn for no useful purpose each time the switch is closed. A somewhat better arrangement is shown in Fig. 6-16a with the corresponding waveforms in Fig. 6-16b. Between the time when the movable contact c is

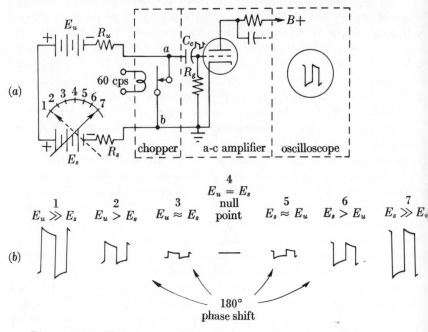

Figure 6-15   Chopper amplifier as a potentiometer null detector: (a) potentiometer input to chopper and oscilloscope readout; (b) waveforms on oscilloscope.

connected to either a or b, the input voltage is zero, on the assumption of no noise pickup during this interval.   This circuit is susceptible to the same limitations of noise interference as that of Fig. 6-15a.   Both are unsuitable where long input leads are used, unless the chopping frequency differs from the 60-cps line voltage which is so readily picked up as an interference.

In order to use the circuits of Figs. 6-15a and 6-16a, it was necessary to make one end of the input signal common with the input amplifier.   In some cases this is impossible, because the measured circuit must operate at a different d-c level from the detector.   This means that either the input is connected to a circuit which is not at ground potential or it is tied to some distant ground point which might not be at the same level as the amplifier ground.   In order to isolate the d-c input from the a-c output, a transformer can be used as shown in Fig. 6-17.   Many potentiometer recorders use the transformer input.   Some step-up of input signal can be accomplished by the transformer when vacuum-tube amplifiers are used.

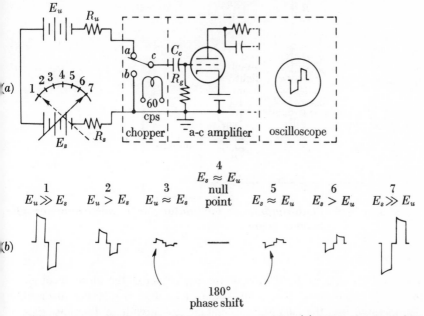

Figure 6-16   *Alternative chopper input circuit: (a) potentiometer in-*
put to chopper and oscilloscope readout; (b) waveforms
on oscilloscope.

There are other methods of modulating the d-c input voltage. Special
capacitors, transistors, and photoconductive detectors can be used, but at
present no modulator has such high inherent null stability as the mechanical
chopper. This might seem strange, considering the problems of vibrating

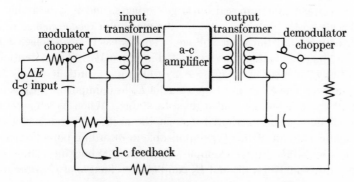

Figure 6-17   *Transformer-coupled chopper amplifier.*

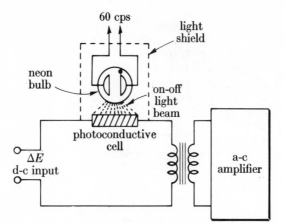

Figure 6-18   Photoconductive modulator for a potentiometer off-balance signal.

contacts, but it is an indication of the perfection of the mechanical choppers. A photoconductive circuit is shown in Fig. 6-18. The neon bulb is operated by the 60-cps line voltage to provide a fluctuating light beam which falls on a photoconductive cell. When the neon tube fires, the light pulse decreases the resistance of the detector cell, and when it deionizes, the cell is in darkness and the resistance increases. This causes a pulsating current in the transformer primary. The a-c voltage from the transformer secondary is fed to an a-c amplifier as with the other modulators.

The problems of noise in the modulator and the a-c amplifier are discussed in more detail in Chap. 7.

Measurement of Small Voltage Changes Superimposed on Large Voltages. In many situations it is necessary to observe small changes of voltage superimposed on large voltages, and it is desirable to have full scale on the potentiometer for the maximum *voltage change* to be observed, rather than the total voltage. This is easily accomplished by providing a "bucking voltage" as illustrated in Fig. 6-19a. The potentiometer is initially balanced with $E_S = 0$ by varying E_B until it equals the initial unknown value E_U. Since the value of E_U is unimportant, E_B is not a calibrated variable voltage, but it must be stable. When E_U changes by ΔE_U, the change can be measured against the accurate variable voltage E_S. A practical circuit of this type applicable in recording potentiometers is shown in Fig. 6-19b. In the example shown here the bucking voltage E_B can be varied from 0 to 1 volt, and E_S can balance changes of E_U from 0 to

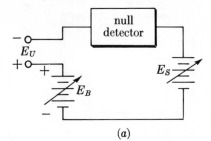

(a)

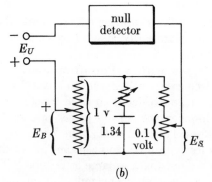

(b)

Figure 6-19   Measurement of small voltage superimposed on large voltages: (a) illustration of method; (b) schematic circuit for specific application.

0.1 volt. Therefore, if E_U is initially 0.90 volt and changes to 0.95 volt, the difference $\Delta E_U = 0.05$ volt would be equivalent to one-half the full scale of potentiometer E_S, rather than a 5 per cent change for a 1-volt scale.

A Constant-Resistance Potentiometer.   The potentiometers described above are all of the voltage-divider type. An alternative, which is known as the "Lindbeck element," is to vary the current I_V through a constant known resistance R_c, as illustrated in Fig. 6-20. The current is varied until the voltage $I_V R_c = E_U$. The current required is determined from the current meter. Obviously the accuracy of the current meter limits the accuracy of voltage measurement, since R_c can be very accurate.

Even though the accuracy is limited by the current meter, the circuit has advantages in measuring very low voltages, as with thermocouples.

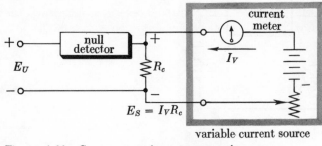

Figure 6-20   Constant-resistance potentiometer.

There are no sliding contacts present in the measuring circuit to introduce spurious thermal voltages. Also, ranges are easily changed by substituting different values of R_c into the circuit.

Measurement of High Voltages with a Potentiometer. The potentiometer is usually designed to measure voltages up to about 2 volts. For higher voltages an accurate voltage divider from fixed resistances is needed, as shown in Fig. 6-21. However, the current passes through the divider even when the potentiometer is balanced so that the "no-current" advantage of the potentiometer is lost. In order to keep the current at a minimum, it is necessary to make the resistance as large as possible. The value of R_1 is dependent on the type of potentiometer null detector and in

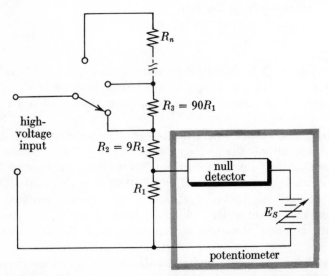

Figure 6-21   Measurement of high voltage with a potentiometer.

general can be quite large with an electronic detector. Therefore, the resistance in series with R_1 can be extremely large, depending on the potentiometer range and the value of the high voltage.

6-3 D-C Current Measurement by Comparison Method

In many laboratory instruments the transducer provides a current related to some phenomenon. This current can be accurately determined by measuring the voltage drop in a standard resistance. Therefore, the current comparison is by a voltage-comparison method. Small changes of current superimposed on large currents are measured in the same way, as illustrated in Fig. 6-19 for voltages.

6-4 Resistance Measurement by a Comparison Procedure

In Sec. 1-5 an ohmmeter is described for resistance measurements. Although this is usually sufficient for the testing of electrical circuits and components, there are many cases where the resistance must be more accurately known. Once again the procedure used for higher accuracy is a comparison procedure.

The Wheatstone Bridge. The Wheatstone bridge shown in Fig. 6-22 provides the most direct and best-known circuit for comparison of unknown R_U against standard resistances.

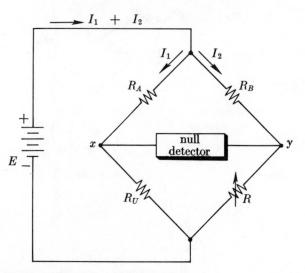

Figure 6-22 Wheatstone bridge.

When the circuit is at balance, there is no current through the detector, indicating no potential difference between terminals x and y, and four significant conditions exist:

1. The current through R_A and R_U is I_1.
2. The current through R_B and R is I_2.
3. $I_1 R_U = I_2 R$.
4. $I_1 R_A = I_2 R_B$.

Therefore, $R_U/R = R_A/R_B$, and

$$R_U = R \frac{R_A}{R_B} \tag{6-2}$$

It can be seen from Eq. (6-2) that the unknown resistance R_U is determined on the basis of three standard resistances: R, R_A, and R_B. It is common practice to make the ratio R_A/R_B some exact fraction or multiple such as 0.01, 0.1, 1, 10, 100, etc., and to refer to it as the "multiplier." Resistance R is made variable in small increments or continuously, so that the dial reading for $R \times$ multiplier equals the unknown resistance R_U.

The main source of error in a Wheatstone bridge is the inaccuracies of

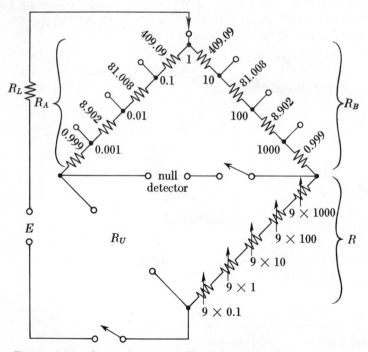

Figure 6-23   General-purpose Wheatstone bridge.

the three standard resistances R, R_A, and R_B. However, these can be made with errors of only about 0.01 per cent. Other factors limiting the accuracy are errors in establishing the null point, thermal emfs, and changes in resistance values due to heating (too high currents). It is important to keep the I^2R loss in the resistors at a safe value, because excessive heating may cause a permanent shift in resistance values. Always stay within the maximum values specified by the manufacturer.

A schematic of a typical general-purpose Wheatstone bridge is shown in Fig. 6-23. The multiplier R_A/R_B varies from 0.001 to 1000 in seven ranges. The total resistance $R_A + R_B = 1000$ ohms. The resistance R is a decade box varying in steps of 0.1 ohm up to a total resistance of 9999.9 ohms.

If a galvanometer is the null detector, the voltage V required across a Wheatstone bridge is given by Eq. (6-3).

$$V = \frac{iR_T}{p}\left(1 + \frac{R_{GC}}{R_{BG}}\right) \tag{6-3}$$

where i is the necessary galvanometer current in amperes to produce a detectable deflection (0.2 mm); R_T is the sum of resistances in the arms $R_U + R + R_A + R_B$; p is the required precision expressed as a fraction (i.e., for 0.1 per cent precision, $p = 0.001$); R_{GC} is resistance of the galvanometer coil; and R_{BG} is resistance of the bridge as seen by the galvanometer.

Use of A-C Supply Voltage for a Wheatstone Bridge. An a-c generator is often used instead of a battery to supply the voltage to the Wheatstone bridge. If resistances in the bridge arms are true resistances, i.e., if there are no reactive components in the standard or unknown resistances, the conditions of bridge balance will be exactly the same as discussed above. There are two advantages in using an a-c supply for the Wheatstone bridge. One is that any d-c voltage source present in the bridge arms will have no effect on the accuracy of the resistance determination. This is because it is the a-c voltage across the bridge which is brought to null, not the d-c. Within the bridge itself, thermal potentials are developed at junctions of dissimilar metals. The component or system whose resistance is being measured often has a d-c component. The conductance cell for measuring solution resistance is the most common example where accurate measurements are made. The error introduced into a d-c measurement of cell resistance by the counter emf of the cell can easily be 100 per cent. The thermocouple effect, though very much smaller, is not insignificant. Assume that the source for a Wheatstone bridge is a 6-volt battery and that the potential across the unknown at balance is 3 volts. If there is a 10-mv thermocouple in the unknown connections, the error would be $(0.01/3)$ $100 = 0.3$ per cent. This accuracy is at least an order of magnitude worse than might be expected on the basis of the accuracy of the standards and the sensitivity of the null detector. The other advantage is that it is simpler to make a very sensitive a-c null detector than a d-c null detector of comparable sensitivity. A simple transistor a-c amplifier and a pair of earphones can equal the sensitivity of an expensive galvanometer. A more sensitive a-c amplifier can be made more easily than a d-c amplifier because there is not the annoying problem of "zero drift" to be overcome (Sec. 4-3).

The difficulty with the a-c-powered Wheatstone bridge is the requirement that none of the bridge arms be very reactive. This requirement confines the frequency of the alternating current to the audio-frequency region. If there is reactance in one of the bridge arms, e.g., in the unknown element, it can be shown that there is no adjustment of the standard resistances which will yield a true null across the bridge. This is because the reactance in the unknown causes a phase shift with respect to the standard side of the bridge which cannot be balanced out by the adjustment of pure resistances. A minimum will be observed rather than a null, but the minimum does not occur at the same setting of the standard that the purely resistive unknown would give. To find the true value of the resistance in a resistive-reactive component, it is necessary to balance the reactive part of the impedance as well as the resistive. This is the subject of the next section.

6-5 Impedance Measurement by Comparison Procedures

The comparison of impedances is accomplished in much the same way as the comparison of resistances, i.e., with a bridge. A bridge for the measurement of impedance is shown in Fig. 6-24. If R_A is equal to R_B, then at balance the impedance Z_s of R_s and C_s must equal the unknown impedance. There are any number of combinations of values of R_s and C_s which would yield an impedance equal numerically to the unknown impedance Z_u, but there is only one combination which will yield the same impedance *and* phase angle as the unknown. To demonstrate that phase balance is necessary for a null, consider the left arms (a, d, c) as an a-c voltage divider for the source voltage. The right arms (a, b, c) also form a divider for the same source. When the impedance Z_s is equal numerically to the impedance Z_u, the magnitudes of the voltages across Z_u and Z_s will be identical. However, these two voltages may be out of phase. The detector sees the potential difference between points d and b. Figure 6-25 shows that a potential difference exists between two equal a-c voltages of different phase. Only when the amplitude *and* the phase of two a-c signals are equal will their voltage difference be zero at all times.

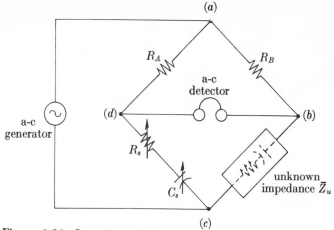

Figure 6-24   Impedance bridge.

It is possible to derive the conditions of balance for the impedance bridge just as was done for the Wheatstone bridge. To make the derivation completely general, the possibility of having a complex impedance in all four arms has been considered, as in Fig. 6-26. At balance, the detector current is zero, and $\bar{I}_1$ and $\bar{I}_2$ flow in the impedances as shown. The bar above the symbols I and Z indicates that the vector quantity is meant, which may be expressed in terms of complex notation (Supplement 3). The two equations resulting from the fact that there is no potential across the detector are

$$\bar{I}_1\bar{Z}_A = \bar{I}_2\bar{Z}_B$$
$$\bar{I}_1\bar{Z}_s = \bar{I}_2\bar{Z}_u$$

From the above

$$\frac{\bar{Z}_A}{\bar{Z}_B} = \frac{\bar{Z}_s}{\bar{Z}_u} = \frac{\bar{I}_2}{\bar{I}_1}$$

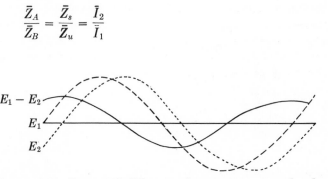

Figure 6-25   Potential difference between two equal voltages of different phase.

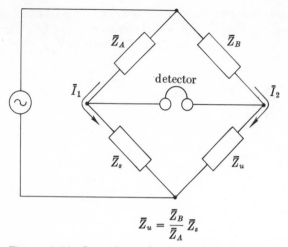

$$\bar{Z}_u = \frac{\bar{Z}_B}{\bar{Z}_A} \bar{Z}_s$$

Figure 6-26   Impedance bridge at balance.

Solving for $\bar{Z}_u$,

$$\bar{Z}_u = \frac{\bar{Z}_B}{\bar{Z}_A} \bar{Z}_s \tag{6-4a}$$

If this equation is applied to the bridge of Fig. 6-24, the following solution for $\bar{Z}_u$ results:

$$\bar{Z}_u = \frac{R_B}{R_A} \left(R_s - \frac{j}{\omega C_s} \right) \tag{6-4b}$$

Equations which contain complex quantities may be separated into two separate and independent equations. One equation will contain all the real terms, and the other equation will contain all the imaginary terms. The complex impedance has both real and imaginary components. The real component is resistive; the imaginary component is reactive. $\bar{Z}_u$ may be separated into its resistive and reactive parts according to Eq. (6-4b). The resistive component of $\bar{Z}_u$ is $R = (R_B/R_A)R_s$, and the reactive component is $X = -(R_B/R_A)(1/\omega C_s)$. The impedance Z_u is thus

$$\frac{R_B}{R_A} \sqrt{R_s^2 + \left(\frac{1}{\omega C_s} \right)^2}$$

and the phase angle

$$\phi = \cos^{-1} \frac{R_s}{\sqrt{R_s^2 + \left(\frac{1}{\omega C_s} \right)^2}}$$

If it is known that the unknown impedance is a series combination of a resistance R_u and a capacitance C_u, the actual values of R_u and C_u can be determined. Substitute $R_u - j/\omega C_s$ for $\bar{Z}_u$ in Eq. (6-4b).

$$R_u - \frac{j}{\omega C_u} = \frac{R_B}{R_A}\left(R_s - \frac{j}{\omega C_s}\right)$$

Separating the above equation into its "real" and "imaginary" parts,

$$R_u = \frac{R_B}{R_A} R_s \tag{6-5}$$

$$C_u = \frac{R_A}{R_B} C_s \tag{6-6}$$

This bridge is called the series-capacitance bridge, and Eqs. (6-5) and (6-6) above are its conditions of balance. Notice that the ratio R_A/R_B comes in as a multiplier, as in the Wheatstone bridge. Notice also that the conditions of balance do not contain a frequency term. Theoretically, then, this type of bridge could be operated from a generator of any waveform, or even from pulses or switching transients.

Suppose that the unknown impedance $\bar{Z}_u$ is composed of a parallel combination of resistance R_u and capacitance C_u. The admittance $\bar{Y}_u$ of the parallel combination is

$$\bar{Y}_u = \frac{1}{\bar{Z}_u} = \frac{1}{R_u} + j\omega C_u \tag{6-7}$$

Equation (6-3) may be rewritten as

$$\bar{Y}_u \bar{Z}_s = \frac{\bar{Z}_A}{\bar{Z}_B} \tag{6-8}$$

because it is easier to work with admittances in a parallel circuit. Substituting of Eq. (6-7) and the values of the arms in Fig. 6-24,

$$\left(\frac{1}{R_u} + j\omega C_u\right)\left(R_s - \frac{j}{\omega C_s}\right) = \frac{R_A}{R_B} \tag{6-9}$$

Expansion of this equation yields

$$\frac{R_s}{R_u} + j\omega C_u R_s - \frac{j}{\omega C_s R_u} + \frac{C_u}{C_s} = \frac{R_A}{R_B}$$

Separating the equation into the real and imaginary terms yields the following equations of balance:

$$\frac{R_s}{R_u} + \frac{C_u}{C_s} = \frac{R_A}{R_B} \tag{6-10}$$

$$\omega^2 C_u C_s R_s R_u = 1 \tag{6-11}$$

When the above equations are solved for C_u and R_u in terms of the known values,

$$C_u = \frac{R_A}{R_B} \frac{C_s}{(R_s{}^2 C_s{}^2 \omega^2 + 1)} \tag{6-12}$$

$$R_u = \frac{R_B}{R_A} \frac{(\omega^2 C_s{}^2 R_s{}^2 + 1)}{\omega^2 C_s{}^2 R_s{}^2} \tag{6-13}$$

Equation (6-11) shows the bridge balance to depend on the frequency, and Eqs. (6-12) and (6-13) confirm this. A bridge with a series combination in one arm and a parallel combination in an adjacent arm is called a Wein bridge. This sort of bridge is useful for measuring resistance and capacitance in terms of standard components and frequency, or it can be used to measure frequency. When a frequency term enters the calculations, as above, it is necessary to have a very stable and accurate oscillator (Sec. 5-5).

There are many other types of bridges which are used for various measurements. Some of these are shown in Fig. 6-27. The choice of bridge arrangement will depend on the approximate value of the components to be measured, the availability of accurate standards, and the necessity of an accurate oscillator. The analysis of each of the bridge types begins with Eq. (6-4) and follows the pattern of the two illustrations exactly.

Because of their frequency and phase sensitivity, certain bridges have been used in the feedback loops of feedback oscillators (Sec. 5-2). By far the most common of these is the Wein bridge (Fig. 6-27). A block diagram showing the Wein bridge in an oscillator feedback loop is shown in Fig. 6-28a. The amplifier is normally a two-stage amplifier with 360° (or 0°) phase shift. In order to have regenerative feedback, there should be no phase shift in the feedback network. The phase angle of the series RC network decreases with increasing frequency, while that of the parallel RC network increases. At the frequency for which the series and parallel impedances are equal, the phase angle will be unchanged in the feedback loop. This condition would exist at the bridge balance point. If the ratio

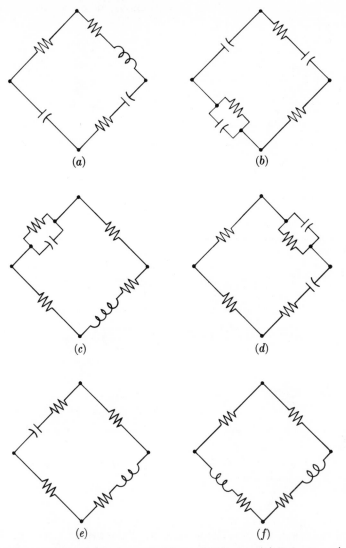

Figure 6-27 Impedance bridges: (a) Owen; (b) Schering; (c) Maxwell;
(d) Wein; (e) Hay; (f) inductance.

R_A/R_B does not satisfy equations of bridge balance [Eq. (6-10)], this cannot affect the feedback voltage phase, since R_A and R_B are pure resistive elements. In fact the oscillator would not operate if the bridge were really balanced, for then the amplifier input would be zero. In practice, R_B is set too small for the true balance conditions. The magnitude of the ampli-

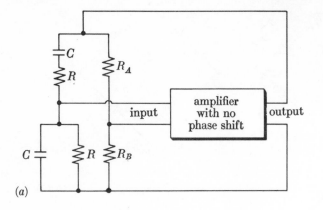

(a)

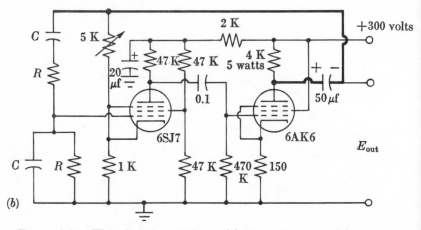

(b)

Figure 6-28 *Wein bridge oscillator: (a) block diagram; (b) schematic of a specific circuit.*

fier input voltage then depends on the fraction of the bridge voltage across the parallel impedance. This voltage is a maximum when the series and parallel impedances are equal. When the frequency increases, the parallel impedance decreases; when the frequency decreases, the series impedance increases. The ratio R_A/R_B is then adjusted so that the circuit just oscillates. This creates a very stable low-distortion oscillator because any frequency other than the balance frequency is not only attenuated in the feedback loop but is also of the wrong phase to sustain oscillation.

The Wein bridge oscillator is usually constructed with the bridge resistors and capacitors equal in value as shown. Under these circumstances the balance equation involving frequency [Eq. (6-11)] is solved for the frequency of oscillation.

$$\omega^2 = \frac{1}{R^2 C^2}$$

$$f_0 = \frac{1}{2\pi RC} \tag{6-14}$$

6-6 Frequency Measurements by the Comparison Procedure

The basic requirements for determining frequency by the comparison procedure are the same as outlined at the beginning of this chapter: (1) a known standard, (2) a system for varying the standard, and (3) a null-point detector.

In Chap. 1, the frequency of a sine wave was determined by comparing the unknown frequency against the frequency of a variable sine-wave generator. The oscilloscope was used as the detector, and the ratio of unknown to known frequencies was indicated by Lissajous figures. Another comparison procedure utilizes a mixer tube that gives an output signal whose frequency is the difference between known and unknown. The difference frequency is often called the "beat frequency," and when it is zero, the known and unknown frequencies are equal. Various a-c detectors (earphones, oscilloscope, etc.) can be used to indicate the beat frequency. The term "heterodyne" is used to identify the process, devices, and methods of mixing two frequencies to obtain the beat.

The accuracy of all comparison procedures depends, of course, on the reliability of the standard. In the United States it is possible to receive the frequency standards that are transmitted regularly from the National Bureau of Standards radio station, WWV. The carrier frequencies of WWV are 2.5, 5, 10, 15, 20, and 25 Mc, and these are accurate within 1 part in 10^9 at the transmitter and better than 1 part in 10^8 at the receiver (after Doppler frequency shift). Standard audio frequencies of 600 and 440 cps and various time pulses are also transmitted on the carriers. The 600-cps signal was chosen because of the large number of useful harmonics and subharmonics, and it is convenient for checking the 60-cps power frequency. The 440-cps signal was chosen because it is the standard musical pitch. These audio frequencies are also stable within 1 part in 10^8. The availability of such reliable standards makes it possible to calibrate secondary standards and the variable oscillators that are ordinarily used for direct comparison with the unknown frequencies.

References

Stout, M. B., "Basic Electrical Measurements," 2d ed., Prentice-Hall, Englewood
Cliffs, N.J., 1960. Detailed descriptions of various types of potentiometers
and bridges and their components. Many references and problems.

"Precision Measurement and Calibration, Electricity and Electronics," National
Bureau of Standards Handbook 77, Vol. I. A collection of basic papers from
the bureau concerning precision measurements. Much useful information on
precision bridges, potentiometers, components, etc.; good bibliography of basic
papers.

Problems

6-1 In the Kelvin-Varley potentiometer, shown in Fig. P6-1, the switch contacts move in pairs so that two series resistors in one branch are always in parallel

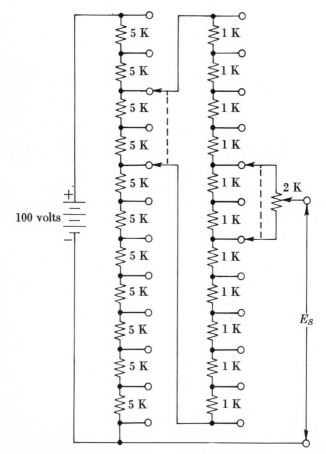

Figure P6-1

with the effective resistance of the next branch; by selection of suitable resistance values, each parallel resistor combination has an effective resistance equal to one of the 11 resistors; therefore, the resistance combination in each branch is equivalent to 10 equal resistors in series, and one-tenth of the voltage across each branch appears at the switch contacts. (a) Determine the range of voltages E_S at the output terminals when the switch contacts are as shown in the diagram and the slider of R_p is varied from one end to the other. Assume that the resolution and accuracy of R_p are 1 per cent. (b) Show where the switch contacts would be to obtain a standard output voltage of 12.50 volts. (c) What factors determine the accuracy of the variable standard voltage E_S? (d) What is indicated if the potentiometer accuracy is stated as "0.1 per cent or ±0.01 volt, whichever is greater"?

Ans.: (a) E_S = 75.00 to 76.00 volts

6-2 A potentiometer is made from a 1-kilohm center-tapped Helipot and a 1.35-volt mercury cell, as shown in Fig. P6-2. Determine the value of the series resistor R_S so that the standard voltage E_S, available at the output terminals, will vary from +0.5 to −0.5 volt. *Ans.:* R_S = 350 ohms

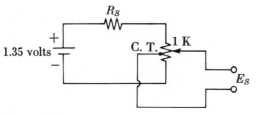

Figure P6-2

6-3 Describe in general terms the factors that determine the precision of a comparison measurement. What factors determine the accuracy?

6-4 For the potentiometer in Fig. 6-7, what value of R_S should be substituted if the span is to be calibrated for 500 mv full scale? *Ans.:* R_S = 20.36 ohms

6-5 For the potentiometer in Fig. 6-9, the current $I = 10$ ma, each of the fixed resistors is 10 ohms, and the slidewire is 11 ohms. What is the output voltage E_{out} for the case illustrated in the figure? *Ans.:* E_{out} = 0.525 volts

6-6 The variable standard voltage E_S for the pH electrometer of Fig. 6-14 is to read from 0 to 14 pH units. At 30° the emf of the cell changes 60 mv/pH unit. Design a specific potentiometer circuit with practical voltage and resistance values to provide the required E_S. Include specific circuitry to compensate for temperature changes from 20° to 40°. (Temperature dependence of cell potential ≈ 0.2 mv/°C per pH unit.)

6-7 Determine specific resistance values for the circuit of Fig. 6-19b, so that the bucking voltage $E_B = 1$ volt, the span of the variable standard voltage $E_S = 0.1$ volt, and the total current drawn from the mercury cell does not exceed 2 ma.

6-8 If the span of $E_S = 10$ mv, determine the value of resistors R_n and R_1 in Fig. 6-21 so that voltages up to 10 volts can be measured with the restriction that the maximum current drawn from the source cannot exceed 1 μa.

Ans.: R_1 = 10 kilohms; R_n = 9.99 megohms (≈ 10 megohms)

6-9   The Wheatstone bridge of Fig. 6-22 is balanced with R_A = 909.09 ohms, R_B = 90.909 ohms, and R = 628 ohms.   What is the unknown resistance R_U?

Ans.: R_U = 6.28 kilohms

6-10   What advantage is to be gained by "heterodyning" when comparing the frequency of two relatively high-frequency sources?

EXPERIMENTS

A potentiometer is made by using the voltage-reference source (VRS) as a variable standard voltage, and it is tested in combination with several null-point detectors.   Reproducibility and stability of the VRS are checked and compared with the accuracy.   The sensitivities of the d-c oscilloscope, chopper scope, and chopper-amplifier scope as null detectors are determined.   A Wheatstone bridge is constructed and used to measure the values of several resistors.

Expt. 6-1   Use of Several Null Detectors in Determining Reproducibility and Stability of Voltage-Reference Source

One of the functions of the VRS is as a Zener-stabilized variable standard voltage in a potentiometer circuit.   If $\frac{1}{2}$ or 1 per cent resistors are used in the divider network, the resistors limit the accuracy.   Information about VRS reproducibility is obtained by measuring the voltage of a mercury cell.   The VRS (after 10-min warmup) is turned to SUM-DIFF position, the POLARITY switched to DIFF, the mercury cell connected to the VRS SIGNAL input, and the VRS OUTPUT terminals connected to the oscilloscope VERT input, as shown in Fig. 6-29.

Turn the oscilloscope to the DC × 1 position, with the gain all the way up, and adjust the voltage from the VRS until the vertical deflection of the beam (line or spot) is zero, as determined by alternately depressing and releasing the ZERO button on the VRS.   Determine the maximum sensitivity of the d-c scope as a null detector, and determine the precision of measuring an unknown voltage with this

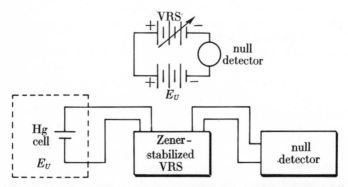

Figure 6-29   Potentiometer circuit with VRS as a variable standard voltage.

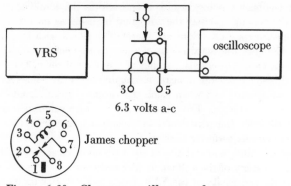

Figure 6-30   Chopper-oscilloscope detector.

detector.   Record the value of the measured voltage for the mercury cell.   Note any drift of the null point.   Leave the mercury cell connected for subsequent experiments.

Chopper-Scope Detector.   Introduce a mechanical chopper across the leads to the oscilloscope, as shown in Fig. 6-30, so that the scope input alternately sees the difference voltage and a shorted input.   To obtain a small external 60-cps synchronizing signal, connect one end of a 2-ft lead to the EXT SYNC binding post on the oscilloscope.   Leave the other end of the lead unconnected.   Switch the selector to EXT SYNC position.   Vary the FINE control about the null point and observe the square wave on the scope.   Note that the phase of the square wave shifts by 180° in passing from one side of the null point to the other.   Establish the null point and determine the reproducibility of measuring the unknown voltage with this detector.   Record the measured voltage for the mercury cell and compare with the previous value.   Observe that the scope can be used on either a-c or d-c with the chopper input, so that zero drift is not a problem.   Switch the oscilloscope to INT SYNC and note that the polarity of the error signal cannot be observed.

Chopper-Amplifier-Scope Detector.   Introduce the power amplifier (constructed in Expt. 4-3) between the chopper and oscilloscope as shown in Fig.

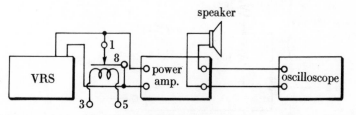

Figure 6-31   Chopper-amplifier-scope detector.   The power amplifier has a 1-kilohm feedback resistor.

6-31. Use a 1-kilohm feedback resistor (negative feedback) in the amplifier circuit and turn the gain all the way up. Detect the null point by listening for the null in the 60-cps output from the speaker. Compare the audible signal with the visual signal on the scope. Compare the sensitivities of these two detectors (audio and visual) with the previous two. Observe the output at the plate of the 6BQ5 power tube (pin 7), and use this signal for null indication. Again record the values for the measured voltage of the mercury cell when using the various output signals from the chopper-amplifier-scope detector. From the recorded voltage values determine the stability of the VRS over the period of this experiment, assuming that the voltage of the mercury cell was perfectly constant.

Compare the reproducibility and stability of the VRS with the accuracy of the VRS as limited by the accuracy of the voltage divider resistors.

Measure or predict the sensitivity of the VTVM as a null detector on its most sensitive scale.

Expt. 6-2   The -5 Position of the VRS

The VRS -5 position on the COARSE control switches the COM output lead to the high end of the last 400-ohm resistor in the divider, as shown in Fig. 6-32. Therefore, the voltage across the OUTPUT terminals is zero when the slider is in the center of the FINE potentiometer, and varies continuously from minus to plus values as the FINE control is adjusted. The output voltage varies continuously from -5 to $+5$ mv on the $\times 1$ RANGE position, -50 to $+50$ mv on the $\times 10$ position, -0.5 to $+0.5$ volt and -5 to $+5$ volts on the $\times 100$ and $\times 1000$ positions, respectively. The -5 position can be used on either the STD VOLT

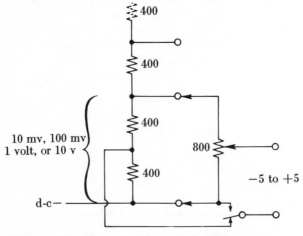

Figure 6-32   The -5 position of the VRS.

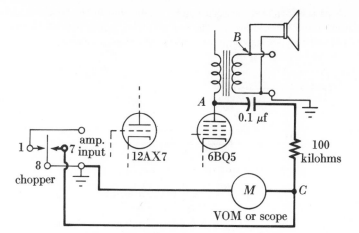

Figure 6-33   Demodulated output from a chopper amplifier as a null-detector signal.

or SUM-DIFF function positions, but if in the SUM-DIFF position the SIGNAL *terminals must be either shorted or connected to a signal source to complete the circuit.*

Determine the relative reproducibility of detecting the null point on the various -5 position with any one of the detectors used in Expt. 6-1. Now introduce the chopper-amplifier-demodulated-voltmeter detector, shown in Fig. 6-33. This is quite similar to the detector illustrated in Fig. 6-31, except that the output from the plate of the 6BQ5 power amplifier is demodulated by using the extra chopper contact. Observe the outputs with the scope connected to points *A*, *B*, and *C*. The pulsating d-c voltage is observed on the most sensitive d-c voltage scale of the VOM, as indicated in Fig. 6-33. Note that the demodulator allows a sensitive d-c meter to be used with the chopper and a-c amplifier. *Disconnect* the VOM and connect the scope between point *C* and ground for subsequent measurements. Observe the waveshape of the off-balance signal. Determine what the null signal should look like by pressing the ZERO button. Compare the VOM signal, the audible speaker signal, and the scope signals at the outputs of the amplifier for sensitivity of detecting the null points on the -5 position. Keep the scope connected at point *C* for the next experiment.

Expt. 6-3   Wheatstone Bridge

Construct the Wheatstone bridge shown in Fig. 6-34, and measure the resistances of several resistors in the substitution box from about 100 ohms to 10 kilohms. Use the VRS for the bridge supply voltage; 1-kilohm precision resistors for R_A and R_B; the decade resistance box for R; and the detector of Fig. 6-33, with the scope as the indicator between point C and ground. Determine the precision of measuring the resistances, and observe what factors would have to be changed to increase the precision and accuracy of the measurements.

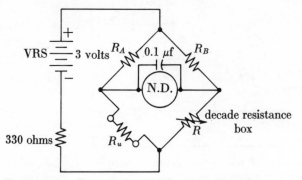

Figure 6-34   Experimental Wheatstone bridge.

chapter seven

Servo Systems

7-1 General Description of Servomechanisms

The word "servo" (often used as an abbreviation for servomechanism) comes from the Latin word *servus*, meaning a slave. A servo, then, could be considered as a slave that submits to a command to carry out a specific request. As a good and reliable slave the servo can compare the result of its effort with the order and make corrections to fulfill the command. The servomechanism is often described as a system that provides power amplification while responding to a command and whose action is continuously determined and controlled by the difference between actual and desired states of the object. Therefore, the servo is part of the "feedback control" family, because it operates on the difference (error) between the actual state and a desired state (which may be a continuously variable function). All devices—electrical, electronic, chemical, mechanical, pneumatic, hydraulic—that enable a specific command to be performed via feedback information can be considered part of a "servo system" or "servomechanism." Note that the servo system is an automatic comparison system wherein the desired position or command movement of an object is compared with the actual position or movement, and action is automatically taken to correct any difference.

Servomechanisms are highly specialized man-made slaves, each designed to perform a specific task. Some are giants capable of keeping huge rockets or ships on commanded courses. Some are midgets that move

291

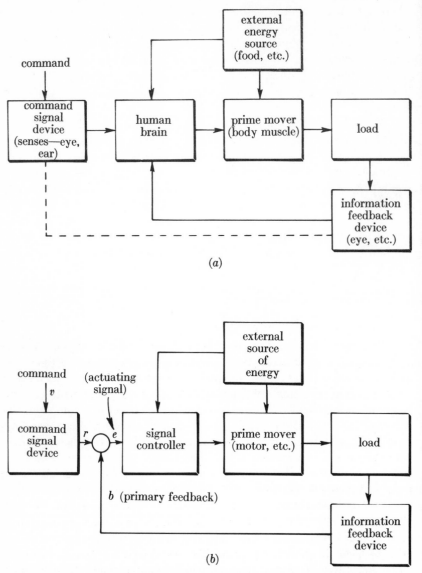

Figure 7-1　Servo block diagram: (a) action of human servo on a load; (b) action of man-made servo on a load.

various loads (such as rods, dials, pens) in small instruments. The "position servo" moves an object to the desired location. The "velocity servo" moves a load at the speed that is commanded. Complete automation becomes a possibility through their use. They not only do many jobs faster and more accurately than man but also do jobs that are humanly impossible. They are at the heart of what has been called a "new industrial revolution," wherein all of men's jobs are performed by servo equipment in automatic factories.

An understanding of the basic components in a servo system can be gained by considering how a human being operates in response to an order to position an object. As shown by the block diagram (Fig. 7-1*a*), the command is picked up by the eye, ear, or touch, and a signal is transmitted to the human brain, which controls the body muscles that exert a force on the load to move it toward the desired location. The eye or other sense acts as an information-feedback device that describes the actual position. The mind compares the command and feedback information and controls the body so as to change the load position in accordance with the error signal—i.e., the difference between desired and actual positions of the object. The man-made servo operates in a similar way, as shown in Fig. 7-1*b*. The command v is picked up by a device that puts it in the form of an acceptable command signal r, and the information on the actual position of the load is put in the form of a feedback signal b. These are usually voltage signals that can be compared to give a difference voltage e that is fed to an electronic signal controller. The controller uses the error signal e to regulate the electrical power to the motor (or other positioner), and the motor operates to move the load to the desired position. When the load is at the desired position, the error (actuating) signal e is essentially zero. Note that the terms "error signal" and "actuating signal" have the same meaning here and are used interchangeably.

7-2 The Automatic Recording Potentiometer—A Simple Servomechanism

The automatic recording potentiometer has become an indispensable instrument in research and development laboratories and in process control. It is a good example of a low-power servo system. Its importance and relative simplicity (as servos go) make it an excellent first example for consideration. As shown in Fig. 7-2, it is the purpose of the recording potentiometer to move a pen (the load) across a chart paper according to some function of the input voltage E_U (the command signal).

Information on the position of the pen is put in the form of a variable standard voltage E_S by coupling a potentiometer circuit to the pen-drive mechanism. The signal controller continuously compares the feedback

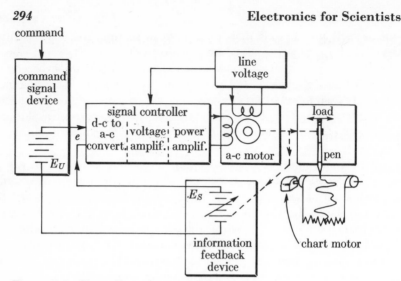

Figure 7-2   Recording servo potentiometer.

information E_S with the command signal E_U and provides the electrical signals that control the motor. The motor turns to move the pen and simultaneously varies E_S so that $E_U - E_S = e = 0$. The circuit must operate so that the pen moves in one direction when $E_U > E_S$ and in the opposite direction when $E_U < E_S$. Since the load is small, a low-power a-c motor is an inexpensive positioner for the pen.

It is apparent that Fig. 7-2 contains the same basic blocks as presented in Fig. 7-1. The chart-drive mechanism is not a part of the pen servomechanism. The chart of most potentiometer recorders is driven by a constant-speed motor to provide a time axis. Therefore, E_U, or some function of E_U, is plotted against time. Recorders of this type are sometimes called *T-Y* recorders. Another servomechanism could be used to move the chart according to another command E_U'. In this case E_U is plotted as a function of E_U', and it is customary to refer to such recorders as *X-Y* recorders.

In the next few sections the servomotor, signal controller, and command and feedback devices of the servo potentiometer are considered in detail. In later sections high-power and more complex servo systems will be briefly considered. The servomotor is considered first, rather than components at the signal input, because this is the way in which parts would often be chosen in practice. It is necessary to select a prime mover that is capable of moving the load rapidly and accurately in response to the command and that also is readily available and reasonable in cost. The prime mover having been chosen, it is necessary to choose a signal controller to match it, so as to accept the input and feedback information and provide the required operational control.

7-3   The Instrument Servomotor

The type of servomotor nearly always used to drive the light loads found in instruments, such as a recorder pen or a spectrophotometer slit, is the a-c two-phase induction motor.   This motor contains two separate stator windings physically perpendicular to each other, as illustrated in Fig. 7-3*a*.   The schematic representation is given in Fig. 7-3*b*.   The rotation of the rotor is a result of a rotating magnetic field produced from out-of-phase alternating currents in the two stator windings.   The rotating magnetic field induces a voltage in the rotor, and the resulting current in the armature produces an interacting field, which forces the rotor to turn clockwise or counterclockwise, in the same direction as the rotating magnetic field.

To produce the rotating magnetic field, it is necessary that the a-c voltage applied to one stator winding be 90° out of phase with the voltage applied to the other winding.   As shown in Fig. 7-4, when the alternating current in coil A leads that in coil B by 90°, the magnetic field rotates counterclockwise.   This is indicated by the top row of circles.   At time t_0, the current is a maximum in A and zero in B, and the direction of the magnetic field is shown by the small arrow in the first circle.   At time t_1, the currents in A and B are equal, and the magnetic field has rotated 45° counterclockwise during the time $t_1 - t_0$.   At time t_2, the current is a maximum in B and is zero in A, so that the magnetic field has rotated 90°

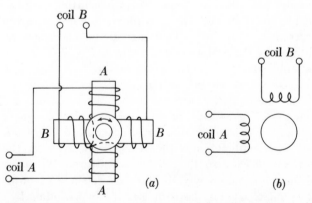

Figure 7-3   The a-c servomotor: (a) coil windings; (b) schematic of two-phase induction motor.

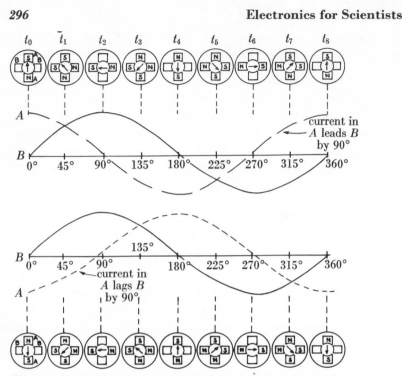

Figure 7-4   Rotating magnetic field in two-phase induction motor.

counterclockwise during the time $t_2 - t_0$. The magnetic field continues to rotate counterclockwise as long as the current in stator winding A leads B by 90°. As soon as the voltage is removed from coil A, the rotating magnetic field is eliminated and the rotor stops. Now, by shifting the phase of the voltage applied to coil A by 180° from the previous case, the current in coil A lags the current in B by 90°. The magnetic field will now rotate clockwise, as indicated by the bottom row of circles in Fig. 7-4.

For the usual applications of the two-phase motor, the voltage applied to one coil winding is fixed at the line voltage, and the other (the control winding) is fed from the controller power amplifier, as shown in Fig. 7-5. It is necessary that the 90° phase shift be provided either in the signal controller which supplies the control winding or in a phase-shift network for the line winding or by a combination of the two. Obviously, when the a-c input to the power amplifier is zero, the rotor does not turn. When a small voltage is applied the rotor turns slowly, the direction depending on whether the current in the control winding leads or lags the line winding by 90°. As the voltage on the control winding increases, the speed increases, the

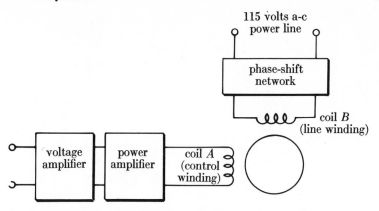

Figure 7-5   Sources for applied voltages to coils A and B.

maximum speed depending on the applied torque, as shown by typical curves in Fig. 7-6.   For this example, the a-c voltage on the line winding is maintained at 115 volts, and the voltage on the control winding is varied from 70 to 115 volts.   If a very sensitive low-noise voltage amplifier precedes the power amplifier, it is possible to observe the motor speed change

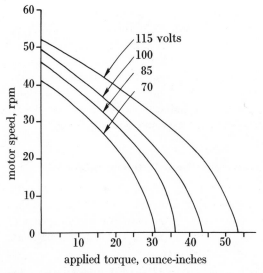

Figure 7-6   Motor speed versus applied torque for various control-winding voltages.

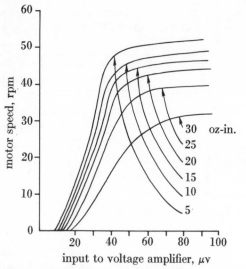

*Figure 7-7   Motor speed versus input to voltage amplifier for various
constant torques.*

as a function of microvolts input, as in Fig. 7-7. The minimum input voltage at which the motor starts turning and the maximum speed are a function of the applied torque.

A d-c motor could also be used as the prime mover. A d-c amplifier
would be required to drive such a unit. The problem of stability in a d-c
amplifier with low-level inputs is a great limitation on the sensitivity of
such a servo.   Another disadvantage is that the amplifier output stage has
to supply all the power for the motor instead of just for a control winding as
in the a-c two-phase induction motor. A potential advantage of the d-c system is a faster response speed, since the amplifier response speed would not
be limited by the necessary control frequency (usually 60 cps).

7-4   The Signal Controller for Servo Potentiometers

The signal controller for the servo potentiometer can be considered as
consisting of three units: the power amplifier, the voltage amplifier, and
the d-c to a-c converter. Although certain characteristics for each of these
components have been discussed in Chaps. 3, 4, and 6, respectively, some
further considerations are presented here.

The Power Amplifier. Various vacuum-tube and transistor-amplifier
circuits have been used to supply the alternating current for the control
winding of the servomotor. One type (used on the Brown balance system)

is shown in Fig. 7-8, where the plates of two vacuum tubes are connected to opposite ends of the secondary on a power transformer. As indicated, the plate voltage on V_1 is positive when it is negative on V_2, and vice versa. Assuming that a 60-cps input voltage e_{in} is applied to V_1, the tube will conduct if the grid and plate voltages are in phase, but only during the half-cycle when both swing positive. The grid of V_2 is tied to that of V_1, but the plate voltages are 180° out of phase. Therefore, if e_{in} is in phase with the plate voltage on V_1, it is 180° out of phase with the plate voltage on V_2 and V_2 cannot conduct on either half cycle. If e_{in} shifts by 180°, then V_2 conducts during one half cycle and V_1 does not conduct on either half cycle. The current pulses in either V_1 or V_2 cause a 60-cps a-c component (superimposed on a d-c component) in the control winding of the servomotor. The current waveshape in coil A is nearly sinusoidal because of the capacitor C_1 and the inductance of the motor winding, which form a 60-cps resonant circuit. The current in the control winding A either leads or lags the current in the line winding B, depending on whether V_1 or V_2 is conducting. The phase relationships in both cases are illustrated by the curves in Fig. 7-9. Note that the current in the motor control winding lags the plate-current pulses by 90°.

Another vacuum-tube power-amplifier circuit is presented in Experiment 7-1. A transistor-servo output stage is shown in Fig. 7-10. It is identical to a conventional Class B amplifier, except that the collector power

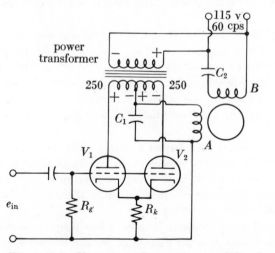

Figure 7-8   Vacuum-tube power amplifier for servomotor.

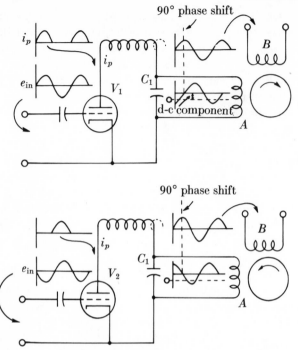

Figure 7-9 *Phase relationships of voltages and currents in the power amplifier and control winding of a servomotor.*

for the transistors is derived from full-wave rectification of the servo power supply.

The Voltage Amplifier. The voltage amplifier found in most recording potentiometers at present is a two-, three-, or four-stage RC-coupled amplifier using 12AX7 vacuum tubes. A three-stage circuit of this type is shown in Fig. 7-11. Amplification is sufficient so that input off-balance signals of 10 to 100 μv can control the servomotor. It is to be expected that compact transistor amplifiers will eventually replace the vacuum-tube circuits.

The D-C to A-C Converter and Input Circuit. The use of various choppers to convert the d-c off-balance signals in potentiometers to a-c signals was described in Sec. 6-2. It is the purpose here to consider the sources of noise in chopper amplifiers and how to reduce them so that low-level signals can be used.

The noise from the chopper contacts is usually less than other noise in the circuit. Since most choppers are plug-in units, the capacitive and resistive coupling between pins can be large in cheap sockets. The most

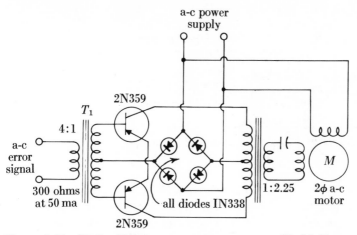

Figure 7-10   High-efficiency servo output stage.   (B. M. Benton, Electronics, September, 1956.)

satisfactory sockets in this respect are those made from Teflon or glazed ceramic.   *A grounded shield helps to reduce the noise component from pickup and leakage.*   The importance of leakage between coil terminals and chopper contacts is obvious if one considers a simple illustration.   If the circuit in-

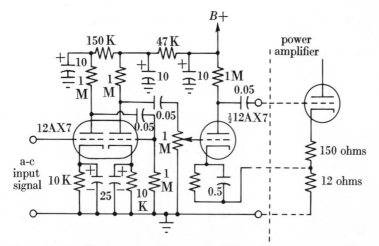

Figure 7-11   Three-stage voltage amplifier for servo potentiometer. (Brown amplifier #358816, Minneapolis Honeywell Bulletin B15-12A.)

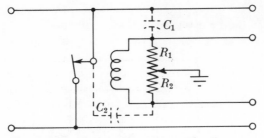

Figure 7-12   Capacitive pickup of noise.

put resistance is 1 megohm and the insulation resistance 10,000 megohms, 1 part in 10^4 of the coil voltage will appear as a noise signal at the amplifier input. Since the coil is normally operated at 6 volts, the noise level at the input would be $6 \times 10^6/10^4 = 600$ μv. The effect of capacitive pickup at the input can be greatly reduced if the coil voltage is balanced to ground as shown in Fig. 7-12. The stray coupling capacitances C_1 and C_2 from either end of the coil can be referenced to ground by grounding the slider of R_1, R_2. The use of R_1, R_2 is usually helpful in reducing electrostatic pickup, especially when the coil leads come out from the base of the chopper. When coil leads are brought out from the top, the isolation is better and lower noise levels are generally possible.

Another type of noise is caused by the leakage resistance R_c of the input coupling capacitor C_c, as shown in Fig. 7-13. When the chopper contacts close, R_c is shunted across R_g to give a grid resistance $R_gR_c/(R_g + R_c)$ instead of R_g. Suppose that $R_g = 1$ megohm and $R_c = 1000$ megohms, so that the grid resistance periodically changes between 1.0000 megohm and 0.9990 megohm as the chopper contacts open and close, respectively.

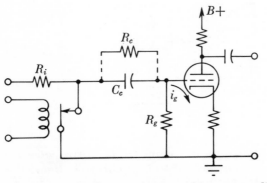

Figure 7-13   Leakage resistance of input coupling capacitor.

If the current i_g is one μa, the voltage between grid and cathode changes from 1.0000 to 0.9990 volt to produce a 1000-μv noise at the input. By using a polystyrene, Teflon, or mica capacitor that is clean, dry, and free of leakage paths, the resistance can be 10^{12} ohms so as to reduce the noise from this source to 1 μv. The grid current can be reduced for the usual 12AX7 tube to about 0.1 μa by operating with proper cathode bias (about 0.8 to 0.9 volt). It is important that all leakage paths be reduced, because the chopper will interrupt any voltage (such as a 250-volt B+ supply) to provide noise at the amplifier input.

Another characteristic of the capacitors that can introduce noise is the "soaking effect," i.e., the ability of the capacitor dielectric to develop a potential difference shortly after complete discharge so as to produce an unwanted d-c voltage across its terminals. This voltage appears as an always-present input voltage, or "offset." Polystyrene capacitors are especially free from this effect.

It is also possible to have "electromagnetic noise" in a chopper circuit. When the chopper contacts ground the grid, there is a ground loop that can intercept magnetic lines of force and generate a voltage across the grid resistance. This is a difficult type of noise to shield against, so that it is necessary to arrange components to eliminate the magnetic fields. Wiring from power-supply chokes and transformers can be a significant source for pickup.

By chopping the d-c input at some frequency other than 60 cps, it is possible to introduce selective filters that reject the 60-cps pickup. Even when chopping the d-c input at 60 cps, a filter that rejects 60-cps noise can be inserted prior to the chopping. This eliminates 60-cps pickup from the input leads, but it does not reject pickup between the chopper and amplifier.

The presence of "thermal junctions" can lead to rather large noise signals. Solder joints, joints of dissimilar metals, and other forms of thermal junctions act as miniature batteries in series with the chopper contacts to produce noise signals. This source of noise can be readily located by blowing a stream of hot air at the suspected spots and observing any change in noise level.

Another type of noise associated with all circuits is the so-called "Johnson noise" caused by random electron motion in conductors, which was described in Chap. 4. This noise is greatly reduced by using an amplifier sharply tuned to the chopper frequency. The Johnson noise level sets the lower limit of input signal that can be observed, if it is considered possible to eliminate all other sources of noise.

7-5   Information-Feedback Device for the Servo Potentiometer

In Fig. 7-2 the information-feedback device, or "feedback element," for the servo potentiometer was shown as a variable standard voltage E_S. Although the methods of obtaining E_S were discussed in Sec. 6-2, several points of importance in recorder applications are now considered. The type of circuit used to obtain E_S depends on the "command" requirements. If the command is simply to move the pen from 0 to 100 chart divisions as E_U changes from 0 to 100 mv, a circuit similar to the one in Fig. 6-7 would be suitable. However, if the command requires that the pen must move from 0 to 100 chart divisions when E_U changes from 80 to 100 mv, the span must be changed to 20 mv and 80 mv of suppression (bucking) voltage must be provided.

The change of span and suppression is easily accomplished with a bridge circuit, as shown in Fig. 7-14. This bridge is similar in form to Fig. 6-22. Note that it is the voltage between points x and y that is compared with E_U. This voltage between x and y is varied by moving the slider on R_s. The voltage span E_{span} is determined by the current I_2 and resistance be-

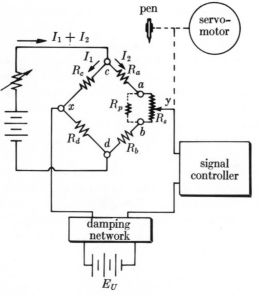

Figure 7-14   Bridge-type feedback element with adjustable span and
suppression.

tween points a and b, and this resistance is determined by the parallel combination of the slidewire resistance R_s and shunt R_p, so that

$$E_{\text{span}} = I_2 \frac{R_s R_p}{R_s + R_p} \tag{7-1}$$

As mentioned in Chap. 6, it is common practice to make the slidewire resistance R_s some exact value, such as 200.0 ohms. Consequently accurate changes of span and suppression can be readily made by substituting precision resistors in the circuit. For example, if I_2 is 1.000 ma with $R_a + R_s + R_b$ in the circuit and $R_s = 200.0$ ohms, then $E_{\text{span}} = 200.0$ mv. This is easily changed to a span of 20.00 mv if I_2 is maintained at 1.000 ma and R_p is added in parallel with R_s so that the parallel combination = 20.00 ohms. However, resistors $R_a + R_b$ must be increased by a total of 180.0 ohms in order to maintain $I_2 = 1.000$ ma. By rearranging the above equation, R_p can be calculated in terms of the specified and known quantities, i.e.,

$$R_p = \frac{E_{\text{span}} R_s}{I_2 R_s - E_{\text{span}}} \tag{7-2}$$

The suppression, or bucking, voltage E_B can be obtained by varying R_b in relation to R_d so that $I_1 R_d - I_2 R_b = E_B$, from which the value of R_b is

$$R_b = \frac{I_1 R_d - E_B}{I_2} \tag{7-3}$$

If $I_1 R_d = 500.0$ mv, $I_2 = 1.000$ ma, and the desired suppression $E_B = 80$ mv, then $R_b = 420.0$ ohms. For the above span of 20.00 mv, $R_s R_p / (R_s + R_p) = 20.00$ ohms; so R_a should equal 560.0 ohms if the voltage between c and d is 1 volt.

The above bridge arrangement is versatile and accurate, but it does require changing three precision resistors R_a, R_p, and R_b, for each change of span, or two resistors R_a and R_b, for a change in suppression only. More simple circuits, though usually less accurate, are available to accomplish changes of span and suppression. One circuit is shown in Fig. 7-15 which is similar to that found on some recorders. In this circuit the voltage across the slidewire (between points c and d) is held constant, and the span voltage E_S is changed by a voltage divider between points x and y. For example, the span can be changed tenfold by changing the resistance ratio $R_2/(R_1 + R_2) = $ from $\frac{1}{4}$ to $\frac{1}{40}$. Sometimes only a fraction of the total slidewire resistance R_s is used to provide the full-scale chart span. In this way the variable resistances R_c and R_d can provide suppression by an amount depending on the fraction of R_s used for the chart span.

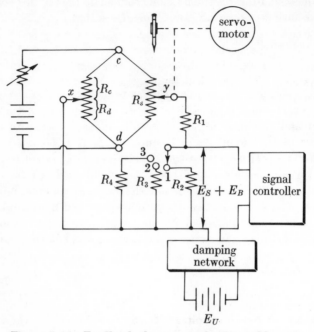

Figure 7-15   Feedback element with adjustable span and suppression.

Other types of feedback elements could be used so that the position of the pen is some function of E_U, such as log E_U. The logarithmic feedback is especially useful in spectrophotometry because of the logarithmic relationship between absorbed radiation and concentration. The logarithmic function can be approximated quite accurately by coupling together two slidewires as in the Photovolt recorder or by a mechanical cam arrangement as in the Sargent recorder. The standardization considerations of servo potentiometers are the same as described in Sec. 6-2.

7-6   The Command Signal—Input Transducers

For the example of the recording servo potentiometer it was stated that the pen was to be positioned on the chart according to a command signal E_U, because the voltage itself was of interest. In many cases, however, it is some other phenomenon that is of interest. For example, we might want the pen to be positioned according to some function of light intensity, or the concentration of hydrogen ions, or the temperature or pressure of a system. In these cases it is necessary to change (transduce) the phenomenon of interest to an electrical signal that can be used by the servo controller. To obtain an electrical signal from the desired phenomenon, devices called "input transducers" are required. These devices have also been called by other names, such as "conversion element" or "pickup," but regardless of the name it is obvious that they are vital parts for the instrumentation of systems. The electrical output from the transducer determines the type and sensitivity of the controller input circuitry that must be used.

7-7   Servo Stability—The Dynamics Problem

If the general characteristics of each of the parts of the servo system, as diagrammed in Fig. 7-1, are known, it is possible to consider more critically the response of the servo system to the command. The ideal position servo would move the load instantaneously to the precise position dictated by the command. If the command varied, the position of the load would respond exactly and without delay to the variations of the command. In practice, no mass can be moved instantaneously, for this would require infinite acceleration and deceleration and therefore infinite force.

Force Balance in the Servo System. The motive force in the servo system is the electromotive torque developed in the servo drive motor (prime mover). This torque acts to accelerate the load and to overcome the frictional and damping forces in the system. For most instrument servomotors (Sec. 7-3) the torque is roughly proportional to the voltage in the control winding. If the error-signal amplifier is linear, the output voltage of the amplifier is proportional to the error-signal input. Finally, if the system is completely linear, the error signal is proportional to the difference between the actual and the command position of the load. Therefore the relationship between the load position c and the motor torque T_m is

$$T_m = K'(c_0 - c) \qquad (7-4)$$

where c_0 is the command position of the load, or that load position which would give no error signal to the amplifier, and K' is a constant with units of torque per load displacement.

For Eq. (7-4) to be true at all times, it is necessary that the amplifier gain, which affects K', is not a function of frequency. For chopper amplifiers, then, the chopper frequency must be high compared with the highest frequency command that the servo is expected to follow. The signal delay in the amplifier (phase distortion) should also be negligible for signals of the fastest expected response speed.

In considering the linear translation of a load, such as the pen in a recording potentiometer, it is more convenient to use the unit "force" than "torque." The force is simply the torque divided by the lever arm. When the load is positioned by a drive pulley concentric to the motor shaft, the lever arm l is a constant and the force developed in the motor, F_m, as applied to the system, is

$$F_m = T_m/l = (K'/l)(c_0 - c) = K(c_0 - c) \tag{7-5}$$

The force which actually accelerates the load, F_a, is the motor force F_m minus the force lost to damping and frictional forces, F_d.

$$F_a = F_m - F_d \tag{7-6}$$

The force F_a is related to the acceleration a of the load by

$$F_a = Ma \tag{7-7}$$

where M is the mass of the load. The damping and frictional forces are generally proportional to the velocity v of the load. The constant of proportionality will be given the symbol D.

$$F_d = Dv \tag{7-8}$$

This assumes that all frictional surfaces are lubricated so that the starting friction and unlubricated sliding friction are negligible. Substituting (7-5), (7-7), and (7-8) into (7-6),

$$Ma = K(c_0 - c) - Dv \tag{7-9}$$

or $\qquad Kc_0 = Ma + Dv + Kc \tag{7-10}$

Expressing the acceleration and the velocity as the second and first time derivatives of c,

$$Kc_0 = M\frac{d^2c}{dt^2} + D\frac{dc}{dt} + Kc \tag{7-11}$$

Response to Step Command. To characterize the response of the system, one of the traditional tests is to apply a step signal at the input, to command that the load, at standstill, be relocated at a new position instantly. From Eq. (7-9), it can be seen that, the greater the command displacement, the greater the accelerating force and, the greater the mass, the less the acceleration.

To consider the effect of the damping term, consider the step response of a system with no damping, i.e., where the damping and frictional forces are negligible ($D = 0$). The load accelerates at a rate of $K(c_0 - c)/M$. As c approaches c_0, the acceleration decreases, but until $c = c_0$, the load has continued to gain speed. At this point the load ceases to accelerate and would just maintain its acquired velocity except that, in going beyond c_0, an accelerating force in the opposite direction is developed by the system. Finally, at some position on the other side of c_0 from the initial position, the load is stopped by the accelerative force which always acts toward c_0.

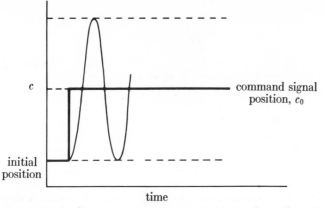

initial
position

time

Figure 7-16   Servo response to step command, no damping.

Now the load, accelerated toward c_0, increases its velocity in that direction until it passes c_0 again.   This sequence is shown as load position plotted against time in Fig. 7-16.   If there are no damping or frictional forces, the load will continue to oscillate about c_0.

When damping or viscous-friction forces are present, the accelerative force is decreased by an amount proportional to the velocity.   Again consider Eq. (7-9) as applied to a load approaching c_0.   As the velocity v increases and the error $(c_0 - c)$ decreases, Dv will, at some c, exceed K $(c_0 - c)$ and the net force becomes decelerative (negative Ma).   The deceleration of the load before c_0 is attained reduces the overshoot of the load.   The overshoot will decrease each half cycle until the load comes to rest at c_0.   This action is called a damped oscillation and is shown in Fig.

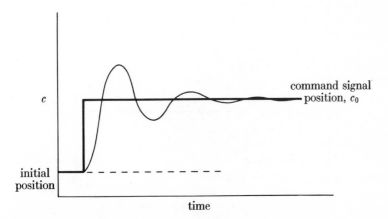

Figure 7-17   Response to step command, some damping.

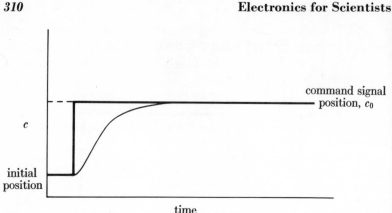

Figure 7-18   Response to step command, damped to eliminate over-shoot.

7-17. If the damping is increased still further, the overshoot can be elimi-nated altogether but the approach to c_0 is much slower. This is shown in Fig. 7-18.

Both overshoot and slow response are distortions of the desired re-sponse to the command signal, and therefore they are important parameters of the servo system. The overshoot is often described as a fraction of the command displacement. That is, if the command was to move the load 10 cm and the initial overshoot was 1 cm, the overshoot would be 0.1, or 10 per cent. A measure of the response speed is the "settling time," the time required for the load to come to the command position within a pre-scribed error tolerance. The measure of overshoot and settling time is shown in Fig. 7-19.

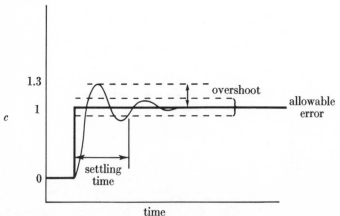

Figure 7-19   Servo response characteristics.

RLC **Analog of Servo Response.** It can be shown that the un-damped servo system is an oscillator as defined in Chap. 5. This is easiest to do by showing that the positioning of the load according to Eq. (7-11) is exactly analogous to the movement of charge in a series-resonant *LC* circuit. When the switch of Fig. 7-20 is closed, the command is to transfer charge to capacitor *C* through inductance *L* and resistance *R*. The sum of the potentials across the circuit elements is equal to the battery voltage. The potential across the resistor is iR: across the inductance, $L(di/dt)$; across the capacitor, Q/C, where Q is the charge on the capacitor. The summation of the potentials in the loop of Fig. 7-20 may be written

$$E = L\frac{di}{dt} + iR + \frac{Q}{C}$$

or since $i = dQ/dt$,

$$E = L\frac{d^2Q}{dt^2} + R\frac{dQ}{dt} + \frac{Q}{C} \tag{7-12}$$

Thus we see that L is analogous to M, R to D, and $1/C$ to K of Eq. (7-11). If there were no resistance, the *LC* circuit excited as in Fig. 7-20 would oscillate at its resonant frequency (where $X_C = X_L$, $Z = 0$), theoretically forever. The introduction of resistance results in a damped oscillation, or *ringing*. The resonant frequency is $f_o = 1/2\pi\sqrt{LC}$ (see Supplement 3). It follows then that the natural frequency of the undamped servo system will be

$$f_o = \frac{1}{2\pi}\frac{K}{M} \tag{7-13}$$

Damping Factor. It is advantageous to know the amount of damping necessary to reduce the overshoot of the system to a tolerable level. The amount of damping required will be larger for a larger mass, because a larger mass acquires less velocity in a given time for the same accelerating force. Also, in order to bring about a deceleration for a particular value of

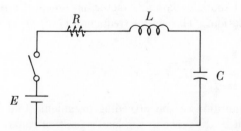

Figure 7-20 Electrical analog of servo system.

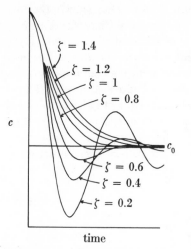

time

Figure 7-21   Servo response as a function of damping factor.

$c_0 - c$, D must be larger for larger values of the motive force K. The following formula for the damping factor ζ shows the relationship between D, K, and M for a constant damping effect:

$$\zeta = \frac{D}{2\sqrt{KM}} \tag{7-14}$$

Figure 7-21 shows the step response as a function of the damping factor. Note that, when the damping factor is less than unity, there are overshoot and damped oscillations. An unnecessarily long time is required to reach command position when the damping factor is greater than 1. A system with a damping factor of unity is said to be critically damped. Most servo systems are operated with a damping factor between 0.6 and 1.0. The lower damping factors give a quicker response and, in spite of the overshoot, a smaller settling time than critical damping. If the damping factor is much below 0.6, the damped oscillations take too long to subside and the settling time is again increased.

Note also from Fig. 7-21 that the damping factor has an effect on the period of the damped oscillation. The actual frequency is given by the following equation when $\zeta < 1$:

$$f = f_o\sqrt{1 - \zeta^2} = \frac{1}{4\pi M}\sqrt{4KM - D^2} \tag{7-15}$$

Saturation.   The assumption of the preceding arguments that the motor torque is proportional to the error in the load's position cannot be true for very large errors. There is a maximum torque for any given motor; there is a maximum output capability of the amplifier. When one of these maxima is reached, the drive system is saturated and a further increase in error signal cannot increase the restoring torque. This characteristic can be seen in the plateaus of Fig. 7-7. Today, most servo systems are designed to saturate with an error which is only a small percentage of the span. For large displacement, therefore, the term $K(c_0 - c)$ in Eq. (7-9) has a maximum value regardless of c.

$$Ma = K(c_0 - c) - Dv$$

This maximum force will be called K_{max}. The initial acceleration of the load will be $a = K_{max}/M$. As the velocity increases, the acceleration decreases until finally the damping force is equal to the driving force and the velocity is constant and maximum. When this is true, $K_{max} = Dv_{max}$. Solving for the maximum velocity,

$$v_{max} = \frac{K_{max}}{D} \tag{7-16}$$

This demonstrates that the maximum velocity in saturation is inversely proportional to the damping; so, here again, excess damping must be avoided if response speed is an objective.

One of the advantages of operating the system in saturation is that the system always responds with its maximum response speed. When the load comes close enough to the command position to bring the system out of saturation, the driving torque decreases and the load decelerates as it approaches c_0. The response of the system operating for a time in the saturated region is shown in Fig. 7-22. In this case, the settling time is a

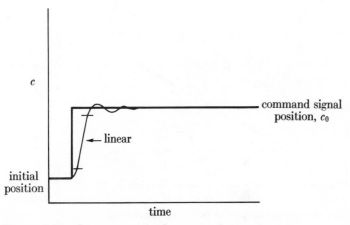

Figure 7-22 **Step response of saturated servo system.**

linear function of the displacement, and the overshoot is a constant fraction of the control-system span, rather than a constant fraction of the input step.

Position Errors. Errors in servo positioning arise from several sources. One of these errors is that the load position does not immediately coincide with the command position. This difficulty has been discussed above. Since it cannot be overcome completely, it is certainly of concern when the load must accurately follow the command signal.

Another source of position error is the "dead zone" of the system. This is the position error for which the error signal is too small to result in a rotation of the servo motor. An obvious way to correct this difficulty is to increase the amplifier gain. This also has the effect of driving the system into saturation for smaller displacements. The limit of practical amplification is when the amplifier is so sensitive that it cannot distinguish between noise and the error signal.

Backlash, due to a looseness in the coupling between the load and the motor, leads to a kind of oscillation. This is due to the momentum built up by the motor rotating through the backlash region. Backlash between the load and the position indicator will cause a hysteresis in the positioning.

An oscillation can also occur owing to a time delay in the feedback control loop. That frequency for which the delay is exactly a half cycle will be fed back in phase rather than out of phase. In most ordinary servos, the delays are so small that the system could not respond to the high frequency at which it would oscillate.

The Ramp Input. Another standard test command signal is the ramp, a linearly increasing potential. The usual response of the linear servo system to the ramp is shown in Fig. 7-23. The servo should move the load at a constant velocity from the initiation of the ramp. The load can-

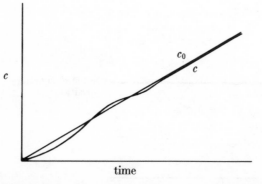

Figure 7-23   Servo response to ramp command.

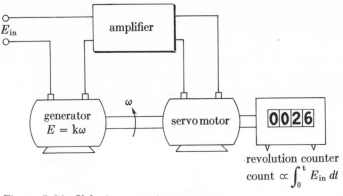

Figure 7-24   Velocity servo integrator.

not be accelerated to that velocity instantly, and so it lags. As the load accelerates to catch up, its velocity exceeds the command velocity and overshoot occurs. The system settles down to follow the command velocity, but the command signal is always a little ahead of the load at any given time. This is due to the fact that, to have the servo motor rotating at a constant velocity, there must be an error signal at the input. It can be seen from Eq. (7-9) that the steady-state displacement error will be proportional to D and v and inversely proportional to K. As the command signal approaches v_{max}, the servo loses the ability even to reproduce the slope of the command signal.

The Velocity Servo. The velocity servo is used, for example, to control the rate of rotation of a shaft rather than the linear position of a load. The effectiveness of a servomechanism in this function was shown in the above case of the ramp command signal. Note from Fig. 7-23 that, while the position is in error during steady state, the shaft velocity reproduces the command velocity very well. An interesting use of a velocity servo is shown in Fig. 7-24. The input voltage E_{in} is compared with the output of a generator whose output is proportional to the speed of rotation, ω, of the servomotor. Thus ω is proportional to the input voltage, and a device that counts the revolutions of the servomotor shaft will read out a number proportional to the time integral of the input voltage. A servo system which has a constant error signal for a controlled velocity is called a Type I servo, or a velocity servo. Some control systems, including those to be discussed in the next chapter, require a constant error signal to maintain a constant output displacement. These are sometimes called type O control systems.

7-8   Antihunt Methods

In Sec. 7-7 the response of an undamped or underdamped servo system was considered. Such systems were found to oscillate back and forth around the desired position, or to "hunt" for the commanded position. The methods of preventing this "hunting" (antihunt methods) are now briefly considered.

One obvious method of eliminating hunting is to provide braking by mechanical friction. This is a relatively simple method, but it generates heat, causes wear, and increases the response time. Therefore, it is only used in certain small low-power servo systems. It is sometimes used on recording servo potentiometers, and damping control is provided by merely a gain adjustment on the amplifier. A magnetic brake is often used on d-c motors. The brake is released by an electromagnet when the motor is energized and applied by a spring when the motor is deenergized.

Damping by electrical feedback in the amplifier is effectively used to eliminate hunting. Usually a damping voltage that is proportional to the speed of the drive motor is applied at some point in the amplifier in opposition to the error voltage. When the desired position is approached at full speed, the error voltage becomes less than the opposing voltage. The torque on the motor then reverses and exerts a braking action. This slows the motor, and the damping voltage decreases so that the reverse torque is decreased and, finally, eliminated when the object reaches the desired position. An induction tachometer can be mechanically coupled by gearing to the motor output, as shown in Fig. 7-25, to provide the damping voltage that is proportional to the motor speed. The damping voltage is fed back to a convenient point in the circuit to produce the desired effect, in this

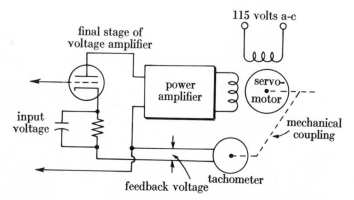

Figure 7-25   Dynamic damping with tachometer feedback.

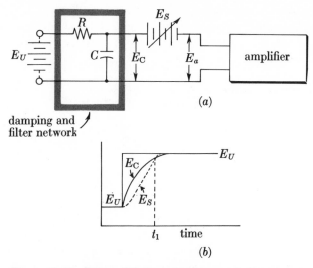

Figure 7-26 *Input RC damping network for servo potentiometer: (a) schematic; (b) response.*

case to the cathode of the final voltage-amplifier stage. The induction tachometer is essentially a two-phase device with a *squirrel-cage* rotor of low resistance. One phase is energized by the a-c line voltage to induce eddy currents in the rotor. When the rotor moves, the space alignment of the eddy-current field is shifted so as to induce a voltage in the other phase. This voltage is directly proportional to the rotor velocity.

In servo potentiometers the damping is often introduced at the input leads for the command voltage E_U (see Fig. 7-14). This is accomplished with a low-pass RC circuit, or "lag network," as shown in Fig. 7-26a, which also serves as a filter for stray a-c voltages that may appear at the input. If one assumes that E_U is suddenly changed to a new value (step input), then the capacitor C will charge at a rate dependent on the RC time constant and the voltage across the capacitor, E_C, will rise exponentially, as shown in Fig. 7-26b. It is the voltage E_C that is compared with E_S to provide the actuating voltage E_a; that is, $E_a = E_C - E_S$. For a large change of E_U the signal E_a is almost immediately large enough to provide full operating voltage and constant speed for the balancing motor. Therefore, E_S varies linearly after the initial time lag. However, at time t_1, $E_S = E_C$, $E_a = 0$, and torque is removed and then reversed as the sign of E_a reverses. The dynamic damping provided by the reversed motor torque brings the system to balance in the shortest possible time if RC is the correct value. If the RC time constant is too large, the system is overdamped and the balance point is gradually approached. If RC is too small, the system is underdamped and overshoot or oscillation occurs. In systems that are inherently overdamped, a high-pass filter, or "lead network," would improve the response time.

7-9 Synchro-Generator–Control-Transformer System

As described in Secs. 7-5 and 7-6, it is necessary to have a command transducer for developing a signal r that is an accurate representation of the command and a load transducer that develops a feedback signal b that accurately indicates the actual state of the load. The difference $r - b$ is the actuating signal e on which the signal controller operates. Because the combination of command and feedback devices provides the error signal e, it is customary to refer to the combination as the "error detector."

There are many combinations of devices that can be used to provide the error signal. Very often the command directs an object, such as a ship or rocket, to follow a desired directional course. Since a course is readily described by angles, it seems logical that both the command and feedback information could be obtained as accurate shaft angles representing the desired and actual course of the object. To convert these shaft angles to voltages that can be easily utilized by an electronic signal controller, there are two commonly used systems, the balanced potentiometer and the synchro generator–control transformer.

The balanced potentiometer is shown in Fig. 7-27. The slider on one resistance is rotated as a function of the command, and the slider on the

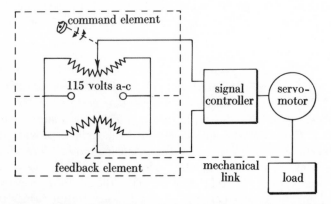

Figure 7-27 *Conversion of shaft angles to voltages with balanced potentiometer.*

other resistance is rotated as a function of actual load position. When the two sliders are at the same percentage travel from the end of the potentiometer, they are at the same potential and the difference between them is essentially zero volts. Movement of the command shaft (and slider) in either direction produces a voltage difference across the two sliders (an error signal), so that the servo positioner operates to move the load on the new course.

The balanced bridge can be operated on either d-c or a-c voltage. In the case of d-c voltage, the polarity of the error signal depends on the direction of displacement of the sliders. If an a-c supply is used, there is the usual 180° phase change about the balance point. These polarity or phase differences are obviously important since they determine the direction in which the positioner shaft turns. The magnitude of the error signal is proportional to the displacement from balance. If the load shaft must rotate through more than one revolution, multiturn helical potentiometers can be used, as well as suitable gearing.

The synchro system consisting of generator G and control transformer CT is represented by several different schematics, three of which are shown in Fig. 7-28. The rotor of the synchro generator is rotated as a function of the command, and the rotor of the control transformer is rotated as a function of the actual position of the load. The two units may be separated by long distances, and a cable containing connecting leads for the three stator windings provides a flexible coupling. When the rotors of G and CT are aligned, as shown in Fig. 7-28, a negligible voltage is induced in the rotor coil of the control transformer. Note that it is the signal from the rotor coil of the control transformer that indicates any error between desired and actual shaft positions. When the command causes the rotor of the synchro generator to rotate clockwise from the balance point, an a-c voltage (the error signal) is induced in the rotor of CT that is in the same phase as that on the coil of the rotor G. For a counterclockwise rotation of G from the balance point, the error voltage is 180° out of phase. The load is moved (and the CT rotor turned) until the error signal is essentially zero. For small error angles (10 to 15°) the magnitude of the error voltage is directly proportional to the displacement between command shaft and controlled shaft.

A pictorial representation of the synchro G and CT as command and feedback elements, respectively, in a servo system is shown in Fig. 7-29. The specific task of this servo is to rotate the huge gun mount to some bearing described by the command shaft and introduced by a small handwheel (or automatic tracking device).

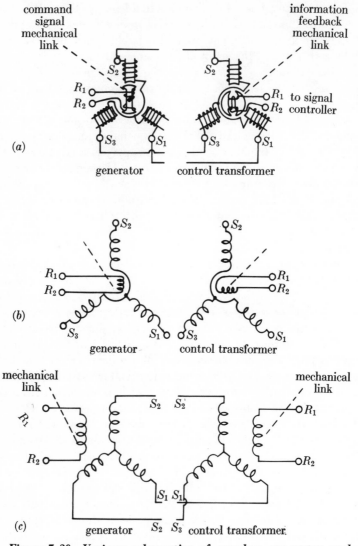

Figure 7-28 *Various schematics of synchro generator and control transformer.*

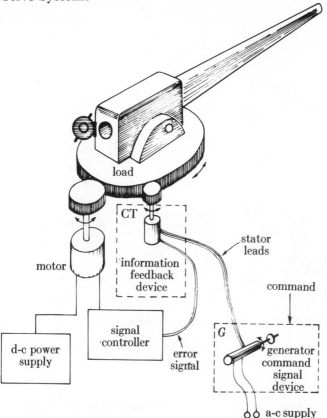

Figure 7-29 *Synchro generator and control transformer as command and feedback elements in a servo system.*

7-10 High-Power Prime Movers and Signal Controllers

The d-c motor is a frequently used prime mover, and some types are capable of high power in servo systems. Both the speed and direction of rotation are easily controlled. The speed of rotation is nearly proportional to the armature voltage if the field flux is constant, and the direction of rotation is reversed by simply reversing the armature current.

The high-power d-c motors use a field winding, as illustrated in Fig. 7-30*a*, which can be separately excited to provide a constant field flux. The low-power d-c motors have a permanent magnetic field, illustrated by Fig. 7-30*b*. The armature current of a small permanent-magnet d-c motor can be provided directly from a push-pull power amplifier using vacuum tubes, for power outputs up to about 25 watts. For heavier loads up to

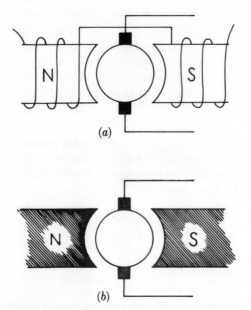

(a)

(b)

**Figure 7-30   *The d-c servo motor: (a) shunt field; (b) permanent mag-*
*netic field.***

several horsepower, a thyratron circuit can be used to supply the armature current of the d-c motor.   Recall from Sec. 5-4 that the thyratron contains an inert gas which ionizes to reduce the cathode space charge and decrease the internal resistance to a very low value.   Therefore, the current
flow is determined almost entirely by the external circuit resistance and
plate-supply voltage when the tube is conducting.   In order to understand

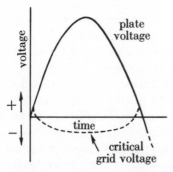

Figure 7-31   *Critical grid voltage of thyratron.*

the operation of a thyratron circuit, it is important to remember that the grid voltage determines whether or not the tube conducts for a given plate voltage but that, once the tube conducts, the grid loses control and conduction can be stopped only by decreasing the plate voltage to a very low value. For each positive plate voltage above the ionization potential, there is a "critical grid voltage" that will just prevent the tube from conducting. This is illustrated in Fig. 7-31. Any grid voltage above the critical value will cause the tube to conduct, but if the grid is more negative, there will be no conduction. These characteristics cause thyratron circuits to be quite different from the usual vacuum-tube amplifier. A thyratron circuit is described that is useful as a signal controller for a d-c motor.

The speed of the d-c motor can be controlled by varying the duration and magnitude of current pulses in the armature. This is easily accomplished with the thyratron circuit shown in Fig. 7-32. When the a-c voltage is applied between plate and cathode of the thyratron, the maximum conduction period is somewhat less than the positive half cycle when the plate swings positive. The fraction of the positive half cycle during which the tube conducts depends on the grid voltage. Therefore the grid voltage determines the average armature current and motor speed. If the grid is supplied with a variable d-c voltage the current can be varied as illustrated in Fig. 7-33a. Another method of "amplitude control" is shown in Fig. 7-33b, where an a-c voltage is shown applied to the grid that is 180° out of phase with the a-c plate supply. A third method of amplitude control uses a fixed d-c grid bias always below the critical voltage and an a-c grid signal that is in phase with the plate supply, as illustrated in Fig. 7-33c. The third method has the advantage that no conduction occurs when the a-c

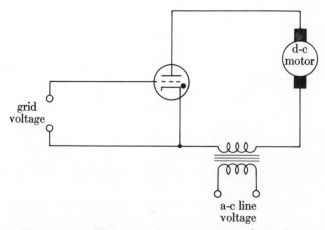

Figure 7-32   Thyratron d-c motor control circuit.

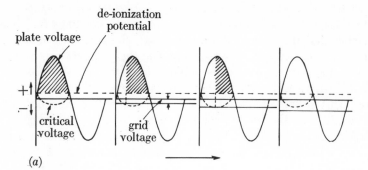

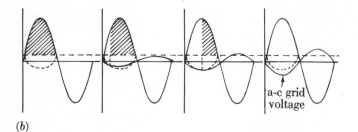

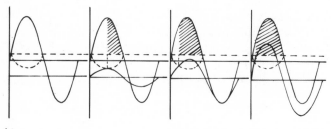

*Figure 7-33   Three methods of amplitude control for thyratron: (a)
d-c grid voltage; (b) a-c grid voltage 180° out of phase with
plate; (c) a-c grid voltage in phase with plate and a fixed
d-c grid bias.*

actuating signal is zero.   In all three cases, however, the current can be
carefully controlled by the grid for only about one-fourth cycle, which is
obvious from Fig. 7-33.   To obtain fine control of current for nearly the full
half cycle, a combination of amplitude and "phase-shift control" is used,
as shown in Fig. 7-34.

With the circuit in Fig. 7-32, the leads to the motor armature must be
reversed in order to reverse the direction of rotation and this is impractical
in servo systems.   To have bidirectional rotation by merely reversing the

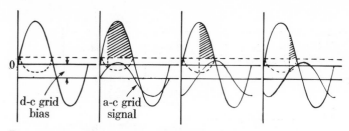

Figure 7-34   Phase-shift control for thyratron.

phase of the actuating signal, two thyratrons can be used in a circuit, as shown in Fig. 7-35. This circuit is designed with fixed d-c bias for each tube so that neither can conduct until an a-c signal is applied to the grid. This circuit is the same as that illustrated by the curves of Fig. 7-33c. The input transformer is connected so that the grid signal on each thyratron is the same phase, but the plate-supply transformer is connected so that the plate voltages are 180° out of phase. Therefore, tube V_1 will conduct when an a-c actuating signal is applied to the grid of V_1 that is in phase with its plate voltage. This means, of course, that tube V_2 will not conduct, since its grid and plate are 180° out of phase. Obviously, then, by reversing the grid signal, tube V_2 conducts and V_1 does not. It is apparent from the circuit of Fig. 7-35 that, when tube V_1 conducts, the armature current is in one direction and, when V_2 conducts, the armature current is reversed, thereby providing the required reversal of motor rotation.

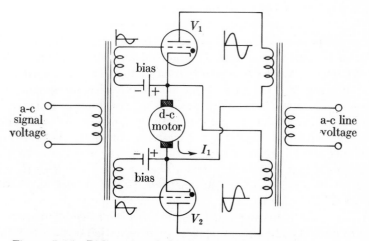

Figure 7-35   Bidirectional thyratron motor control.

command

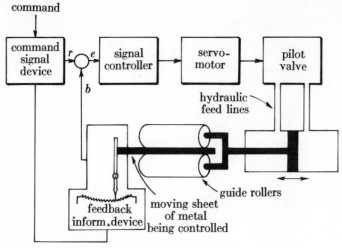

Figure 7-36   Hydraulic servo system.

For huge heavy-duty d-c motors, d-c generators can be used to supply an armature current of several hundred amperes. The d-c generator output can be controlled by varying its field current, which is controlled by a servo vacuum-tube amplifier. In this way an actuating signal of 1 mw can produce an output from the generator of several hundred kilowatts, an over-all power gain of several hundred million. Three of the well-known rotating amplifiers are known as the Ward-Leonard system, the Rototrol generator, and the Amplidyne generator. Each consists essentially of a generator driven at 1800 or 3600 rpm, and each depends on a small field current producing a large armature current.

The other common method of producing large power output is with hydraulic components. They have the advantage of producing several times larger torques than electrical equipment of similar size and weight. The hydraulic servos are consequently used in applications requiring hundreds of horsepower. The definite advantage of minimum apparatus-to-horsepower ratio must be weighed against the disadvantages of working with oil lines rather than wires and the relatively slow response of hydraulic systems. Also, hydraulic systems are relatively expensive. An illustration of a hydraulic servo is given in Fig. 7-36. Two large guide rollers are positioned by a ram-type hydraulic system. The command is to keep the edge of the metal sheet moving along an exact line. The feedback information device "feels" the edge of the metal and provides the feedback signal b, and once again the actuating signal e is obtained from the difference $r - b$ between command and feedback signals. Any deviation of the metal from the desired position yields an amplified actuating signal and operates a servomotor controlling the pilot valve which regulates the oil flow in the hydraulic system. The movement of the hydraulic ram provides the necessary horizontal motion of the guide rollers so that the edge of the metal sheet stays on the desired line.

7-11 Standard Block Diagram and Terminology

The AIEE has recommended standard symbols for feedback control systems, and these are shown with a general block diagram (Fig. 7-37) that contains the basic elements and variables. The definitions are as follows:

The *command v* is the input which is established by some means external to and independent of the feedback control system.

The *reference input elements a* produce a *reference input r* which is proportional to the command.

The *control elements* g_1 produce the *manipulated variable m* which is applied to the controlled system. The manipulated variable is generally at a higher energy level than the actuating signal and may also be modified in form.

The *controlled system* g_2 is the device that is to be controlled.

The *controlled variable c* is the quantity that is directly measured and controlled. It is the output of the controlled system.

The *feedback elements h* produce the *primary feedback b*, which is a function of the controlled variable and which is compared with the reference input to obtain the *actuating signal e*. Therefore, $e = r - b$, and this signal is usually at a low energy level and is fed to the control elements.

The *indirectly controlled variable q* is the output quantity and is related through the *indirectly controlled system z* to the controlled variable. It is outside the closed loop and is not directly measured for control.

The *ultimately controlled variable* is a general term that refers to the indirectly controlled variable. In the absence of the indirectly controlled variable, it refers to the controlled variable.

The *idealized system* g_i is one whose performance is agreed upon to define the relationship between the *ideal value i* and the command.

The *ideal value i* is the value of the ultimately controlled variable that would result from an idealized system operating from the same command as the actual system.

The *system error* y_e is the ideal value minus the value of the ultimately controlled variable.

The *disturbance u* is the unwanted signal that tends to affect the controlled variable. The disturbance may be introduced into the system at many places.

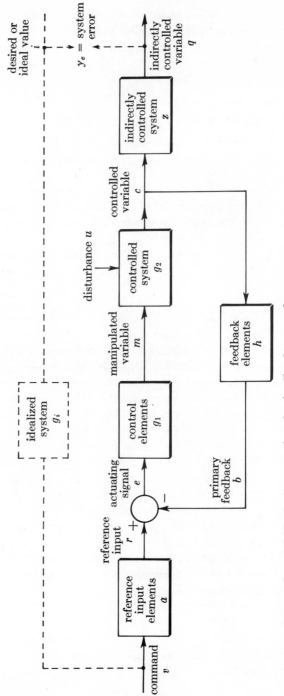

Figure 7-37 General block diagram for the feedback control system.

7-12   Open-Loop Control

All the systems described in this chapter have been "closed-loop control systems." In all cases the information about the controlled device was fed back and compared with the command, to provide a closed loop. Many devices, however, are controlled without a feedback loop and are called "open-loop systems." With this system the difference between the actual state and the desired state of the controlled device has no influence on its action.

The desired output of an open-loop system is predetermined by calibration of the input device, and the actual output depends on the correctness of the calibration. If the system components vary because of temperature, contamination, pressure, and other variables, there is nothing to warn that there are errors in the state of the controlled device and no corrections are possible. In many such cases a human being steps in to act as a feedback element and closes the loop.

A good example of open-loop control is the adjustment of water temperature at the beginning of a shower, hoping that it will remain comfortable until the shower is completed.

References

Ahrendt, W. R., and C. J. Savant, Jr., "Servomechanism Practice," 2d ed., McGraw-Hill, New York, 1960. Primarily contains material on circuitry, electrical and mechanical components, and practical problems encountered in servo design.

Lauer, H., R. N. Lesnick, and L. E. Matson, "Servomechanism Fundamentals," 2d ed., McGraw-Hill, New York, 1960. Introduces the principles underlying the theory of servomechanisms. The treatment has been kept both simple and rigorous.

Pearson, E. B., "Technology of Instrumentation," Van Nostrand, Princeton, N.J., 1958. Stresses fundamentals of servomechanisms and dynamic measurements.

Taylor, P. L., "Servomechanisms," Longmans, New York, 1960. Divides the presentation of material into three parts: Part I provides introductory background for the subject; Part II expands the subject with a preliminary study of some practical systems; Part III treats more rigorously the mathematical analysis of systems.

Problems

7-1   Determine the approximate amplifier gain required to obtain 100 volts rms on the control winding of a servomotor (Fig. 7-5) with a 50-μv d-c input signal. Assume a chopper input similar to the circuit shown in Fig. 6-15.

Ans.: Gain $\approx$ 6 million

7-2   Explain how "noise" would affect the sensitivity and accuracy of a servo recorder.

7-3   Design a bridge-type input circuit (as in Fig. 7-14) that has a *span* of 10 mv, a *suppression* of 100 mv, and a current drain from the bridge supply that does not exceed 2 ma.

7-4   List some practical applications of *zero suppression* for a servo recorder.

7-5   For the self-balancing potentiometric input circuit in Fig. P7-5, *show* why it would be feasible to specify the span as variable from 50 to 100 mv.

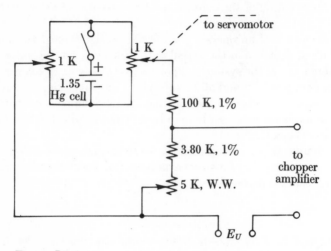

Figure P7-5

7-6   Calculate the minimum and maximum spans available with the self-balancing potentiometer of Fig. 7-38.

  Ans.: Assuming the slider of R_S moves from end to end,
    minimum span 9.5 mv on "10" position
    maximum span 206 mv on "100" position

7-7   For the servo constant current source of Fig. 7-43, $E_{supply} = 1.5$ volts, $E_{comparison} = 100$ mv, $R = 100$ ohms, and the load $R_L \approx 170$ ohms. Calculate how low E_{supply} can drop before the current changes from 1.00 ma.

  Ans.: $E_{supply} = 0.6$ volt

7-8   For a servo constant voltage supply (Fig. 7-43) to maintain a constant voltage $E_R = 0.200$ volt across R, calculate (*a*) the range of currents if R varies from 10 to 200 ohms, and (*b*) the value of the motor-driven slidewire, assuming no resistance in the circuit other than R and R_S, and a supply voltage of 2 volts.

  Ans.: (*a*) from 20 ma to 1 ma; (*b*) a 2-kilohm control would be suitable.

EXPERIMENTS

The servo system is studied as a self-balancing recording potentiometer, a constant current source, and a constant voltage source. After examination and familiarization with the components in the servo system, the various characteristics are investigated.

With the servo connected in its normal way as a self-balancing potentiometer, various voltage *spans* are obtained, and the recorder is finally *calibrated* to have full-scale spans of 10 mv and 100 mv. An *attenuator* (voltage divider) for input voltages up to 100 volts is also connected to expand the range of input voltages. Zero *suppression* is tested by using the wired bridge circuit and also the voltage reference source (VRS).

The effect of amplifier *gain* on *dead zone* and *damping* (antihunting) are observed. The *phase* of voltages on the control and line windings of the two-phase a-c motor is observed while reversing the sign of the unbalance signal. The increase of *noise* pickup at high input impedance is demonstrated.

The servo system is temporarily converted for two other applications. A *servo constant current supply* is connected, wherein any changes of load resistance or supply voltage are compensated by the servo to maintain a constant current through the load. The circuit for the *constant voltage supply* is essentially the same as for the constant current supply, but the voltage across the load terminals is maintained constant even though the load resistance varies.

The servo system is finally reconnected as a self-balancing recording potentiometer, and the spans are rechecked before completing the experiments.

Expt. 7-1 Familiarization with Basic Components of Servo Recorder

Remove the rear and top panels of the EUW-20 recorder to expose all components. Identify the major parts by referring to the block diagram of Fig. 7-2 and the schematic diagrams in Supplement 1, Sec. S1-9. The bridge, amplifier, and power-supply wiring are all exposed by removing the rear panel. The servomotor, the multiturn slidewire drive and coupling system, and the chart drive motor and gears are easily accessible by removing the top panels. Note that there are several convenient connecting terminals in the potentiometer circuit. These enable rapid modifications for multipurpose laboratory applications and performance of the subsequent experiments.

(*Note:* In the following experiments, switch the recorder to STANDBY or OFF when making circuit connections. Remember that B+ is ON in the standby position.)

Expt. 7-2 Voltage Spans for the Self-Balancing Potentiometer

a. 100-mv Span. The input bridge circuit for the potentiometer is shown in Fig. 7-38. The full-scale voltage span, E_{span}, is determined by several factors: the voltage across the three-turn slidewire R_S; the fraction of R_S used to provide full-scale movement of the pen; and the fraction of bridge voltage that is compared with the input signal voltage E_U. In Fig. 7-38 the supply voltage ($E_{Hg} = 1.35$ volts) is shown directly across the slidewire, and the slidewire drive ratio provides for about 2.7 turns of the three-turn slidewire for the pen to move across the 10-inch chart. Therefore, the change in bridge output voltage E_V is about $1.35(2.7/3) = 1.2$ volts as the pen moves from one end of the chart to the other.

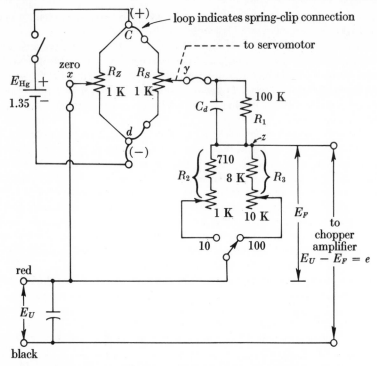

Figure 7-38   Recording potentiometer input circuit.

With the range switch in the "100" position, the fraction of E_V that is compared with E_U depends on the resistance ratio $(R_3/(R_1 + R_3))$; therefore, $E_{span} \approx 1.2[R_3/(R_1 + R_3)]$. Since $R_1 = 100$ kilohms, the resistor R_3 should be slightly larger than 8 kilohms to provide a maximum comparison voltage of 100 mv. The resistance R_3 is an 8-kilohm fixed resistor and a series variable resistor. Rather than make the variable resistor just large enough for calibration of the 100-mv range, it is about 10 to 15 kilohms so that the maximum full-scale reading can be calibrated for any voltage between about 100 and 200 mv.

Calibrate the recorder for 100 mv full scale as follows: Connect the voltage reference source (VRS) to the input terminals and switch it to the ×10 RANGE, and move the COARSE and FINE controls to 0. Now set the zero-adjust control of the recorder to 0 on the scale, and switch the COARSE control of the VRS to 10 (100 mv). Adjust R_3 (the lower screwdriver control on the side) until the pointer moves exactly full scale. Depress the ZERO button of the VRS and see if the pointer returns to 0 on the scale. Alternately release and depress the ZERO button and adjust the *damping control* of the recorder, so that the pointer comes to rest without significant overshoot or oscillation. Turn the VRS RANGE switch to ×1 and rotate the COARSE switch by 10-mv steps with chart on. Repeat several times and determine the reproducibility and accuracy of the scale readout when compared to the input voltages. Determine whether the position of the damping control influences the precision and accuracy on the 100-mv range.

Now vary R_3 until the pointer is one-half of full scale. Check the 0. Switch the VRS from 100 mv to 200 mv, and adjust R_3 for a full-scale span of 200 mv. Check the precision and accuracy with the 200-mv span.

Determine the maximum span available by varying R_3 to its maximum value. Observe why a single-turn variable resistor of larger resistance would not be too desirable.

Calibrate for a 200-mv span before proceeding with the next part of the experiment.

b. 10-mv Span. Switch the recorder to the 10-mv position. The same considerations hold for the 10-mv span as for the 100-mv span, but the fraction of E_V used as the comparison voltage is determined by the resistance ratio $R_2/(R_1 + R_2)$. Resistance R_2 is also made variable to provide a calibration so that the full-scale reading can be for any value between about 10 and 20 mv.

After observing the limits of the span by varying R_2, calibrate for a full-scale reading of 10.0 mv. Note that on the "10" position the recorder damping control is switched out of the circuit to increase the gain.

c. 20- to 200-mv Continuously Variable Range. The maximum value of the variable voltage E_V can be decreased by connecting a variable resistor in series with the mercury cell, as shown in Fig. 7-39. Disconnect the negative lead to the mercury cell from point d, and connect a 10-kilohm variable control resistor between the negative end of the mercury cell and point d. Use spring-clip leads to make the connections.

Switch the recorder to the "100" position. Vary the 10-kilohm control to give full-scale spans of 20 mv, 200 mv, and other voltages between the two extremes. Note that the damping control must be varied to give reliable readings for spans from one extreme to the other. Although the 10-kilohm control can provide a span of 10 mv, observe that the reproducibility of the readings is not good. Explain.

Remove the 10-kilohm control and reconnect the negative lead of the mercury cell to point d. Calibrate for a 100-mv full-scale span by adjusting R_3.

d. High-Voltage Ranges. Input voltages greater than a few tenths of a volt can be measured with the self-balancing potentiometer by using a voltage

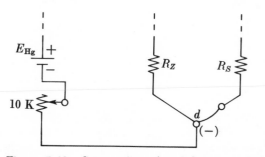

Figure 7-39   Connection of 10-kilohm control for a 20- to 200-mv variable span.

divider at the input. The disadvantage of this procedure is that current flows from the input source, even at balance. However, the resistance of the divider can be relatively large to decrease the current. Unfortunately, the greater the resistance of the divider the greater the chance of noise pickup at the input.

To make voltage measurements up to 100 volts, connect a voltage divider (attenuator) as shown in Fig. 7-40. Switch the recorder to the 100-mv span, and connect 100 volts across the 1000:1 attenuator of Fig. 7-40. Trim (with parallel resistors) one of the attenuator resistors to give exactly a full-scale reading for a 100-volt input. Check the precision and accuracy by rotating the VRS COARSE control to provide 10-volt increments at the attenuator input.

Remove the 10-megohm resistor and replace with a 1-megohm resistor to provide a 100:1 attenuator, and proceed as above to provide a 10-volt full-scale reading.

Expt. 7-3   Zero Suppression

In many laboratory applications it is important to observe small changes superimposed on large signals. For example, the transducer output voltage might be 1 volt, but the total change over the operating range might only be 0.01 volt (10 mv). Therefore, to spread the useful 10-mv signal across the full scale of the recorder, it is necessary to effectively *suppress* the scale 0 many chart widths of scale.

a. Zero Suppression with the VRS. The VRS is a good zero-suppress unit because it is very stable, continuously variable over a wide range, and all necessary terminals are built in. By using the VRS in its DIFF position, the recorder becomes, in effect, a linear off-balance indicator for the change of input voltage.

Let a 1-volt output from the transistor power supply simulate the output from some transducer, and connect it to the SIGNAL terminals of the VRS. Connect the recorder across the OUTPUT terminals of the VRS. Set the VRS switches in the same positions as used to calibrate the VRS, and adjust the VRS COARSE and FINE controls to the null point, with the recorder switched for the 10-mv span. Observe that a 10-mv variation of the input signal causes full-scale travel of the pen. In other words, a simulated 1 per cent change of input signal causes full-scale indication. Since changes of input signal of less than 0.1 mv are readily observed, relative signal changes of less than 1/10,000 can be recorded. With the chart ON,

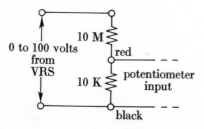

Figure 7-40   Voltage divider for recording high voltages.

determine the stability of the transistor supply over a period of time, assuming the VRS is absolutely stable over the same period.

Disconnect the input signal and switch the VRS to give a STD VOLTAGE output of 100 mv. Do not forget to switch POLARITY to the NORMAL position.

b. Zero Suppression within the Bridge Network. Disconnect the slidewire at the + side of the bridge and insert a 1-kilohm resistor, as in Fig. 7-41. Switch the recorder to the "100" range. Note, however, that the 100-mv span has been reduced to 50 mv by adding the 1-kilohm resistor in series with the 1-kilohm slidewire. Observe that the recorder "0" can be suppressed two span widths by varying the zero adjust control. Therefore, an input voltage variation of 50 to 100 mv gives full-scale pen travel if the scale 0 is set with a 50-mv input signal.

Observe the span and amount of zero suppression (in terms of span) when a 3900-ohm resistor is substituted for the 1-kilohm resistor.

Remove the resistor and reconnect the end of the slidewire to the positive end of the bridge.

Rewire the bridge circuit so the 1-kilohm resistor is between the end of the slidewire and the negative end of the bridge. Note that the zero suppression is now reversed.

Rewire the bridge circuit so that it is the same as at the start of the experiment.

Expt. 7-4 Dead Zone of the Servo Recorder

The dead zones on the normal "10" and "100" positions are so small that they are difficult to measure. Therefore, the dead zone is purposely made larger for easy observation. Wire an 8200-ohm resistor in the bridge circuit in series with the + end of the slidewire as in the preceding experiment. Switch the recorder to the "100" position. This decreases the span to about 10 mv but keeps the *damping* control in the circuit. Turn the damping control completely clockwise and slowly vary the FINE control of the VRS until the pen moves. The *dead zone* is the change of input voltage required to move the pen.

Turn the damping control completely counterclockwise and repeat the above test.

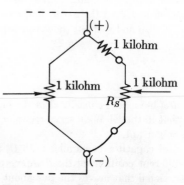

Figure 7-41 Zero suppression.

Replace at least one of the 12AX7 tubes with a lower-gain 12AU7 tube, and determine the dead zones with the damping control in the two extreme positions. Compare the dead zones for the different cases.

Put the recorder back to normal operation by replacing the 12AU7 tubes with the 12AX7 tubes, and removing the 8200-ohm resistor.

Expt. 7-5   Phase Relationship of the 60-cps Voltages on the Line and Control Windings of the Servomotor

Caution: In this experiment, one side of the power line is connected to the scope and recorder chassis, which presents a potential hazard. Check with your instructor before proceeding.

The phase is observed by connecting the vertical plates of the oscilloscope to the *control winding* and the horizontal plates to the *line winding*. Use patch cords fitted with insulated alligator clips on one end, and *be sure* that the clip connection is *firm* and *not shorting* between two terminals. Connect the scope GND to the recorder chassis, the VERT IN to pin 7 of the power tube (6BQ5), and the HOR IN to one side of the line winding (easily clipped on at the fuse terminal). Switch the recorder to the "100" position and turn to maximum damping.

Switch both the vertical and horizontal scope amplifiers to $\times 100$ AC. Connect a d-c voltage from the VRS to the input of the recorder so that the pen travels about full scale. Now alternately depress and release the ZERO button on the VRS, and observe the phase relationship during the short period (about 1 sec) of unbalance. Adjust the vertical gain of the scope so that the scope pattern is within complete view during the unbalance period.

The phase on the control winding is affected by changing one or more 0.01-μf capacitors that are connected between *ground* and the *grids* of the 12AX7 tubes. A 0.1-μf capacitor is easily clipped in parallel with the 0.01-μf capacitor between ground and pin 2 of the second 12AX7 tube. Observe how the increase of capacitance affects the phase. Use the same procedure of alternately depressing and releasing the ZERO button of the VRS to obtain an unbalance signal, or run the pen to the ends of the scale.

Observe that the pen is easily moved by hand to various points of rest either side of the null point when the 0.1-μf capacitor is in the circuit. Slowly turn the FINE control of the VRS, first in one direction and then the other, and observe the scope patterns. Note the dead zones, both with and without the 0.1-μf capacitor in the circuit.

Expt. 7-6   Damping (Antihunting)

Although *damping* and the *damping control* have been considered in the previous experiments, it is important to observe that in the EUW-20 servo recorder the value of the capacitor C_d (Fig. 7-38) is very important.

Switch to the "100" position. Clip a 1-μf capacitor in parallel with C_d and determine how the damping is affected for different positions of the damping control. Alternately apply and remove an input signal that moves the pen about full scale when testing the damping.

Note that the recorder 10-mv position might be somewhat underdamped because the damping control is removed on this position. Removal of the damping control provides added gain that prevents the 10-mv range from being sluggish.

Expt. 7-7   Servo Constant Current Supply

A simple modification of the self-balancing potentiometer converts it into a controller to compensate for changes of supply voltage or load resistance in an external circuit, so that a *constant current* is maintained through a load.   In the case of the self-balancing potentiometer an internal bucking voltage is automatically adjusted to match the input signal voltage.   For external control applications, the controlled element (the multiturn slidewire R_S) is disconnected from the internal circuit and connected in an external circuit.   A signal voltage is developed in the external circuit that varies as a function of the controlled variable.   This signal voltage is maintained equal to a *constant reference voltage* E_C by automatically varying the control element R_S, and in so doing the controlled variable (current I in this case) is maintained constant.

Prior to any wiring of the controller, *disconnect* all spring clips from the terminal posts.   The slidewire R_S is thus disconnected from the bridge and can be readily connected in an external circuit.   The constant reference voltage E_C is provided by connecting the mercury cell voltage E_{Hg} and the divider, as shown in Fig. 7-42a, which are normally in the potentiometer circuit.   (Note, of course, that it would also be possible to introduce an external reference voltage source.)   The spring-clip connections that are necessary to provide the E_C from the mercury cell and divider are illustrated in Fig. 7-42b.

Note in Fig. 7-42a that the 1.35 volts is connected directly across one of the series resistor combinations, $(R_1 + R_2)$ or $(R_1 + R_3)$, depending on whether the servo is in the "10" or "100" position, respectively.   The voltage E_C is a fraction of the 1.35 volts and depends on the ratios $R_3/(R_1 + R_3)$ and $R_2/(R_1 + R_2)$. Switch to the "100" position to obtain a reference voltage adjustable from 100 to 200 mv.

A current source is connected with a load R_L, controlled resistance element R_S, limiting resistance R_{il}, and a standard resistance R.   All resistances are in series with a voltage source E_{supply} and a milliammeter (full scale, 1.5 ma), as shown in Fig. 7-43.   It is the IR voltage drop E_R that is maintained constant by the servo system, so that the difference (error) voltage $e = E_R - E_C$ is kept equal to zero. Therefore, the desired current I through the load can be selected by using specific values of R and changing E_{supply} so that the control element R_S is within its balancing range.   For example, if a constant current of 1.00 ma is required and the internal comparison voltage $E_C = 100$ mv, then a standard resistance $R = 100$ ohms should be selected so that $IR = 100$ mv and $e = E_R - E_C = 0$.   If the load resistance R_L increases, the slidewire resistance R_S decreases to maintain $E_R = E_C$ and therefore maintains a constant current value.   Likewise, the resistance R_S varies to maintain a constant current when the supply voltage varies or when another source of emf is introduced into the circuit.   The resistance R_{il} is only to limit the current if R, R_S, and R_L should all be switched or moved to very low values.

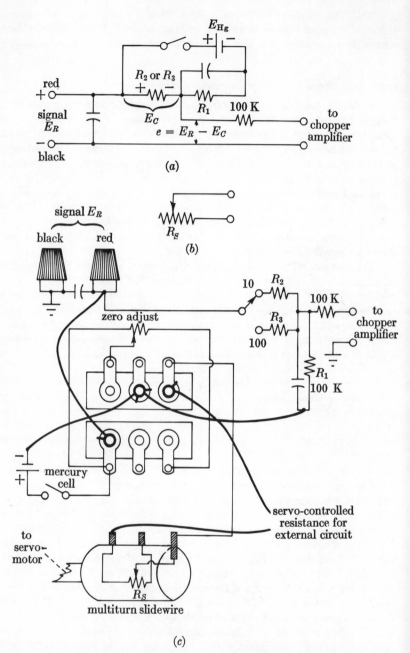

Figure 7-42   *Servo controller:* (a) *schematic of internal reference volt-*
age; (b) *the controlled element* R_s; (c) *connections to*
terminal posts.

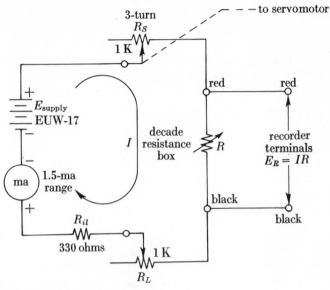

Figure 7-43   Current source.

It is important which end of R_S is used, in order that the servomotor varies the resistance in the correct direction to maintain the current constant. Note that when the motor and input circuit are connected in the normal way (pen moves from from right to left) the correct end terminal is the one closest to the slidewire shaft.

With the servo controller in STANDBY or OFF, switch the decade resistance box so that $R = 100$ ohms, move the pen carriage to about mid-scale, turn on the transistor supply, and gradually increase the voltage to provide a current of about 1 ma. Vary R_S, R_L, and E_{supply} to determine whether all are controlling the current, and again adjust so that current is about 1 ma and pen carriage is about mid-scale.

Connect the output of the decade resistance box to the respective red and black leads of the servo controller, as shown in Fig. 7-43, and turn the controller ON. If the circuit is connected correctly it will come to balance quickly near 1 ma. Set the reference voltage to 100 mv by adjusting R_3 until the current reads 1.00 ma on the meter (full scale, 1.5 ma).

Vary the load resistance R_L, and note how the current continually seeks 1.00 ma until the slider of R_S drives to either end of its travel. Determine whether the resistance ratio R_L/R_S is significant in providing *precise* and *accurate* control of current. Observe how R_S varies to compensate for changes of supply voltage.

Switch the decade resistance box so that $R = 200$ ohms, and decrease the supply voltage and/or increase R_L so that R_S is within its operating range. Record the current on the meter and again observe how the current is affected by changes of E_{supply} and R_L.

Repeat the above operation for $R = 500$ ohms and $R = 67$ ohms.

Switch the servo controller to the "10" position and adjust the decade resistance box so that $R = 10$ ohms, and again determine the response of the system as a constant current source.

Return the controller to the "100" position, determine how to obtain a constant current of 0.965 ma, and test your method.

Expt. 7-8   Servo Constant Voltage Supply

The circuits of Expt. 7-7 are not changed for this experiment, but only the considerations.   Assume that it is desirable to maintain the voltage constant across the terminals of R (input to the servo), regardless of how R changes or whether another emf is introduced.   By connecting a VTVM across R, demonstrate that E_R remains constant as R changes, and determine the limits of the servo control. Be careful to change ranges on the current meter, and do not exceed a current of 20 ma.

Expt. 7-9   Recording Potentiometer

Restore the circuit to its normal use as an automatic-balancing recording potentiometer, according to the terminal connections shown in the EUW-20 manual or on the back cover of the recorder.

chapter eight

Operational Amplifiers for Measurement and Control

The development of the stable high-gain d-c amplifier (Sec. 4-3) has made possible the development of all-electronic systems for the precision control of electrical quantities. Commercially available instruments employing electronic control are now common in the scientific laboratory. Direct-current power-supply voltage regulation is the most common example of electronic control. In addition, many sophisticated instruments rely on electronic control for their operation: constant-current supplies, line-voltage regulators, some electrometer voltmeters, spectrophotometers, analog computers, and many others. Recently the widespread availability of d-c control amplifiers (sometimes called operational amplifiers) has made it possible for research workers to develop precision control circuits to suit their own problems and applications. In general, operational amplifier control systems are simple, precise, fast, and relatively inexpensive. The characteristics of the amplifiers, the principles of their operation, and many examples of their application are presented in this chapter. The regulated power supply is discussed in some detail. Some of the methods for electronically controlling high-power devices such as magnets and furnaces are indicated.

8-1 An Amplifier Designed for Feedback Control

In Chap. 7 the technique of using an amplifier, servomotor, and me-chanical linkages for feedback control was presented. As indicated, these servo systems can be and are applied to the problem of controlling purely electrical quantities. An example of servo control of voltage is shown in Fig. 8-1. The d-c voltage across the load, e_o, is to be kept constant and equal to the reference voltage e_{ref}, despite changes in the load resistance and the power-supply voltage. If the output voltage is not equal to the reference voltage, a d-c error voltage e_s will exist at the input of the ampli-fier and the servomotor will drive the slider of the variable resistance to correct the output voltage. In short, the error signal is converted to me-chanical movement, and mechanical movement is converted back into an electrical quantity so that the error signal decreases toward zero. There are many examples where the servomotor controls a Variac, or generator, in order to control some electrical quantity.

Since electrically actuated devices, such as transistors and vacuum tubes, can also be used to control electrical quantities, it is not necessary in many cases to go through the mechanical linkages of the servo. Figure 8-2 shows a completely electronic circuit for voltage control. A vacuum tube replaces the rheostat of Fig. 8-1. In effect, the vacuum tube becomes a variable series resistance controlled by the amplifier. If the load voltage e_o increases, the current in the load must decrease to bring e_o back to the reference value e_{ref}. The required decrease in current can be provided by making the grid potential of the series tube V more negative. In other words, for regulation of e_o, the amplifier must provide a polarity reversal, so that when e_o goes positive the amplifier output (and grid of the series tube) goes negative, and vice versa. The potential advantages of electronic

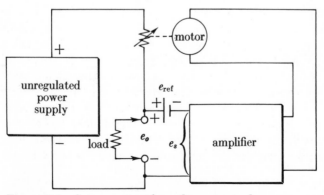

Figure 8-1   Servo system for voltage control.

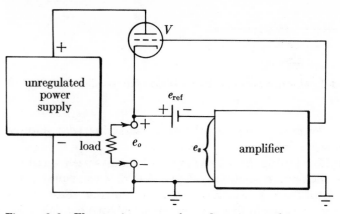

Figure 8-2   Electronic system for voltage control.

control, compared with servo control in this case, are greater simplicity and faster response.   It is important now to consider those characteristics which make an amplifier suitable for control.

It has been shown in the above example, that the amplifier must be *inverting* or else the amplified error signal would only augment the error and cause the system to run out of control.   Recall that it is *negative feedback* which leads to a stable system.   The control amplifier must also be a *d-c amplifier* so that it can respond to the slow changes of input voltage that are common in control applications.   The d-c amplifier should have *high gain*.   Assume that the amplifier output voltage has been adjusted so that the proper bias voltage is supplied to the grid of V when e_s is zero. In this case there is no error, since e_o is exactly equal to e_{ref}.   If the output voltage of the unregulated power supply then changes by 10 volts, the grid voltage of the control tube must change by $10/\mu$ volts to maintain a constant e_o.   If V is a 6AS7, a popular control tube with a μ of 2, the amplifier output voltage would change 5 volts.   The error signal e_s would thus be 5 volts/A, where A is the gain of the amplifier.   An amplifier with a gain of 1000 would give a 5-mv error in this case.   *The error signal decreases as the amplifier gain increases*, which accounts for the design of control amplifiers with very high gains.

For precise control, it is also important that the amplifier have good d-c stability, so that the output voltage is constant for a constant input voltage.   This stability can be obtained by careful design and use of very stable power supplies.   As other control applications are discussed it will become apparent that other desirable amplifier characteristics are *high input impedance* (since the amplifier is a voltage-sensitive device), *low output impedance* (since the amplifier must sometimes supply current while maintaining control), and *good high-frequency response* (so that the control

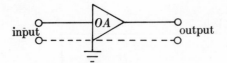

Figure 8-3   Operational amplifier: schematic symbol.

response can be rapid). The capability of producing both positive and negative output voltages is often necessary.

An amplifier having the above characteristics has been found to be so versatile, to perform so many operations, that it is commonly called the *operational amplifier*. In combination with precision resistors, capacitors, potentiometers, and other devices the operational amplifiers perform mathematical operations, such as adding, multiplying, integration, and differentiation. It is this ability to perform precise mathematical operations that makes it the key element in analog computers.

The schematic symbol for an operational amplifier OA is the triangle shown in Fig. 8-3. The dotted line indicates the common connection between the input signal, the output signal, and the power supply. For simplicity this connection is usually omitted from the circuit diagram.

The operational amplifier is of little value when connected as shown in Fig. 8-3. Because of the very high gain, an input signal of a few millivolts would drive the output voltage to its maximum value. Since a few millivolts would be a typical value for noise and drift within the amplifier, it follows that the amplifier is not suitable for signals smaller than a few millivolts. It is the use of a negative-feedback path (the control loop) with the operational amplifier that results in a stable circuit suitable for accurate control and precise computation.

Feedback Circuits. There are three general feedback circuits which are used with an operational amplifier. All three are shown in Fig. 8-4. The first feedback circuit shown (Fig. 8-4a) is the conventional voltage-feedback circuit discussed in Sec. 4-7. A fraction β of the output voltage is fed back in series with the input voltage. Recall that this circuit has the characteristics of low output impedance, high input impedance, reduced noise and distortion, reduced gain, and increased gain stability. The circuit is shown with the triangular amplifier symbol as well as with the more familiar block symbol. In the current-feedback amplifier (Fig. 8-4b), a voltage proportional to the output current is fed back in series with the input voltage. The characteristics of this circuit are similar to those of the voltage-feedback amplifier except that the output impedance is high and the no-load voltage gain is not reduced.

The third feedback circuit is shown in Fig. 8-4c. It is a kind of voltage feedback. The output voltage is connected through an impedance R_f to the amplifier input at point S *in parallel* with the input signal. It is the

only feedback circuit shown in Fig. 8-4 which has a common ground connection for the input signal, the output signal, and the power supply.   It
is this type of feedback which is used when the amplifiers are connected to
perform mathematical operations on the input signal.   For this reason it is
called operational feedback.

Operational feedback provides all the beneficial effects of normal voltage feedback except that the input impedance is very low.   This is because the input-signal source is connected through R_f to the output voltage,
which is of opposite sign and A times greater than the input voltage.

$$e_o = -Ae_s \tag{8-1}$$

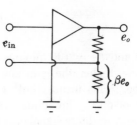
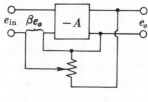

(a)

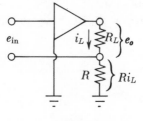
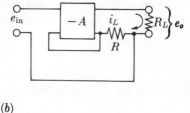

(b)

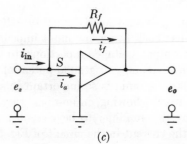

(c)

Figure 8-4   Feedback circuits: (a) voltage; (b) current; (c) operational.

The voltage across R_f is $e_s - e_o = e_s(1 + A)$. The current i_f through R_f is thus

$$i_f = \frac{e_s - e_o}{R_f} = \frac{e_s(1 + A)}{R_f} \tag{8-2}$$

Upon applying Kirchhoff's law to the junction S (Fig. 8-4c), the current from the signal source i_{in} equals i_f plus the current to the amplifier input i_a. The input impedance of the amplifier itself is normally so large (1 to 100 megohms) that i_a can be neglected.

$$i_{in} = i_f \tag{8-3}$$

Therefore, the input resistance $R_S = e_s/i_{in}$ is found from Eqs. (8-2) and (8-3) to be

$$R_S = \frac{e_s}{i_{in}} = e_s \frac{R_f}{e_s(1 + A)} = \frac{R_f}{1 + A} \tag{8-4}$$

or $R_S \approx R_f/A$ when $A \gg 1$. If $A = 10,000$ and $R_f = 100$ kilohms, the input resistance would be about 10 ohms. The higher the gain and the lower R_f, the lower the input resistance will be. This means that, as far as the signal source is concerned, a resistance of only a few ohms is connected from the input terminal to ground. Only very large signal currents, then, could cause the input voltage e_s to be significantly different from ground potential. For this reason point S is called a "virtual ground." Such a low input resistance is much better for a current-sensing device than for a voltage amplifier. In fact, it can be easily shown that the output voltage is a linear function of the input current.

Solving Eq. (8-2) for e_s, and substituting $i_f = i_{in}$ from Eq. (8-3),

$$e_s = \frac{R_f i_{in}}{1 + A} \tag{8-5}$$

Substituting e_s from Eq. (8-5) into (8-1),

$$e_o = -Ae_s = -\frac{A}{1 + A} R_f i_{in} \tag{8-6}$$

For large values of A, then, e_o is very nearly equal to $-R_f i_{in}$. Thus, the amplifier with operational feedback has a low input impedance ideal for a current-sensitive circuit, an output voltage proportional to the input signal current, and an input which is virtually at ground potential.

The concept of the virtual ground is so important in studying operational amplifiers that it is worth showing, in another way, how the input potential e_s is controlled by the amplifier to be virtually zero. Consider the problem of measuring the current in the circuit of Fig. 8-5a. Whether

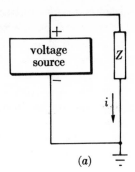

(a)

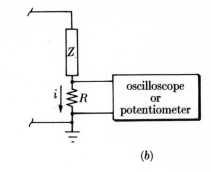

(b)

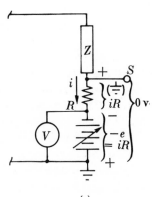

(c)

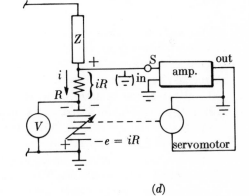

(d)

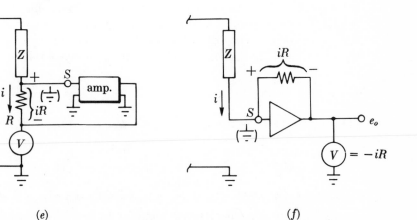

(e)

(f)

Figure 8-5   *Application of control to the measurement of current.*

an ammeter is introduced in the circuit or a resistor is used to measure the iR drop as in Fig. 8-5b, the magnitude of the current will be affected by the measurement device. Furthermore, the impedance Z is no longer grounded, which may be undesirable from other points of view. If the measurement is made at some other place in the circuit, either the voltage source or the ammeter will not be grounded.

One remedy for the above problems is to offset the iR drop in the circuit with an external voltage source as shown in Fig. 8-5c. If the battery voltage is exactly equal and opposite to the iR drop, the circuit performs as though undisturbed and as though the impedance were connected directly to ground. If the battery voltage has been set correctly, the voltage at point S will be zero. The ground symbol in parentheses indicates a virtual ground. A voltmeter, reading the battery voltage, indicates the iR drop across R. The voltmeter, drawing current, now causes no error in the current measurement. The battery voltage could be automatically adjusted with a servomechanism, as shown in Fig. 8-5d. If there is an error signal at point S, the servomotor changes the battery voltage to correct it. The d-c output voltage of a control amplifier can take the place of the servomotor and battery as shown in Fig. 8-5e. If the iR drop increases, the output voltage becomes more negative to compensate. This circuit can be redrawn as Fig. 8-5f and is identical to Fig. 8-4c. Thus, it is shown by this example that the operational amplifier always tries, by means of its output signal and a feedback path, to control its input potential to be virtually that of ground. Within the gain, output current, and voltage limitations of the amplifier, this control will be achieved.

To connect a signal-voltage source to an amplifier with operational feedback, it is necessary to interpose an impedance to keep from overloading the voltage source. The resulting circuit is shown in Fig. 8-6a. For clarity, the common ground connection has been shown, but in subsequent circuits the convention of not showing the ground circuit, as in Fig. 8-6b, will be followed. The signal voltage e_{in} is connected to point S through resistance R_{in}. The current drain i_{in} on the signal source will be

$$i_{in} = \frac{e_{in} - e_s}{R_{in}} \tag{8-7}$$

Substituting for i_{in} from Eq. (8-7) and i_f from Eq. (8-2) in Eq. (8-3),

$$\frac{e_{in} - e_s}{R_{in}} = \frac{e_s - e_o}{R_f} \tag{8-8}$$

Eliminate e_s by substituting $e_s = -e_o/A$ from Eq. (8-1), and solve for e_o,

$$e_o = \frac{-e_{in}(R_f/R_{in})}{1 - (1 + R_f/R_{in})/A} \tag{8-9}$$

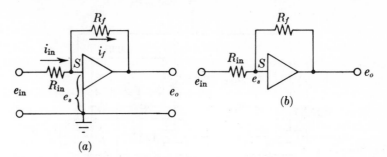

Figure 8-6   *Operational feedback voltage amplifier.*

From an amplifier gain of -10^4 or more, it is readily seen that $-A \gg 1 + R_f/R_{\text{in}}$, unless the ratio R_f/R_{in} is unusually large. Therefore the denominator reduces to unity, and

$$e_o = -\frac{R_f}{R_{\text{in}}} e_{\text{in}} \tag{8-10}$$

The remarkable fact indicated by Eq. (8-10) is that the output voltage is now a precise multiple of the input voltage, independent, within predetermined limits, of the amplifier characteristics and the output load. In other words, if the resistances R_f and R_{in} are accurate within 0.1 per cent and are in the ratio $R_f/R_{\text{in}} = 10$, then $e_o = 10.00e_{\text{in}}$. The use of other impedances Z_{in} and Z_f to replace R_{in} and R_f, respectively, enables other precise mathematical operations to be performed, as described in subsequent sections. In many texts, the circuit including the amplifier with operational feedback and a series input impedance as shown is called the operational amplifier. Through usage, however, the amplifier itself, designed for use with operational feedback, has come to be known as an operational amplifier, even though it can also be used with conventional voltage- and current-feedback circuits. In this text, an amplifier having the characteristics necessary for d-c control circuits will be called an operational amplifier. The type of feedback employed in the working circuit will be separately termed voltage, current, or operational, as in Fig. 8-4.

    The Operational-Amplifier Circuit. The circuit of a typical operational amplifier is shown in Fig. 8-7. The input stage is the difference amplifier described in Chap. 4 (Fig. 4-23). The gain of this stage, according to Eq. (4-9), is 76. The input stage is d-c-coupled to the second stage of amplification. About one-third of the signal is lost in the coupling divider. The gain of the second stage is 30. The final stage is a cathode follower

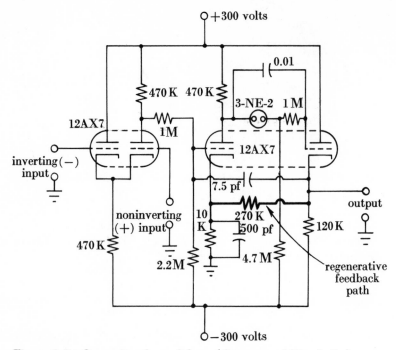

Figure 8-7   Operational amplifier. (Courtesy of Heath Co.)

for low output impedance. The coupling to this stage, through neon glow tubes, involves little signal loss. The gain of the cathode-follower stage is, of course, somewhat less than 1. The over-all gain of the amplifier is then about $76 \times \frac{2}{3} \times 30 = 1520$. Additional gain is sometimes obtained through the use of regenerative feedback. The regenerative-feedback path in this amplifier is shown in Fig. 8-7. In this case the amplifier gain is brought up to 8600. The high-frequency gain is improved by the 500-pf bypass capacitor in the cathode circuit of the second stage. However, with so much regenerative feedback, too much high-frequency gain could result in a high-frequency oscillation. The 7.5-pf capacitor between the amplifier output and the grid of the second stage is a *negative*-feedback path to reduce the very high-frequency gain and thus prevent oscillation.

The reasons for the difference-amplifier input stage are threefold: the positive, or noninverting, input provides a convenient place to apply a potential to adjust the zero level of the amplifier; the difference amplifier is less susceptible to drift caused by variations in the supply voltages; and, occasionally, the + input is used as a signal input, as will be shown later.

D-C-Level Adjustment. With a direct-coupled amplifier such as that of Fig. 8-7 it is necessary to adjust the d-c level of the amplifier so

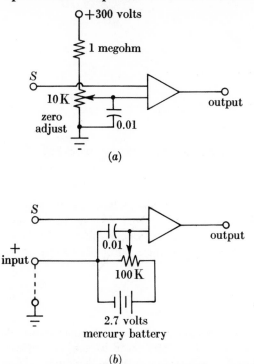

Figure 8-8 *Biasing the operational amplifier:* (a) *using the power-supply voltage;* (b) *battery bias.*

that the output voltage is zero when there is no input signal. The means of making this adjustment must be reasonably convenient, because aging or replacement of components or changes in power-supply voltage will cause a d-c level change in the amplifier. The amplifier of Fig. 8-7 requires about a 1.3-volt bias at the positive input to adjust the d-c level. Two circuits for applying this voltage are shown in Fig. 8-8. Figure 8-8*b* allows the use of the positive input for a signal if desired. In subsequent figures, the bias-adjustment circuit will be omitted for simplicity. The positive (noninverting) input will also be omitted, unless specifically required in the circuit.

Effect of D-C Offset. It is very important in most applications of the operational amplifier that the d-c level throughout the amplifier be adjusted and maintained so that the output voltage is zero when there is no input signal. The effects of using an amplifier which has a d-c offset with operational feedback can be illustrated by the following discussion. Suppose that the amplifier with no feedback has an output of B volts when there is no input signal (point S connected to ground). When an input

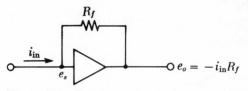

Figure 8-9   Current measurement.

signal e_s is then applied to point S, the output voltage would be

$$e_o = -Ae_s + B \tag{8-11}$$

showing the constant output offset voltage B. This amplifier is now wired with operational feedback as shown in Fig. 8-9. When there is no input signal ($i_{in} = 0$), i_f is zero and there is therefore no voltage drop across R_f. In other words $e_s = e_o$. Substituting e_s for e_o and solving Eq. (8-11) for e_o,

$$e_o = e_s = \frac{B}{1 + A} \tag{8-12}$$

The operational feedback no longer keeps point S at ground potential, but rather at a potential of $B/(1 + A)$. The error in the virtual ground, $B/(1 + A)$, is called the d-c offset referred to the amplifier input. The zero-adjust control can be used to adjust the offset voltage to zero. Once adjusted, a typical amplifier will drift, to cause an average offset referred to the input of 5 to 50 mv. How serious this drift might be depends on the application.

Consider the effect of offset on the voltage amplifier of Fig. 8-6b. Offset will cause the voltage at point S to be $B/(1 + A)$. When there is no input-signal voltage (input e_{in} short-circuited to ground), the offset potential appears across R_{in} and an input current of $-B/R_{in}(1 + A)$ is generated. This current will cause an output voltage of $(R_f/R_{in})[B/(1 + A)]$. Thus, the offset voltage is amplified by the same factor as the input voltage. This amplifier circuit with e_{in} grounded and a gain of 10 or 100 is often used for the adjustment of the d-c level control.

It might seem from Eq. (8-12) that a higher-gain amplifier would have less offset. However, the d-c instability is most critical in the first stage of amplification, and subsequent amplification to increase A will only increase B proportionately. A very well-regulated power supply is required for d-c stability. Regulation of better than 1 per cent is essential, and 0.05 per cent is not uncommon.

8-2   Operational Amplifiers for Electrical Measurements

The operational amplifier is used to aid in making electrical measurements by serving as an isolation amplifier with a precise gain between the circuit being measured and the measurement device. In every case, the operational amplifier disturbs the circuit less than would the usual meters, recorders, or oscilloscopes. The amplifier presents a lower output impedance to the indicating device than would the circuit itself. In addition, certain measurements can be made by using operational amplifiers which are very difficult by other means.

Current Measurements. The output voltage of a high-gain amplifier with operational feedback (Fig. 8-9) is a precise function of its input current, i.e., $e_o = -i_{in}R_f$ [Eq. (8-6)]. If R_f is 1 megohm, the output will be 1 volt/μa of input current. If the amplifier gain is $-50,000$, the resistance presented at the current input terminals by the amplifier is only 1 megohm/50,000 = 20 ohms (Eq. 8-4). By comparison, a dropping resistor to give a 1-mv recorder a full-scale deflection of 1 μa would be 1000 ohms. Furthermore, with the amplifier circuit the meter, or indicator, used to measure the amplifier output voltage may draw reasonable currents without affecting the accuracy of the current measurement.

Since the input impedance is so low, currents from several circuits may be brought to the input as in Fig. 8-10 and the output voltage will be proportional to the sum of the input currents. The operational amplifier input is commonly called the summing point (S) because the sum of all the signal currents plus the feedback current must equal zero. The input circuits will not interfere with one another, because the input is so near ground potential. By use of this circuit, current measurements can be made to better than 0.1 per cent accuracy. With a very large value for R_f, currents as low as 10^{-11} amp can be measured accurately. However, such low current measurements usually require a balancing, or compensating, cur-

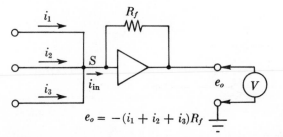

$$e_o = -(i_1 + i_2 + i_3)R_f$$

Figure 8-10   Measurement of the sum of currents.

rent to be fed to the summing point. This is to compensate for leakage currents into the wiring and into the amplifier input.

Voltage Measurements. The circuit of Fig. 8-6 has been discussed as a voltage amplifier. The gain is a constant (independent of the amplifier characteristics) times the input voltage. Precise gains up to 1000 are practical. Since point S is a virtual ground, the input resistance of this amplifier will be R_{in}. If the maximum practical R_f is 1 megohm for a particular amplifier and a gain of 100 is desired, R_{in} will be 10 kilohms. Thus this amplifier has a rather low input resistance. It is important to distinguish between the input to the amplifier circuit with input impedance and operational feedback as shown in Fig. 8-6 and the input to the operational amplifier itself. To avoid confusion, the latter input will be referred to only as point S, or the summing point.

Several voltage inputs may be used with the operational feedback amplifier as shown in Fig. 8-11. The output voltage is the simple sum of the amplified signal voltages. Each input voltage can be amplified by a different factor if desired. The input circuits are all effectively isolated from one another because the potential at the summing point is virtually ground.

The voltage-feedback amplifier shown in Fig. 8-12 can also be used to measure potential. Suppose that a signal voltage of the sign shown is applied to the input. The output voltage will go negative until the potential across R_2 is equal to that of e_{in} and has the polarity shown. Now the potential between point S and ground is virtually zero and the system is stable. The output voltage e_o is divided across R_1 and R_2 so that $e_f = e_o[R_2/(R_1 + R_2)]$. For amplifiers with high gains, $e_f = -e_{in}$, so that

$$e_o = -e_{in} \frac{R_1 + R_2}{R_2} \tag{8-13}$$

This amplifier has the advantage over the operational feedback amplifier that it draws negligible current from the potential source being measured.

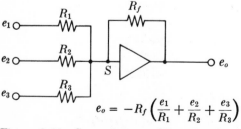

$$e_o = -R_f \left(\frac{e_1}{R_1} + \frac{e_2}{R_2} + \frac{e_3}{R_3} \right)$$

Figure 8-11   Summing amplifier circuit.

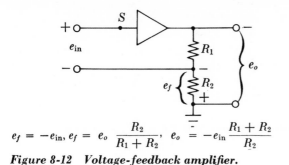

$$e_f = -e_{in}, e_f = e_o \frac{R_2}{R_1 + R_2}, \quad e_o = -e_{in} \frac{R_1 + R_2}{R_2}$$

Figure 8-12 *Voltage-feedback amplifier.*

Neither input terminal is ground or can be grounded; however the connection to point S is a virtual ground. Note that there is no way by which several input voltages could be summed at the input of the voltage-feedback amplifier except by connecting them in series. This illustrates an important point: *When it is necessary to sum signals at an amplifier input, operational feedback must be used;* it is important to remember that *with operational feedback the signal currents are being added, not the potentials.*

The Voltage Follower. A voltage-measuring circuit which offers even greater isolation of the input circuit is shown in Fig. 8-13. This circuit is known as the voltage follower because the output voltage is identical to the input voltage in sign and magnitude. This circuit makes use of the noninverting, or positive, input of the operational amplifier. When the voltage at the noninverting input goes positive, the output goes positive. The entire output voltage is fed back to the inverting input, which is *not*, in this case, maintained at virtual ground. The gain of a feedback amplifier was shown in Eq. (4-17) to be $A/(1 - \beta A)$. In this case β is -1, and the gain is therefore $A/(1 + A)$, which, when A is large, is indistinguishable from unity. The follower, by presenting a very high impedance to the signal and a very low impedance to the load, very effectively isolates the signal and measurement circuits. Input and output impedances are typically 100 megohms and less than 1 ohm, respectively.

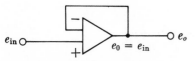

Figure 8-13 *Voltage follower.*

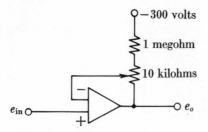

Figure 8-14   Power-supply biasing of the voltage follower.

The follower may be biased in one of two ways. The battery bias method shown in Fig. 8-8b is suitable, since the positive input is available. Another method, shown in Fig. 8-14, adds the bias voltage in the feedback loop. The feedback signal is attenuated by 0.995 by the bias network, giving the amplifier a slight gain (about 1.005).

The Integrator.   Charge may be measured by using the basic operational feedback circuit and letting the feedback current accumulate on a capacitor. The circuit is shown in Fig. 8-15. As charge passes the summing point, the output establishes a potential on the capacitor so that all the charge is accumulated on the capacitor and the summing point remains at ground potential. The potential across the capacitor is the same as the potential of the output with respect to ground and may be measured continuously with any device which does not require an unreasonable amount of current. Capacitance may be defined by the equation $C = Q/V$, where V is the potential across the capacitor and Q is the charge on the capacitor. Q is the current-time integral, i.e., $Q = \int_0^t i\,dt$. Upon substituting for Q and solving for V, $V = -(1/C)\int_0^t i\,dt$. Thus the output voltage at any time t is the current-time integral of the input-current waveform. If a potential

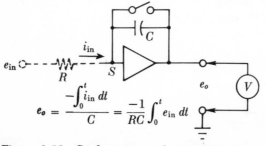

$$e_o = \frac{-\int_0^t i_{in}\,dt}{C} = \frac{-1}{RC}\int_0^t e_{in}\,dt$$

Figure 8-15   Coulometer, or integrator.

is to be integrated, a resistor is put in the input circuit so that the input current is proportional to the signal voltage. The output voltage would then be

$$e_o = -\frac{1}{RC}\int_0^t e_{in}\, dt \tag{8-14}$$

since $i_{in} = e_{in}/R$. Of course a summing integrator would result if current from more than one source were brought to the summing point.

Consider the integration of the succession of peaks shown in Fig. 8-16. During each peak, charge is accumulated on the feedback capacitor proportional to the area under the peak. Between the peaks, when the signal voltage is zero, the integral is constant. After each peak, the integrator output voltage is greater. The output of the integrator is returned to zero in preparation for the next integration by short-circuiting the integrating capacitor with a switch or relay contact. Integration is resumed when the switch is reopened.

The integrating capacitor accumulates all charge passing the summing point, whether from the signal or any other source. Errors can arise from any or all of the three following sources: (1) Zero-level offset. Recall that, when the zero level is not adjusted properly, the summing point tends to be

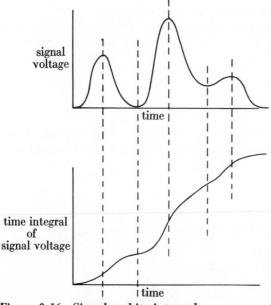

Figure 8-16   Signal and its integral.

controlled at some potential other than ground. It can be seen from Fig. 8-15 that if this is the case, when e_{in} is zero (ground potential), there will still be an i_{in} and thus a changing integral. Unless the operational amplifier is properly balanced and very stable, integration of small currents over long periods of time is impossible. (2) Current leakage to the summing point. Any currents leaking to the summing point from nearby power-supply leads or other sources will be integrated and confused with the signal current. The solution to this problem is to shield the summing-point wiring. (3) Capacitor leakage. As a potential develops across the capacitor dielectric, some charge will leak through the capacitor, resulting in an error current and an unstable integral. Care must be taken to select high-quality integrating capacitors such as those using polystyrene dielectrics.

It is tempting and, in fact, sometimes convenient to use the integrator to shift a sine-wave signal 90° in phase or make a triangular wave out of a square wave. The integration of the error currents and any d-c component of the signal, however, will cause the d-c level of the integrator output to increase steadily. Once the amplifier's maximum positive or negative output voltage is reached, the amplifier is no longer in control and the output is no longer the integral of the input.

The Differentiator. The rate of change of potential may be measured by interchanging the capacitor and resistor of the integrator. The resulting circuit, shown in Fig. 8-17, gives the time derivative of the input signal. When the input voltage changes, a current must pass through the feedback resistor to keep the summing point at ground potential. The magnitude of this current is directly proportional to the size of the capacitor and the rate of change of the input voltage. The output voltage necessary to supply this current is, of course, proportional to the size of the feedback resistor. From the above, then,

$$e_o = -RC\frac{de_{in}}{dt} \tag{8-15}$$

where de_{in}/dt is expressed in volts per second. The problems of drift do not exist with the differentiator circuit because it is a-c-coupled from the

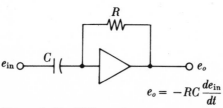

$$e_o = -RC\frac{de_{in}}{dt}$$

Figure 8-17   Differentiator.

signal to the summing point and d-c-coupled from the output to the summing point.

Noise pulses, having a high rate of change of potential, are amplified by the differentiating circuit. Thus, with R and C chosen to differentiate a potential change of moderate speed, high-frequency noise can predominate in the output. The high-speed response of the circuit can be reduced to decrease the noise sensitivity. This is done by putting a small capacitor in parallel with the feedback resistor or a small resistor in series with the input capacitor. This will, of course, have the effect of making the derivative of the signal somewhat less than perfect.

A Voltage or Current Comparator. Comparison measurements may be made using the operational amplifier as a difference detector. The summing capability makes it possible to compare two grounded current sources with a grounded detector. The circuit is that of Fig. 8-10 with two inputs. The current to be measured is fed to one input, while an adjustable standard opposing current source is fed to the other. When the two currents are equal, the output voltage will be zero. The sensitivity is increased by increasing the value of R_f. A similar voltage comparator may be made using the similar circuit of Fig. 8-11. In all these applications, the maximum practical sensitivity is limited by the zero-level stability of the amplifier.

8-3   The Chopper-Stabilized Operational Amplifier

The problems arising from d-c instability in the operational amplifier have been mentioned in the previous section. Efforts to keep the offset less than a few millivolts in a direct-coupled amplifier add greatly to the cost and complexity of the amplifier and supplies and offer only modest improvement. Direct-current amplifiers with excellent d-c stability can be built by chopping the d-c input signal to a-c, amplifying the a-c signal, and demodulating to regain the d-c output. Chopper amplifiers, however, have very poor high-frequency response, the upper limit usually being of the order of 1 to 10 cps when the chopper frequency is properly filtered from the d-c output. While the response speed of a chopper amplifier is generally too slow for use as a computing or control amplifier, it can be used as a control amplifier to detect and counteract slow drifts in the d-c-coupled amplifier.

The chopper amplifier detects offset by measuring the potential at the summing point of the operational amplifier. This potential was shown in Sec. 8-1 to differ from ground potential when an offset exists. If there is a potential at the summing point, it is amplified by the chopper amplifier and applied to the bias input to correct the offset. A simplified circuit for the stabilization of an operational amplifier by a chopper amplifier is shown in Fig. 8-18. A positive voltage at point S indicates a positive offset in

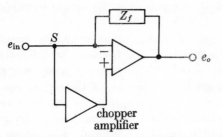

Figure 8-18   *Chopper amplifier controlling d-c drift in operational amplifier.*

the output voltage. To correct this, a negative change in the bias voltage at the positive input should be made. The chopper amplifier should then be inverting. If a 10-mv chopper-amplifier output voltage is required to correct the offset at a particular time and the gain of the chopper amplifier is 1000, the voltage at point S must then be 10 mv/1000 = 0.01 mv. In other words the drift and offset of the operational amplifier would ideally be reduced by the gain of the chopper amplifier. This provides a dramatic improvement in stability.

The Chopper Amplifier.   The circuit of a typical chopper amplifier is shown in Fig. 8-19. The d-c input voltage is chopped with a 60-cps chopper. The a-c voltage is amplified by two stages of triode amplification, V_1 and V_2. After being inverted twice, the signal at the plate of V_2 is now in phase with the chopped signal at the grid of V_1. The alternate half of the chopper is used to short-circuit the amplified a-c signal. This leaves only the negative half cycles if the d-c input voltage is positive, and vice versa. Thus the a-c voltage has been converted back to d-c, and the polarity has been inverted as required by Fig. 8-18. Figure 8-19*b* shows the waveforms at points A to E of Fig. 8-19*a*. If the a-c signal at the plate of V_2 had simply been diode-rectified, there would have been no way of knowing, from the output, the polarity of the input voltage. Following the output chopper in Fig. 8-19, there is a filter to reduce the chopper-frequency component in the output. It is this filter which makes the amplifier response so slow.

Because the filtering of the a-c component in the output voltage is not perfect, the chopper amplifier will introduce some noise of the chopper frequency into the operational amplifier circuit. The higher the chopper frequency, the easier it is to filter out and the faster the response of the amplifier can be. Mechanical choppers can be used at 400 cps, which offers some improvement over 60 cps. Solid-state choppers operating at frequencies well over 100 kc are used in at least one model. The resulting amplifier is fast enough and has sufficient gain to use directly as an operational amplifier.

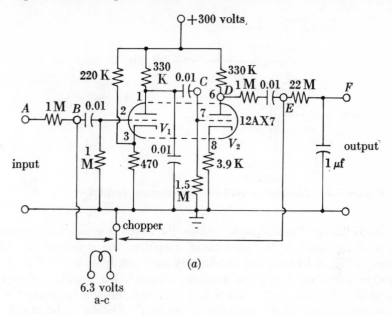

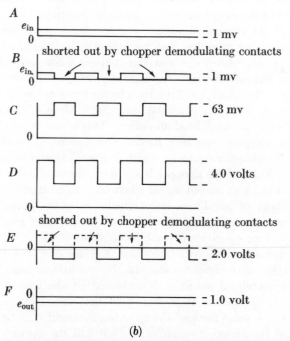

(a)

6.3 volts
a-c

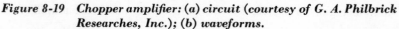

(b)

Figure 8-19   *Chopper amplifier: (a) circuit (courtesy of G. A. Philbrick Researches, Inc.); (b) waveforms.*

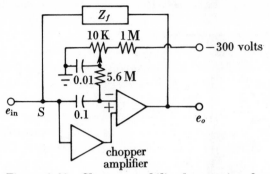

Figure 8-20   Chopper-stabilized operational amplifier.

Stabilizing Techniques. Since the stabilizing amplifier requires the positive input of the operational amplifier, the stabilized amplifier shown in Fig. 8-18 must use the battery bias supply shown in Fig. 8-8b. Another stabilizing circuit which avoids a battery bias supply is shown in Fig. 8-20. The signal at point S is a-c-coupled through the capacitor to the inverting input of the operational amplifier. The d-c signal at point S is amplified by the inverting chopper amplifier and applied to the non-inverting input of the operational amplifier. The bias supply is used to establish the d-c level at the inverting input. The bias is adjusted initially so that the output of the chopper amplifier is zero. Subsequent drift is controlled by the stabilizing amplifier, but the initial adjustment reduces the required stabilizer output voltage and thus reduces noise and offset.

The Effects of Stabilization. As explained above, the chopper amplifier should reduce the offset and drift by a factor equal to the gain of the amplifier. However, there is a practical lower limit, often in excess of the ideal, for the offset of the stabilized amplifier. This is due to an offset occurring within the chopper amplifier itself. One source for such an offset is noise from the chopper contacts, which is amplified and demodulated at the output. Noise of the chopper frequency generated within the amplifier will also result in an output signal when there is no input signal. This is particularly true of amplifiers using 60-cps choppers. However with good shielding and a quality chopper, even a 60-cps chopper amplifier can reduce the offset of an operational amplifier to about 100 μv.

In addition to reducing the drift and offset, the use of a stabilizing amplifier alters certain other characteristics of the operational amplifier. The d-c gain of the stabilized amplifier is increased by the gain of the chopper amplifier. It is obvious from Fig. 8-20 that the d-c signal is amplified by the chopper amplifier and the operational amplifier in succession. If the gain of the chopper amplifier is 1000 and the operational-amplifier gain is 50,000, the d-c gain of the stabilized amplifier will be

50,000 $\times$ 1000 = 50,000,000. The d-c control of the stabilized amplifier is thus very precise. For control of rapid fluctuations, the gain of the operational amplifier alone determines the precision.

Under certain circumstances, the maximum output voltage or current of the operational amplifier may be insufficient to maintain control and keep the summing point at virtual ground. This could occur with the integrator circuit, for instance, if the current integral exceeds the value $Ce_{o,\text{max}}$, where C is the value of the integrating capacitor and $e_{o,\text{max}}$ is the maximum operational-amplifier output voltage. Under such circumstances, the operational-amplifier output will be the maximum available output signal, and the amplifier is said to have reached its "limit." Ordinarily, the operational amplifier will come out of limit and regain control as soon as the demand on the output ceases to exceed the output capability. However, with the stabilizing circuit of Fig. 8-20, the recovery from limit can take several seconds to a minute. This is explained in the following way: During the limit period, the potential at the summing point is not a virtual ground. The chopper amplifier amplifies the voltage at the summing point and applies a high output voltage to the operational-amplifier input to correct the offset. The large filter capacitor in the chopper-amplifier output thus is charged to a high potential. When the limit conditions are removed, this capacitor must discharge through the high resistance of the filter. The operational amplifier will remain at limit until the capacitor is discharged. It is important, therefore, in using stabilized amplifiers, to avoid circuits which would cause the amplifier to limit even for a fraction of a second.

Stabilizing the Follower. The stabilizing circuit of Fig. 8-20 cannot be used for the follower, since the positive input is required. Furthermore, the input of the follower is not at ground potential. An offset

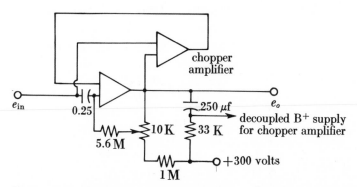

Figure 8-21 Stabilized follower amplifier. (Designed by D. D. DeFord, Northwestern University.)

exists in the follower amplifier if the output voltage is not equal to the input
voltage. The stabilizing amplifier is wired to measure the difference
between the input and output voltage and apply the correction signal to
the inverting input. The circuit is shown in Fig. 8-21. Again, the input
signal is a-c-coupled to the operational-amplifier noninverting input. The
d-c input signal is amplified and inverted by the chopper amplifier and
then amplified and reinverted by the operational amplifier. The d-c-gain,
offset, and limit-recovery considerations for the stabilized follower are the
same as those for the stabilized inverting amplifier.

8-4   The Generation of Precise Voltages and Waveforms

An amplifier with a precisely known and constant gain can be used
to amplify the potential from a standard voltage reference cell to provide a
wide range of accurate voltages. To keep from drawing current from the
standard cell, the voltage-feedback amplifier is used. The voltage reference source is shown in Fig. 8-22. When 0.1 per cent resistors are used in
the feedback divider, the output voltage will be accurate to 0.1 per cent.
Current may be drawn from the output with virtually no change in the
potential or any damage to the standard cell.

The most common application of the operational amplifier as a precision waveform generator is to generate a linear-sweep voltage. With a
constant input signal the integrator shown in Fig. 8-23 will produce an
output voltage which is a linear function of time. The switch S is opened to
begin the sweep and closed to return the output voltage to zero. Switch S
may be a device which short-circuits the capacitor at regular intervals, or
whenever the output voltage reaches a particular value in order to repeat
the sweep automatically. For instance, the thyratron may be used as
switch S, in a way similar to the relaxation oscillator of Fig. 5-16. The
advantages of the operational-amplifier sweep circuit of Fig. 8-22 over
that of Fig. 5-16 are (1) the near-perfect linearity of the sweep because of

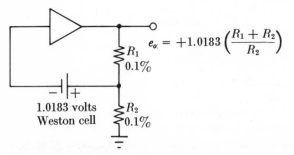

$$e_o = +1.0183 \left(\frac{R_1 + R_2}{R_2} \right)$$

R_1
0.1%

1.0183 volts
Weston cell
R_2
0.1%

Figure 8-22   Voltage reference source.

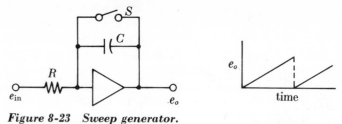

Figure 8-23   *Sweep generator.*

the constant charging current and (2) the ability to draw current from the operational-amplifier output without affecting the sweep rate or linearity. With a high-quality integrating capacitor and a reasonably stable high-gain operational amplifier, a sweep linear to at least 0.1 per cent should be expected.

Oscilloscope Sweep Circuits. As discussed in Chap. 1, a sweep voltage is used to display the time axis when an oscilloscope is used to observe a waveform. The accurate measurement of the period of time between parts of the observed waveform is facilitated by a sweep voltage which increases linearly with time. In other words, the horizontal velocity of the dot should be constant over the entire sweep. The operational-amplifier sweep circuit can obviously be used to advantage for oscilloscope sweep voltages or to provide a linear time base for use with an X-Y recorder.

The accuracy of measurements made with an oscilloscope is usually of the order of 1 to 3 per cent. This is a function of the linearity of the deflection of the CRT and the ratio of the size of the dot to the size of the screen. Greater accuracy can be obtained only by using the oscilloscope as a comparison instrument to compare the waveform with another which is a standard of voltage and/or time. In general a linearity of more than 1 per cent for an oscilloscope sweep would be superfluous. The operational amplifier can, in this case, be of lower gain and simpler design than that of Fig. 8-7.

The Miller Sweep Circuit. A simple operational-amplifier sweep circuit is shown in Fig. 8-24. The operation of the circuit is as follows: Switch S is normally closed, and the bias voltage $-E_{cc}$ is such that the tube is not cut off. The output voltage e_o is thus $E_{bb} - i_b R_L$. The integrating capacitor C is connected to the bias supply. When switch S is opened, the summing point SP is freed and the circuit can operate as an operational-amplifier integrator. As positive charge accumulates on the SP side of C, the grid potential tends to increase, increasing i_b and lowering e_o. Since the change in e_o is $-A$ times the increase in grid voltage, most of the change in the charge on C appears as the decrease in e_o. The potential at SP remains relatively constant. When S is closed, the grid

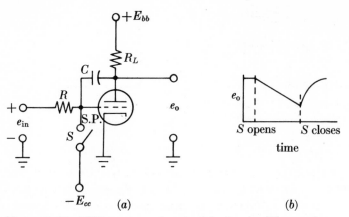

Figure 8-24   Miller sweep circuit: (a) circuit; (b) waveform.

is returned to potential $-E_{cc}$ and the output voltage regains its initial value as the capacitor C charges through R_L. The voltage e_{in} is some well-regulated source, usually $+E_{bb}$.

When the sweep duration is very short, it is desirable to be able to start and stop the sweep with an electrical signal. The circuit of Fig. 8-25 is called the suppressor-gated Miller sweep. This sweep circuit is turned on and off (analogous to opening and closing a gate) by a signal e_{c3} applied to the suppressor grid. Normally a negative potential large enough to cut off the plate current is applied to the suppressor grid. Since $i_b = 0$, the plate voltage and e_o are equal to E_{bb}. The control grid is at the saturation point, $e_{SP} = 0$ (Sec. 3-3), because the large resistance R will not allow any appreciable grid current. The capacitor C is thus charged up to E_{bb} volts. When the suppressor grid is raised to ground potential, the tube conducts and the plate voltage e_o suddenly drops. The potential across C cannot change instantly, because it cannot lose its charge instantly; so the control-grid voltage drops an amount equal to the plate-voltage drop, giving the control grid a negative bias. As the input current E_{bb}/R enters the summing point, the output voltage decreases linearly with a comparatively small increase in control-grid voltage. The plate and grid waveforms are shown in Fig. 8-25b. When the suppressor signal again cuts the plate current off, the capacitor C recharges to E_{bb} through R_L and the control grid returns to ground potential.

Other circuits for the generation of linear-sweep voltages generally use some technique which provides a constant capacitor charging current for the duration of the sweep.

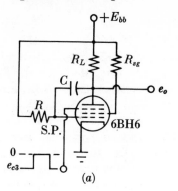

(a)

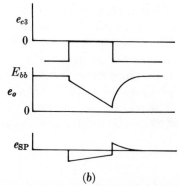

(b)

Figure 8-25   Suppressor-gated Miller sweep: (a) circuit; (b) output waveform.

Operational Amplifiers for Oscillators.   Operational amplifiers may be used with positive feedback for any of the feedback oscillator circuits of Chap. 5.   Except for very low-frequency oscillators, they have very little advantage over the more often used a-c-coupled amplifier.

Through the use of operational-amplifier circuits for summing, integrating, and differentiating, the output waveform from a sine- or square-wave generator may be altered to suit a particular need.   For discussions of various oscillator and wave-shaping circuits using operational amplifiers, see the References listed at the end of this chapter.

8-5   The Precise Control of Current and Voltage

A few devices used for physical and chemical measurements have an output voltage which is related to the quantity being determined. Such devices include glass electrodes for pH, photovoltaic cells for light, microphones for physical displacement, etc. However, the majority of devices used for translating physical and chemical quantities into electrical signals (termed transducers) require the establishment of particular electrical conditions within the transducer in order to obtain the desired response. For example, radiation will not produce a current from a photocell or Geiger tube unless a potential source has been connected to the electrodes; the platinum-resistance thermometer will not respond to temperature changes unless a current is passing through the wire. In some cases the voltage or current imposed on the transducer must be very carefully controlled. For example, the current in the magnet coils of a mass spectrometer or a nuclear magnetic resonance spectrometer must be held very constant. For quantitative response, the potential across sensitive radiation detectors must be very stable. In these and many other cases, the problems of measurement include the problems of control. Operational amplifiers have been widely used in the design of the necessary control circuits. Precise control can be maintained despite sudden changes in the controlled system or the control command.

Voltage-Feedback Control Circuits. The now familiar voltage-feedback amplifier is shown as a control amplifier in Fig. 8-26. The potential across Z_2 of Fig. 8-26a is controlled to be equal to that of e_{ref}. This will be true regardless of the values of Z_1 and Z_2 as long as the output-voltage and current capabilities of the operational amplifier are not exceeded. With this circuit, the potential at any point in a complex network or device can be controlled while the power is supplied through some other element of the device.

The potential control circuit of Fig. 8-26a is to be distinguished from the controlled or regulated output voltage provided by Fig. 8-22. A voltage-regulator circuit such as that of Fig. 8-22 does not control the potential across any particular segment of the circuit but rather maintains a constant potential across the entire circuit which is supplied by the voltage source. The regulated power supply, which is basically the constant voltage supply of Fig. 8-22 modified to supply higher power, is discussed in detail in the next section.

If Z_2 in Fig. 8-26a is a resistance of constant value, a constant current will flow through Z_1. This is shown in the constant-current source of Fig. 8-26b. The voltage drop across R_{std}, i.e., $I_L R_{\text{std}}$, must equal e_{ref}, and thus the current through the load Z_L is independent of the nature or value of the load.

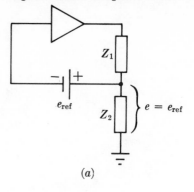

(a)

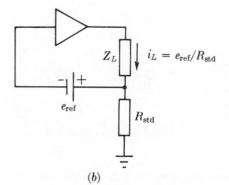

(b)

Figure 8-26   Voltage-feedback control: (a) voltage control; (b) current control.

Operational-Feedback Control Circuits.   The current in the operational-feedback path is precisely equal to the input current.   Thus the current through Z_L in Fig. 8-27a is determined by the input signal e_{ref} and R.   The advantages of this circuit over Fig. 8-26b are: (1) The reference voltage source has one terminal connected to ground. (2) The output voltage is that voltage required to pass the controlled current through Z_2 (a desired measurement in some cases). (3) Although Z_L is not grounded at one terminal, one terminal is at least connected to a virtual ground. The disadvantage of Fig. 8-27a is that e_{ref} must supply a current equal to the control current.   This limits the use of this circuit to low currents and certain types of reference sources.

A voltage control circuit employing operational feedback is shown in Fig. 8-27b.   Adding the currents to the summing-point junction, $e_{ref}/R_1 + e_{Z2}/R_f = 0$.   Solving for the potential across Z_2, $e_{Z2} = -e_{ref}(R_f/R_1)$. This circuit has the disadvantages that the feedback current passes through

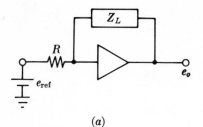

(a)

(b)

Figure 8-27   Operational feedback control: (a) current control; (b) voltage control.

Z_1 and that the impedance to the reference voltage is rather low (R_1). On the other hand, a grounded reference source can be used. In fact, several reference voltages may be connected to the summing point through resistors. The potential across Z_2 will be controlled to be

$$E_{Z2} = -R_f[(e_1/R_1) + (e_2/R_2) + (e_3/R_3) + \cdots]$$

A voltage follower can be put in the feedback loop, as shown, to supply the current for the operational feedback path.

Considerations of Control-Circuit Design. A common problem in electrochemistry is to apply just enough current between two electrodes in an electrolytic cell so that one of them maintains a particular potential with respect to a third, or reference, electrode. A device which will control the potential of an electrode under such conditions is called a potentiostat. The voltage-control circuits of Fig. 8-26a or 8-27b can be used as potentiostats when connected to the electrolytic cell as in Fig. 8-28a and b. The

high-frequency gain

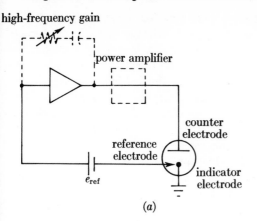

(a)

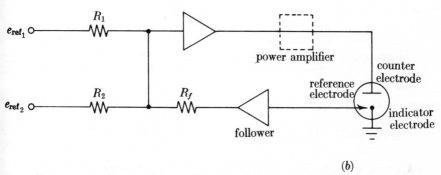

(b)

Figure 8-28   Potentiostats: (a) voltage feedback; (b) operational feed-
back.

operational amplifier supplies current to the counter electrode to maintain
the potential of the indicator electrode with respect to the reference electrode at the potential e_{ref}. In these circuits, the current through the reference is negligible; so polarization of the reference electrode is avoided.

Power. If the current output of the operational amplifier is insufficient, the operational amplifier may be followed by a stage of power
amplification, as shown in Fig. 8-28. This stage can be a simple cathode-
follower or emitter-follower amplifier and need not be especially stable,
because the operational-amplifier control will compensate for any insta-
bilities in the system. In this way circuits controlling many amperes can
be easily devised.

Speed. Operational amplifiers with very fast response speeds of the order of 1 μsec are available. If the power amplifier also has good high-frequency response, rapid control can be maintained even at high currents. Capacitive loads such as an electrolytic cell have a doubly bad effect on the response time of a potentiostat. The first is that an amplifier's response speed falls off badly when it has to supply a capacitive load. The second is that, in order to change the potential of a capacitor quickly, a very high current is required for a brief instant. This effect makes the design of the power amplifier very important.

Stability. A crucial problem in control circuits is stability. It is, of course, necessary for stable operation of the operational amplifier that the feedback be negative or out of phase. The upper frequency response of the usual operational amplifier has been cut off purposely so that those frequencies which are shifted very much more than 180° in phase are attenuated in the output. However, if there is delay in the feedback network, so that the signal getting back to the summing point is regenerative, the circuit becomes an oscillator. Even when the signal delay is not sufficient to cause a sustained oscillation, a damped oscillation may occur. One remedy for this effect is to reduce the phase distortion in the operational amplifier and the other elements in the control loop. If ringing or oscillation still occurs, it is necessary to cut down the amplifier gain at high frequencies until the oscillation ceases. A high-frequency gain control is shown in Fig. 8-28. This control should be adjusted so that the amplifier responds as quickly as possible to a step change in e_{ref} without overshoot or ringing.

Switching. In switching operational-amplifier circuits to change ranges, select various loads, change the mode of operation, etc., the amplifier circuit must be stable at all times. If the feedback loop is opened momentarily, a stabilized amplifier will limit and apply full output voltage to the load for several seconds when the loop is closed again. An unstabilized amplifier will recover more quickly. This means that shorting (make-before-break) switches should be used in the feedback circuit. Shorting switches cause momentary short circuits between the switched components which may be undesirable. There is not yet a simple foolproof answer to the switching problem.

8-6 Computation and Simulation

Commercially available operational amplifiers were designed primarily for analog computers. An analog computer performs mathematical operations on potentials which are analogous to the numbers in the problem. Circuits which add, subtract, multiply by a constant, differentiate, and integrate have been discussed. Assemblies of these circuits can be interconnected to solve many mathematical problems. Analog computers are not so accurate as digital computers, but they are usually much simpler and therefore less expensive. A discussion of the proper application or even the possible applications of analog computers to the solution of mathematical problems is beyond the intention of this text. However, it was thought to be interesting and instructive to include a few examples of problem types which the analog computer is capable of solving quite easily. In addition, an analog computer can simulate the response of any system whose response can be described mathematically. This point is illustrated by a circuit which simulates the response of the servo system discussed in the previous chapter.

Solving Simultaneous Equations. Consider the general case of simultaneous equations with two unknowns x and y.

$$a_1x + b_1y = c_1$$
$$a_2x + b_2y = c_2 \tag{8-16}$$

Since adding and multiplying by a constant are easily performed operations, the equations can be solved electronically. When the coefficients a_1, b_1, etc., are greater than 1, an amplifier must be used for multiplication by the constant, but when the multiplier is a fraction, a simple voltage divider may be used. For the sake of simplicity, it is therefore desirable to divide the equations so that most or all of the coefficients are fractions. The following equations result:

$$\frac{x}{b_1} + \frac{y}{a_1} - \frac{c_1}{a_1b_1} = 0$$
$$\frac{x}{b_2} + \frac{y}{a_2} - \frac{c_2}{a_2b_2} = 0 \tag{8-17}$$

The above equations are solved by using two summing amplifiers as shown in Fig. 8-29. The value of the output voltage of amplifier 1 is the numerical solution of Eq. (8-17) for x, and amplifier 2 gives the solution for y. Amplifier 1 sums a fraction $1/b_1$ of x, a fraction $1/a_1$ of y, and a constant $-c_1/a_1b_1$ to satisfy the first equation. Amplifier 2 is set up to satisfy the second equation. The outputs must then be the solution to the equations.

The effect on the solution of altering the values of any of the constants is seen immediately. The constant in the equations, c_1/a_1b_1 or c_2/a_2b_2, could be time-variant voltages, and the outputs would be the correct solution of the equations as a function of time.

Equations with more unknowns can be solved in the same way. For instance for five equations and five unknowns, one would need 5 amplifiers,

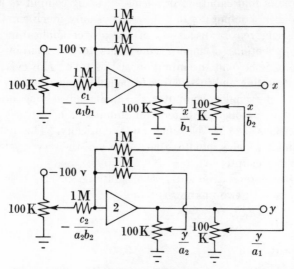

Figure 8-29   Method of solving simultaneous equations.

25 output-dividing potentiometers, 5 voltage sources for the constants, and 30 precision resistors to connect the voltages to the summing point.

Solving Differential Equations. The integrating and differentiating circuits employing operational amplifiers are useful for solving many types of differential equations. The very simple case of the falling-body problem is illustrated here. A mass falling with no friction under the influence of the gravitational force g obeys the equation

$$\frac{d^2y}{dt^2} = g \tag{8-18}$$

where y is the vertical position of the mass. To solve Eq. (8-18) for y, it is necessary to integrate twice. The circuit is shown in Fig. 8-30. A voltage analogous to g is integrated to yield the negative of the first derivative of y or the velocity. This quantity is integrated to yield the actual position y of the mass. Of course the position of a mass falling free in a gravitational field is a function of time. The position-time relationship can be observed by plotting y as a function of time on a recorder or an oscilloscope.

The solution to the problem begins with the mass at rest $(dy/dt = 0)$ at a reference position $(y = 0)$. This is the situation when the switches S are closed. The integrations begin when both switches are opened and the mass begins to accelerate. If the time constant RC of the integrating circuit is 1 sec, e.g., 1 megohm $\times$ 1 μf, the observed time axis will correspond exactly to the time required for an actual fall. The integrator

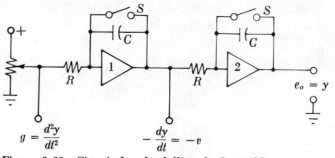

$$g = \frac{d^2y}{dt^2} \qquad\qquad -\frac{dy}{dt} = -v$$

Figure 8-30 *Circuit for the falling-body problem.*

can operate on any time scale; however, if a quicker solution to the problem is desired, a shorter time constant can be used.

Analog Simulation of a Real System. While the previous circuit solved a differential equation, it also simulated the vertical motion of a free mass in a gravitational field. Simulation of system response is one of the most common uses of analog computing systems. The following is a description of a circuit for simulating the response of a servo system whose response obeys Eq. (7-11):

$$Kc_0 = M\frac{d^2c}{dt^2} + D\frac{dc}{dt} + Kc$$

The reference position c_0 of the servo indicator is taken to be at $c = 0$; so $Kc_0 = 0$. Equation (7-11) is then divided by M and rewritten,

$$-\frac{d^2c}{dt^2} = \frac{D}{M}\frac{dc}{dt} + \frac{K}{M}c \qquad\qquad (8\text{-}19)$$

The circuit of Fig. 8-31 will solve this equation. To obtain the quantities dc/dt and c, the quantity d^2c/dt^2 is integrated first by amplifier 1 and then by amplifier 2. dc/dt and c must then be multiplied by $-D/M$ and $-K/M$, respectively, and then added to obtain d^2c/dt to satisfy Eq. (8-19). The damping adjust potentiometer divides the quantity $-dc/dt$, which is then amplified ten times by amplifier 4. This gives a range of 0 to 10 for the factor D/M. The quantity c is similarly divided by the torque control and amplified ten times by amplifier 3. Amplifier 3 also serves to add in the quantity $(D/M)(dc/dt)$ so that the output of amplifier 3 is $-[(D/M) \times (dc/dt) + (K/M)c]$. The quantity d^2c/dt^2 is thus obtained from the output of amplifier 3.

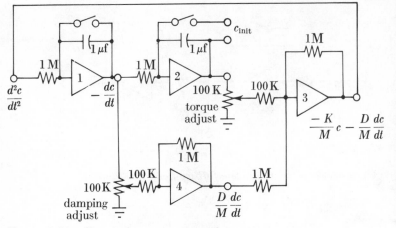

Figure 8-31   Circuit for a servo simulator.

According to Eq. (8-19) the system will come to rest when $c = 0$. The voltage c_{init} imposes an initial displacement on the system by charging the integrating capacitor of amplifier 2 when the integrator switches are closed. When the integrator switches are opened, the value of c will reproduce the response of a linear servo following a step-input command of c_{init}. The effect of torque and damping on the step-response characteristics is readily observed.

8-7 The Regulated Power Supply

The regulated power supply has become a common and almost indispensable piece of apparatus in most laboratories. When experiments are being performed with an apparatus requiring a power supply, accuracy is increased and frustration is decreased when changes in line voltage and load current do not influence the data obtained. The accuracy and stability of most modern scientific instruments depend on the careful regulation of the voltages supplied to critical circuits within the instrument. Some instruments, such as the precision oscilloscope, may contain half a dozen or more regulated supply voltages.

Regulator Characteristics. A power-supply regulator using operational-amplifier control is shown in Fig. 8-32. This is basically the controlled-voltage source of Fig. 8-22. A power-amplifier stage has been added so that the necessary power is available at the output. As mentioned in the section on control (Sec. 8-5), the power amplifier can simply be a high-current cathode- or emitter-follower stage powered by an unregulated source. The reference-voltage source has been moved from the negative-feedback loop (Fig. 8-22) to the positive input as in the case of the voltage follower (Fig. 8-13). With the reference voltage in this position, a grounded reference source may be used, but the amplifier must be a difference amplifier (Sec. 4-4).

The voltage-regulator circuit (Fig. 8-32) is a voltage-feedback circuit. The fraction of the output voltage fed back, β, is $R_2/(R_1 + R_2)$. From Eq. (4-17) for the gain of a voltage-feedback amplifier,

$$e_o = e_{\text{ref}} \frac{A}{1 - \beta A} \tag{8-20}$$

where A is the gain of the operational-amplifier–power-amplifier combination. In this case the gain of the cathode follower is near unity; so A is essentially the gain of the operational amplifier. In the case of the controlled-voltage source (Fig. 8-22), it is important that the product βA be very much greater than unity so that the output is a precisely known function of e_{ref}, essentially independent of A. In the case of the regulated power supply, the output voltage does not have to be precisely predicted from the values for e_{ref} and β; it is usually adjusted to the desired value. The essential thing is that the output voltage be constant. The factors which can alter the output voltage of the regulated supply are changes in the reference voltage, the feedback factor, the unregulated d-c voltage to the power amplifier, and the current drawn by the load, R_L. Assume for the present that the reference voltage and the feedback divider are suf-

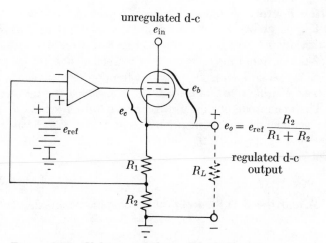

Figure 8-32   Voltage regulator: block diagram.

ficiently stable. The practical means of obtaining stability in these components will be discussed later.

Output Resistance. Consider first the influence of the load current i_L on the output voltage e_o. The change in output voltage for a given change in load current is the output resistance R_o.

$$R_o = \frac{\Delta e_o}{\Delta i_L} \qquad (8\text{-}21)$$

The lower the output resistance, the less the output voltage will change with changes of load current. The output resistance of the voltage-feedback amplifier is given in Eq. (4-26) as the unfedback output resistance divided by $1 - \beta A$. The unfedback output resistance of the cathode-follower power amplifier of Fig. 8-32 is given by Eq. (3-55) as being approximately equal to $1/g_m$. The output resistance of the regulator of Fig. 8-32 is thus approximately

$$R_o = \frac{1}{g_m(1 - A\beta)} \qquad (8\text{-}22)$$

Typical values for a regulator might be g_m for a 6L6 (triode connection), 5000 μmhos, $\beta = \frac{1}{3}$, and $A = -150$. In this case the output resistance would be $1/(5 \times 10^{-3} \times 51) = 4$ ohms. Of course the output resistance could be made even lower by using an amplifier with higher gain or an output tube with a larger transconductance. Equation (8-22) should be regarded as only approximate. In addition to the assumptions made in the derivations of Eqs. (3-55) and (4-26), it is assumed that the output resistance of the unregulated d-c source is smaller than the plate resistance of the power-amplifier tube.

Stabilization Factor. Perhaps the most important quality of the regulator circuit is its ability to hold a constant output voltage despite changes in the unregulated voltage e_{in}. If e_{in} of Fig. 8-32 drops, the voltage e_c on the grid of the output tube must increase to keep a constant voltage across R_L. Since a change in e_c is an amplified fraction of a change in e_o, the output voltage will have to change a little to produce the necessary change in e_c. The magnitude of the effect on e_o can be approximated by considering the incremental voltage relationships in Fig. 8-32. From the cathode-follower plate to ground, $\Delta e_{\text{in}} = \Delta e_b + \Delta e_o$. If the regulator is reasonably effective, $\Delta e_o \ll \Delta e_{\text{in}}$; so

$$\Delta e_b \approx \Delta e_{\text{in}} \qquad (8\text{-}23)$$

From Eq. (8-23) and the definition of μ for the power-amplifier tube, $\mu = -\Delta e_b/\Delta e_c$,

$$\Delta e_c = -\frac{\Delta e_{\text{in}}}{\mu} \qquad (8\text{-}24)$$

A fraction β of Δe_o is amplified A times to yield Δe_c; so

$$\Delta e_c = A\beta \, \Delta e_o \tag{8-25}$$

Combining Eqs. (8-24) and (8-25) to eliminate Δe_c and solving for Δe_o,

$$\Delta e_o = \frac{\Delta e_{\text{in}}}{-\mu A\beta} \tag{8-26}$$

The change in the input voltage is thus diminished at the output by the factor $-\mu A\beta$. The quality of voltage regulation is usually given as the stabilization factor S.

$$S = \frac{\% \text{ change of } e_{\text{in}}}{\% \text{ change of } e_o} \tag{8-27}$$

From Eq. (8-26) the stabilization factor for the regulator of Fig. 8-32 is thus

$$S = \frac{\Delta e_{\text{in}}/e_{\text{in}}}{\Delta e_o/e_o} = -\frac{e_o}{e_{\text{in}}}\mu A\beta \tag{8-28}$$

Again, upon taking typical characteristics for the regulator of Fig. 8-32, $A = -150$, $\beta = \frac{1}{3}$, $\mu = 8$, $e_o/e_{\text{in}} \approx \frac{3}{4}$, the stabilization factor $S = 300$. In other words, the input voltage may change 30 per cent while the output voltage is constant to 0.1 per cent.

Practical Regulator Circuits. Most regulator circuits would not use a commercial operational amplifier in a circuit as shown in Fig. 8-32. One reason is that the operational amplifier itself requires positive and negative supply voltages, both highly regulated. Another reason is that the extreme gain of the operational amplifier is not required in most cases. A practical power supply providing well-regulated output voltage is shown in Fig. 8-33. A full-wave voltage-doubler rectifier and π-section filter supply the unregulated d-c power to the regulator circuit and load.

The amplifier is a 6BH6 common-cathode circuit. The cathode is held at $+108$ volts by the OB2 regulator tube. The voltage across the regulator tube is e_{ref}, and the cathode of the 6BH6 is the positive amplifier input. The voltage divider across the output voltage selects the fraction β of the output voltage which is compared with the voltage across the OB2. The output voltage of the 6BH6 amplifier is connected directly to the grid of the 6L6 power tube. If the output voltage tends to drop owing to a drop in line voltage or increase in load current, the grid of the 6BH6 becomes more negative with respect to the cathode. The voltage at the plate of the 6BH6 becomes more positive, making the 6L6 more conductive in order to maintain a constant output voltage.

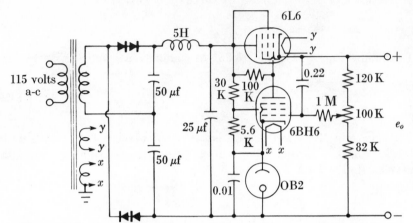

Figure 8-33   1 per cent voltage regulator.   (Courtesy of Heath Co.)

The output voltage is adjusted by the potentiometer in the output divider, which changes the feedback fraction β. The output voltage will be controlled to a value such that the voltage at the 6BH6 grid is about $+105$ volts. The output-voltage range of this regulator might then be expected to be adjustable from 375 to 160 volts.

Note that the screen and plate voltage for the 6BH6 amplifier is obtained from the unregulated input voltage. This causes the regulation to be somewhat poorer than Eqs. (8-22) and (8-28) predict. When the input voltage decreases, the screen and plate voltages of the 6BH6 would tend to decrease, partially offsetting the positive change in plate voltage required for a constant output voltage. An alternative is to power the amplifier from the regulated output voltage. This offers improved regulation, but to maintain proper operation of the amplifier circuit, the output voltage can only be adjusted over a narrow range.

The 0.22-μf capacitor in the grid circuit of the 6BH6 serves to improve the a-c gain of the regulator by coupling the rapid output changes unattenuated to the amplifier input. The 6L6 cannot use the grounded heater supply of the 6BH6, because at output voltages greater than 180 volts the maximum heater-to-cathode voltage of the 6L6 would be exceeded.

A 0.1 Per Cent Regulator. To obtain very precise and stable power-supply voltages, several refinements of the circuit of Fig. 8-33 must be introduced. These improvements are embodied in the regulator circuit of Fig. 8-34. The operation of the circuit is the same as that of Fig. 8-32. The amplifier is a two-stage difference amplifier. The first stage V_1 is the difference amplifier with a difference output which was shown in Fig. 4-19. The second stage V_2 has a difference input and a single-ended or grounded

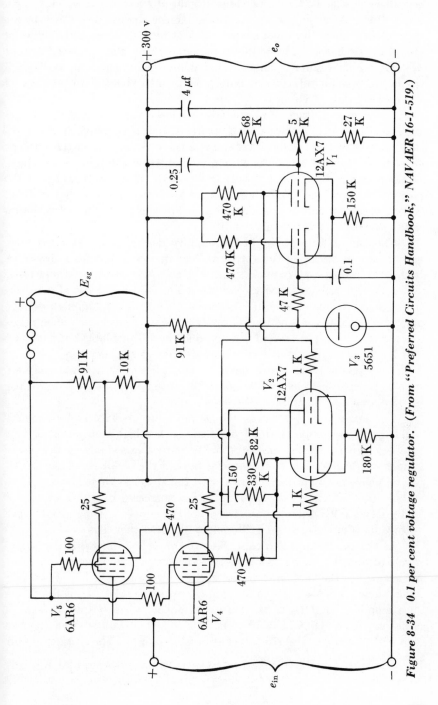

Figure 8-34 0.1 per cent voltage regulator. (From "Preferred Circuits Handbook," NAVAER 16-1-519.)

output as in Fig. 4-23. The combined gain of these stages is very high, about 3000. As explained in Sec. 4-4, difference amplifiers of this type are quite stable, since the usual sources of drift tend to affect both halves of the stage similarly. The amplifier is powered by the regulated output voltage, which results in improved stability and regulation, but which limits the possible adjustment output voltage to about ±10 per cent of the nominal output voltage.

A reference voltage of 87 volts is developed across the 5651 voltage-regulator tube V_3. Notice that this circuit, too, is supplied by the regulated output voltage. The circuit maintains a very nearly constant current through the regulator tube to minimize changes in the reference voltage. In the circuit of Fig. 8-33, a change in the input voltage or a change in the current through the 6BH6 will change the current through the OB2. Since a regulator tube's characteristics are never perfect, a small variation in the reference voltage would result.

Considering the stability of the amplifier and reference voltage source, special care in designing the output-voltage divider is justified. Resistors with a low temperature coefficient and a high wattage rating should be used.

A further refinement of the circuit of Fig. 8-34 is the use of pentodes in the power-amplifier circuit. As shown by Eq. (3-28), the high voltage gain of a pentode can greatly improve the stabilization ratio. The maximum available output current is determined by the available input current and by the maximum plate current of the power-amplifier tube. In Fig. 8-34, two power tubes which have a current rating of 100 ma each are used to provide as much as 200 ma at the output. As many power tubes as necessary may be paralleled with V_4 and V_5.

The large capacitor across the output prevents any high-frequency oscillation which might result from using such a high-gain amplifier in a feedback circuit. It also ensures that the output impedance of the power supply will be low even at frequencies beyond the bandpass of the amplifier. The output impedance from d-c to 200 kc is less than 0.5 ohm. The stabilization ratio S is over 1500 and can be increased by another factor of 10 by using a VR tube in the screen voltage supply. The output ripple voltage for a moderately well filtered input is less than 1 mv.

A Transistorized Voltage Regulator. A transistorized-voltage-regulator circuit is shown in Fig. 8-35. This circuit is a direct semiconductor analogy to the vacuum-tube voltage regulator of Fig. 8-33. A 4.6-volt Zener diode takes the place of the voltage-regulator tube. Q_1 is the difference amplifier, and Q_2 is the power amplifier. The output voltage is adjustable from about 11 to 15 volts. Up to 300 ma can be drawn by the load with the single 2N1183 power transistor shown. The rectifier circuit is a half-wave voltage doubler.

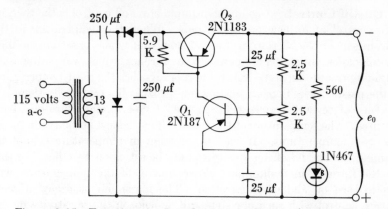

Figure 8-35 *Transistorized voltage regulator. (From Electronics, July 23, 1961, p. 62.)*

8-8 Control for A-C-Operated Loads

The feedback control circuits discussed in this chapter thus far are most suited for control with loads operating from direct current. Alternating current of small to moderate power could be provided to a load by using an a-c voltage for e_{ref}. The control of circuits and loads operating directly from the a-c line is also of great importance. Many loads such as reactive circuits, transformer-powered circuits, certain types of motors, etc., cannot operate properly from d-c power sources. In the case of large motors, ovens, high-intensity lights, etc., the high power required makes the problem of providing and controlling a d-c source much greater than the problem of controlling the a-c power line.

A-C Control Elements. To control power from the a-c line, some electrically driven control element is required. An obvious control element is the Variac autotransformer (Fig. 2-3), which could be driven with a servomotor. The servo-controlled Variac is used in some types of line-voltage regulators. The Variac output voltage is rectified and compared with a reference voltage. A servo amplifier (Sec. 7-4) amplifies any difference and applies a voltage to the control winding of a servomotor to rotate the Variac commutator and correct the error.

Alternating-current control elements which would act as a variable resistance in the a-c circuit would not be desirable for high-power applications. A large amount of power would be wastefully dissipated in the control element, which would necessarily be bulky and expensive. For this reason most a-c control circuits work on a switching basis—actually turning the a-c power to the load on and off. In this way no power is dissipated except in the load.

On-Off Control. A common example of on-off control is the thermostatic control of furnace pumps or fans. When the temperature in the environment of the thermostat drops below that which is set on the dial, a switch closes, supplying a-c power to the furnace, which warms the room containing the thermostat. When the room reaches the right temperature, the thermostat switch opens, turning the furnace off. Ordinarily there is a difference of several degrees between the "turn-on" and "turn-off" temperatures. The temperature of the room will cycle back and forth between these two temperatures. If such a variation in temperature cannot be tolerated, the on and off temperatures may be set closer together. In this case the furnace, in maintaining closer control of the temperature, will have to turn on and off more often. The maximum accuracy of temperature control with such a system will depend on the sensitivity of the thermostat, the response speed of the thermostat (the possibility of positive feedback), and the maximum practical frequency with which the furnace can be switched on and off. The average temperature of the room will depend on what fraction of the time the furnace is turned on.

Several electrically actuated devices suitable for switching high currents are available. The most common are the relay, the thyratron tube, and the silicon controlled rectifier. The use of electrically actuated switches allows rapid switching and the use of very sensitive electrical temperature sensers such as the thermistor and the platinum-resistance thermometer. The temperature of ovens and mantles with low thermal lag and good insulation can be controlled to very close tolerances with such a system.

Often the burden on the temperature-control system is eased considerably by using two heating elements. The larger is connected to a Variac which is adjusted so that the temperature is maintained just below the desired temperature. The on-off controller is connected to the other heating element. The advantages of this arrangement are that there is always a flow of heat, making the changes due to the on-off control less severe, and that the control system does not have to carry the entire heating current. The disadvantage is that a certain amount of manual adjustment is necessary if the control conditions change very much.

Electrically Actuated Switches. Relay contacts act just like a switch in controlling a-c power; the power is connected to the load regardless of the magnitude or direction of the current. When the thyratron or silicon controlled rectifier (SCR) is used, conduction can take place only during half the cycle. For conduction in both directions, two thyratrons or SCR's must be used—each conducting current in the opposite direction. The thyratron is turned on by removing the negative-bias voltage on the grid. (Until its operation is explained, the SCR can be considered equivalent to the thyratron.) Thus, by changing the grid-bias voltage from quite negative to zero, the full-load current will be switched on and off.

When the thyratron grid-bias voltage is held at an intermediate value, the thyratron will conduct during only part of the half cycle (see Fig. 7-33a). Thus the bias voltage on the thyratron will determine the fraction of the cycle during which current is supplied to the load. In this way some current will be supplied to the load during each cycle or at least every 17 msec. For many loads, such as lights, heating elements, capacitors, and some motors, a pulse of current every 17 msec can be considered a continuous source of power. In other words, for such loads the thyratron switch gives the efficiency of on-off control and the smoothness and accuracy of continuously variable power control. To take advantage of this method of control, the controlled variable must vary according to the fraction of the cycle during which power is supplied. In addition, the controlled-variable sensing element must have an output which is a continuous function of the controlled quantity. In other words, a platinum-resistance thermometer or thermistor, which has a temperature-dependent resistance, would be suitable, but an "on-or-off" element like a bimetallic contactor or mercury-thermometer contact would not be suitable.

Figure 7-33b and c shows that the amplitude of a power-frequency signal which is in phase or 180° out of phase with the power voltage can be used to control the on period of the thyratron. In addition, the phase angle of a constant-amplitude signal can control the on time or firing angle, as in Fig. 7-34. This method is called phase control and is generally preferred because it allows control over the entire half cycle as shown.

A Thyratron Control Circuit. A thyratron phase-controlled circuit is shown in Fig. 8-36. A single 3D22 thyratron tube is connected in series with the heating coil across the Variac output voltage. The phase of the thyratron control grid voltage is determined by the state of balance of a Wheatstone bridge which contains a platinum-resistance thermometer. The Wheatstone bridge is powered by a 60-cycle signal. The off-balance signal from the bridge will be either in phase or 180° out of phase with the power voltage, depending on whether the temperature is too high or too low. The off-balance signal is amplified by V_1 and added to a phase reference signal which leads the power signal by 135°. The sum of the two signals will vary from the 135° phase angle depending on the direction and magnitude of the bridge unbalance. After amplification by V_2, the control signal lags the power signal by about 45°, which allows current to flow during the last half of the conduction half cycle. The circuit is designed in this way because the control is most sensitive (greatest change in power for a given change of phase angle) when the firing angle is near the peak of the conduction half cycle. The Variac is adjusted so that approximately the correct temperature will be maintained with a 45° firing angle.

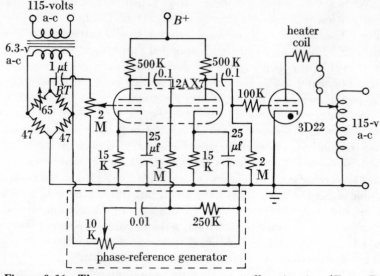

Figure 8-36   Thyratron temperature-controller circuit.   (From R. B. McFee, Rev. Sci. Instr., 23, 52, 1952.)

The Silicon Controlled Rectifier.   A silicon controlled rectifier is pictured in Fig. 8-37.   When the supply voltage is positive at the anode, the two "end" p-n junctions J_1 and J_3 are forward-biased, but the "middle" n-p junction J_2 is reverse-biased.   The reverse bias of J_2 prevents ordinary diode conduction.   When a current of sufficient magnitude is introduced into the gate, conduction across J_3 and J_2 can take place as in the case of an n-p-n transistor.   Thus electrons are conducted across the reverse-biased p-n junction J_2.   The resulting conduction of J_1 makes the

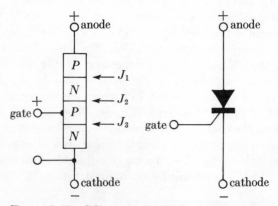

Figure 8-37   Silicon controlled rectifier: pictorial and schematic.

p-n-p section act like a transistor, and holes are conducted across J_2. The middle n and p regions become saturated with electrons and holes which remove the reverse bias of J_2. The SCR will now conduct like an ordinary p-n diode even when the gate current is removed. All that is needed to initiate conduction is a pulse of gate current. The magnitude of gate current required to initiate conduction, or "trigger" the SCR, depends on the potential between the anode and cathode in much the same way as in the case of the thyratron. To stop conduction in the SCR, as in the thyratron, it is necessary to interrupt the anode-to-cathode current. When the cathode is positive with respect to the anode, junctions J_1 and J_3 are reverse-biased and no conduction through the SCR is possible. The advantages of the SCR over the thyratron are: (1) no filament current required; (2) smaller size; (3) higher current-handling capacity; (4) much smaller voltage drop across the "on" SCR.

The source for the current pulses for triggering the SCR is often the unijunction-transistor relaxation oscillator of Fig. 5-17c. Recall that current through the resistance R charges the capacitor C until the emitter peak-point voltage is reached. At this potential the emitter-base diode becomes forward-biased and the capacitor discharges through R_1, creating a pulse across R_1.

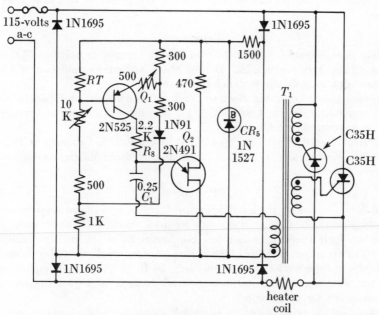

Figure 8-38   Silicon-controlled-rectifier temperature control.   (From G. E. Controlled Rectifier Manual.)

The application of the SCR and the unijunction-transistor trigger circuit is illustrated by the temperature controller of Fig. 8-38. Two SCR's are arranged in series with the heating coil so that conduction can take place during both half cycles. The trigger pulse is supplied to the SCR gates through the transformer T_1. The time delay between the beginning of the half cycle and the trigger pulse determines for what fraction of time the load will receive current.

The trigger-pulse generating circuit is powered by an unfiltered full-wave bridge rectifier. The Zener diode CR_5 keeps the voltage to the transistors from exceeding 22 volts during each half cycle. A thermistor temperature-sensing element RT is used in a Wheatstone-bridge circuit. The transistor Q_1 is in the position of the null detector of this bridge. The magnitude of the off-balance voltage controls the magnitude of the current through R_8 which charges capacitor C_1. When the potential across capacitor C_1 reaches the emitter peak-point voltage of the unijunction transistor Q_2, C_1 is discharged through Q_2 and the primary of T_1, creating a pulse to turn on whichever SCR is forward-biased. At the end of the half cycle, the SCR turns off, and the voltage across the bases of Q_2 drops, causing any charge on C_1 to be discharged. A small trigger pulse generated at this time cannot trigger an SCR, because the power voltage is nearly zero. If the controlled temperature becomes too high, the resistance of RT increases, the current through R_8 decreases, and the trigger pulse is generated later in the half cycle, reducing the power to the heater as required.

References

"Applications Manual for Philbrick Octal Plug-In Computing Amplifiers," George A. Philbrick Researches, Inc., Boston, Mass., and other manufacturers' literature contain useful application information.

"General Electric Controlled Rectifier Manual," Semiconductor Products Dept., General Electric Co., Liverpool, N.Y. Theory, applications, and ratings of silicon controlled rectifiers.

"Preferred Circuits Handbook," NAVAER 16-1-519, U.S. Government Printing Office, Washington, D.C. Practical circuits and design information on voltage regulator circuits.

Problems

8-1 (a) Calculate the input resistance R_S of an operational amplifier whose open-loop gain is 7500 when used with a feedback resistance of 10,000 ohms as in Fig. 8-9. (b) If a recorder with a full-scale sensitivity of 100 mv were connected directly to the output of the amplifier of part (a), what would the full-scale current sensitivity of the recorder and amplifier be? (c) If the operational amplifier were not used, what size measurement resistor would be required to yield the same current sensitivity for the recorder?

Ans.: (a) $R_S = 1\frac{1}{3}$ ohms; (b) 10 μa full scale; (c) 10,000 ohms

8-2   A voltage amplifier of the type shown in Fig. 8-6 is to be wired. What is the highest voltage gain, accurate to 1 per cent, obtainable with an amplifier whose open loop gain is (a) 1000? (b) 10,000? (c) 10,000,000?

Ans.: (a) 10; (b) 100; (c) 100,000 (although this would be unobtainable with most units because of noise and drift).

8-3   The circuit of Fig. 8-6 is used to measure a d-c voltage of 10 volts having a source resistance of 1 kilohm. If $R_1 = 10$ kilohms, and $R_f = 100$ kilohms, calculate e_o.   *Ans.:* -91 volts

8-4   The operational amplifier of Fig. 8-15 limits at an output voltage of ± 50 volts. The offset referred to the input is 5 mv, $R = 100$ kilohms, and $C = 0.1$ μf. (a) How long will it take the amplifier to limit after the switch is opened if $e_{in} = 0$? (b) What is the output voltage when the switch is closed? (c) What average signal voltage is required to yield an integral accurate to 1 per cent? (d) How long can the integration of part (c) proceed before limit? (e) What is the maximum tolerable offset for a 1000-sec integration accurate to 1 per cent when the signal integral at 1000 sec is about 25 volts?

Ans.: (a) 100 sec; (b) 5 mv; (c) 0.5 volt; (d) 1 sec; (e) 2.5 μv

8-5   The input resistance of a chopper-stabilized amplifier is about 1 megohm. After stabilization the amplifier of Fig. 8-20 has an offset of only 100 μv. (a) What input current will be required by the stabilized amplifier itself? (b) What is the approximate a-c input impedance of the amplifier itself?

Ans.: (a) 10^{-10} amp; (b) about 1 megohm

8-6   (a) What is the low-frequency 3-db point f_1 for the high-pass filter in the noninverting input circuit of Fig. 8-20? (b) Trace the amplification path in Fig. 8-20 for signals above f_1. (c) Trace the amplification path for frequencies below f_1. (d) On the basis of the above, explain why the circuit remains a d-c amplifier in spite of the 0.1-μf "blocking" capacitor. (e) Why must a different stabilization configuration be used for voltage followers?

Ans.: (a) 2.6 cps; (b) through high-pass filter to the inverting input; (c) through chopper amplifier to noninverting input; (e) input of the follower is not virtual ground.

8-7   The operational amplifier of Fig. 8-26 is said to limit when the output current or voltage reaches values of ± 1 ma or ± 50 volts, respectively; $e_{ref} = 10$ volts, Z_2 is a resistive load, and $Z_1 = 0$. (a) What is the voltage across Z_2? (b) Over what range of R_2 will the amplifier control?

Ans.: (a) 10 volts; (b) Z_2 greater than 10 kilohms

8-8   Referring to Fig. 8-26, $e_{ref} = 1$ volt, $Z_2 = 10$ kilohms. (a) What current will flow in the load Z_1 if the amplifier limits are not exceeded? (b) If the limits of the amplifier are ± 1 ma or ± 50 volts, over what range of R_1 will the system control the current?   *Ans.:* (a) 0.1 ma; (b) from 0 to 490 kilohms

8-9   To solve a set of seven linear, simultaneous equations containing seven unknowns, how many of each of the following are required? (a) Operational amplifiers; (b) voltage sources; (c) coefficient potentiometers; (d) precision resistors. (e) If the amplifiers limit at ± 50 volts, and the coefficient potentiometers are all 100 kilohms, what must the amplifier output current rating be?

Ans.: (a) 7; (b) 7; (c) 49; (d) 56; (e) 3.5 ma

8-10   The output resistance of the voltage regulator shown in Fig. 8-34 is about $\frac{1}{2}$ ohm.   (a) What is the expected percentage change in the 300-volt output from no load to full load (200 ma)?   (b) What size output filter capacitor would be required to give a $\frac{1}{2}$-ohm output impedance at 120 cps for an unregulated supply?

Ans.: (a) 0.03 per cent; (b) 2660 μf

8-11   Compare the advantages of supplying the amplifier and the voltage reference in a regulated power supply from (a) the unregulated side of the series tube; (b) the regulated side.

8-12   The voltage-regulator circuit of Fig. 8-33 may be wired as a controlled current source.   Show how the voltage divider across the output would have to be modified to include the load and a standard resistance.   What standard resistance should be chosen for a controlled current of about 50 ma?   What should its wattage rating be?

Ans.: 2-kilohm, 5-watt dissipation, but use 25 or 50 watts for stability.

EXPERIMENTS

These experiments are designed to illustrate the most important applications and principles of feedback as applied to measurement, computation, and control. After gaining a familiarity with the operational amplifier, measurement and control circuits are studied by feedback type.   Advanced experiments in control, computation, and simulation are also suggested.   A study of the voltage-regulated power supply is carried out.

For the study of operational-amplifier circuits, an operational-amplifier system as described in Supplement 1 is used.   This system contains four high-gain operational amplifiers, a high-current cathode-follower amplifier, and regulated supplies for $+$ and -300 volts.   The voltage-regulator section of the universal power supply studied in Chap. 2 and used in previous experiments is used to study the voltage regulator.

Expt. 8-1   Familiarization with Operational-Amplifier System

Remove the cover plate and the base plate.   With the unit upright and facing you, observe the $+300$ volts supply at the left rear and the -300 volts supply at the right rear.   The rear transformer provides the high voltages for the supplies. The transformer in the middle of the chassis contains the three filament windings. Note the positions of the $+$ and -300-volt adjustment controls.   The four operational amplifiers are arranged behind the front panel, each consisting of a pair of 12AX7 tubes.   The pair of 6BQ5 tubes at the far right of the chassis make up the power amplifier (high-current cathode follower).   Amplifier 1 (far left) can be connected in the usual inverting manner, or it can be used as a voltage follower or a difference amplifier.   A switch located near the center of the chassis is used to select the mode of operation of amplifier 1.

Turn the chassis over to expose the under-chassis wiring.   Locate the high-voltage and filament-voltage fuses at the rear apron of the chassis.   An auxiliary octal power socket is also located on the rear apron.   To help identify the major components observed, refer to the complete schematic in Supplement 1.

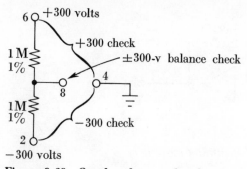

Figure 8-39 Octal socket on the chassis rear apron.

Expt. 8-2 Preliminary Adjustments

Power-Supply Adjustment. With the VTVM measure the + and − supply voltages at the rear-apron power socket. The power socket connections are shown in Fig. 8-39. Adjust both supply voltages to 300 volts. (The unit should have been on for at least 10 min to allow voltages to stabilize.) To obtain a better balance of the supply voltages, adjust one of the regulated voltages so that the potential between pins 4 and 8 of the power socket is zero.

Amplifier Adjustment. Connect amplifier 1 as a gain-of-ten amplifier with operational feedback as shown in Fig. 8-40. *Use ONE HAND only, and BE CARE-FUL when making connections to the front panel when the high voltage is ON.* Measure the output voltage with the input grounded as indicated. Adjust the balance control so that the output voltage is zero.

Repeat for amplifiers 2 through 4. The amplifier balance must be checked from time to time throughout the following experiments.

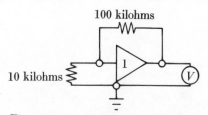

Figure 8-40 Connections for balance adjustment.

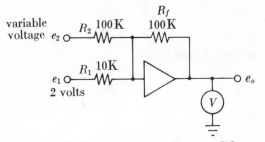

Figure 8-41   Weighted summing amplifier.

Expt. 8-3   Operational-Feedback Amplifier

Using the voltage-reference source (VRS), adjust the transistor power-supply output to exactly 2.00 volts. Connect the 2.00 volts from the transistor power supply to the input of a gain-of-ten amplifier as shown in Fig. 8-41. Measure the output voltage of the amplifier using the voltage-reference source and a null indicator.

Connect the voltage-reference source to a unity gain second input, and note that the output voltage is the sum of the two input currents times R_f; that is, $e_o = -(e_1/R_1 + e_2/R_2)R_f$. Use voltages of both polarities from the VRS.

Expt. 8-4   Voltage- and Current-Feedback Circuits

Voltage Amplifiers. Wire the voltage-feedback voltage amplifier shown in Fig. 8-42. Use the decade resistance box for R_1 and a 1-kilohm precision resistor for R_2. The signal to be amplified is supplied by the VRS. Ground the case of the VRS to the common of the operational-amplifier system. Set the VRS output at 50 mv and adjust R_1 to 99 kilohms. Connect the VOM or VTVM (50-volt scale) to the amplifier output. The amplifier gain should be 100; the output voltage, 5.00 volts. At this high-gain and low-signal level, it will be necessary to check the amplifier balance often simply by depressing the zero button on the VRS. Adjust

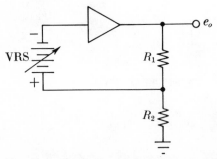

Figure 8-42   Basic voltage or current feedback circuit.

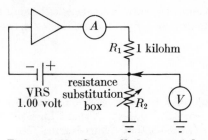

Figure 8-43   Controlled potential source.

R_1 to 199 kilohms, 299 kilohms, . . ., 999 kilohms so that the amplifier gain is increased to 200, 300, . . ., 1000. Note the deviations from the theoretical output voltages at high gains and relate them to the open-loop gain of the operational amplifier. Be sure that the amplifier is balanced when making these measurements.

Constant Current Source. The circuit for this experiment is essentially the same as Fig. 8-42. Set the resistance of the decade resistance R_1 at 1 kilohm and the VRS output voltage at 0.1 volt. Connect the VOM (150-μa range) in series with the decade resistance box. The VOM thus measures the current through R_1. If the amplifier is properly balanced, the current should be $E_{\text{VRS}}/R_2 = 100$ μa. If necessary, the problem of amplifier drift may be reduced by using $E_{\text{VRS}} = 1.00$ volt and $R_2 = 10$ kilohms. Determine the range of R_1 over which the current is a constant. R_1 represents a variable load resistance. Measure the amplifier output voltage when R_1 is at the high end of the range.

Controlled Potential Source. A voltage feedback, controlled potential source is shown in Fig. 8-43. The circuit is identical to Fig. 8-42, except that the resistance substitution box is used for R_2 and the output voltage is measured across R_2. *Put the current meter on the 15-ma scale.* Set the resistance decade box R_1 at 1 kilohm and the substitution box at 10 kilohms. Measure the output voltage with the VTVM. Measure the range of R_2 for which the output voltage is a constant. Measure the load current at the low end of the range of R_2. The current limitation of the amplifier causes the errors at low values of R_2.

Introduce the power amplifier as shown in Fig. 8-44. This amplifier will supply

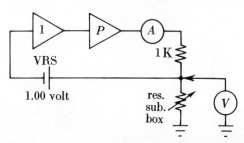

Figure 8-44   Controlled potential source with a power amplifier.

up to 20 ma. Drains in excess of this figure may result in damage to the amplifier or power supply. Decrease R_2 and note that the output voltage is constant up to 20 ma.

Expt. 8-5   Voltage Follower

When the selector switch (inside top cover, center of chassis) for amplifier 1 is in the follower position, it is wired as shown in Fig. 8-14.   Ground the input terminal and adjust the balance control so that the output voltage is zero.   Connect a voltage of 5.00 volts to the input, using the VRS.   Measure the output voltage. Using the VTVM, measure the difference in potential between the output and input.   A slightly higher output voltage is explained by the bias circuit, which reduces the feedback to slightly less than 1.

Connect the resistance substitution box as a load on the follower output and measure the output voltage as the load resistance is decreased.   Start with the load at 10 kilohms.   When the output voltage drops, it is due to the output current limitation of the amplifier, which could be remedied by using the power amplifier as above.

The follower input current can be estimated by measuring the voltage dropped across a large input resistor.   Carefully balance the follower.   Connect a 10-megohm resistor from the input to ground and measure the output voltage.   An input current of 10^{-8} amp will cause an input voltage (and thus an output voltage) of 0.100 volt.

Expt. 8-6   Integration and Differentiation

Connect the integrating and differentiating circuits as shown in Fig. 8-45.   A shorting wire can serve as the switch S.   Connect a 1.0-volt, 100-cps square wave from the sine-square generator to the integrator input.   The input capacitor is to

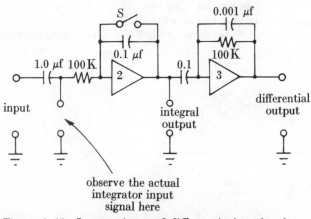

Figure 8-45   Integrating and differentiating circuits.

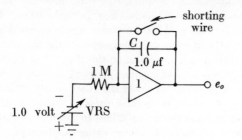

Figure 8-46   Linear sweep generator.

eliminate the d-c component from the square-wave signal. Observe the square wave and its integral with the d-c input of the oscilloscope. When the integral signal wanders off the scope face, bring it back by shorting switch S momentarily to discharge the capacitor. If the integrator output wanders rapidly, the amplifier balance should be checked. Observe the differentiator output and compare with the original signal.

Connect a 1-volt, 100-cps sine wave to the integrator input. Measure the phase angle between the input sine wave and its integral.

Expt. 8-7   Linear Sweep Generator

Determine the time required for the output to rise from 0 to 10, 20, 30, and 50 volts for the circuit shown in Fig. 8-46. The amplifier must be well warmed up and the bias carefully adjusted. Capacitor C is kept shorted until the integration is to begin. Determine whether the rate of charge of the capacitor is within the component tolerances of the theoretical value. Repeat the integration and stop the integration at a specific value on the voltmeter by pressing the zero button on the VRS. (When the input signal is 0, the output integral does not change.)

Expt. 8-8   Operational-Amplifier Applications

If time permits, one of the practical circuits given in Chap. 8 may be built and tested. Suggested circuits are:
Fig. 8-27*b* (operational-amplifier feedback voltage control).
Fig. 8-29 (solution of simultaneous equations).
Fig. 8-30 (solution of the falling-body problem).
Fig. 8-31 (servo-system simulator).
Fig. 8-20 (stabilized operational amplifier using the stabilizer of Fig. 8-19).

Expt. 8-9   Voltage-Regulator Characteristics

Remove the top cover and bottom plate from the universal power supply. Turn the center switch to REGULATED, and connect the VOM (150-ma scale) from the $B+$ terminal on the front panel to terminal P_1 on the underside of the power supply. This connects the load resistors across the regulated output. Use the VTVM to measure the output voltage. With the power supply upside down, the output voltage as a function of load current is measured. Turn the voltage selector switch to the far right (OFF position). Turn on the $B+$. Now increase the load stepwise (decreasing resistance across output). Measure the output voltage for each load current, and at three preset values of $B+$, such as 200, 275, and 350 volts. *Do not exceed 100 ma.* Readings at the high currents should be taken quickly and the currents reduced to more moderate values to avoid overheating the load resistors. From the observed values of voltage change and current, calculate the output resistance of the regulated power supply.

Repeat the above experiment using the 6L6 connected as a triode, by moving the jumper on the terminal strip near the 6L6 socket (Fig. 8-47).

Restore the clip connections to their normal connections.

A switch is provided at the power-transformer primary that selects turns ratios between primary and secondary. This simulates line-voltage changes from about 105 to 115 to 125 volts for the three positions. This switch may be used to determine the line-voltage regulation characteristics of the regulator. For three preset values of $B+$, measure the output voltage as a function of input voltage. Adjust the load current to about 40 ma. Try to calculate S, the stabilization factor. The stability factor is much lower and more easily measured when the 6L6 is connected as a triode.

Check to see that the 6L6 is reconnected as a pentode, and set the line-voltage switch in the NORMAL position.

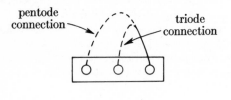

Figure 8-47 Pentode and triode connections for the 6L6 regulator tube.

chapter nine

Electronic Switching
and Timing and Digital
Counting Systems

9-1 Counting, Switching, and Timing

To count rapid events, such as the number of disintegrations from a radioisotope, it is necessary to use electronic switching and pulse circuitry. The general technique, as illustrated in Fig. 9-1, is to transduce each event into an electrical signal, to modify the signal to a pulse that can control an electronic switch, and to operate the indicator that registers each event.

The same basic pulse and switching components can be used for determination of time intervals between events. Even time intervals in the microsecond range, and less, can be accurately determined. An electrical pulse is developed at the start of an event that closes a switch, and another

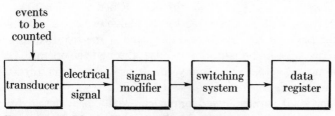

Figure 9-1   *Block diagram of a counting system.*

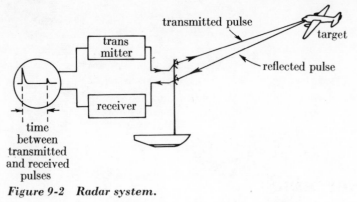

Figure 9-2   Radar system.

pulse at the end of the event opens a switch. The switch operates timing circuitry to display the time interval. The timing circuitry could consist of a stable oscillator for producing pulses at a fixed frequency f and a counting circuit for determining the number of pulses N during the unknown time interval t_u (when the switch is closed), so that $t_u = N/f$. For example, if, during the unknown time interval, 1000 pulses are counted from an oscillator operating at 1,000,000 cps, then $t_u = 1000/1,000,000 = 0.001000$ sec. Note that if $f = 10$ mc/sec (stable to 1 part in 10^7), then N would be 10,000 during the above time interval and the accuracy of measuring t_u would be 1 part in 10^4.

In *radar* [1] a time interval can represent a distance. As illustrated in Fig. 9-2, a short burst or pulse of electromagnetic radiation is transmitted from a highly directional antenna, and this transmitted pulse starts the timing period; when the transmitted radiation hits a distant target, a part of the radiation is reflected back, and an echo pulse is picked up by a receiver. The time interval between transmitted and echo pulses provides an accurate measure of the target distance. It has been established that radar pulses travel at the speed of light; so it takes 12.4 μsec for a radar pulse to travel to a target one nautical mile [2] away and back again.

In the first 10 sections of this chapter, the circuits necessary for providing suitable pulses, rapid switching, counting, and timing are described, and in the final sections these basic circuits are tied together to perform specific operations, such as illustrated by the above examples. But before discussing the basic circuits let us examine some of the requirements for a specific counting task and qualitatively follow through the operation of the counting circuit. In this way, many functions of the circuitry will be apparent prior to a detailed study.

A "proportional counter," used for nuclear events, provides an interest-

[1] Contraction for *r*adio *d*etection *a*nd *r*anging.
[2] The nautical mile is 6080 ft, as compared with 5280 ft for a statute mile.

ing example that contains circuits typical of digital systems. The proportional counter must determine the relative energy distribution of nuclear
particles from radioactive materials. Transducers are available to produce
electrical pulses that are proportional to the energy of the nuclear particles,
as illustrated in Fig. 9-3a. Although instruments are available with
hundreds of channels so as to obtain a well-defined energy spectrum, the
principle can be illustrated with a three-channel *pulse-height discriminator*,
as shown in the block diagram Fig. 9-3b. The pulses from the transducer
are fed into discriminator circuits that provide one rectangular output pulse
for each input pulse above a preselected voltage level. For example, each
pulse above voltage level l_4 will produce an output pulse from discriminator
4; discriminator 3 produces one output pulse for each input pulse above
voltage level l_3, etc. Now, to isolate pulses in the energy levels $l_4 - l_3$,
$l_3 - l_2$, or $l_2 - l_1$, it is necessary to use anticoincidence circuits. As illustrated in Fig. 9-3b, the anticoincidence circuit prevents simultaneous pulses

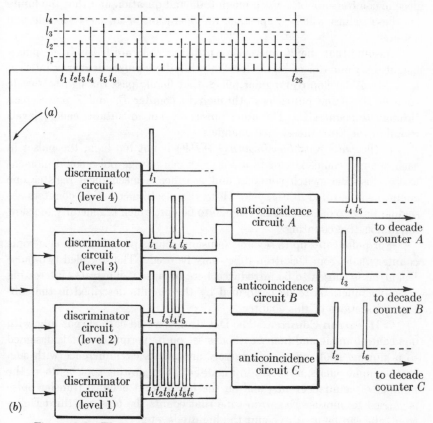

*Figure 9-3   Three-channel pulse-height analyzer: (a) output from
transducer; (b) block diagram.*

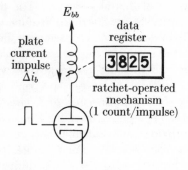

Figure 9-4　Electromechanical register.

from passing through to the decade counter, thereby isolating pulses representative of a given energy interval.　Note that all pulses sent to the decade counters are of a given magnitude and duration and that the limits on these values will be important for operation of an electronic decade counter.

Assume that the 26 pulses shown in Fig. 9-3a are fed into the pulse-height discriminator of Fig. 9-3b.　Only the three pulses in energy interval $l_4 - l_3$ will develop rectangular pulses that finally pass through to decade counter A.　Nine pulses pass through to counter B, and 7 pulses pass through to counter C.　The other pulses are not in suitable energy levels to fall in the three preselected channels.

If the *pulse repetition frequency* (PRF) is not too high, the pulses in each channel could be sent to a relay.　Each voltage pulse could momentarily close the switch contacts and advance a mechanical register one count, as illustrated in Fig. 9-4.　However, electromechanical counters are seldom built to operate faster than 20 to 60 cps, which is generally too slow for radioactive counting.

For pulse rates up to several thousand counts per second an electronic counter made from Dekatron tubes may be used.　The so-called two-pulse Dekatron is chosen to be introduced here because it illustrates interesting circuitry functions to be performed by the circuits described in the subsequent sections of this chapter.

A Dekatron Counter.　The Dekatron is a cold-cathode gas tube with one central anode and many cathodes set on its periphery.　It is designed so a glowing spot moves successively around its circumference with successive input pulses, as shown in Fig. 9-5a.　The glowing spot lights up the number of counted events, and on the tenth input event a transfer pulse is carried to another Dekatron tube that counts the tens.　A third Dekatron tube can be used to count the hundreds, etc.

For the Dekatron to indicate the correct count, each event must produce signal waveforms of sufficient magnitude and duration to stimulate three glow transfers, as illustrated in Fig. 9-5b. The tube contains a single anode, 10 cathodes (K_0, K_1, K_2, ..., K_9), 10 $1G$ guide electrodes ($1G_1$, $1G_2$, ..., $1G_0$), and 10 $2G$ guide electrodes ($2G_1$, $2G_2$, ..., $2G_0$). Cathodes $K_1 - K_9$ are tied together, and K_0 is used for an output terminal. All $1G$ electrodes are tied together, and all $2G$ electrodes are tied together. Both the $1G$ and $2G$ guide electrodes are normally held at a positive bias, as shown. Switch S is normally closed but is opened for resetting to zero.

When the "reset" switch S is open, K_0 is the most negative electrode and gas discharge occurs between K_0 and the anode A. With switch S closed and a large negative input pulse applied to $1G$, the glow discharge transfers from K_0 to $1G_0$. The duration of the negative pulse should be about 80 μsec to ensure transfer. A delayed negative pulse is applied to the

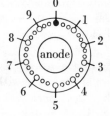

(a)

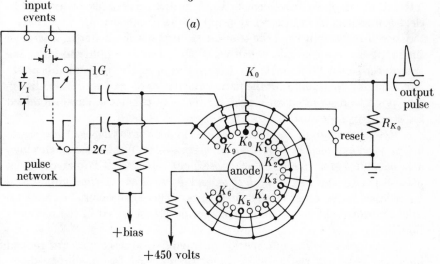

(b)

Figure 9-5   Dekatron counter: (a) face of Dekatron; (b) input pulses and circuit for glow transfer in a Dekatron.

$2G$ electrode so that $2G_0$ remains negative after $1G_0$ returns to its positive-bias value, and the glow discharge moves smoothly to $2G_0$. The subsequent removal of the negative pulse from $2G_0$ moves the discharge to the next closest and most negative electrode, which is K_1. The glow discharge on K_1 lights up the number 1 on the face plate. A second pair of negative pulses moves the discharge to $1G_1$, $2G_1$, and then to K_2, whereby the number 2 is illuminated. The current for the discharge is supplied by the anode voltage source; the input pulses are only used to stimulate the movement of the discharge from one K electrode to the next. In summary, a single event must produce a pair of sequential negative pulses of suitable magnitude and duration so as to induce the progression of the glow discharge to the next higher indicating position. For this type of Dekatron, typical values for each pulse would be 60 volts in magnitude and 80 μsec duration. Note that negative pulses sent first to the $2G$ electrode, and then to the $1G$ electrode, can reverse the direction of glow transfer and cause *subtraction* of counts.

Let us now relate some of the requirements and characteristics specified in the above example to general considerations that are found repeatedly in digital circuits, wherein individual events are counted, timed, and programmed.

Some General Circuit Considerations. As in Chap. 7, it is again assumed that individual scientists are familiar with the transducers most important in their area of work. It is expected that a phenomenon of interest, in the above case nuclear disintegrations, is readily transduced to electrical signals of known relationship to the phenomenon. The characteristics of the signals from the transducer output will, of course, determine the input electronic circuitry. Often this will be an amplifier to boost the transducer signal to a usable level for subsequent electronic modification. Note that for the example of the proportional counter any amplitude distortion prior to discrimination could significantly affect the curve obtained for the energy spectrum.

Referring again to Fig. 9-3, there are circuits for *sorting* electrical signal information and *modification* of electrical pulses to suitable *shape*, *duration*, and *magnitude* for operation of subsequent circuits. Characteristics of pulses such as *rise time*, and *fall time*, and *duration* are of great importance for reliable operation of electronic circuits. These characteristics are considered throughout this chapter and specifically identified in the next section.

Circuits for sorting information or providing selectivity are of general interest. Whereas the *anticoincidence circuit* used for the proportional counter prevents passage of simultaneous pulses, a *coincidence circuit* (*AND gate*) allows passage of only simultaneous pulses. Both these circuits are described in Sec. 9-4.

Referring back to Fig. 9-5, two pulses must be produced for each input pulse, and these must be *related in time* to be useful. In many other circuits it is important for a single pulse to produce two or more signals related in time in order to control subsequent circuitry. Sometimes all that is necessary is to produce several pulses delayed by approximate amounts relative to each other. In other cases, the time relationship is critical and must be accurately set. Several of the specific circuits considered in subsequent sections provide control pulses of precise time relationships.

The important functions of *adding, subtracting, scaling down* by 10, *carrying* 1 pulse out of 10 to the next stage, and *storage* of information are all illustrated by the Dekatron. The neon-filled Dekatron requires about 80 μsec for each of the three glow transfers, so that the *resolving time* per event is about 250 μsec. Therefore, the maximum pulse repetition rate is about 4000 input events per second. Some Dekatrons are filled with gas mixtures that have shorter deionization time than the neon-filled tubes, but they still do not have the speed and general utility of the binary circuits discussed in Sec. 9-6. However, the Dekatron requires relatively simple circuitry compared with the binaries and, where applicable, provides economy, especially since it provides *visual decimal readout* without additional components. In general, though, the basic functions of the Dekatron and binaries of Sec. 9-6 are similar.

9-2   Characteristics of Pulses and Pulse Amplifiers

Pulse Shape. For many applications the ideal voltage or current *pulse* might be represented by Fig. 9-6. Note that the leading edge rises and the trailing edge falls at infinitely rapid rates, and the top of the pulse is flat. In other words, such a pulse would be ideal for instantaneous starting and stopping of events and holding a voltage or current at a precise value for a small increment of time. Real pulses, however, are seldom ideal. The time required to charge or discharge a capacitor is a major factor in determining pulse shape. In Fig. 9-6b an expanded pulse is shown that illustrates some typical distortions from ideality. The quality of this pulse can be described in terms of the *rise time* T_R and the *tilt* E_t. The rise time can be given as the time required to go from 10 to 90 per cent of the maximum voltage E. The tilt is expressed as a percentage, $100E_t/E$. Another pulse that is characteristic of the electrical output signals from some transducers and electronic circuits is illustrated in Fig. 9-6c. This pulse may be described in terms of the following characteristics: the *delay time* T_d is the time required for the pulse to rise to one-half its maximum value; the *rise time* T_R may be defined as above; the decay, or *fall, time* T_f may be defined as the time required for the pulse to drop from the maximum to 10 per cent of the maximum value.

The effect of RC circuits on ideal and real pulses is considered in detail in the next section.

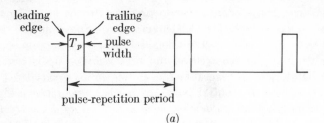

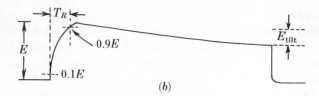

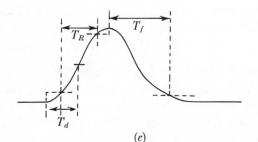

Figure 9-6   Ideal and real pulses: (a) ideal pulse; (b) expanded real pulse; (c) nonideal output pulse.

Pulse Amplifiers. The characteristics required for pulse amplifiers have all been discussed in a general way in Chaps. 3 and 4. The important considerations include frequency response, gain, noise, polarity of output, stability, linearity, input and output impedances, and distortion.

As described in Supp. 3, high harmonics must be amplified without significant reduction in gain or change in phase to prevent pulse distortion. The necessary amplifier gain depends on the magnitude of the input and in some applications may vary a millionfold. For example, in nuclear-radiation detection the output of the transducer might vary from about 100 μvolts to 10 volts. Since output voltages of 10 to 100 volts are often required for electronic pulse-height discrimination, the gain requirement might be 10^5 to 10^6 for the amplifier. Attenuators are, of course, necessary to provide a coarse gain control over such a wide range of input signals, to avoid overdriving the amplifier.

The stability of the amplifier is often important to maintain proportionality between input pulse height and output, and good regulation of the power supplies is essential. Linearity is obtained by proper choice of operating points for the amplification elements and by the use of negative feedback.

The pulse amplifier is usually divided into two parts. The preamplifier is made small and compact and connected by short leads to the transducer. This reduces distributed capacitance, which decreases rise time. The preamplifier gain is usually about 1 to 100. It might consist only of a cathode follower to drive the cable that connects to the main amplifier. The final stage of the preamplifier is usually a cathode follower so that a cable can be used to connect the main amplifier at least a few feet away.

A typical two-stage RC-coupled pulse amplifier followed by a cathode follower and negative feedback is shown in Fig. 9-7. The pulse rise time of an amplifier with n identical stages and no feedback is

$$T_R = R_L C_d \sqrt{2\pi n} \tag{9-1}$$

where R_L is the plate load resistance and C_d the distributed capacitance. Therefore, with two identical stages of $R_L = 5$ kilohms and $C_d = 20$ pf,

$$T_R = 5 \times 10^3 \times 20 \times 10^{-12} \times \sqrt{4\pi} = 0.35 \ \mu\text{sec}$$

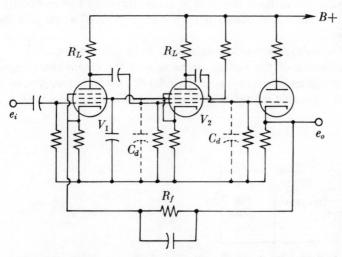

Figure 9-7 **Pulse amplifier with negative feedback and cathode-follower output.**

An expression that gives an approximate relationship between the upper half-power frequency response and the rise time in a multistage amplifier is

$$T_R \approx \tfrac{1}{3}f_2 \tag{9-2}$$

Therefore, for a rise time of 0.35 μsec, the upper half-power frequency response should be about 1 Mc. Note again that the rise time can be improved (decreased) by decreasing R_L. This, of course, is done at the expense of gain.

9-3   Wave Shaping by the RC Circuit

It was indicated, through the examples and discussion in Sec. 9-1, that the shapes of electrical signals must often be modified to be in a suitable form for operation of circuits. Interestingly, the simple RC circuit often plays a part in the formation of suitable waveforms. Also, it often distorts signals in an undesirable way. Therefore, although the reader has been repeatedly referred to Supplement 3, as specific aspects of the RC network were met, it is considered important to review and add a few final words on this important simple circuit before launching into the subsequent switching and timing circuits.

Recall, first of all, the important basic factors or rules governing the simple RC circuit of Fig. 9-8. Observe in the figure that a source of voltage E (of negligible internal resistance) may be suddenly impressed across the RC circuit by flipping the switch.

1. At every instant, the voltage across the capacitor is directly proportional to the stored charge (Q); that is, $e_C = Q/C$, where C is the capacitance.

2. The voltage across the resistor $e_R = iR$ (Ohm's law).

3. The sum of the voltage drops around the circuit must equal the impressed voltage at every instant (Kirchhoff's law); that is, $E = e_C + e_R$

4. The current is the same in all parts of a series circuit at a given

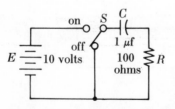

Figure 9-8   Simple RC circuit.

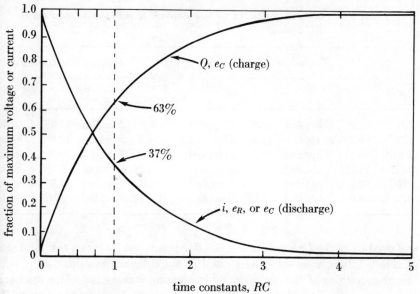

fraction of maximum voltage or current

time constants, *RC*

Figure 9-9   *Charge and discharge curves in the RC circuit.*

nstant, and it is equal to the net voltage divided by the resistance; that is,
$i = (E - e_C)/R$.

Suppose that the switch has been OFF for sufficient time so that $Q = 0$. Therefore $i = 0$, $e_R = iR = 0$, $e_C = Q/C = 0$. Now flip the switch ON. At the instant of closing, the capacitor has not had a chance to charge, and $e_C = 0$. Therefore, $i = (E - e_C)/R = E/R = 10/100 = 0.1$ amp, and $e_R = 10$ volts. Immediately the flow of electrons starts to charge the capacitor; so Q and e_C increase and i and e_R decrease, all exponentially, as shown in Fig. 9-9. The current at any time t after turning the switch ON is given by Eq. (9-3),

$$i = \frac{E}{R} e^{-t/RC} \tag{9-3}$$

After a time $t_1 = RC$, the current $i_t = (E/R)e^{-RC/RC} = (E/R)e^{-1} = (E/R) \times 0.368$. In other words at time $t_1 = RC = 100 \times 1 \times 10^{-6} = 10^{-4}$ sec, the current is 36.8 per cent of the current at the instant of impressing voltage E. This means that at time $t_1 = RC$ the voltage across the resistor is only 36.8 per cent of its initial value and the capacitor is charged to 63.2 per cent of the impressed voltage. The time $t_1 = RC$ is

Table 9–1   Output voltages across capacitor and resistor in series RC circuit

Time	Capacitor charging		Capacitor discharging	
	e_C	e_R	e_C	e_R
RC	63.2% E applied	36.8% E applied	36.8% E initial	36.8% E initia
$2RC$	86.5% E applied	13.5% E applied	13.5% E initial	13.5% E initia
$2.3RC$	90.0% E applied	10.0% E applied	10.0% E initial	10.0% E initia
$3RC$	95.0% E applied	5.0% E applied	5.0% E initial	5.0% E initia
$4RC$	98.2% E applied	1.8% E applied	1.8% E initial	1.8% E initia
$4.6RC$	99.0% E applied	1.0% E applied	1.0% E initial	1.0% E initia

referred to as the *time constant* of the RC circuit, and is given the symbol τ
Table 9-1 tabulates values of e_C and e_R for different multiples of τ, bot
for the charging of the capacitor by impressing voltage E and for discharg
ing a capacitor that is charged to a voltage E. Note that when $t = 4.6R($
the capacitor is charged to 99.0 per cent of the impressed voltage and $e_,$
is only 1 per cent of its initial value. For practical purposes the capacito
is often considered to be fully charged when $t = 5\tau$.

It is important to keep in mind that the voltage across the capacito
does not change instantly. The changes of capacitor voltage are *exponen
tial*. From one point of view, the capacitor may be considered a shor
circuit at the first instant of impressing a sudden voltage change. From
another viewpoint, an instantaneous change of voltage represents a
infinitely high frequency so that the reactance of the capacitor is zero.

By observing the output of the series RC circuit, first across the resisto
and then across the capacitor, various waveshapes similar to those in Fig
9-10 can be observed if a rectangular pulse is fed to the input. It is im
mediately obvious that the output waveform is greatly dependent on th
relationship of RC time constant τ to pulse width T_p. It is interesting t
observe that the leading edge of the output across the resistor is alway
steep, assuming a steep leading edge for the input voltage. In contras
the leading edge of the capacitor output is always changing exponentiall
Note that the sum of voltages across the capacitor and resistor equals th
input voltage at each instant, for a given RC time constant. This can b
observed by comparing the pairs of curves in (c), (d), and (e) of Fig. 9-1(

It is worthwhile to observe that sharp positive and negative pulse
can be obtained across the resistor when the RC time constant is muc
shorter than the pulse width. This finds application in many circuits. I

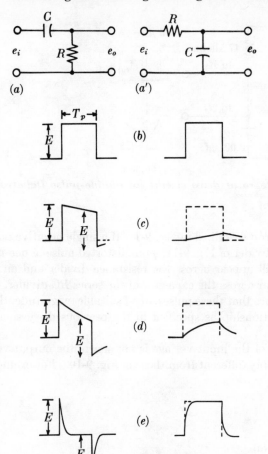

Figure 9-10 *The RC series circuit: (a) output taken across resistor; (a′) output taken across capacitor; (b) input voltage; (c) output voltages across R and C, respectively, when $\tau \gg T_p$; (d) $\tau \approx T_p$; (e) $\tau \ll T_p$.*

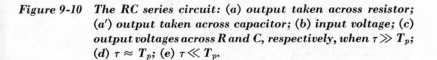

ig. 9-10c the voltage across the capacitor is a rather linear sawtooth volt-ge. This suggests that the circuit can act as an integrator when the time onstant is long compared with pulse width. In fact, when the output is aken across the capacitor, the *RC* circuit is often referred to as an "inte-rator."

An interesting application of this integrator characteristic of the *RC* ircuit is for developing the two negative pulses of proper time sequence

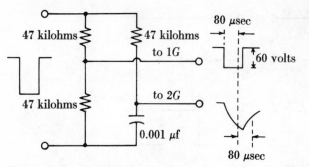

Figure 9-11   *An integrator drive circuit for double-pulse Dekatrons*

for the two-pulse Dekatron described in Sec. 9-1. If a single negative pulse is impressed across the divider of Fig. 9-11, an undistorted pulse of one-half the input magnitude will appear across the resistance divider and an integrated pulse will appear across the capacitor of the series RC divider. It can be seen from the figure that these pulses are of suitable magnitude, time duration, and time relationship as specified in the previous discussion of Dekatrons.

If the leading edge of the input voltage is not sharp, the output voltages may look considerably different from those in Fig. 9-10. For example

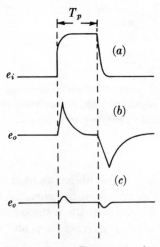

Figure 9-12   *Response of an RC circuit to a nonideal pulse (e_o across resistor): (a) input pulse; (b) output for $\tau < T_p$; (c) output for $\tau \ll T_p$.*

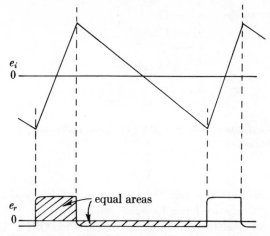

Figure 9-13 *"Differentiated" rectangular output voltage from an RC circuit with sawtooth input voltage.*

observe the output across the resistor of an RC circuit, as in Fig. 9-12, where a nonideal pulse is applied to the input.

When a sawtooth wave is applied across a series RC circuit, the voltage across the resistor will be a rectangular pulse, as shown in Fig. 9-13, if the RC time constant is much shorter than the period of the sawtooth. The output signal from this RC circuit is thus proportional to the rate of change of input. For this reason, the circuit is frequently called a "differentiator."

9-4   Diode Switching Circuits

In Chap. 2, diodes were used as switches to rectify sine waves. A diode is ON when it is forward-biased, i.e., when the anode is positive with respect to cathode, and it is OFF when it is reverse-biased. Diodes may be arranged in different ways so that their switching action performs various functions. They are used repeatedly as *clippers*, *clamps*, AND and OR gates, and in other circuits that are discussed in this section.

Diodes are superior to electromechanical switches or relays with respect to speed, but their electrical characteristics are not as good. The switching time is usually only a few microseconds, or even less. The Zener diode can be switched about the avalanche point with switching times considerably less than 1 μsec. In fact the silicon Zener has a theoretical switching time of about 10^{-9} sec. However, when a mechanical switch is closed, or ON, the resistance between the contacts is low (only a fraction

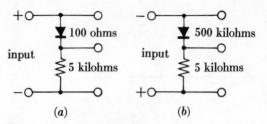

Figure 9-14   *Diode-resistor series circuit: (a) forward-biased; (b) reverse-biased.*

of 1 ohm) and the resistance is nearly infinite in the open, or OFF, position. In comparison, the vacuum diodes have forward resistances, $R_f \approx 1000$ ohms when ON, and reverse resistances, $R_b \approx 10^9$ ohms, when OFF. This provides a back-to-forward resistance ratio of about 10^6:1. For semiconductor diodes, $R_f \approx 10$ ohms, and $R_b \approx 1$ megohm, to provide a back-to-forward resistance ratio of about 10^5:1. These less-than-ideal ratios can cause disturbances in circuits and must be considered in the circuit design.

The Diode Clipping Circuit. The so-called *clipper circuit*, or *limiter*, is useful in a variety of ways in wave-shaping circuits. Limiters are used to prevent voltages from swinging too far in either the positive or the negative direction, to cut off either a positive or a negative pulse, to convert a sine wave into a rectangular wave, and to isolate or eliminate various sections of waveforms.

When a diode is in series with a resistor as shown in Fig. 9-14, it is

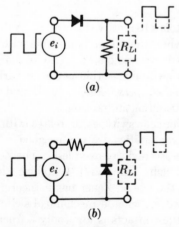

Figure 9-15   *Limiters: (a) series; (b) shunt.*

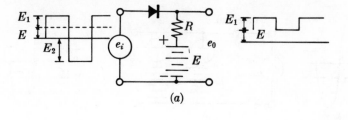

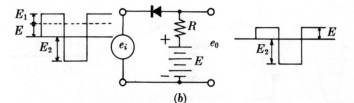

Figure 9-16   Clipping above and below a fixed voltage level: (a) clipping below E; (b) clipping above E.

apparent that the circuit may be analyzed like a voltage divider. When the diode is forward-biased (Fig. 9-14a), most of the input voltage appears across the resistor. When it is reverse-biased (Fig. 9-14b), only a small fraction of the voltage appears across the resistor. From the assumed forward and back resistances for a semiconductor diode, 100 ohms and 500 kilohms, respectively, it can be seen that this diode is not an ideal switch but is quite adequate in most cases.

The diode-resistor circuit of Fig. 9-14 can be used as a limiter by connecting the load either in *series* with the diode or in *shunt* with the diode. The diode-resistor circuit of Fig. 9-14 is redrawn in Fig. 9-15a to illustrate the *series limiter* and in Fig. 9-15b to illustrate the *shunt limiter*. By reversing the diodes the positive peaks can be clipped off. Note that a d-c return through the input voltage source e_i is necessary so that the clipper does not become a clamp (see below).

In some cases it is desirable to clip off the part of the signal that is either below or above a fixed bias voltage E. This can be accomplished by the circuit illustrated in Fig. 9-16. When the diode is connected as in Fig. 9-16a, it will not conduct until the input voltage swings more positive than E. Therefore all the input signal more negative than E is clipped off. Likewise, by reversing the diode (Fig. 9-16b) all the signal more positive than E will be clipped off, because it will not conduct when the input voltage swings more positive than E.

A limiter that clips signals above and below fixed voltage limits is

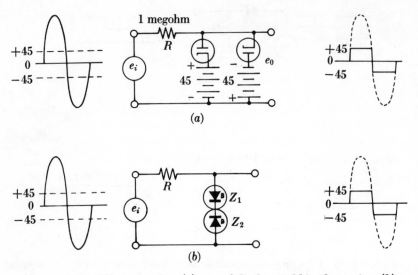

Figure 9-17   *Slicer circuits: (a) use of diodes and bias batteries; (b) use of Zener diodes.*

shown in Fig. 9-17a.   It is sometimes called a *slicer,* because it slices out a section of the input voltage.   In effect, the diodes alternately switch the batteries across the load.   The same type of clipping can be obtained by using two Zener diodes in a back-to-back configuration, to replace both the regular diodes and bias batteries, as shown in Fig. 9-17b.

During the positive half cycle, Zener diode Z_1 appears as a short circuit, and Zener Z_2 conducts only when the breakdown potential V_Z is exceeded.   During the next half cycle this condition reverses.   Zener diodes can also be used as replacements for the bias batteries and regular diodes in other clipper circuits.

The Diode Clamping Circuit.   The *clamping circuit* is usually designed to "clamp" the top or bottom of a waveform to a fixed d-c level, which may be zero, while preserving its shape and amplitude.   It is sometimes called a *d-c restorer,* because it can restore the d-c component that is lost in coupling circuits.   A simple d-c restorer is illustrated in Fig. 9-18, together with the equivalent circuits for positive and negative applied voltages and the initial waveforms during d-c restoration.

The input voltage is a 500-cps square wave with amplitude varying from $+10$ to -10 volts, or 20 volts peak-to-peak.   Assume that the capacitor is uncharged and that the square wave is suddenly applied as shown by the input waveform in Fig. 9-18.   The $+10$ volts is applied across the diode so that it conducts.   The effective resistance is now 1 kilohm in parallel with 1 megohm, if it is assumed that the diode resistance is 1 kilohm. Therefore the time constant for charging the capacitor is short ($1 \times 10^{-6} \times 10^{3} = 10^{-3}$ sec). Since the period between alternations of the square wave is 0.001 sec, the capacitor will charge to 63 per cent of the applied voltage, or about 6.3 volts, before the input voltage drops to -10 volts. The instant the voltage drops, the diode stops conducting, and the effective resistance is the 1-megohm resistor of the circuit. Now the time constant for the discharge of the capacitor is very long ($1 \times 10^{-6} \times 10^{6} = 1$ sec), and it does not discharge significantly during the 0.001 sec of this input negative half cycle.

On the next positive half cycle the diode does not conduct until the voltage has exceeded 6.3 volts, because this is the voltage retained on the capacitor from the previous cycle, and it opposes the applied input. The net voltage applied across the diode at the start of the second cycle is 10 −

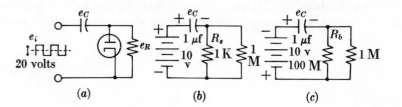

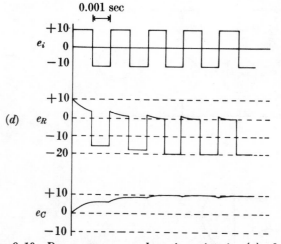

Figure 9-18   **D-c restorer or clamping circuit: (a) clamping circuit; (b) equivalent circuit with diode conducting; (c) equivalent circuit with diode not conducting; (d) waveforms.**

6.3 = 3.7 volts. During the second positive half cycle the capacitor will charge some more and will add 2.3 volts (63 per cent of 3.7 volts) to the previous 6.3 volts, to give a total of 8.6 volts. Again during the negative cycle the discharge of the capacitor is insignificant so that the 8.6 volts on the capacitor opposes the positive swing of the third half cycle. The capacitor continues to charge to 63 per cent of the remaining voltage until the charge is essentially 10 volts.

After the capacitor is charged to 10 volts, it is apparent that, during each positive half cycle of the input, the output will be 0 volts. During each negative half cycle of the input, the output will be $-10 - 10 = -20$ volts. In effect the entire input waveform has shifted downward at the output so that the top is on the zero axis. The bottom of the waveform could be clamped to the zero axis by simply reversing the diode. *In the case of narrow pulses it is necessary to clamp to the base and not the peak.*

A d-c restorer can be biased to clamp the bottom or top of the waveform at some preselected voltage by placing a battery in series with the cathode of Fig. 9-18a. The circuit will then *clamp* at the battery voltage.

The Diode AND Circuit. In many counting applications it is necessary to register an event only when it occurs simultaneously with another

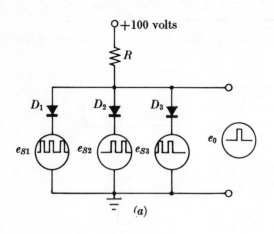

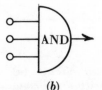

Figure 9-19   AND gate: (a) schematic; (b) logic symbol.

event. This can be accomplished with the so-called *AND*, or *coincidence*, *circuit*. The name *AND circuit* is derived from logic terminology. An output is obtained only when input pulses are simultaneously applied at input 1 *AND* input 2 *AND* any other input. This operation may be described as "event discrimination."

A diode AND circuit is shown in Fig. 9-19. If the internal resistances of the three pulse sources and the three conducting diodes are very small compared with the series resistance R, the voltage drop across the output terminals will be small and close to zero volts. In other words, the output terminal to which the three anodes are tied is normally held close to ground potential because of the low resistance of the conducting diodes.

As illustrated in Fig. 9-19, the first positive pulses appear simultaneously only at D_1 and D_3. This causes reverse bias on diodes D_1 and D_3, and they stop conducting, but D_2 remains conducting and holds the output close to ground potential. The second pulse appears simultaneously across all three diodes so that the output voltage now rises to a value corresponding closely to the amplitude E of the input pulses. In effect, this is equivalent to putting a battery of magnitude E briefly across the output terminals. The third input pulse appears at D_1 and D_2, but not at D_3. Therefore D_3 remains conducting and holds the output close to zero volts. The obvious conclusion is that pulses must appear simultaneously at all inputs in order to obtain an output pulse. The *logic* symbol for this AND gate is shown in Fig. 9-19*b*.

The AND gate could be achieved by using reverse-biased Zener diodes and switching about the avalanche point. As previously mentioned, this provides very rapid switching. As illustrated in Fig. 9-20, a 10-volt bias supply is applied to both cathodes of two 5.6-volt Zener diodes. This

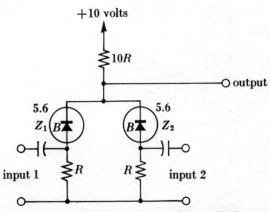

Figure 9-20   AND circuit with Zener diodes.

maintains the diodes in avalanche conduction. If a positive pulse is applied to input 1, diode Z_1 will be gated out of the avalanche region but diode Z_2 holds the output at 5.6 volts. If positive pulses appear simultaneously at inputs 1 and 2, both diodes are gated out of the avalanche region and the output rises to the 10-volt supply voltage during the input pulse interval. This produces a positive 4.4 volts (10 − 5.6) output coincidence pulse.

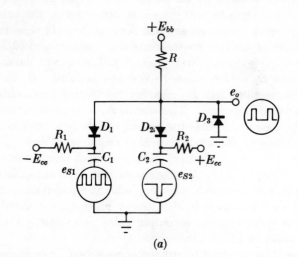

(a)

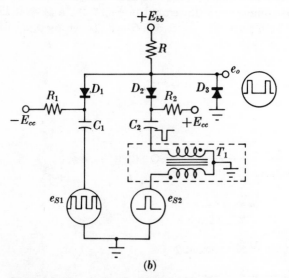

(b)

Figure 9-21   Anticoincidence circuits.

The Diode Anticoincidence Circuit. The diode anticoincidence circuit, frequently called a NOT-AND, or INHIBITOR, circuit, is shown in Fig. 9-21. The basic operation of the circuit is shown in Fig. 9-21a. Diode D_2 is normally cut off by the $+E_{cc}$ bias. Diode D_1 is normally conducting because of the negative bias $-E_{cc}$. Positive pulses appearing at the input e_{s1} cause D_1 to cut off. This allows e_o to rise to $+E_{bb}$ for the duration of each positive pulse, as for the AND gate. When the positive pulse at input e_{s1} occurs simultaneously with a negative pulse at input e_{s2}, diode D_2 conducts and the output voltage e_o cannot rise much above 0 volts. In other words, the output is *inhibited* when a positive pulse appears at input e_{s1} and a negative pulse appears at e_{s2} simultaneously. Diode D_3 is a clamp that prevents the output from going negative toward $-E_{cc}$ when D_1 is conducting.

Figure 9-21b is similar to Fig. 9-21a, except that it provides the necessary inversion for input e_{s2} when all input pulses are positive. This was the case with the pulse-height analyzer illustrated in Fig. 9-3. The transformer T_1 inverts the positive input pulse to a negative inhibit pulse such that the circuit operates exactly as described for Fig. 9-21a.

The Diode OR Circuit. The OR gate derives its name from the fact that it provides an output pulse when a pulse appears at input 1 OR input 2 OR any other input. Its greatest application is as a *buffer*. That is, it prevents interaction of input sources while bringing their outputs to a common terminal. An OR circuit may be achieved by tying the cathodes of the diodes together, returning them through a resistor to a negative voltage, and then applying the inputs to the anodes, as shown in Fig. 9-22.

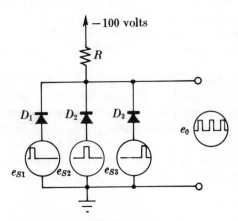

Figure 9-22   OR circuit.

The three diodes all conduct when the input signals are at the same level. However, if the voltage levels of the input signals are different, only those diodes will conduct which have the greatest potential difference from the return voltage (-100 volts in this example). Therefore, if a positive 10-volt pulse is applied only to D_1, it will conduct and provide a 10-volt output pulse. This pulse reverse-biases D_2 and D_3, and the high resistances of these nonconducting diodes isolate, or *buffer*, their signal inputs from the output.

9-5 Amplification Elements as Switches

Whereas diodes are somewhat analogous to a toggle switch, the vacuum-tube and transistor amplification elements can be operated so that they are somewhat analogous to a relay switch. The grid or base of these devices controls the conducting path between plate-cathode or collector-emitter. They can be biased to be either at cutoff or at saturation, and a sufficiently large voltage applied suddenly to the grid or base causes a rapid transition to the opposite state. In other words, a control element determines whether the device is ON or OFF. This is somewhat similar to the way a relay coil controls its switch contacts to be ON or OFF.

The three-electrode devices can achieve the same switching action as diodes, but they also have a linear transition region in which there is proportional coupling between input and output, and they have the inherent possibility of amplification. These advantages will become apparent in the applications of these elements as switching devices in the subsequent sections.

Vacuum Triode or Pentode Switches. A triode (12AU7) that is biased OFF is shown in Fig. 9-23a. From the average plate characteristics for the 12AU7, it can be seen that, with a 300-volt plate supply E_{bb}, a grid supply $-E_{cc}$ that is more negative than -20 volts will cut off the tube completely. Note that the plate voltage equals the plate-supply voltage, because there is no voltage drop across the load resistor when the tube is cut off.

In Fig. 9-23b, the triode is biased ON by tying one end of the 1-megohm grid resistor to $+E_{bb}$ rather than to $-E_{cc}$. At first glance it might seem that this would make the grid very positive, but it should be remembered that the grid and cathode form a diode with a forward resistance r_c of about 1 kilohm. This 1-kilohm resistance is in series with the 1-megohm resistor R_g, which forms a voltage divider across the 300-volt plate supply, as shown in Fig. 9-23c. Note that the grid voltage E_c is a small fraction of the plate supply, i.e.,

$$E_c = \frac{E_{bb}r_c}{R_g + r_c} \tag{9-4}$$

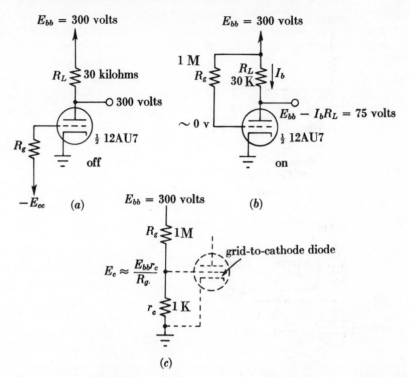

Figure 9-23 *Triodes biased for switching: (a) triode biased OFF; (b) triode biased ON; (c) d-c equivalent grid circuit of (b).*

In this example,

$$E_c = \frac{300 \times 10^3}{10^6 + 10^3} = +0.3 \text{ volt}$$

This is approximately 0 volts, and from the 30-kilohm load line for the 12AU7 it is determined that $I_b = 7.5$ ma. Therefore, when the tube is ON, the plate voltage is given by

$$E_b = E_{bb} - I_b R_L \qquad (9\text{-}5)$$

and in this case

$$E_b = 300 - 7.5 \text{ ma} \times 30 \text{ kilohms} = 75 \text{ volts}$$

It should be emphasized that the job of the triode in switching applications is to hold a load at one of two voltage levels and to switch from one voltage level to the other level in the shortest possible interval of time. In some cases it is necessary that the transition occur in about 10^{-8} sec. Un-

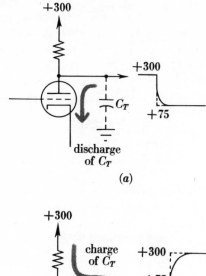

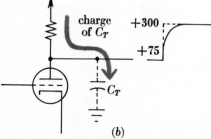

Figure 9-24   *Charge and discharge of capacitors as seen by the plate:*
(a) tube conducts; (b) tube cuts off.

fortunately, the inherent capacitance in the amplification elements and the
connections of the circuit tend to integrate the signal and prevent the rapid
transition.   This is illustrated in Fig. 9-24, where the capacitor shown in
the drawing is the sum of all capacitances as seen by the plate of the tube.
Part of this capacitance is from interelectrode capacitances and part from
the wiring to the grid of the next stage.   Note that C_T discharges through
the tube when the tube is driven ON and that C_T charges through the plate
resistor when the tube is driven OFF.   With another tube connected that
drives ON at the same time, C_T includes $(1 + \mu)C_{gp}$ of the other tube
(Miller effect).

The rise and fall times of the pulse can be decreased by decreasing the
total capacitance and the plate resistance.   This can be achieved by selecting tubes, careful wiring, and using a lower value of plate resistor.   Power
pentodes have a low resistance and small C_{gp} and are often used where a
very sharp fall time is desired.   Keep in mind that connecting wires that
are long and run close to the chassis add considerable capacitance to the

circuit. Although a very small resistance provides a small plate-voltage change, it is necessary to lose efficiency to achieve a very fast rise time.

Transistor Switches. Transistors may be used as switches in the same manner as tubes. In some respects transistors are better switches. When a transistor is saturated, the base, emitter, and collector are all at essentially the same potential; hence there is an extremely small voltage drop across transistor switches, indicating a relatively small resistance when ON. The most important disadvantages are the slowness of response and the inability to withstand high voltages. Figure 9-25 shows the ON and OFF bias conditions for a *p-n-p* transistor.

For a *p-n-p* transistor the base need be only a few tenths of a volt more negative than the emitter to cause saturation. When saturated, the collector is approximately at the emitter potential, or 0 volts. To bias a *p-n-p* transistor OFF, a base voltage of about 0.1 volt is sufficient, and the base bias supply V_{BB} is generally a 1.5-volt cell. The transistor switch when OFF presents a complication which is not present with tubes, i.e., the relatively low resistance between the collector and emitter. Transistors are not as "off" as vacuum tubes. With the exceptions noted above, and with the fact that the grid of a tube must be moved through larger voltages than the transistor to change from ON to OFF or from OFF to ON, transistors and vacuum tubes serve similar functions in the circuits to be described in the remainder of this chapter. By interchanging transistors and tubes and selecting the proper polarity and magnitude of supply voltages, the subsequent circuits will, in general, present very similar characteristics. The base will be analogous to the grid, the emitter to the cathode, and the collector to the plate. Although the volt-ampere characteristics of the devices are vastly different, the transition region is rapidly passed through

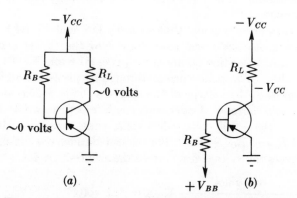

Figure 9-25   Transistors biased for switching purposes: (a) p-n-p transistor biased ON; (b) transistor biased OFF.

when the three-electrode device is driven between the extremes of cutoff and saturation.

The finite switching time in transistors arises from the fact that the charge concentration in the material must readjust to a new value and the charge flow mechanisms are inherently slow. This is especially true in the base region, where the charge must change from a very high to a very low value in going from saturation to cutoff. Switching times are faster with transistors that have thinner base regions and thus less volume for charge storage. Since the "high-frequency cutoff" of transistors varies inversely with base thickness, this will provide a measure of the transistor switching speed.

9-6 The Bistable Multivibrator

One of the most useful and important building blocks in digital systems is the bistable multivibrator, more commonly called the *binary*, or *flip-flop*. The terms are meant to indicate that it is a circuit with two stable states and remains indefinitely in one of the stable states until forced into the other by means of an external trigger pulse. Its action is somewhat analogous to that of a toggle switch, which can exist in one of two stable positions and can remain there until pushed into the other stable state. Like the toggle, the flip-flop requires a push, in the form of a trigger pulse, to get it into the other stable state.

Flip-flops have many applications. They can be arranged to add, subtract, multiply, divide, and store information. Also, their signals can be used for gating other circuits or actuating relays and indicator devices.

Fixed-Bias Binary. A flip-flop that uses a fixed negative bias E_{cc} is shown in Fig. 9-26. Note that the plate of each tube is direct-coupled through a resistor to the grid of the opposite tube. To start with, assume that V_1 is ON (conducting) and V_2 is OFF (not conducting) and on this basis analyze the circuit.

Now let us quantitatively show that with V_1 ON and V_2 OFF the circuit is truly in a stable state and then show how the circuit can be triggered so that a rapid transition occurs and V_1 goes OFF and V_2 ON.

If V_2 is OFF, there is no plate current through its plate-load resistor R_{L2}. Consider then what the voltage at the grid of V_1 (Fig. 9-27a) would be if there were no grid current. Under such conditions there would be a voltage, $E_{bb} - E_{cc} = 200 + 100$ volts $= 300$ volts, across the series voltage divider made up of $R_{L2} + R_{C2} + R_{g1}$. The current through the divider i_d multiplied by R_{g1} gives the voltage drop across the grid resistor, i.e.,

$$i_d R_g = \frac{300 \text{ volts}}{10K + 220K + 150K} 150K = 118 \text{ volts}$$

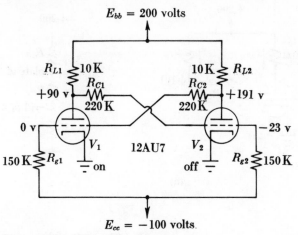

Figure 9-26   Fixed-bias binary.

Therefore, the grid of V_1 would be 118 volts $-$ 100 volts $= +18$ volts with respect to ground (the cathode).

It is well known, of course, that a slightly positive voltage on the grid causes grid current to flow, and the grid-to-cathode resistance r_c drops to only about 1 kilohm. As shown in Fig. 9-23, this means that the grid is tied closely to ground and is essentially 0 volts. Therefore, the tube V_1 is in saturation and clearly ON.

By drawing the 10-kilohm load line for a 200-volt plate supply with the 12AU7 tube, it is determined that plate current $I_{b1} = 11$ ma when the grid is at 0 volts. Therefore the plate voltage of V_1 is

$$E_{b1} = E_{bb} - I_{b1}R_{L1} = 200 - 11 \text{ ma} \times 10 \text{ kilohms} = 90 \text{ volts}$$

As shown in Fig. 9-27b, the grid voltage of V_2 may now be determined by observing that the voltage $90 + 100 = 190$ volts is across the series-resistance divider $R_{C1} + R_{g2}$, and the grid voltage of V_2 is readily calculated to be -23 volts. From the plate characteristics of a 12AU7 tube with a 200-volt plate supply it is seen that the grid cutoff voltage $E_{co} = -15$ volts. Therefore the grid of tube V_2 is below cutoff by 8 volts, and tube V_2 is indeed OFF.

The small current I_{c2} (Fig. 9-27a) causes a small voltage drop of about 9 volts across R_{L2} so that the voltage at the plate of V_2 is $200 - 9 = +191$ volts.

In introducing flip-flop circuits, the question always arises as to whether a third stable state could exist, whereby both tubes would be

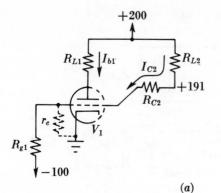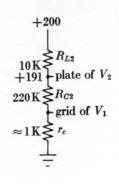

(a)

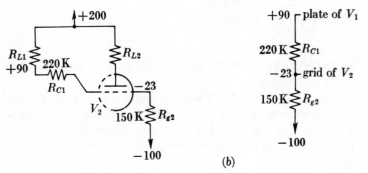

(b)

Figure 9-27   Binary circuit of Fig. 9-26 redrawn for analysis: (a) ON tube; (b) OFF tube.

drawing identical plate currents. This would be analogous to a spring-actuated switch stopping at dead center. By careful balancing the toggle might momentarily be stopped at the center, but the slightest disturbance quickly releases the spring force that moves the device to one of its stable states. Suppose that when the flip-flop circuit is turned ON the plate currents in the two tubes are momentarily equal. It is characteristic of tubes, especially in warming up, that the currents and voltages in the circuit change appreciably. The slightest unbalance in the two tubes causes a larger unbalance because of the regenerative feedback between plate and grid of each tube. For example, if the plate current in V_1 increases slightly, its plate voltage decreases. Since the plate of V_1 is coupled directly to the grid of V_2, the grid of V_2 goes more negative. This causes the plate current of V_2 to decrease, and the plate of V_2 goes more positive. The plate of V_2 is directly coupled to the grid of V_1, and so the grid of V_1

goes more positive. This causes still a further increase in plate current of V_1. This reasoning may be continued to illustrate that the slightest unbalance at any moment causes the flip-flop to plunge rapidly into one of its stable states if the loop gain is > 1. It is this same regenerative function that allows a trigger pulse to push the flip-flop from one stable state to the other.

Triggering the Flip-Flop. There are many different ways of triggering the flip-flop so that it undergoes a *transition of states*. The requirement is to raise the OFF tube above cutoff or to push the ON tube below saturation so that the regenerative process of the circuit causes the stable states to reverse.

One of the common triggering methods for many applications is shown in Fig. 9-28. A negative pulse is fed to two "steering" diodes that have their anodes connected to the plates and their cathodes returned to $B+$ through resistance R. If V_1 is ON and V_2 OFF, as shown in Fig. 9-28, diode D_2 will *steer* the negative pulse to the plate of V_2. Diode D_1 is reverse-biased and does not conduct, because the plate of V_1 and anode of D_1 are at $+90$ volts, whereas the cathode of D_1 is at $+200$ volts. The negative pulse that reaches the plate of V_2 is direct-coupled to the grid of V_1 and drives the tube below saturation. In fact, if the negative pulse is sufficiently large, it pushes the grid from saturation to cutoff. If not that large, it sets in motion the regeneration process. The plate of V_1 jumps to a higher voltage as its plate current decreases, and this causes the grid of

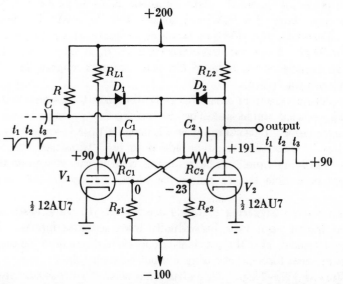

Figure 9-28 Symmetrical plate triggering of bistable multivibrator.

V_2 to become more positive and to raise above cutoff and conduct. Conduction of V_2 causes its plate, thus the grid of V_1, to go more negative, so that V_1 cuts off and V_2 drives to saturation. The voltages on the tubes are now reversed from the way shown in the diagram of Fig. 9-28. The point labeled OUTPUT drops from $+191$ to $+90$ volts at time t_1. The next negative pulse reverses the tubes again so that V_1 is ON and V_2 is OFF, and the OUTPUT jumps from $+90$ to $+191$ volts at time t_2. It is not necessary, of course, to take the output from the plate of V_2. The output can be taken from either of the plates depending on the application.

The purpose of capacitors C_1 and C_2 has not been described up to this time. The reason for their use, however, is quite apparent if the discussion is recalled from the previous section about charging and discharging the capacitance as seen by the plate of the tube. Note that this causes integration of the pulse and an exponential instead of sharp rise of voltage at the grid. If the trigger pulse is of short duration, its driving action could cease before the grid drops far enough to switch the states. By adding the "crossover," or "commutating," capacitors (C_1 and C_2) the sharp leading edge of the pulse is seen immediately at the grid. Therefore, the tubes can undergo a sharp rapid transition of states. C_1 and C_2 are sometimes called "speed-up" capacitors.

C_1 and C_2 may also be considered as compensating capacitors (Sec. 4-3) because R_{c1} and R_{c2} form uncompensated attenuators with the effective input capacitance C_i in parallel with either R_{g1} or R_{g2}. Therefore $C_1 = C_2 = C_i R_g / R_c$. When both tubes are conducting during a transition, the input capacitance C_i (Sec. 4-1) is influenced greatly by the Miller-effect capacitance $(1 + \mu)C_{gp}$, which might be about 20 to 30 pf for a 12AU7 tube. The capacitance due to wiring, socket, and C_{gk} might be about 5 to 20 pf. Therefore, the effective input capacitance might range from about 25 to 50 pf. Since the resistance ratio R_g / R_c is often near unity, the speed-up capacitors would be of the same order of magnitude as C_i. Their values are not critical.

The speed-up capacitors must charge or discharge to the new voltage levels of the reversed stable states before the flip-flop is ready to accept another trigger pulse. This charging or discharging time is known as the "settling time." This time must be added to the "transition time" to obtain the "resolving time." The resolving time is the minimum time between two successive trigger pulses for which the circuit will switch reliably.

The alternative triggering methods are many. In some cases it is desirable to trigger each tube individually from separate inputs. The only change necessary from the previous circuits is to disconnect the diodes and rearrange them for separate trigger input to each tube.

Self-Biased Flip-Flop. In instruments where two separate power supplies are not economical, a self-biased binary can be used. In this way

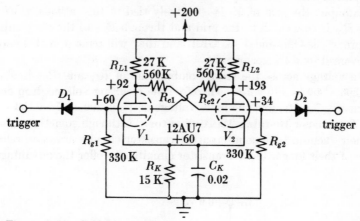

Figure 9-29   Self-biased binary.

the E_{cc} bias supply is eliminated. The self-biased binary works on the same principles as self-biased amplifiers, with a capacitor across the cathode resistor. As shown in Fig. 9-29, a common-cathode resistor is used for the two tubes. Since the two tubes draw about the same current when either is ON, it is only during the transition period that the cathode voltage might change significantly. However, the small capacitor in parallel with the cathode resistor holds the cathode voltage relatively constant during the short transition period of a few microseconds or less.

A brief analysis of the circuit in Fig. 9-29 provides the expected voltages at the grids, plates, and cathode and reveals that V_1 and V_2 will exist in two stable and opposite states, either ON or OFF. A look at the plate-characteristic curves for the 12AU7 shows that grid cutoff $E_{co} = -15$ volts for a plate supply $E_{bb} = 200$ volts. For a 42-kilohm (27 + 15 kilohm) load line the saturation plate current $I_b = 4$ ma. If one tube V_2 is assumed OFF and only V_1 is ON, then the cathode voltage

$$E_K = I_b R_K = 4 \text{ ma} \times 15 \text{ kilohms} = +60 \text{ volts} \qquad (9\text{-}6)$$

with respect to ground. The plate of V_1 is at a voltage

$$E_{b1} = E_{bb} - I_b R_L = 200 - 4 \times 27 = +92 \text{ volts}$$

The voltage at the grid of V_2 is determined by the 92 volts applied across the voltage divider $R_{c1} + R_{g2}$, that is,

$$E_{g2} = E_{b1} \frac{R_{g2}}{R_{C1} + R_{g2}} = 92 \frac{330}{330 + 560} = +34 \text{ volts} \qquad (9\text{-}7)$$

with respect to ground. Therefore, the grid of V_2 is -26 volts ($34 - 60$ volts) with respect to the cathode. Since the grid cutoff $E_{co} = -15$ volts, it is apparent that V_2 is truly OFF. By the same reasoning as in the previous example, the grid of V_1 is effectively tied to the cathode, since the resistor R_{c2} is connected to the grid and through R_{L2} to the plate supply. Therefore, V_1 is ON, and V_2 is OFF, and they will remain in these states until reversed by a trigger pulse.

The voltage across the series combination of R_{L2} and R_{C2} is $E_{bb} - E_{g1} = 200 - 60 = 140$ volts. Therefore the resulting voltage drop across R_{L2} is nearly 7 volts, and the plate voltage of V_2 is $200 - 7 = 193$ volts.

A Transistor Bistable Multivibrator. Although sometimes slower than their vacuum-tube counterparts, transistor circuits are more reliable because of their longer life. Transistor circuits also offer the advantage of

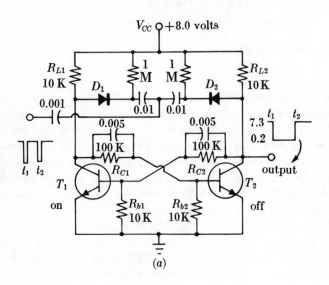

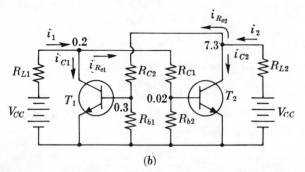

Figure 9-30   Transistor binary: (a) schematic; (b) schematic redrawn for circuit analysis.

low power consumption, which is quite important in instruments such as digital computers having thousands of binaries. The small size is also a desirable feature for complex instruments.

The transistor circuit shown in Fig. 9-30a is similar in operation to the vacuum-tube equivalent. It is redrawn in Fig. 9-30b for easier analysis. Transistor T_1 is shown as saturated (ON) and has the collector, base, and emitter all at about the same potential. The OFF transistor T_2 has a negligibly small collector current i_{C2}, and the current i_{Rc2} is only about 70 μa. The OFF collector voltage V_{CE2} is given, therefore, by

$$v_{CE2} = V_{CC} - i_2 R_{L2} \approx 8 - 70 \times 10^{-6} \times 10^4 = 7.3 \text{ volts}$$

The base voltage v_{BE2} of T_2 is given by

$$v_{BE2} = v_{CE1} \frac{R_{b2}}{R_{c1} + R_{b2}} = 0.2 \frac{10K}{100K + 10K} \approx 0.02 \text{ volt}$$

The 0.02 volt is sufficiently low to hold T_2 in a cutoff condition. Many n-p-n transistors require about 0.1 volt to trigger into conduction.

The negative trigger pulses are applied to the input coupling capacitors and steering diodes that are connected to the collectors of T_1 and T_2. A negative input pulse is steered to the collector of the OFF transistor and is directly coupled to the base of the ON transistor. The base voltage of the ON tube therefore drops abruptly, the collector voltage of T_1 and base of T_2 increase, and the familiar regenerative flip-flop process takes place, so that T_1 is flipped OFF and T_2 ON. A second negative pulse again reverses states, and so T_1 goes ON and T_2 OFF.

9-7 Schmitt Trigger (Cathode-Coupled Bistable Multivibrator)

The Schmitt trigger is a modified bistable multivibrator that is widely used as a voltage discriminator, such as in the nuclear radiation pulse-height analyzer, illustrated in Fig. 9-3. Also, the Schmitt trigger is useful as a "squaring circuit." It is often used in a sine-square generator to convert the output of a sine-wave oscillator to a square wave.

A typical circuit is shown in Fig. 9-31. The direct coupling from the plate of V_1 to the grid of V_2 is the same as for the conventional bistable multivibrator, but the plate-to-grid connection from V_2 to V_1 is eliminated. Instead, the common-cathode resistor R_K provides the other necessary coupling for regeneration between stages. It is this feature that classifies the circuit as the *cathode-coupled bistable multivibrator.*

When the input signal is below a preset voltage value, one tube conducts and the other tube is cut off. The moment the voltage exceeds the preset value, there is a rapid transition of states. The circuit remains in the new stable states as long as the input remains above a voltage level that

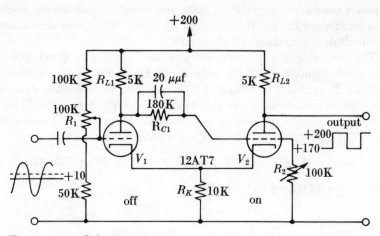

Figure 9-31   Schmitt trigger.

is slightly lower than the initial triggering voltage. As soon as the voltage drops below this second level, there is another rapid transition of states back to the original states. Input signals below the preset voltage level do not provide an output signal. They are discriminated against.

The triggering level can be set by a potentiometer R_1, which determines the average grid voltage E_{g1} of tube V_1. With E_{g1} sufficiently low, V_1 is cut off and R_2 is adjusted so that V_2 is conducting heavily but not clamped (e.g., grid bias of about -1 volt on V_2). The plate current I_2 of V_2 causes a voltage drop E_K across the common-cathode resistor R_K. The difference between the value E_{g1} set by the potentiometer R and the cathode voltage is the grid bias $(E_{g1} - E_K)$ of V_1. Since the transition of states occurs the moment the cutoff voltage E_{co} is exceeded, it is the voltage difference E_t between E_{co} and grid bias that determines the triggering level, i.e.,

$$E_t = E_{co} - (E_{g1} - E_K) \tag{9-8}$$

For example, if $E_{co} = -4$ volts, $E_K = 64$ volts, and $E_{g1} = 50$ volts, then the triggering level

$$E_t = -4 - (50 - 64) = 10 \text{ volts}$$

In other words, a minimum signal of $+10$ volts would be required, in this case, to raise V_1 above cutoff. At this point V_1 starts conducting, its plate voltage and the grid of V_2 decrease, causing a decrease in plate current of V_2; the resulting drop of cathode voltage E_K increases the plate current of V_1, and the regeneration process continues until V_2 is OFF and V_1 is ON. The output from the plate of V_2 jumps to the plate-supply value because of the transition.

When V_1 is ON, it acts as a cathode follower so that E_K tends to follow the input signal E_s, and the tube does not cut off when the grid falls to the initial triggering level. Usually the grid must go more negative by a few volts in order to return the tubes to the original stable states with V_1 OFF and V_2 ON. This is known as the "hysteresis effect," and it can be compensated by various techniques.

To produce a sharp voltage spike at the output, the plate resistor R_{L2} of V_2 is sometimes replaced by an inductor L, as shown in Fig. 9-32. This forms an RL high-pass circuit, consisting of L and $R = r_p$ of V_2. Recall that the voltage across an inductor is $L(di/dt)$. The rate of current change

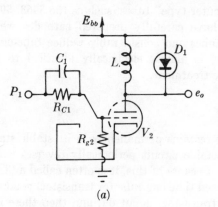

(a)

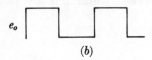

(b)

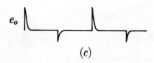

(c)

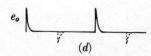

(d)

Figure 9-32   Peaking coil in a Schmitt circuit: (a) replacement of R_{L2} with L and D_1; (b) output with R_{L2}; (c) output with L; (d) output with L and diode D_1.

is very high when V_2 is suddenly cut off or turned on, thereby producing positive and negative voltage spikes.

A diode D_1 may be used to clip the negative spike. It is called a "plate-catching diode" because it does not allow the output to go negative. In other words it "catches" the plate at E_{bb}. The diode may be reversed to clip the positive peak. Some resistance in parallel with the inductor is necessary to prevent oscillation. The diode must have a sufficient peak-inverse rating to withstand the effects of large pulses.

Schmitt triggers are capable of discriminating voltage levels of about 0.1 volt. However, the supply voltage E_{bb} must be carefully regulated, and wire-wound resistors should be used to avoid resistor aging effects. It is also preferable to use "computer-type" tubes, such as the 5963, 5965, 5814, and 5844. These tubes have carefully prepared cathodes which lengthen the service life of the tubes and considerably reduce tube-aging effects. The 5963, for instance, is almost electrically identical to the 12AU7 but has improved cathode treatment.

9-8 Astable Multivibrator

Whereas the bistable circuit remains permanently in its stable states until externally triggered, the astable circuit periodically reverses states without any external triggering. Because of this, it is often called a "free-running" multivibrator. For a fixed time one tube (or transistor) conducts heavily, and the other tube (or transistor) is cut off, and then there is a rapid transition of states, which remain stable for another fixed time before reversing again. The time intervals between transitions are primarily

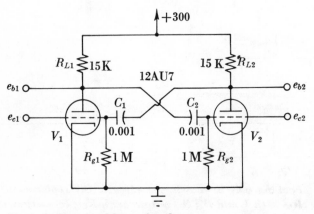

Figure 9-33   Astable multivibrator.

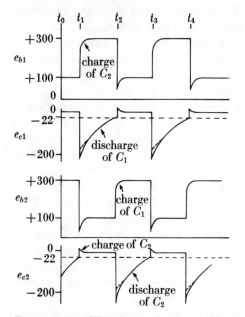

Figure 9-34   Waveforms from astable multivibrator.

fixed by the RC time constants and voltage supplies of the circuit. Therefore, the frequency of the output can be easily varied.

The astable circuit in Fig. 9-33 resembles an RC-coupled amplifier, with the output of the second stage coupled back to the input of the first stage. There is no d-c coupling, only the coupling capacitors C_1 and C_2. These capacitors transmit instantaneous voltage changes from plate to grid, but the grid voltages always decay toward the potential to which the grid resistors are tied (to ground potential in Fig. 9-33).

The operation of the circuit of Fig. 9-33 is best understood by reference to the waveforms in Fig. 9-34. Assume that at an arbitrary time t_0 tube V_1 is ON and V_2 is OFF. The plate voltage e_{b2} of V_2 is therefore at the plate-supply voltage ($+300$ volts), and e_{b1} of V_1 is about $+100$ volts (as determined with the 15-kilohm load line on the plate characteristics for the 12AU7-A tube, which gives about 13.3 ma plate current when $e_{c1} = 0$). The grid voltage e_{c1} of V_1 is at 0 volts, and e_{c2} of V_2 is below cutoff. However, e_{c2} is rising toward 0 volts as the capacitor C_2 discharges through R_{g2}. When the grid voltage e_{c2} reaches cutoff at time t_1, tube V_2 begins to conduct. This causes e_{b2} to decrease, and the voltage decrease is immediately coupled to the grid of V_1. Consequently the plate current of V_1 decreases, and e_{b1} increases. The increase of e_{b1} is coupled to the grid of V_2, so as to increase the plate current of V_2 even more, and the regenerative process continues until V_1 is cut off and V_2 is fully conducting. The grid of V_1 is now much below cutoff, and it will remain below cutoff until capacitor C_1 discharges sufficiently so that e_{g1} reaches cutoff. The transition of states then occurs again at time t_2. This periodic *switching* of states produces continuously the waveforms shown in Fig. 9-34.

The general shapes of the waveforms in Fig. 9-34 are quite obvious from considerations in the previous sections. Not quite so obvious are the reasons for the voltage spikes that occur immediately following a transition of states. But as might be expected, they are a result of charging one of the coupling capacitors. This is easily seen by referring to Fig. 9-35, which shows both the charge path for C_2 and the discharge path for C_1, following the transition at time t_1, wherein V_1 is suddenly cut off and V_2 made conducting. Capacitor C_2 must charge from its pretransition voltage of $+100$ volts to the $+300$-volts plate-supply voltage. The charge path for C_2 is through the plate-load resistor R_{L1} of V_1 and through the grid-to-cathode conducting diode of V_2 (with resistance r_c of about 500 ohms). The grid of V_2 is thus forced several volts positive, and the plate current of V_2 increases to drop the plate voltage e_{b2} briefly to a value considerably below the steady value of $+100$ volts. The RC time constant for the charging of C_2 is only about 15 μsec so that C_2 will be charged to 90 per cent of its final value in about 40 μsec. The approximate voltages in the circuit at a time $t_1 + 40$ μsec are shown in Fig. 9-35.

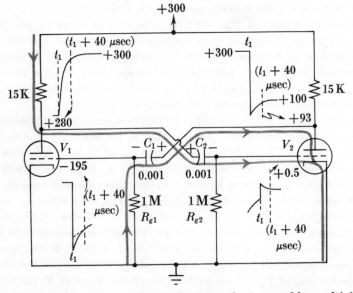

Figure 9-35 Charge and discharge paths in astable multivibrator.

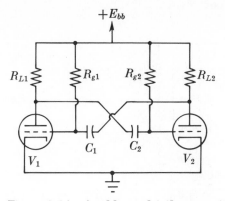

Figure 9-36   Astable multivibrator with positive grid return.

The capacitor C_1 must discharge from its pretransition voltage of $+300$ volts toward the steady value of $+100$ volts that will be on the plate of V_2 about 75 μsec after the transition. The discharge path of C_1 is through the 1-megohm grid resistor R_{g1} and the plate resistance r_p of V_2, which makes a long time constant and slow discharge. Therefore, the grid of V_1 changes slowly from about -200 volts ($E = 300 - 100$) toward ground potential, but a transition occurs at time t_2, when grid cutoff $E_{co} = -22$ volts is reached.

The time interval from the transition at t_1 to the transition at t_2 is calculated from the equation for capacitor discharge,

$$t_2 - t_1 = RC \ln \frac{E}{E_{co}} = 10^6 \times 10^{-9} \ln \frac{300 - 100}{22} = 2.2 \text{ msec}$$

The time interval $t_3 - t_2$ is also 2.2 msec because the circuit is symmetrical. Therefore the total period is 4.4 msec, and the frequency is 227 cps.

Astable Circuit with Positive Grid Return. In most astable multivibrators the grid resistors are returned to the plate-supply voltage E_{bb}, as shown in Fig. 9-36. The advantage of connecting the grid resistors in this way is that the discharge of the coupling capacitors will be toward the $+E_{bb}$ voltage instead of ground potential. Consequently, the rate of voltage change on the grid is steeper in the region of cutoff, and the duration of the switching period is more reproducible.

Transistor Astable Multivibrator. The transistor astable circuit of Fig. 9-37 is similar to the vacuum-tube circuit of Fig. 9-36. The base resistors are tied back to the collector supply V_{CC} so that the coupling capacitors discharge toward $+V_{CC}$. Note that the base resistors in this example are not the same value; so the time constants for the discharge of

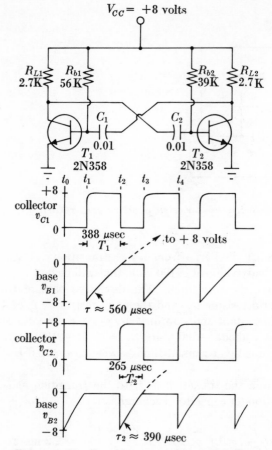

Figure 9-37   Transistor astable multivibrator.

C_1 and C_2 are different, and the waveforms are unsymmetrical. The time constants are $\tau_1 = R_{b1}C_1 = 560$ μsec, and $\tau_2 = R_{b2}C_2 = 390$ μsec. The periods between transitions may be calculated from the approximate equations

$$T_1 = t_2 - t_1 = R_{b1}C_1 \ln \frac{2V_{CC}}{V_{CC}}$$

$$T_2 = t_3 - t_2 = R_{b2}C_2 \ln \frac{2V_{CC}}{V_{CC}}$$

(9-9)

and, for this example,

$$T_1 = 56 \times 10^3 \times 10^{-8} \ln 2 = 388 \ \mu\text{sec}$$

$$T_2 = 39 \times 10^3 \times 10^{-8} \times 0.693 = 265 \ \mu\text{sec}$$

These calculations are based on the assumption that the collector drops instantaneously from $+V_{CC}$ to 0 volts, but, of course, shunt capacitance prevents this from being perfectly true. Also, it is assumed that the ON transistor is a short circuit and the OFF transistor an open circuit. Note that the charge and discharge paths for the transistor circuit are similar to those illustrated in Fig. 9-35 for the vacuum-tube circuit, during the period t_1 to t_2.

Synchronization of the Astable Multivibrator. In some applications free-running multivibrators must by synchronized to increase the frequency stability. Sine waves or pulses from a carefully stabilized oscil-

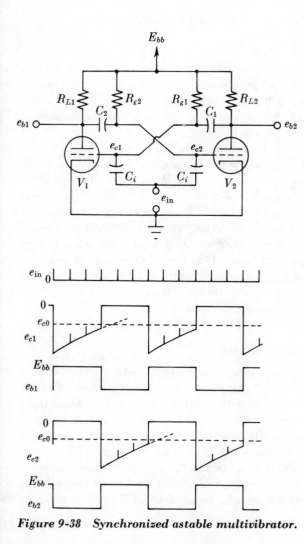

Figure 9-38   Synchronized astable multivibrator.

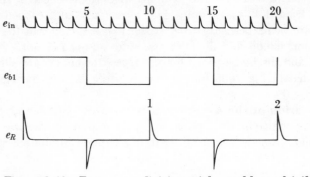

Figure 9-39   Frequency division with astable multivibrator.

lator can be used in these cases to *drive* the astable circuit. The most satisfactory method is with pulses, as shown in Fig. 9-38. By feeding the positive pulses to both grids, the grid voltage of the OFF tube is brought up to cutoff voltage in each period by one of these pulses superimposed on the discharge voltage from the coupling capacitor.

Frequency Division by Astable Multibrator. The synchronization technique shown in Fig. 3-38 also suggests the possibility of frequency division. Suppose, for example, that the circuit constants were chosen so that the tubes would switch states on every fifth pulse. Therefore, the output from the plate e_{b1} of V_1 would be a square wave as shown in Fig. 9-39. If this square wave is fed across an RC differentiator, the voltage across the resistor e_R will consist of one positive and one negative pulse for each cycle. It is apparent, then, that there is one *positive* output pulse for every 10 input pulses of constant repetition rate. In other words, the input frequency has been divided by 10. Other multiples may be selected by varying the values of circuit components.

9-9 Monostable Multivibrator

The monostable multivibrator is a hybrid between the bistable and astable circuits. The circuit remains permanently with one tube ON and one tube OFF, until triggered with a suitable input pulse. Once triggered, the tubes reverse states. However, the tubes will revert back to the original permanent states after a period T. Once back in the original states no further switching occurs until it is again triggered with an external pulse. In other words, it is a "one-shot," or "start-stop," device. One pulse produces one, and only one, cycle. One tube starts to conduct when triggered but stops after a period T determined by the circuit values. The names *one-shot* and *start-stop multivibrator* and *univibrator* are commonly used to identify the monostable circuit. Because the circuit can produce rectangular gating pulses of fixed duration and can delay events by fixed times, it is frequently found in electronic instruments.

Cathode-Coupled One-Shot Multivibrator. A one-shot circuit is shown in Fig. 9-40. The plate of V_1 is capacitively coupled to the grid of V_2 in the same way as for the astable circuit. The coupling from V_2 to V_1 is through the common-cathode resistor R_K, whence the classification *cathode-coupled*.

The voltage E_{cc} on the grid of V_1 is set by the potentiometer R_p to a value so that V_1 is cut off. Tube V_2 is clamped ON by connecting its grid resistor to the plate supply E_{bb}. A negative input trigger pulse on the plate of V_1 is coupled immediately to the grid of V_2, where it decreases the plate current and causes the voltage drop e_k across the cathode resistor R_K to decrease. If the cathode voltage decreases sufficiently, tube V_1 starts to conduct. Plate current in V_1 causes its plate voltage to drop, and regenerative switching occurs so that V_2 goes OFF and V_1 goes ON. Capacitor C_2 will now discharge. When C_2 has discharged so that the grid bias of V_2 is less than cutoff, the plate current in V_2 increases the cathode voltage, which increases the grid bias of V_1 and decreases its plate current. This increases the plate voltage of V_1, which is coupled to the grid of V_2, and the familiar multivibrator switching occurs, so that V_1 is again OFF and V_2 ON. This completes the cycle ON-OFF-ON for V_2 and OFF-ON-OFF for V_1, which was instigated by the negative trigger pulse.

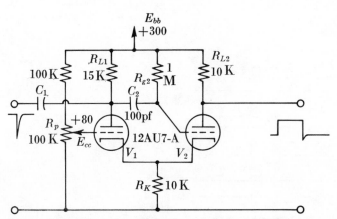

Figure 9-40   One-shot cathode-coupled multivibrator.

The waveforms in Fig. 9-41 show the voltage values around the circuit. Let us now calculate these values at various times and in this way gain a better understanding of the monostable circuit. First, assume that V_1 is OFF and V_2 is ON, the condition prior to the trigger pulse at time t_1. Now, determine the plate current of V_2 at zero grid bias, using the tube curves for the 12AU7-A, a 300-volt plate supply, and a 20-kilohm load line (10 + 10 kilohms). The plate current i_{b2} is found to be about 11 ma; so

$$e_k = i_{b2}R_K = 11 \text{ ma} \times 10 \text{ kilohms} = 110 \text{ volts}$$

and the plate voltage e_{b2} of V_2 is

$$e_{b2} = 300 \text{ volts} - 11 \text{ ma} \times 10 \text{ kilohms} = 190 \text{ volts}$$

Since the grid-to-cathode voltage of V_2 is about zero, the grid voltage $e_{c2} = e_k$ and $e_{c2} = 110$ volts. If E_{cc} were set for +80 volts, then the grid bias e_{c1} of V_1 would be

$$e_{c1} = E_{cc} - e_k = +80 - 110 = -30 \text{ volts}$$

Since the plate-to-cathode voltage of V_1 is 190 volts (300 − 110), it can be determined from the tube curves that cutoff voltage $e_{co} = -15$ volts. Therefore, the grid bias $e_{c1} = -30$ volts is more than adequate to hold V_1 below cutoff, and since the plate current of V_1 is zero,

$$e_{b1} = 300 \text{ volts}$$

The values of $e_{b1} = 300$, $e_{c2} = 110$, $e_{b2} = 190$, and $e_k = 110$ remain fixed until a trigger pulse occurs to switch states temporarily. Immediately

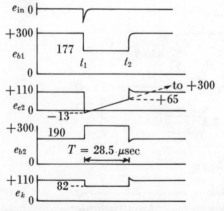

Figure 9-41   Waveforms for the one-shot multivibrator of Fig. 9-40.

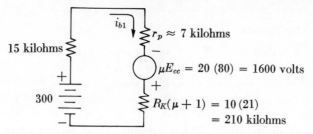

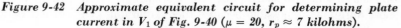

Figure 9-42 *Approximate equivalent circuit for determining plate current in V_1 of Fig. 9-40 ($\mu = 20$, $r_p \approx 7$ kilohms).*

following the transition, the above voltages change, and the new values can be roughly determined by the following method.

Tube V_1 is now conducting, and the plate current i_{b1} can be determined by the approximate equivalent circuit of Fig. 9-42 * and is found to be 8.2 ma (1900 volts/232 kilohms). From this it follows that

$$e_k = i_{b1}R_K = 8.2 \times 10^{-3} \times 10^4 = 82 \text{ volts}$$

and $$e_{b1} = E_{bb} - i_{b1}R_{L1} = 300 - 8.2 \times 10^{-3} \times 15 \times 10^3$$

$$= 177 \text{ volts}$$

The grid voltage e_{c2} drops by 123 volts (300 − 177 volts) almost immediately after the transition at time t_1 and then starts to approach cutoff as capacitor C_2 discharges toward +300 volts. From the tube curves for the 12AU7-A, it can be seen that a plate-to-cathode voltage of 218 volts (300 − 82) has a grid-voltage cutoff of about −17 volts. Therefore, when e_{c2} has climbed from an initial value of −13 volts (110 − 123) to a value of +65 volts (82 − 17), tube V_2 starts to conduct and the tubes switch at time t_2; so V_2 is again ON, and V_1 is OFF. The circuit will now remain in this condition until another trigger pulse is applied at the input.

The period T between t_1 and t_2 is an important value that has many applications. It can be calculated, as previously, by the simple relationship,

$$T = t_2 - t_1 = R_{g2}C_2 \ln \frac{300 + 13}{300 - 65} = 29 \ \mu\text{sec}$$

One useful feature of the above circuit is that the period T is a linear function of E_{cc} over a considerable range.

The plate-coupled univibrator is a direct hybrid of the bistable and astable circuits described in Secs. 9-6 and 9-8. Its operation is readily analyzed by consideration of the basic bistable and astable circuits.

* Pettit, p. 145.

9-10 Blocking Oscillators

An oscillator that cuts itself off after one or more cycles because of the accumulation of a negative charge on the grid capacitor is called a "blocking oscillator." It can be designed to perform many of the same functions as multivibrators, and can be free-running or driven like a one-shot multivibrator but cannot have a bistable form. Its most important application is as a source of sharp pulses of high current. High-current pulses of short duration are possible because there is no quiescent current between pulses.

Driven Blocking Oscillator. The free-running and driven blocking oscillators are similar in design except that the latter is purposely biased far below cutoff, as shown in Fig. 9-43. Therefore, the tube is nonconducting until a sufficiently large positive trigger pulse is applied to the grid. The trigger pulse starts the flow of plate current which provides a di/dt in the transformer primary, producing a secondary voltage that causes the grid to swing positive. In turn, this signal increases the plate current even more, and the familiar regenerative action occurs until the tube reaches its maximum current. At this point there is no further change of current, and the secondary voltage drops. The capacitor C also starts to decay toward E_{cc} (-80 volts) at a rate determined by the time constant $R_g C$. One of these effects predominates to decrease the plate current, and the di/dt in the transformer primary now drives the grid end of the secondary winding in the negative direction. The negative voltage on the grid decreases the plate current even more, and the regenerative action rapidly drives the grid far below cutoff. Typical waveforms at the grid and plate are shown in Fig. 9-44.

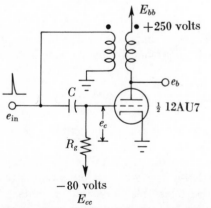

Figure 9-43 Driven blocking oscillator.

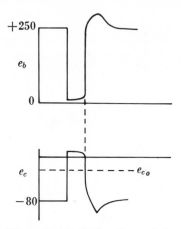

Figure 9-44   Pulses from driven blocking oscillator.

The output voltage can be taken from the grid or plate, or, as is often done, a third transformer winding provides for the e_b waveform to be isolated from the d-c plate supply. If a cathode resistor R_K is included in the circuit of Fig. 9-43, the output voltage can be taken across R_K. In this case the output will be free of the negative voltage swing of the trailing edge as seen on the grid, since the cathode cannot fall below ground potential.

The free-running blocking oscillator has its grid resistor R_g tied back to the cathode instead of to a negative bias. Therefore, the negative charge that builds up on the grid side of the capacitor during the grid-cathode diode conduction leaks off and decreases the grid bias until cutoff is reached and the tube conducts. The R_gC time constant determines the pulse repetition frequency.

9-11   The Triggered-Sweep Oscilloscope

Several of the circuits described in the previous sections are utilized in the triggered-sweep oscilloscope, as shown in the block diagram of Fig. 9-45. The triggered sweep, as indicated in Sec. 1-8, has a great advantage for displaying nonrecurrent signals or transients and is found on most modern research-type oscilloscopes.

To provide a very linear time base, the Miller sweep, shown in Fig. 8-25, if often used. The sweep may be started (triggered) either by the signal to be observed or by a different external trigger source, which might be the trigger that initiates the signal to be observed. A Schmitt binary

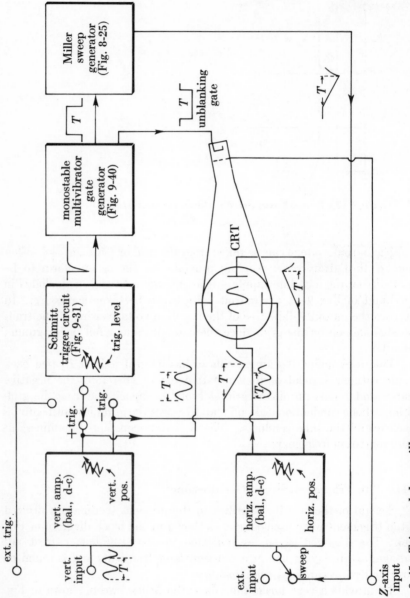

Figure 9-45 *Triggered d-c oscilloscope.*

is often used to produce a trigger pulse at a preset d-c level of the input signal. The output from the Schmitt binary is fed to a monostable multivibrator that produces a rectangular gate. The duration T of the gate is readily adjustable and determines the length of the sweep. A negative gate is also fed to the cathode of the CRT to decrease the grid bias and *unblank* the tube, so that the electron beam reaches the fluorescent screen. Since the negative gate is also of period T, there is no retrace on the CRT screen from the trailing edge of the sweep signal. Also, high beam intensities may be used without fear of burning the phosphor screen, because the electron beam is OFF for much of the time and is ON only during the actual sweep.

Carefully regulated power supplies and quality components are used in the general-purpose oscilloscope for the reasons of stability and accuracy previously described for the individual circuits. A Z-axis input is also shown in Fig. 9-45 to provide intensity modulation, as described in Sec. 1-8.

9-12 Scalers and Electronic Counters

Dekatron Scaler and Counter. The Dekatron tube and associated circuitry, described in Sec. 9-1, provide one output pulse for every 10 input events. In other words, the number of output pulses with respect to input is *scaled down* by a factor of 10 by each Dekatron stage. As shown in Fig. 9-46, a second sequential Dekatron counts the tens, and its output with respect to the input on the first Dekatron is scaled down by a factor of 100. Therefore, a third Dekatron will count the hundreds, and the output from the third stage is scaled down by a factor of 1000.

Since the maximum input rate that most Dekatrons can tolerate is a few thousand cycles per second for reliable operation, the maximum output rate from the third Dekatron cannot exceed a few cycles per second. Many ratchet-type counters can operate up to 20 cps; so the third Dekatron can be followed by an inexpensive electromechanical register. With a three-digit register and three Dekatron stages the total count can be 999,999. For the example shown in Fig. 9-46, the total count is 372,825.

The input circuitry depends on the magnitude of the input pulses from the transducer. In most cases, it is necessary to modify each input pulse so that it has the correct shape for obtaining the double pulse necessary for a one-digit transfer in the Dekatron tube. If the integrator network of Fig. 9-11 is used to obtain the double pulse for driving the Dekatron, then the input rectangular pulse of about 120 volts amplitude and 80 μsec duration can be supplied from a one-shot multivibrator of the type shown in Fig. 9-40. Preceding the one-shot multivibrator, it is necessary to have an amplifier if the input pulses are small.

Binary Scalers and Counters. The binary circuits of Sec. 9-6 are also scalers because output pulses are obtained that are scaled down by a

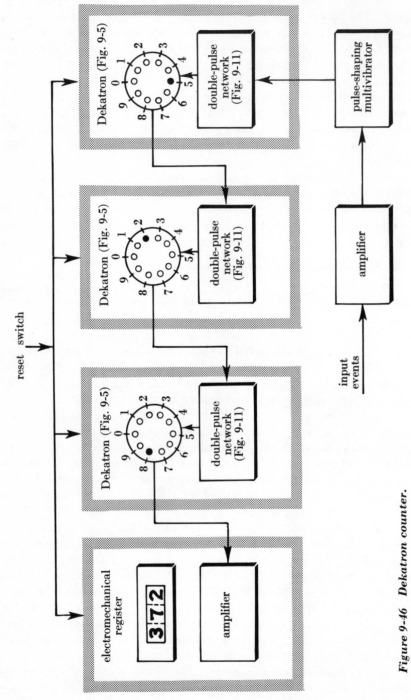

Figure 9-46   Dekatron counter.

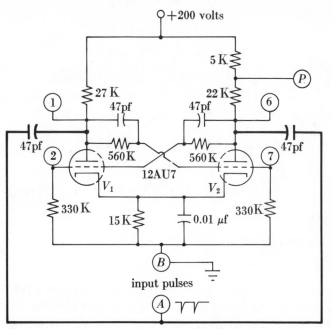

Figure 9-47   Binary with symmetrical plate triggering.

factor of 2 with respect to the input. A circuit similar to the self-biased binary of Fig. 9-29 is shown in Fig. 9-47, but with the plates connected via coupling capacitors for symmetrical triggering. For each negative pulse there is a transition of states. The output at point P is taken from a divided load resistor for V_2. Note that two negative pulses at the input produce one negative pulse after differentiation of the output from point P. With this arrangement it is possible to cascade many binaries, as illustrated with three binaries in Fig. 9-48.

For simplicity each identical binary circuit of Fig. 9-47 is represented by a symbol that indicates the connecting points for the other circuitry necessary in scaling and counting operations. In Fig. 9-48 the output from point P of one stage is fed to the input point A of the next stage. Only the negative pulses are of sufficient magnitude to trigger a transition. If it is assumed that V_2 of each binary is ON and V_1 OFF at the start, then the four sequential negative pulses at the input of the first stage provide two negative pulses at the input of the second stage and one negative pulse at the input of the third stage.

If, at the start, the V_1 tube in each binary is OFF, then the plate (point 1) of each V_1 tube is at $+193$ volts. Each V_1 plate is individually connected to a neon light in series with a current-limiting resistor and back

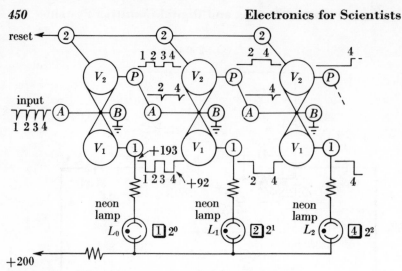

Figure 9-48   *Three binaries cascaded for counting.*

to the plate supply. The 7-volt difference between $+200$ and $+193$ volts is insufficient to ionize the gas in the neon lamp; so all lamps are OFF at the start. However, when the first negative pulse is applied to the first stage, point 1 drops to $+92$ volts. Now the voltage across neon lamp L_0 is sufficient for firing, and L_0 lights to indicate the number 1. A second input pulse reverses states in both the first and second stages. Therefore, lamp L_0 goes OFF, and the second neon lamp L_1 goes ON, indicating a number 2. A third negative input pulse reverses states in only the first binary; so L_0 goes ON, and L_1 remains ON. The sum of the two lamps indicates the number 3. A fourth negative input pulse causes transitions to occur in all three binaries. Therefore, lamps L_0 and L_1 go OFF, and lamp L_2 in the third stage goes ON to indicate the number 4. All binaries can be put in the start position (with V_1 OFF and V_2 ON) by applying a negative trigger pulse to the reset terminal (point 2) which is connected directly to the grids of the V_1 tubes.

If the ON neon lamp is represented by a 1 and an OFF neon lamp by 0, Fig. 9-49 indicates the waveforms and lamp condition for a series of four cascaded binaries. Note that, in counting from 1 to 16, the binary equivalent number is indicated by the vertical column reading from the bottom up. For example, the decimal number 5 is 0101 in binary, and the decimal number 9 is 1001 (that is, $2^3 + 0 + 0 + 2^0 = 8 + 1 = 9$). On the sixteenth input pulse all four binaries return to their start condition, and a "carry pulse" is sent to a subsequent stage or other circuitry. The first four binaries then repeat the same sequence for the next 16 input pulses.

The advantage of the binary as a scaler in comparison with the Dekatron is the much faster response time. The obvious disadvantage is the less familiar binary readout. For this reason binaries have been connected with feedback systems to provide a *scale of* 10. Such units are sometimes called "binary decades." They require four binaries to obtain a scale of 10, whereas the same number of binaries provide a scale of 16 with binary readout. In computers, binary arithmetic (addition, subtraction, multiplication, and division) is simpler to perform than decimal arithmetic. Therefore, the operations are usually performed in binary, with a final conversion to decimal readout.

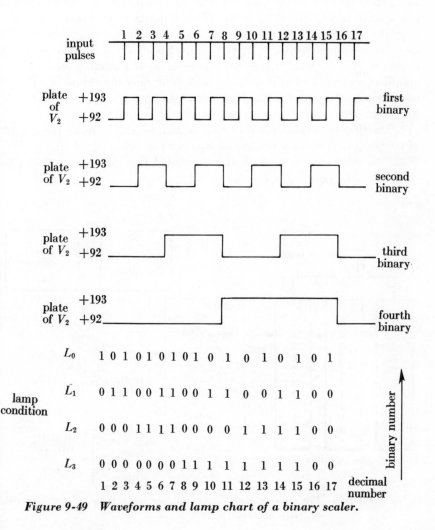

Figure 9-49 Waveforms and lamp chart of a binary scaler.

9-13 Frequency and Time-Interval Meters

Counting Frequency Meters. The most accurate type of frequency meter makes use of the counters described in the previous section. The principle is very simple. The unknown input frequency is amplified and modified to produce one pulse for each cycle, and the pulses are allowed to enter the decade counters for a precise time interval Δt. If the time interval Δt is 1 sec, the decade counters read out directly in cycles per second.

There are various types of gates that can be opened and closed to allow passage of pulses for only the desired time interval. One type of gate is provided by a 6AS6 tube which is constructed so that the suppressor grid acts as a second control grid. If the suppressor grid is several volts negative with respect to the cathode, the tube remains cut off even with input pulses applied to the regular control grid. If a positive pulse of duration Δt is applied to the suppressor grid, the input pulses will be amplified and passed to the decade counters for only the period Δt. Three decades could be added to the three decades shown in Fig. 9-50 to provide direct readout of frequency up to 1 Mc.

The time-interval signal is often produced by scaling down the output of a crystal oscillator operating at frequencies of 100 kc, 1 Mc, or 10 Mc. With the crystal in a small thermal-regulated box the frequency can be controlled to 1 ppm. The time interval generated by dividing the crystal-

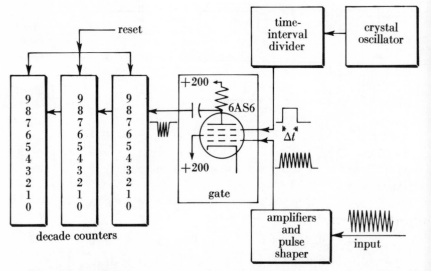

Figure 9-50 Frequency meter (events per unit time, time interval, or ratio meter).

oscillator frequency has the same accuracy as the oscillator. Therefore, the accuracy of frequency measurement is often dependent on the number of counts. In starting and stopping the counting there is the chance of losing either the first or the last input cycle, so there is an uncertainty of ± 1 cycle. If the frequency is about 100,000 cps, the accuracy is 0.001 per cent. If the frequency is low, the accuracy is low, for example 1 per cent for 100 cps.

For better precision at low frequencies, the functions of unknown input frequency and standard crystal oscillator can be reversed. The duration Δt of 1 cycle of unknown frequency provides the time interval for counting the pulses from the crystal oscillator. If the unknown frequency f_u is 100 cps, then $\Delta t = 1/f_u = 0.01$ sec. During this time interval a crystal oscillator operating at a frequency $f_s = 1,000,000$ cps would pass 10,000 counts. The error for determining low frequencies is thus decreased from 1 to 0.01 per cent by the alternative method. With this procedure, the unknown frequency $f_u = f_s/N$, where N is the number of counts read off the decade counters.

From the above example it is apparent that the same general system can be used for *time-interval measurements*. The start of an event opens the gate, and the end of the event closes the gate. With an oscillator feeding pulses to the counter at a rate of 1 Mc, the counter reads directly in microseconds. One hundred counts indicates a time interval of 100 μsec. By using a standard frequency of 1000 cps, the time intervals can be read directly in milliseconds.

The ratio between two unknown frequencies f_x and f_y may also be determined by the same general technique. One cycle of the lowest frequency f_x is used to provide the time interval for counting the number of cycles from frequency f_y. For example, if $f_x = 100$ cps and $f_y = 8$ kc, the number of counts will be 80 and the ratio $f_y/f_x = 80:1$.

Counting-Rate Meters. Although the circuits described in this section can be used to determine counts or events per unit time, the circuitry is rather elaborate and the accuracy more than sufficient in many cases. A much simpler type of circuit is often used to provide inexpensive and portable *count-rate meters*, especially for radioactive monitoring.

Most of these meters work on the basis of converting each input event into a pulse of fixed amplitude and duration and then determining the average current from these pulses, with an ordinary D'Arsonval meter. If a capacitor C_1 is completely charged by a pulse of voltage amplitude E, the charge $Q = C_1 E$. For n pulses in time interval Δt, each adding a charge Q, the total change in charge $\Delta Q = n C_1 E$, and the rate of change of charge, or average current i_{av}, in period Δt is

$$i_{av} = \frac{\Delta Q}{\Delta t} = \frac{nCE}{\Delta t} \qquad (9\text{-}10)$$

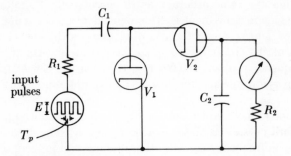

Figure 9-51   Diode pump for a count-rate meter.

From Eq. (9-10), it is apparent that if a circuit can be arranged to accept a charge Q from each input pulse, and to measure the average rate of change of charge, then the current registered on the meter will be directly proportional to the number of pulses per unit time.   Therefore, a current meter can be made direct-reading in count rate.

In the above method it is important that each input pulse contributes the same charge Q to the meter current.   This is accomplished by the so-called *diode pump*, or *storage counter*, shown in Fig. 9-51.   When the positive voltage pulse of amplitude E is applied to the circuit, diode V_1 conducts and C_1 charges to the voltage E if the RC charge time is much less than the pulse width T_p.   For practical purposes $T_p > 5R_1C_1$ is satisfactory, on the assumption that the diode resistance of V_1 is negligible compared with R_1.   The charge Q on C_1 is now $Q = C_1E$.   When the input pulse drops back to zero, the cathode of V_2 is E volts negative with respect to the anode, so that V_2 conducts and capacitor C_1 discharges through diode V_2, the current meter, and the resistances R_1 and R_2.   The capacitor C_2 is used to average the current through the meter, and it should be much larger than C_1.   Circuit values are chosen so that C_1 discharges essentially completely before the next input pulse.   Therefore, the input circuit is in

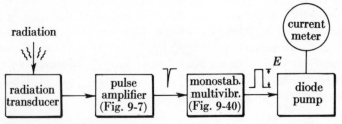

Figure 9-52   Count-rate meter.

the same condition as for the previous input pulse, and another pulse of amplitude E will again provide a charge $Q = C_1E$. Again this charge will be *pumped* through the meter when the input pulse returns to zero.

It is obvious from Eq. (9-10) that the average current through the meter can be changed by changing the capacitance of C_1 or the amplitude E of the input pulses. Therefore, the sensitivity, or range, of the meter in terms of count rate can be varied by changing either C_1 or E or both.

The method of providing the pulses of amplitude E from a radiation detector, such as a Geiger tube, is illustrated in Fig. 9-52. The output from the detector is amplified and fed to a monostable multivibrator, such as that shown in Fig. 9-40, to produce pulses of constant amplitude E and duration T_p. These are the pulses that are fed to the diode pump of Fig. 9-51.

Direct-Reading Frequency Meter. A frequency meter, utilizing the same readout principles as the radiation count-rate meter, is shown in Fig. 9-53. A Schmitt trigger is used to convert the sine wave into a square wave. By feeding this square wave into an RC differentiator, one sharp negative trigger pulse is obtained for each cycle at the input. The negative trigger pulses are fed into a monostable multivibrator, as in the count-rate meter, to obtain uniform pulses of amplitude E and period T_p. The output of the one-shot multivibrator goes to the diode pump, which produces a current directly proportional to the pulse rate. Since the pulse rate is equal to the input frequency, the meter can be made to read frequency directly. Again, the sensitivity, or range, may be changed by varying C_1 or E, as for the count-rate meter.

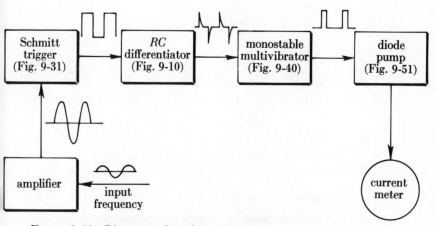

Figure 9-53 Direct-reading frequency meter.

9-14 Electronic Digital-to-Analog Converters

The count-rate and direct-reading frequency meters described in Sec. 9-13 can be considered as digital-to-analog converters, because a current or voltage is developed that is representative or analogous to the number of input events. There are, of course, many other examples of such converters, such as the following.

Binary-Number to Analog Voltage Conversion. Each digit of a binary number could be represented by a voltage from a battery of suitable value. Therefore, for the binary number 1010 ($1 \times 2^3 + 0 \times 2^2 + 1 \times 2^1 + 0 \times 2^0 = 1 \times 8 + 0 \times 4 + 1 \times 2 + 0 \times 1 = 10$), 8- and 2-volt batteries could be connected in series across the output to provide a 10-volt analog signal, as illustrated in Fig. 9-54. Note that in this example the 4- and 1-volt batteries, representing the third and first digits of the binary number, respectively, are bypassed by the switches.

The switches can be the contacts of single-pole double-throw relays, and each binary number can be fed to the relays so that its analog voltage appears at the output. Relays are relatively slow, however, and an all-electronic converter, as shown in Fig. 9-55, can convert binary numbers to analog voltages at the rate of about 100,000 numbers per second. The circuit uses one-shot multivibrators (or flip-flops if it is desired to hold the digital state) to produce 100-volt pulses for each digit of the binary number that is a 1. Precision resistors are used to provide output currents in the ratio 8, 4, 2, and 1. Therefore, various combinations of 8, 4, 2, and 1

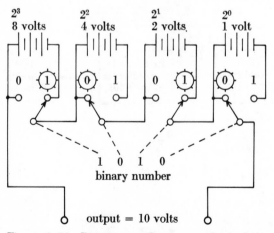

Figure 9-54 Binary-number to analog voltage conversion with relays and batteries.

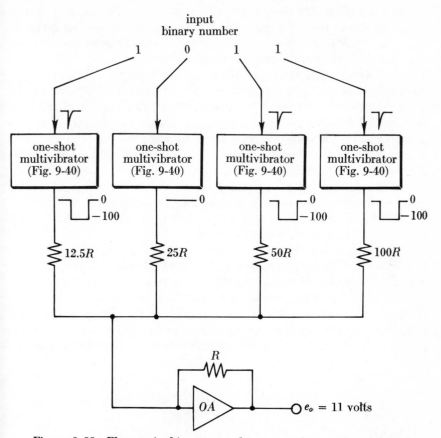

Figure 9-55   Electronic binary-number to analog voltage converter.

can be summed by the operational amplifier to provide an output voltage that is the analog of the input binary number. Note the example in Fig. 9-55, whereby the input binary number 1011 produces an 11-volt analog at the output.

9-15   Analog-to-Digital Converters

The outputs from most transducers are analog-type signals. Pressures, temperatures, light intensity, and many other phenomena are commonly transduced into analog voltages that are measured with various meters. For digital operations with these quantities, it is necessary to convert the analog signal to digital representations or pulse codes. There are many types of analog-to-digital converters that are commercially available, and the number of specific designs is growing rapidly. The purpose of this section is not to present a survey of the various converters but rather to show that typical converter types contain many of the same basic circuits that were presented in the other sections of this chapter.

Converter with Sawtooth Comparison Voltage. The principle of operation of one type of analog-to-digital converter is illustrated by the block diagram in Fig. 9-56. The voltage sample to be coded in digital form is compared with the voltage from a linear sawtooth generator. The programmer starts the sawtooth generator at time t_0 and simultaneously feeds a start pulse to the start-stop circuit (a binary multivibrator, Fig. 9-29) that opens the gate and allows pulses from the master oscillator to feed into the digital counter. When the voltage from the sawtooth rises to a value equal to the sample voltage to be encoded, the comparison circuit senses the null point and sends a stop pulse (time t_1) to the start-stop circuit, which closes the gate and stops the counters.

There are many different comparison circuits, and one type is shown in Fig. 9-57. The sample voltage e_{in} is compared with the sawtooth e_{ref}. When e_{in} is greater than e_{ref}, the diode is reverse-biased and there is no current in the transformer winding in series with it. The tube V_1 is conducting because it is in clamp, and the plate of V_1 is therefore at a low value. When the sawtooth voltage starts to exceed the sample voltage, the diode conducts and the feedback loop around V_1 is closed so that the

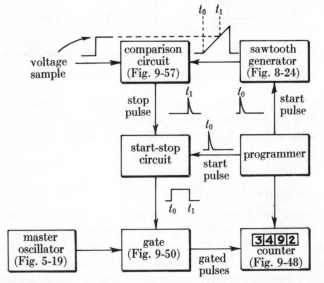

Figure 9-56   Analog-to-digital converter with sawtooth comparison voltage.

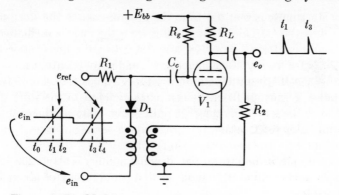

Figure 9-57   Multiar comparison circuit.

cathode swings positive and tube V_1 cuts off. This produces a positive pulse at the output that can be used as the stop pulse to close the gate.

Converter with Staircase Comparison Voltage.   The same general idea of voltage comparison used in Fig. 9-56 has also been used in a different analog-to-digital conversion system, as illustrated in Fig. 9-58.

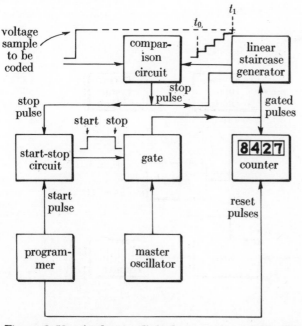

Figure 9-58   Analog-to-digital converter with staircase comparison voltage.

Once again a start pulse is sent out from the programmer to the start-stop circuit that opens the gate and allows pulses from the master oscillator to reach the digital counter. The pulses are also fed to the linear staircase generator * so that a fixed voltage increment is added to its output for each input pulse. When the resulting staircase voltage equals the sample voltage, a stop pulse is sent out from the comparison circuit to the start-stop circuit that closes the gate and stops the pulses from entering the counter. After the termination of counting, the programmer sends out a reset pulse to clear the counter for the next conversion cycle.

The conversion time for a three-digit decimal number is about 200 μsec. Circuits can be made sufficiently stable so that an accuracy of about 0.1 per cent is possible.

* The staircase generator is similar to the diode pump of Fig. 9-51, except that the meter and resistor R_2 are eliminated and the output across C_2 is fed to a circuit of high input resistance. Therefore, there is insignificant discharge of C_2 over the period of staircase generation, and each input pulse adds a fixed charge and *voltage step*, or increment, across C_2, within the limitations described for the diode pump.

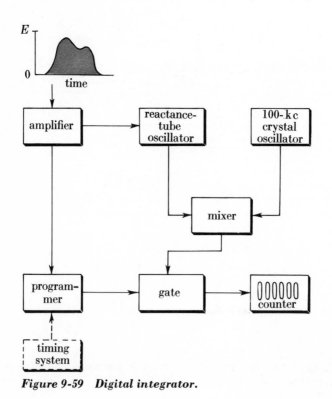

Figure 9-59   Digital integrator.

Digital Integrator. There are many cases where it is desirable to obtain the integral of some phenomenon over a given period, and the circuit of Fig. 9-59 provides an interesting way of integrating a voltage analog from some transducer and converting simultaneously to a digital readout. The circuit is similar in principle to the model 270 integrator of the Allegany Instrument Co.

The output frequency of a reactance tube oscillator is mixed with a stable 100-kc signal from a crystal oscillator to obtain a difference beat frequency that is fed to the counters. The reactance tube oscillator is adjusted so that its output frequency is 100 kc when the input voltage is zero, thereby giving a zero difference-frequency output from the mixer, and no counts are registered on the counter. The reactance tube oscillator is designed and adjusted so that an input voltage of 1 volt changes its frequency by 10 kc. Input voltages varying from 0 to 1 volt provide a linear change in frequency from 100 to 110 kc in the reactance tube oscillator and a 0 to 10 kc difference frequency that feeds the counters. To integrate the voltage under the entire curve, all that is necessary is to open the gate before the signal is applied and close the gate after the signal is completed. Fractions of the input signal can be integrated over selected time intervals by connecting a timing system to the programmer.

References

Millman, J., and H. Taub, "Pulse and Digital Circuits," McGraw-Hill, New York, 1956. A thorough quantitative treatment of digital circuits at an advanced level.

Pettit, J. M., "Electronic Switching, Timing, and Pulse Circuits," McGraw-Hill, New York, 1959. A selected example is presented for each type of the important switching and pulse circuits; each example is developed in a clear way.

"Basic Theory and Application of Transistors," TM 11-690, U.S. Government Printing Office, Washington, D. C., 1959. Contains thirty pages on transistor pulse and switching circuits.

"Radar Electronic Fundamentals," NAVSHIPS 900,016, U.S. Government Printing Office, Washington, D.C., 1944. An elementary and qualitative description of waveshaping and basic multivibrator circuits.

Problems

9-1 For the radar system illustrated in Fig. 9-2, determine the sweep rate (inches/second) so that the echo from an airplane at a range of 100 nautical miles will appear on the scope at 4.00 in. from the start of the transmitted pulse.

Ans.: Sweep rate $= 3230$ in./sec

9-2 A 10-volt rectangular pulse with a 1-msec pulse width is applied at time t_0 to a series RC circuit, as shown in Fig. 9-10, with $R = 100$ kilohms and $C = 1000$ pf. Calculate the voltages across R and C at $t = t_0$, 0.1 msec, 0.3 msec,

0.5 msec, 1 msec, 1.1 msec, 1.3 msec, and 1.5 msec, and plot the results. *Note:* Use Fig. 9-9 or Table 9-1 to determine answers.

Ans.: at t_0 $E_R =$ 10   volts $E_C =$ 0   volts

     $t = 0.1$ msec $E_R =$ 3.7 volts $E_C =$ 6.3 volts

     $t = 0.3$ msec $E_R =$ 0.5 volt $E_C =$ 9.5 volts

     $t = 0.5$ msec $E_R \approx$ 0   volts $E_C \approx$ 10   volts

     $t = 1$ msec $E_R = -10$ volts $E_C = 10$ volts

     $t = 1.1$ msec $E_R = -3.7$ volts $E_C =$ 3.7 volts

     $t = 1.3$ msec $E_R = -1$ volt $E_C =$ 1   volt

     $t = 1.5$ msec $E_R \approx$ 0   volts $E_C \approx$ 0   volts

9-3 Repeat Prob. 9-2 for the case where R is changed to 1 megohm, and calculate E_R and E_C for times $t = t_0$, 0.5 msec, 1 msec, and 1.5 msec.

Ans.:   at t_0 $E_R = 10$ volts $E_C = 0$ volts

     $t = 0.5$ msec $E_R = $ 6 volts $E_C = 4$ volts

     $t = 1$ msec   This is at the end of the pulse, and E_R changes from 3.7 to -6.3 volts, and $E_C = 6.3$ volts.

     $t = 1.5$ msec $E_R = -2.5$ volts $E_C = 3.8$ volts

9-4 A 20.00-volt square wave, symmetrical about zero volts, is applied to the series limiter of Fig. 9-15a. ($R = 10$ kilohms.) Calculate the maximum output voltage for: (*a*) a semiconductor diode, $R_f = 100$ ohms; (*b*) a vacuum diode, $R_f = 1000$ ohms.   *Ans.:* (*a*) 9.99 volts; (*b*) 9.1 volts

9-5 A 10.0-volt square wave, symmetrical about zero, is applied to the clipping circuit of Fig. 9-16a. Calculate the peak-to-peak output voltage for the following voltages: (*a*) $E = +6$; (*b*) $E = +3$; and (*c*) $E = -3$.

Ans.: (*a*) zero; (*b*) 2 volts; (*c*) 8 volts

9-6 A 100-volt peak-to-peak sine wave is applied to the circuit of Fig. 9-17b. Z_1 is a 30-volt Zener diode. The output voltage is 55 volts peak-to-peak. Calculate the breakdown potential of Z_2.   *Ans.:* 25 volts

9-7 A 100-volt square wave having a PRF of 1 kc is applied to the clamping circuit of Fig. 9-18. The diode has forward resistance of 500 ohms and C is 1 μf. Approximately how many cycles are required to reach a clamped condition after applying the square wave to the circuit?

Ans.: $R_f C = T_p = 0.5$ msec; need about 5 cycles

9-8 A square wave is applied to the grid of a 12AU7 through a large capacitor in a circuit similar to Fig. 9-23b. $E_{bb} = 250$ volts, $R_L = 10$ kilohms, and $R_g = 1$ megohm. Calculate the peak-to-peak output voltage of the circuit for the following input voltage amplitudes: (*a*) 100; (*b*) 40; (*c*) 10.

Ans.: (*a*) 135; (*b*) 135; (*c*) 100

9-9 Calculate the voltages at the plates and grids of a 12AU7 for a binary similar to Fig. 9-26. $R_L = 47$ kilohms, $R_c = 220$ kilohms, $R_g = 220$ kilohms, $E_{bb} = 250$ volts, and $E_{cc} = -100$ volts. Consider V_1 ON.

Ans.: $E_{g1} \approx 0$ volts; $E_{g2} \approx -30$ volts; $E_{b1} = 40$ volts; $E_{b2} = 206$ volts

9-10 (*a*) Calculate the value of R_g necessary to provide $E_{c2} = -30$ volts in a circuit similar to Fig. 9-29. Assume V_1 is ON. $V_1 = V_2 = \frac{1}{2}$ 12AU7, $E_{bb} = 250$ volts, $R_L = 33$ kilohms, $R_c = 1$ megohm, and $R_K = 10$ kilohms. (*b*) Calculate E_K, E_{g1}, E_{g2}, E_{b1}, and E_{b2}.

Ans.: (*a*) 310 kilohms; (*b*) $E_K = 50$ volts; $E_{g1} \approx 50$ volts; $E_{g2} = 20$ volts; $E_{b1} = 85$ volts; $E_{b2} = 244$ volts

9-11 The 12AT7 tube of Fig. 9-31 is replaced by a 12AU7 and $E_{c2} = -1$ volt. Calculate the following: (a) R_2 required to maintain $E_{c2} = -1$ volt; (b) E_{b1}; (c) E_{b2}; (d) E_K; and (e) the voltage of G_1 above ground necessary to cause a transition.

Ans.: (a) $R_2 = 105$ kilohms; (b) $E_{b1} \approx 200$ volts; (c) $E_{b2} = 163$ volts; (d) $E_K = 75$ volts; (e) 60 volts

9-12 A transistor astable multivibrator similar to Fig. 9-37 has the following circuit parameters: $T_1 = T_2 = $ CK768; p-n-p transistors; $R_L = 10$ kilohms; $R_b = 100$ kilohms; $C = 1000$ pf; $V_{CC} = -15$ volts. Calculate: (a) the peak-to-peak output voltage; (b) the square-wave frequency.

Ans.: (a) about 15 volts; (b) 725 cps

9-13 (a) Calculate the stable-state voltages for a cathode-coupled monostable multivibrator as shown in Fig. 9-40: $R_L = 10$ kilohms, $R_K = 5$ kilohms, $V_1 = V_2 = $ 12AU7, $R_{g2} = 1$ megohm, $C_2 = 500$ pf, $E_{cc} = 20$ volts, $E_{bb} = 250$ volts. (b) What is the peak-to-peak output voltage?

Ans.: (a) $E_{b1} \approx 250$ volts; $E_{b2} = 155$ volts; $E_K \approx E_{g2} = 43$ volts; $E_{g1} = 20$ volts

9-14 What value of C_1 should be chosen to provide an output current of 1 μa with a 1-volt, 1-kc input square wave for the diode pump circuit of Fig. 9-51? What is the maximum value of R_1?

Ans.: $C_1 = 1000$ pf; $T_p \approx 5R_1C_1$; $R_1 \approx 100$ kilohms

EXPERIMENTS

All three basic types of multivibrators are constructed and investigated in the following experiments, using both transistor and vacuum-tube circuits. The scaling and counting capabilities of the bistable multivibrator are first observed. A low-frequency pulse source is constructed to aid in these observations. The bistable Schmitt trigger is also constructed, and its applications as a "squaring circuit" and discriminator are illustrated. The production of gates of varying widths is demonstrated with the monostable multivibrator. The ability of a "free-running" astable multivibrator to produce various asymmetrical rectangular oscillations is observed. Included in the experiments with multivibrators are RC differentiation and RC integration.

Expt. 9-1   Bistable Multivibrator

Construction and Voltage Measurements. Construct the binary shown in Fig. 9-60, but *do not connect* the speed-up capacitors C_1 and C_2. With the VTVM measure the voltages at pins 1, 2, 3, 6, and 7 of the 12AU7, determine which tube is OFF and which tube is ON, and compare the measured voltages with the calculated values for the similar circuit shown in Fig. 9-29. It is possible to trigger the circuit with pickup of noise on the VTVM probe. Therefore, make sure that a transition does not occur while obtaining a complete set of voltages at the above points. A transition is easily observed by the neon light going ON or OFF while the measurements are made. Now connect the speed-up capacitors C_1 and C_2, and then try to measure the voltages at the pins.

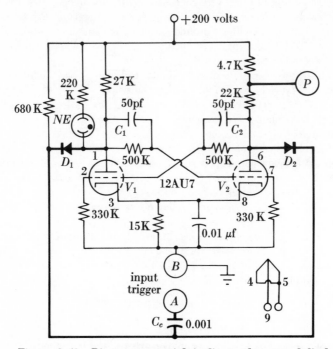

*Figure 9-60   Binary stage with indicator lamp and diode plate trigger-
ing.*

Source of Low-Frequency Negative Trigger Pulses. The thyratron
sweep circuit of Fig. 9-61 provides a convenient source of repetitive negative pulses
for reliable triggering of the binary circuit. After constructing the trigger circuit,
observe with the oscilloscope the sweep output at pin 6. Note that the output
sweep rate can be readily changed by varying the grid-to-cathode voltage between
-0.5 and -2 volts with the fine control on the VRS. Measure the magnitude of
the sweep voltage at a few values over the range. Now observe the negative trigger
pulse at the output of the RC differentiator, which results from the rapid flyback
of the sweep voltage and short RC time constant. These negative trigger pulses
are used in the subsequent experiments.

Triggering and Binary Characteristics. Connect the pulse output from
Fig. 9-61 to the input terminals A and B of Fig. 9-60. With the oscilloscope connected between terminals A and B, set the VRS fine control so that about *one pulse
per second* is observed on the scope. While watching the trigger pulses on the scope,
observe out of the corner of your eye the neon lamp in the binary. Observe that
two negative pulses are required for each ON-OFF cycle of the neon lamp.

Vary the pulse rate, and observe both the input trigger signal and the square-
wave output on either plate of the binary and at point P. To obtain a faster pulse

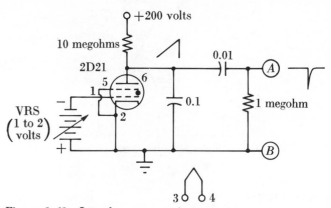

Figure 9-61   Low-frequency trigger source.

rate so that the square wave can be easily observed on the scope, shunt the 10-megohm resistor in Fig. 9-61 with a 1-megohm resistor.

For high-speed triggering, connect the square-wave output of the sine-square generator between terminals *A* and *B*. Set the frequency to 20 kc, the range switch on 10 volts, the amplitude at maximum, and observe the output at point *P*. Vary the amplitude control of the square-wave generator to determine the minimum voltage necessary to provide reliable triggering.

By alternately observing the input at point *A* and the output at point *P*, note that the frequency of the output square wave with respect to the input is scaled down by a factor of 2.

Set the amplitude control of the sine-square generator to the maximum (10 volts), and increase the frequency until the frequency ratio of input to output is no longer 2:1. Record the shapes of the input and output waves at the maximum frequency for reliable operation, and measure the rise times.

Expt. 9-2   Binary Counting

If Experiment 9-1 is performed in a laboratory with other workers, two or more students may cascade their binaries to make a counter, as shown in Fig. 9-62. Use the low-frequency trigger (about *one pulse per second*), and observe the operation of the neon lamps for successive trigger pulses. Use the high-frequency trigger pulse, and observe the relationship between input frequency and the output square-wave frequencies of successive stages.

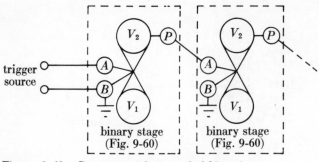

Figure 9-62   Counter with cascaded binaries.

Expt. 9-3   Schmitt Trigger

Construction and Voltage Adjustments.   Construct the Schmitt circuit shown in Fig. 9-63, but do not connect the parts shown in dotted lines.   Make the voltage adjustments by varying R_1 and R_2 in the following sequence: First, adjust R_1 so that the grid of V_1 is at ground.   Now vary R_2 so that the grid-to-cathode voltage of V_2 is -0.5 volt as measured by a VTVM.   *Do not change this adjustment.*

Connect the VTVM (on the 500-volt range) across the output.   Gradually decrease the bias of V_1 by varying the potentiometer R_1 until a sudden increase in voltage at the output indicates a transition.   Measure the grid-to-ground voltage

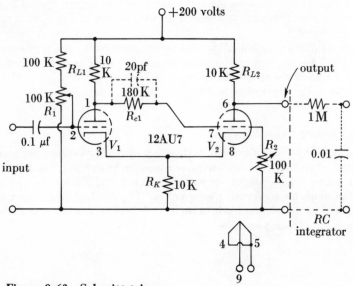

Figure 9-63   Schmitt trigger.

of V_1 at the transition point. Also note the magnitude of the voltage change at the output.

Connect the sine-wave output of the sine-square generator to the input of the Schmitt circuit, and turn the amplitude control to maximum on the 10-volt range. Using the oscilloscope, note the relationship between input and output at a few frequencies from about 25 cps to 25 kc. At each frequency, slowly vary potentiometer R_1, and note the relationship between the bias on V_1 and the widths of the asymmetrical rectangular output wave. Now connect the 20-pf capacitor across R_{c1}, and observe the effect on the output, especially at the higher frequencies.

Set the frequency of the sine-wave input at about 300 cps. Connect the RC integrator circuit (shown in dotted lines in Fig. 9-63) across the output. Now observe the relationship between the square-wave output from the Schmitt trigger and the RC integrator output for different bias values on V_1, as set by varying R_1.

Refer to the circuit diagram in the instruction manual for the sine-square generator, and note that the square-wave output from the generator is produced by a Schmitt trigger fed by the output from a sine-wave oscillator.

Make a series of measurements that will demonstrate the usefulness of the Schmitt trigger as a *discriminator circuit*.

Expt. 9-4   Monostable Multivibrator

Construction and Waveform Observations. Construct the monostable multivibrator shown in Fig. 9-64. Set the frequency of the input square wave at about 10 kc and the amplitude control at maximum on the 10-volt range. Start with $C = 0.00022$ μf, and record the waveforms of the input pulse and those at each collector and at each base of the circuit.

Determination of Gate Width. Now connect the scope between point P and ground, and vary C. Record how the width of the gate changes as a function of capacitor C. Determine how well the observed value checks with the calculated

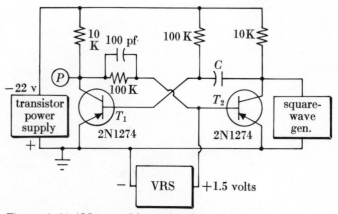

Figure 9-64   Monostable multivibrator.

value of gate width. Vary the input frequency over a wide range, and observe how the ratio of gate width to period between input pulses varies.

Expt. 9-5   Astable Multivibrator

Construction and Waveform Observations. Construct the circuit of Fig. 9-65. Start with capacitors $C_1 = C_2 = 0.005$ μf. Observe the waveforms at each base and collector, and measure the frequency of the output. Change the values of C_1 and C_2 to both increase and decrease the output frequency. Compare the observed and calculated frequency values.

Change the relative values of C_1 and C_2 (for example, 0.001 and 0.005) to produce an asymmetrical waveform. Record the waveforms at the base and collector of each transistor. Compare the calculated and observed ON and OFF values for each transistor.

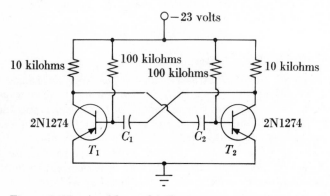

Figure 9-65   Astable multivibrator.

Supplements

supplement 1

An Integrated System of Instruments, Test Equipment, and Rapid-Connect Parts

In this section the new "solderless" electronic construction kits and specially designed instruments are described. These together with the specified test equipment enable all experiments in the book to be performed efficiently and rapidly. The system is universal in that it can be used for the rapid assembly and testing of practically any vacuum tube or transistor circuit. These instruments and kits are ideal in teaching basic electronics and scientific instrumentation and are also valuable in research, engineering development, and control. The system was originated by H. V. Malmstadt and C. G. Enke to teach the principles and use of electronic circuits and instruments in scientific applications. The units have all been engineered, developed, and made commercially available by the Heath Co. (Benton Harbor, Michigan).

A complete list of the equipment necessary to perform all the experiments in this text is given below. The Heath number for each group or unit has been used for convenience.

EUW-12. *Wired test equipment.* A group of standard electronic test equipment, substitution boxes, and a tool kit.

EU-13. *Universal experimental chassis and parts.* A set of chassis and electronic components especially designed for efficient and realistic construction of electronic circuits.

EU-14. *Special experimental chassis and parts.* A set of tubes, transistors, and other special parts required to perform the specific experiments described in this book.

EUW-15. *Universal power supply.* A regulated power supply to be used for the experimental circuits, and also designed for instruction in rectification, filtering, and regulation.

EUW-16. *Voltage reference source.* A source of accurately known voltages from a fraction of a millivolt to 100 volts. This unit is used as a calibrator, a d-c signal source, and a potentiometer throughout the experiments.

EUW-17. *Transistorized power supply.* A low-voltage power source for supplying transistor experimental circuits in each chapter.

EUW-18. *Laboratory meter with shunts.* This unit illustrates the adaptation of the meter movement in the Experiments of Chap. 1 and is a generally useful current meter throughout the experiments.

EUW-19. *Operational amplifier system.* The operational amplifiers in this unit can be connected for the precise control of voltage or current, the precision amplification of voltage and current signals, the addition and time integration of electrical signals, and analog computation and simulation as described in Chap. 8.

EUW-20. *Servo recorder.* This is a true potentiometric recorder with very good characteristics. The servo system can be used in a variety of applications and is used in the Experiments of Chap. 7 to illustrate the principles of servo systems. Though not required, the servo recorder is a convenient readout device for many of the other experiments.

The authors feel that the maximum instruction will be obtained when the experiments are performed by students working individually. If experiments from each chapter are to be performed, a complete experimental setup (all the above units) will be required for each student in a section. If more than one section of the course is to be run, it is suggested that there be additional EU-13 and EU-14 units at each desk so that students can leave some of their circuits wired from one laboratory period to the next without incurring a parts shortage.

The complete specifications, circuits, and applications for each of the above units are presented in the following sections of this Supplement. The authors greatly appreciate permission from the Heath Co. to use illustrations and other portions of the Heath EU manuals in presenting the complete system.

S1-1 EUW-12. Wired Test Equipment

These seven standard test instruments and the set of tools are used throughout the experiments. The characteristics of the Heath test equipment which proved suitable in developing all the experiments are listed below. Other test equipment can be substituted if the characteristics are equivalent or better than the listed equipment. Note in particular that a d-c oscilloscope with identical horizontal and vertical d-c amplifiers is necessary for many of the experiments.

Vacuum-Tube Voltmeter (VTVM). Specifications. *Meter scales:* D-c and a-c (rms), 0 to 1.5, 5, 15, 50, 150, 500, 1500 volts full scale. A-c peak-to-peak, 0–4, 14, 40, 140, 400, 1400, 4000. *Resistance:* 10-ohm center scale ×1, ×10, ×100, ×1000, ×10 kilohms, ×100 kilohms, ×1 megohm. Measures 0.1 ohm to 1000 megohms with internal battery. *Meter:* $4\frac{1}{2}$-in. 200-μa movement. *Multipliers:* 1 per cent precision type. *Input resistance d-c:* 11 megohms (1 megohm in probe) on all ranges. *Circuit:* Balanced bridge (push-pull) using twin triode. *Accuracy:* D-c ± 3 per cent, a-c ± 5 per cent of full scale. *Frequency response:* ±1 db, 25 cps to 1 Mc (600-ohm source).

Volt-Ohm-Milliammeter (VOM). Specifications. *Sensitivity:* 20,000 ohms/volt d-c, 5000 ohms/volt a-c. *Range a-c and d-c volts:* Full scale, 1.5, 5, 50, 150, 500, 1500, 5000. *Direct current:* 150 μa, 15, 150, 500 ma, 15 amp. *Ohmmeter:* 0.2 ohm to 20 megohms in three ranges. *Decibels:* −10 to +65 db. *Resistors:* 1 per cent precision type.

D-C Oscilloscope. Specifications (vertical and horizontal channels identical). *Bandwidth:* D-c to 200 kc (2-db point). *Sensitivity:* 0.1 volt (peak-to-peak) per $\frac{1}{4}$ in. (uncalibrated). *Attenuator:* Three-position compensated type. *Gain control:* Continuously variable. *Input impedance:* 3.6 megohms shunted by 35 pf. *Coupling:* Either alternating or direct current, switch-selected. *Relative phase shift between channels:* Less than 5°. *Sweep generator (recurrent type):* Linear sawtooth produced by multivibrator-type generator covering 5 cps to 50 kc in four overlapping ranges. "External-capacity" binding post for lower sweep rates. *Sync provision:* Either internal or external, switch-selected.

Sine-Square Generator. Specifications. *Sine wave: Frequency range,* 20 cycles to 1 Mc. *Output volts* (rms), 0 to 10 volts, 0 to 1 volt, 0 to 0.1 volt, or 0 to 0.01 volt, working into a high-impedance load. *Source impedance* (±10 per cent), 10-volt range, 0 to 3.5 kilohms; 1-volt, 0.1-volt, and 0.01-volt range, 600 ohms. *Distortion,* less than 0.25 per cent, 20 to 20,000 cycles. *Frequency response,* ±1.5 db, 20 cycles to 1 Mc. *Square wave: Frequency range,* 20 cycles to 1 Mc. *Output volts* (peak-to-peak; ±5 per cent), 0 to 10 volts, 0 to 1 volt, 0 to 0.1 volt, into a high-impedance load. *Source im-*

pedance (±10 per cent), 10-volt range, 0 to 220 ohms; 1-volt and 0.1-volt ranges, 52 ohms. *Rise time,* less than 0.15 μsec. *General:* Frequency accuracy, ±5 per cent.

Decade Resistance Box. Resistance values from 1 to 999,999 ohms in 1-ohm steps available across terminals, $\frac{1}{2}$ per cent accuracy, 1-watt resistors.

Resistor Substitution Box. Resistors ranging in values from 15 ohms to 10 megohms available across terminals, 36 EIA standard 10 per cent, 1-watt resistors.

Capacitor Substitution Box. Capacitors ranging in value from 0.0001 to 0.22 μf are selected by 18-position panel switch, silver-mica and plastic molded capacitors in standard EIA values, rated at 600 volts with the exception of the three largest, which are rated at 400 volts.

Tool Kit. A combination midget wire stripper and diagonal cutters, midget long-nose pliers with plastic-covered handles, three screwdrivers ($\frac{1}{8}$ in. with 3-in. blade, $\frac{3}{16}$ in. with 4-in. blade, and $\frac{3}{32}$ in. with 3-in. blade and pocket clip), a Weller model 8200K Dual-Heat soldering gun, solder joint brush, a set of five nut drivers ($\frac{3}{16}$, $\frac{1}{4}$, $\frac{5}{16}$, $\frac{3}{8}$, $\frac{1}{2}$ in.), a nut starter, and a combination metal two-way soldering aid tool.

S1-2 EUW-13. Universal Chassis and Parts

A unique system of quick-connect electronic parts and chassis is described in this section. With this system circuits can be constructed, tested, and modified in a small fraction of the time that would be required if soldered connections were used. Without this system it is impossible to complete the experiments described in this book in 15 afternoons of laboratory work. As an additional advantage, the parts in these circuits are connected by the "point-to-point method" just as they would be if wired permanently in a conventional chassis. Economy in time and parts is also provided, since all potentiometers, resistors, capacitors, leads, tube sockets, and other parts can be used over and over again. Also, any extra parts or components not already in the system can be easily connected into the circuits because of the versatility of the connectors.

Four years of classroom experience has proved this system to be a valuable aid in electronics instruction. It is also useful for circuit development in research and development laboratories. The circuits built with these rapid-connect parts can be used permanently, if desired, after they have been tested and optimized.

A simple circuit wired on an experimental chassis is shown in Fig. S1-1. It can be seen that a $\frac{1}{8}$-in. post is used wherever a solder lug would ordinarily occur with standard chassis components. Wherever a wire would be soldered to a lug, a spring clip is used to make the connection to the post.

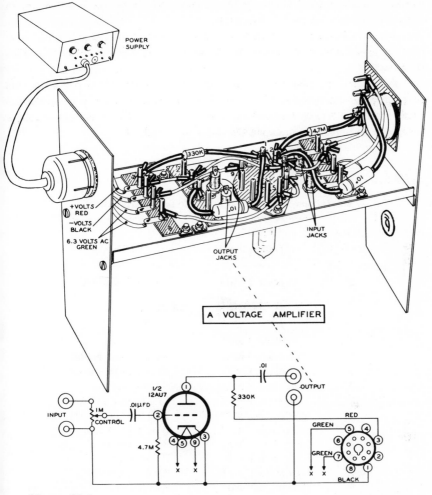

Figure S1-1

As many clips as necessary can be connected to each post. Resistors, capacitors, and connecting leads all have insulated sleeving and a spring clip on each end. The contacts have excellent electrical characteristics, and the circuit is wired in a very realistic way. The modular experimental chassis are designed and constructed with many convenient and time-saving features. One set of tie points are already connected to the power-supply socket and to input and output banana jacks. Therefore, test circuits can be rapidly and safely connected to the power supply, input-signal sources, and output-measuring devices. When more than one experimental chassis is used, they can be quickly and easily connected together with the "connector-plate" brackets.

A more complete description of the chassis units and components, and how to use them, is included in the section on Circuit Assembly Procedures.

Tubes and transistors are not included with the other parts for this unit, because the types needed depend on the specific circuits to be assembled. All the tubes, transistors, and other miscellaneous special parts necessary to perform the experiments in this book are included in EU-14.

Parts List

Resistors with Clips and Sleeving Installed

Parts per kit	Description	Color code
2	15 ohms 1 watt	Brown-green-black

2	47 ohms 1 watt	Yellow-violet-black
2	100 ohms 1 watt	Brown-black-brown
2	150 ohms 1 watt	Brown-green-brown
2	220 ohms 1 watt	Red-red-brown
2	330 ohms 1 watt	Orange-orange-brown
2	470 ohms 1 watt	Yellow-violet-brown
2	680 ohms 1 watt	Blue-gray-brown
4	1000 ohms 1 watt	Brown-black-red
2	1500 ohms 1 watt	Brown-green-red
2	1800 ohms 1 watt	Brown-gray-red
2	2200 ohms 1 watt	Red-red-red
2	3300 ohms 1 watt	Orange-orange-red
2	3900 ohms 1 watt	Orange-white-red
2	4700 ohms 1 watt	Yellow-violet-red
2	6800 ohms 1 watt	Blue-gray-red
2	8200 ohms 1 watt	Gray-red-red
4	10 kilohms 1 watt	Brown-black-orange

| 2 | 15 kilohms $\frac{1}{2}$ watt | Brown-green-orange |
| 2 | 18 kilohms $\frac{1}{2}$ watt | Brown-gray-orange |

Parts List (Continued)

Parts per kit	Description	Color code
2	22 kilohms $\frac{1}{2}$ watt	Red-red-orange
2	27 kilohms $\frac{1}{2}$ watt	Red-violet-orange
2	39 kilohms $\frac{1}{2}$ watt	Orange-white orange
2	47 kilohms $\frac{1}{2}$ watt	Yellow-violet-orange
2	56 kilohms $\frac{1}{2}$ watt	Green-blue-orange
2	68 kilohms $\frac{1}{2}$ watt	Blue-gray-orange
2	82 kilohms $\frac{1}{2}$ watt	Gray-red-orange
4	100 kilohms $\frac{1}{2}$ watt	Brown-black-yellow
2	180 kilohms $\frac{1}{2}$ watt	Brown-gray-yellow
2	220 kilohms $\frac{1}{2}$ watt	Red-red-yellow
2	270 kilohms $\frac{1}{2}$ watt	Red-violet-yellow
2	330 kilohms $\frac{1}{2}$ watt	Orange-orange-yellow
2	390 kilohms $\frac{1}{2}$ watt	Orange-white-yellow
2	470 kilohms $\frac{1}{2}$ watt	Yellow-violet-yellow
2	510 kilohms $\frac{1}{2}$ watt	Green-brown-yellow
2	680 kilohms $\frac{1}{2}$ watt	Blue-gray-yellow
2	820 kilohms $\frac{1}{2}$ watt	Gray-red-yellow
4	1 megohm $\frac{1}{2}$ watt	Brown-black-green
2	2.2 megohms $\frac{1}{2}$ watt	Red-red-green
2	4.7 megohms $\frac{1}{2}$ watt	Yellow-violet-green
2	10 megohms $\frac{1}{2}$ watt	Brown-black-blue

Precision Resistors. Precision 1 per cent resistors (Fig. S1-2) of the following values are included: two each of 1, 10, and 100 kilohms, and one 50 kilohms. All values with clips and sleeving installed.

Power wire-wound resistors (Fig. S1-3) in the following values are included: one each of 1, 2, and 5 kilohms at 7 watts rating, and one 10 kilohms at 5 watts rating.

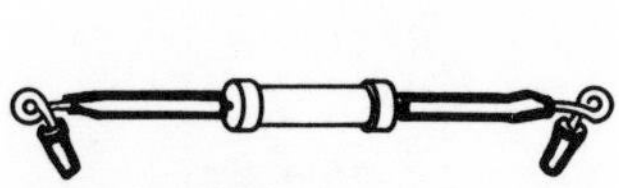

Figure S1-2

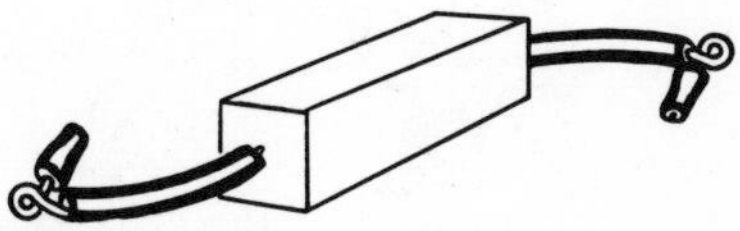

Figure S1-3

Figure S1-4

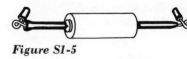

Figure S1-5

Capacitors with Clips and Sleeving Installed. Four each of the following *ceramic-disk capacitors* (Fig. S1-4): 10, 20, 50, 100, 200, 470 pf (μμf).

Four each of the following *paper tubular capacitors* (Fig. S1-5) either 400 or 600 volts rating: 0.001, 0.0022, 0.0047, 0.01, 0.022, 0.047, 0.1, and 0.22 μf; and two each of 0.5 and 1.0 μf rated at 200 volts.

Two each of the following *electrolytic capacitors* (Fig. S1-6): 20 μf 150 volts, 40 μf 150 volts, 100 μf 50 volts.

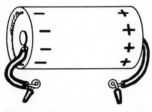

Figure S1-6

Potentiometer Controls. Two each of the following controls: 1000 ohms 2 watts, 10 kilohms 2 watts, 100 kilohms 2 watts, and 1 megohm $\frac{1}{4}$ watt. The potentiometer controls are mounted on an insulator plate and solder-connected to three posts as shown in Fig. S1-7. Potentiometers and other similar parts may also be used with the system by soldering a wire with spring clips to each terminal.

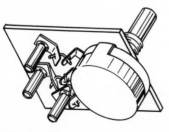

Figure S1-7

Patch Cords. The following patch cords have banana plugs at both ends (Fig. S1-8): one each of 12-in. red and 12-in. black, three each of 24-in. red and 24-in. black, two each of 36-in. red and 36-in. black.

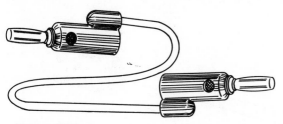

Figure S1-8

The following patch cords have banana plugs at one end and spring clips on the other (Fig. S1-9): two each of 6-in. red and 6-in. black, 12-in. red and 12-in. black.

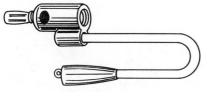

Figure S1-9

Connecting Wires. The following connecting wires have spring clips and insulation on each end (Fig. S1-10): sixteen 2-in. black, twelve $3\frac{1}{2}$-in. brown, ten 5-in. red, eight 7-in. orange, four 12-in. yellow.

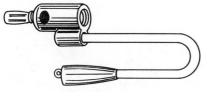

Figure S1-10

The two power cables (Fig. S1-11) are for interconnecting experimental chassis and universal power supply.

The line cord with insulated clips is for bringing line voltage directly to the $\frac{1}{8}$-in. tie posts. (*Danger.* Make clip connections before plugging into line.)

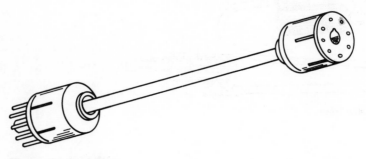

Figure S1-11

Solderless Tube Sockets. Three octal, four 9-pin, and three 7-pin sockets are shown in Fig. S1-12. The same sockets are also useful as the tie points for connection of transistors.

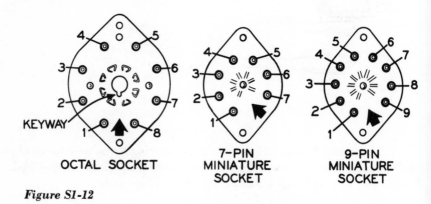

OCTAL SOCKET

7-PIN
MINIATURE
SOCKET

9-PIN
MINIATURE
SOCKET

Figure S1-12

Experimental Chassis. See Fig. S1-13 and description under Circuit Assembly Procedures. Four preassembled chassis units, with tie points and power socket, are each drilled for the interchangeable tube sockets.

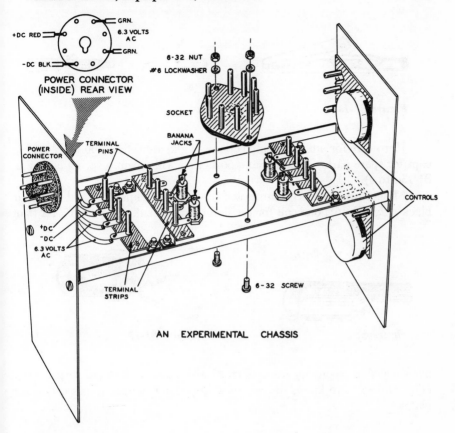

Figure S1-13

Hardware. Hardware for mounting interchangeable tube sockets and control potentiometers: twenty 6-32 × $\frac{3}{8}$-in. screws, twenty 6-32 nuts, ten control nuts, twenty No. 6 lockwashers, and ten control lockwashers (Fig. S1-14a to e, respectively).

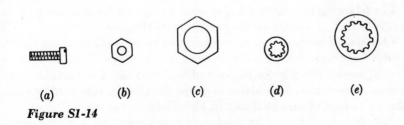

Figure S1-14

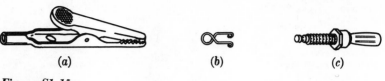

(a)   (b)   (c)

Figure S1-15

Hardware for auxiliary connections: 8 alligator clips, 100 extra spring clips for spare parts, and 6 banana posts that will accept a spring clip (Fig. S1-15a to c).

Miscellaneous. Insulators for the alligator clips, four red and four black (Fig. S1-16); one coil for oscillator experiments (Fig. S1-17); 5 ft of

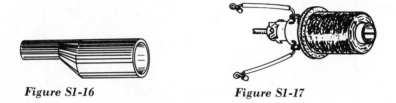

Figure S1-16   *Figure S1-17*

black sleeving, fiberglass lining (Fig. S1-18a); 2 ft of black sleeving, plastic (Fig. S1-18b); two knobs for control potentiometers; six chassis connector plates.

Figure S1-18

Circuit Assembly Procedures

The following information is provided as a guide for learning how to assemble your test circuits on the experimental chassis.

Chassis. The chassis are assembled except for the tube sockets, which are interchangeable for versatility. Sockets are fastened to the chassis with 6-32 screws, No. 6 lockwashers, and 6-32 nuts (see Fig. S1-13). Controls can be mounted either above or below the chassis, with control lockwashers and control nuts as shown in Fig. S1-19.

Note in Fig. S1-13 that an octal male power connector is permanently mounted on the back plate and pins 1, 3, 5, and 7 are connected to the four

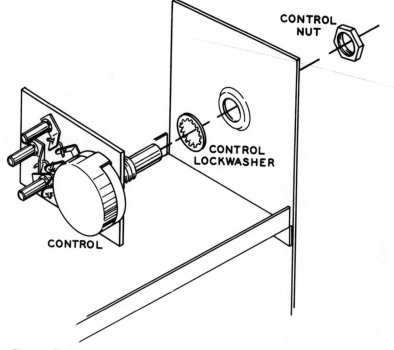

CONTROL NUT

CONTROL LOCKWASHER

CONTROL

Figure S1-19

$\frac{1}{8}$-in. posts at the rear of the chassis. These same pins are connected on the female octal socket of the universal power supply. Pin 1 (black lead) connects to $-$DC, pin 3 (red lead) connects to $+$DC (through the meter or jumper), and pins 5 and 7 (green leads) are for the filaments. Two other tie-point strips, each with four $\frac{1}{8}$-in. tie posts, are also mounted on the chassis, and two posts of each strip are connected to two banana jacks. These jacks are normally used for input and output circuits.

Tube Sockets. The tube sockets are specially designed for the system with $\frac{1}{8}$-in.-diameter posts connected to the tube socket pins. If you are unfamiliar with the correct method of numbering the pins of the different tube sockets, refer to Fig. S1-12. The correct pin number for each element of each tube is usually marked on a schematic diagram. Tube pin numbers can also be looked up in a tube manual.

Connection of System Parts. To fasten a part or wire in place, squeeze the clip, slide it down over the terminal pin, and then release it (see Fig. S1-20). The electrical size, in microfarads or micromicrofarads, is marked on the side of each capacitor. The electrical size, in ohms (Ω), of most resistors is indicated by the color bands on the resistor. Refer to the color-code information on the end paper. The sleeving on the leads of

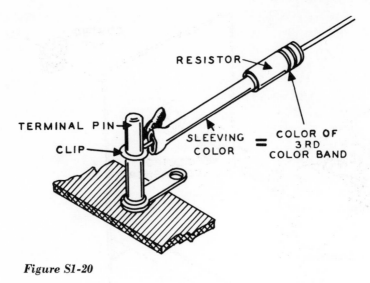

RESISTOR

TERMINAL PIN

CLIP

SLEEVING COLOR = COLOR OF 3RD COLOR BAND

Figure S1-20

each resistor is the same color as the third color band; this will aid you to identify quickly the sizes of resistors.

Figure S1-21 shows how connections can be made between patch cords, banana plugs, banana jacks, and resistors or other parts. Usually the banana jacks are used to conduct signals in and out, from devices such as signal generators, or to connect external measuring devices, such as meters or oscilloscopes, to an experimental circuit. The hybrid patch cords with a spring clip on one end and a molded banana plug on the other enable direct connection between banana jack and $\frac{1}{8}$-in. posts.

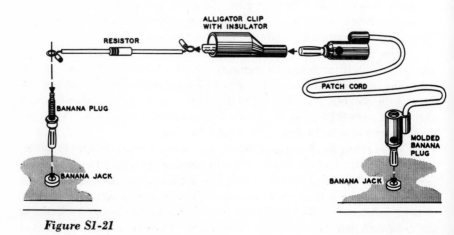

RESISTOR

ALLIGATOR CLIP WITH INSULATOR

PATCH CORD

BANANA PLUG

BANANA JACK

MOLDED BANANA PLUG

BANANA JACK

Figure S1-21

Connection of Extra Parts. Although the EU-13 experimental kit contains parts with a wide range of values, sufficient to build all experimental circuits in this book and many other circuits without any additions, there will undoubtedly be specific parts, such as relays, transformers, and special-valued resistors, that will have to be added to construct some other circuits. These parts can be readily connected into the quick-connect system by several methods. If the specific part is to be permanently incorporated in the quick-connect system, it is best to solder spring clips on the component leads. Extra clips have been included in the kit for this purpose.

Figure S1-22 shows how one of the extra clips can be fastened to a resistor or capacitor lead. Use the following steps for each lead:

1. Cut some fiberglass-lined sleeving to the same length as the lead. Put this sleeving over the lead.

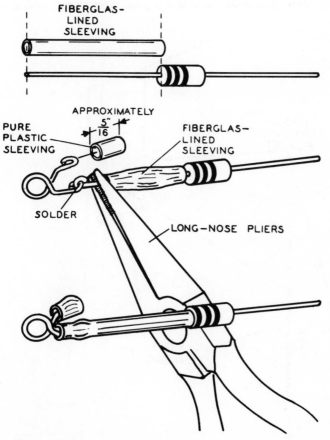

Figure S1-22

2. Press the sleeving back toward the body of the resistor or capacitor, and fasten the end of the lead to one of the eyes in the clip.

3. Hold the sleeving back with long-nose pliers, and solder the clip and lead together.

4. Slide the sleeving over the soldered connection. Place a $\frac{5}{16}$-in. length (approximately) of plastic sleeving over the other eye of the clip.

Another method of preparing extra parts for circuit connection is to cut a spring-clip lead in two pieces and then solder each piece onto a lead or terminal of the specific new part.

The hybrid patch cords are useful for temporarily including an extra part in a quick-connect circuit. The molded banana plug is fitted with an insulated alligator clip which is clipped onto a lead or terminal of the extra part. The other end of the hybrid patch cord has a spring clip that fits over the $\frac{1}{8}$-in. tie-point posts in the EU-13 chassis.

Interconnection of Chassis. When several interrelated circuits are assembled, it is often important to make a good mechanical connection

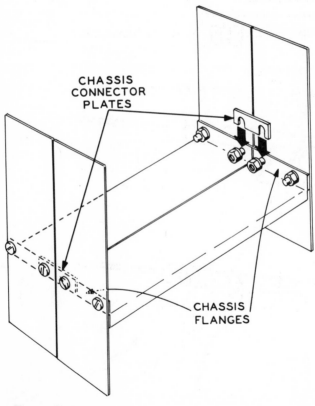

CHASSIS
CONNECTOR
PLATES

CHASSIS
FLANGES

Figure S1-23

between all the chassis used. Figure S1-23 shows how the chassis are fastened together. First, loosen the corner screws of each chassis. Then place the chassis connector plates between the lockwasher and the end panels, and retighten the screws.

Experimental Circuits. Figures S1-1, S1-24, and S1-25 show three different circuits constructed from the universal chassis and rapid-connect

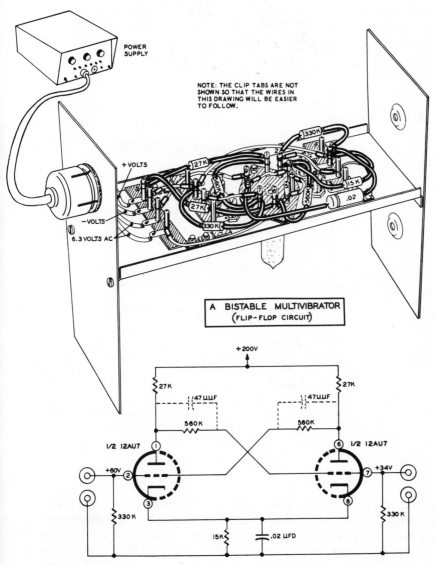

Figure S1-24

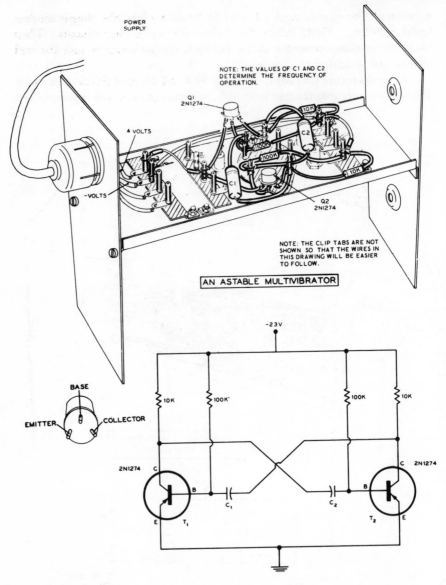

Figure S1-25

parts. Two circuits use tubes, and one uses transistors. The schematic diagram for each circuit is also shown. Many different arrangements are possible in connecting the circuits, but in general most parts should be connected so that they lie flat near the chassis, as illustrated by the examples in the three figures.

S1-3 EU-14. Special Experimental Parts

The specific tubes, transistors, diodes, chopper, multitapped signal transformer, and miscellaneous parts used for the experiments in the book have been grouped together. Many of the same components are useful as spare parts in the other units of the complete system. For example, the chopper and several tubes can be used in the servo recorder (EUW-20).

Also, all the necessary parts are included in this group to build a utility power amplifier by use of conventional solder techniques. An output transformer and loudspeaker are included. This amplifier is intended to give students practice in soldering and layout of standard parts, as well as to furnish instruction in power amplifiers and feedback, and to provide an auxiliary amplifier for other experiments. The amplifier is easily disassembled at the end of a course and the more expensive parts saved for use by another class. The number of power amplifiers at each EU-100 station should be the same as the number of students using the station during the duration of a particular course.

Parts List

Tubes. Two each of 12AU7 and 12AX7, and one each of 6BH6, 2D21 thyratron, and 6BQ5.

Diodes with Clips. Two germanium diodes (Fig. S1-26) and one 6.8-volt Zener reference diode (Fig. S1-27).

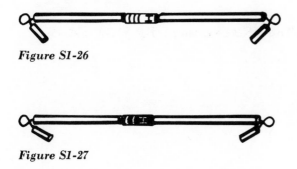

Figure S1-26

Figure S1-27

Transistors. Two 2N1274 *pnp* transistors and one TS610 power transistor. Clips can be connected to the transistor leads as shown in Fig. S1-28, or wires and clips can be connected to a transistor socket and the transistor plugged in.

Figure S1-28

Chopper.   One James Electronics type 1800 or equivalent chopper (Fig. S1-29).   6.3-volt coil; 50- to 70-cps drive frequency; base fits standard octal socket; spdt contacts.

Figure S1-29

Neon Lamps.   Two NE-2 neon lamps (Fig. S1-30) with clips.

Figure S1-30

Switch. One dpdt rotary switch (Fig. S1-31) with clips.

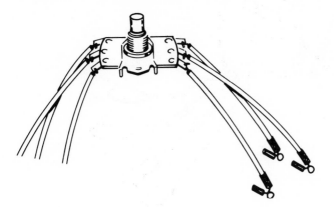

Figure S1-31

Variable Capacitor. One 350-pf variable capacitor (Fig. S1-32) with wires and clips.

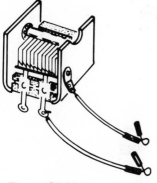

Figure S1-32

Multitapped Signal Transformer with Insulated Clips. One transformer (Fig. S1-33) with 117 volts, 60 cps primary (black leads), and secondary voltages of about 25, 50, 75, and 100 volts, 5 ma maximum a-c current. Between brown lead and red lead = 25 volts rms; brown to yellow = 50 volts; brown to green = 75 volts; and brown to blue = 100 volts.

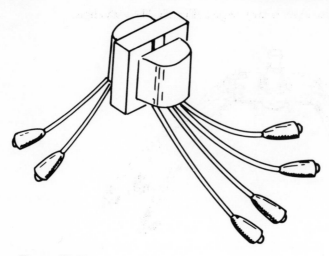

Figure S1-33

Miscellaneous.   One antenna coil with clips (Fig. S1-34), and one earphone-microphone with clips (Fig. S1-35).

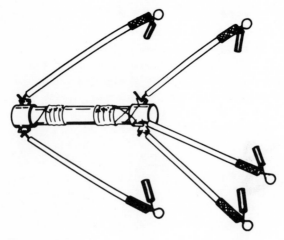

Figure S1-34

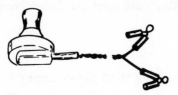

Figure S1-35

Power-Amplifier Parts. One each of $\frac{1}{2}$-watt resistors, 100 ohms, 1500 ohms, 220 kilohms, and 470 kilohms.

One 500-kilohm potentiometer and knob, one output transformer, one 4-in.-round permanent-magnet loudspeaker, and loudspeaker mounting panel.

One 50-μf electrolytic capacitor 25 volts, and two 0.1-μf tubular capacitors.

One octal power plug, and two 9-pin tube sockets for 12AX7 and 6BQ5 tubes.

Hardware for mounting all parts, input and output banana jacks, solder lugs, rubber grommets, hookup wire, and chassis punched for mounting all components.

S1-4 EUW-15. Universal Power Supply

The model EUW-15 universal power supply serves two purposes: it is both a well-regulated power supply for general laboratory applications and an experimental unit that can provide many different types of power-supply circuits. The unit is normally used as a regulated voltage-doubler power supply, as shown on the main schematic diagram. As the specifications in the next section show, this unit will perform well as a power source for critical laboratory applications.

A number of the leads in the rectifier, filter, divider, and regulator circuits are the rapid-connect clip leads; so they can be quickly changed to connect different types of rectifiers and filter circuits. These leads also allow the unit to be used with pentode or triode voltage-regulator circuit or with a power-supply bleeder or variable internal load. Half-wave, full-wave, bridge, and voltage-doubler rectifier circuits, and several *LC* and *RC* filter networks can be connected in a matter of minutes. Both the output load and the a-c input voltage can be varied for studies of power-supply stability.

Experimental circuits requiring filament and B+ voltages can be powered also by plugging in a power cable or by connecting leads to the five-way binding posts. While other power supplies can be used to supply power for the experimental circuits, this supply has been specifically designed for experimentation in rectifier, filter, and regulator design, as described in Chaps. 2 and 8.

Specifications

The following specifications are for the EUW-15 power supply when it is wired for voltage-doubler operation:

B+ voltage output	200 to 350 volts d-c regulated, at 0 to 100 ma continuous
Filament voltage output	6.3 volts a-c at 3 amp
B+ regulation	Output variation less than 1 per cent from no load to full load at 300 volts. Output variation less than ±1 volt for a ±10-volt variation in the a-c line input
B+ ripple	Less than 10 mv rms ripple, jitter, and noise
B+ output impedance	Less than 10 ohms from 5 to 100,000 cps
Divider voltages (unregulated)	Approximately 500, 400, 300, 200, and 100 volts
Voltage divider	Internal, using five 1500-ohm 10-watt resistors; also can be used as a variable internal load
Variable load	Divider can be connected as a variable load, but current must not exceed 80 ma
Tube complement	One 6L6, series regulator One 6BH6, control amplifier One OB2, voltage regulator
Controls and switches	DIVIDER-VOLTAGE (or variable-load) switch. DIVIDER-REGULATOR switch. REGULATOR-VOLTAGE (MIN.-MAX.) control. POWER (ON-OFF) switch. HIGH-VOLTAGE (ON-OFF) switch
Output terminals	DC+ and DC− Filament (6.3 VAC) Meter Chassis ground
Power requirements	105 to 125 volts a-c, 50/60 cps

Circuit Notes

See Chap. 2, Experiments, for a more complete description.

Front-Panel Controls. See Fig. S1-36, and relate to schematic diagrams, Fig. S1-37 and Fig. 2-33.

Voltage Doubler. Read the description in Chap. 2, and study both the simplified schematic, Fig. S1-37, and the complete schematic, Fig. S1-38. Note that the rapid-connect clip leads are indicated by dotted lines.

DIVIDER VOLTAGE SWITCH

Connects any one of five available DC output voltages to the output terminals.

DIVIDER-REGULATOR SWITCH

Switches the unit so it operates either as a regulated power supply, or as an unregulated power supply with a voltage divider output.

REGULATOR VOLTAGE CONTROL

Adjusts the voltage regulator circuit, varying the DC output between 200 and 350 volts.

OUTPUT TERMINALS

Five-way binding posts make the following connecting points available: 6.3 volts AC, -DC volts, +DC volts, and chassis ground. A connecting terminal is also provided so a milliammeter (MA) can be easily connected in series with +DC output.

INDICATOR LIGHT AND HIGH VOLTAGE SWITCH

Switch connects +DC volts to front panel connectors. Indicator light shows that +DC voltage is present at these connectors.

OCTAL POWER SOCKETS

6.3 volts AC and -DC volts available at these sockets at all times. +DC volts available only when the +DC and the MA connecting terminals are connected together by a jumper wire or milliammeter.

POWER SWITCH AND INDICATOR LIGHT

Indicator light shows when switch is turned on; switch connects power to the unit.

Figure SI-36

495

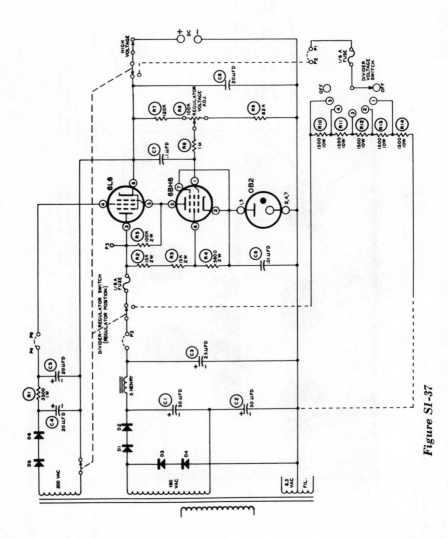

Figure S1-37

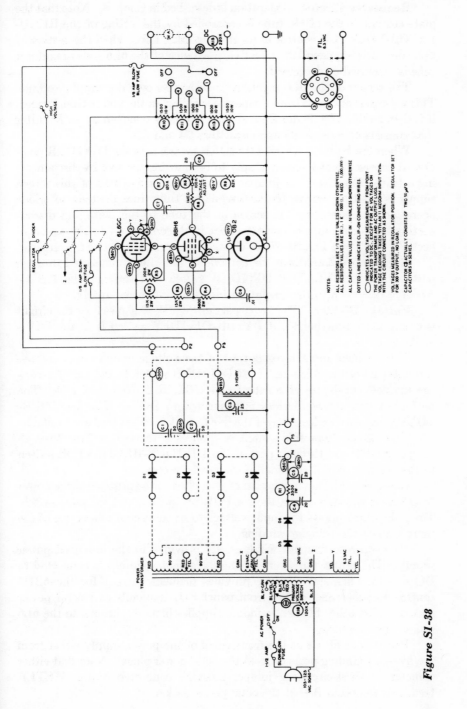

Figure S1-38

Regulator Circuit. Operation is described in Chap. 8. Note that the plate current in the 6BH6 tube is controlled by the setting of the REGU-LATOR-VOLTAGE control in its grid circuit. Thus, when the setting of this control is changed, the effective resistance of the 6L6 series-regulator tube is increased or decreased.

The screen of the 6L6 regulator tube has its own d-c supply voltage. This voltage is obtained from a separate winding on the power transformer; it is then rectified by diodes D5 and D6. Ripple is removed by an RC filter that consists of resistor R1 and capacitors C4 and C5.

When the REGULATOR-DIVIDER switch is in the DIVIDER position, it causes the 6L6 screen supply to become inoperative by disconnecting a transformer lead. A jumper wire in the positive lead of this screen supply is used to change the 6L6 regulator tube from pentode to triode operation by connecting the screen of the tube to the plate and disconnecting the screen supply circuit. That is, disconnect P4 to P6, and connect P6 to P5 (see Fig. S1-37) to change from pentode to triode regulator.

Regulated voltage from the cathode of the 6L6 is connected through part of the REGULATOR-DIVIDER switch and through the HIGH-VOLTAGE switch to the output terminals of the power supply.

Voltage Divider. The lower part of Fig. S1-37 shows how the circuit is connected when the REGULATOR-DIVIDER switch is in the DIVIDER position.

The rectified and filtered output of the voltage doubler is connected through part of the REGULATOR-DIVIDER switch to the top of a voltage divider, consisting of resistors R10, R11, R12, R13, and R14. The bottom of this voltage divider is connected to DC−. The DIVIDER-VOLTAGE switch selects one of the five output voltages that are available.

The output from this switch is connected through a fuse, through jumper P1-P2, and through part of the DIVIDER-REGULATOR switch to the positive output terminal of the power supply.

General. The a-c input voltage is applied to the primary of the power transformer through a fuse, the a-c POWER switch, and the slide switch. The slide switch allows the input voltage to be connected to any one of the three taps on the primary winding.

Two separate filament windings are provided in the universal power supply. The center tap of one of these filament windings is connected to DC−. This filament winding provides filament current for the 6BH6 control amplifier and to the front-panel FIL terminals and octal power sockets. The other filament winding supplies filament current to the 6L6 series-regulator tube.

Power is available at the front panel of the power supply either from the five-way binding posts or from the octal power plugs. Note that either a meter or short-circuiting jumper must be connected to the METER terminals to obtain B+ at the octal power socket.

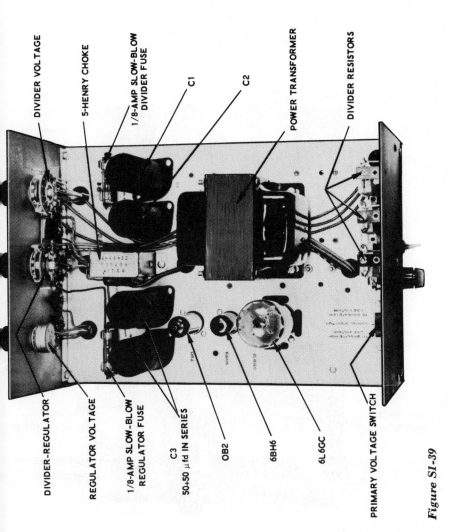

DIVIDER VOLTAGE

5-HENRY CHOKE

1/8-AMP SLOW-BLOW DIVIDER FUSE

C1

C2

POWER TRANSFORMER

DIVIDER RESISTORS

DIVIDER-REGULATOR

REGULATOR VOLTAGE

1/8-AMP SLOW-BLOW REGULATOR FUSE

C3 50-50 µfd IN SERIES

OB2

6BH6

6L6GC

PRIMARY VOLTAGE SWITCH

Figure S1-39

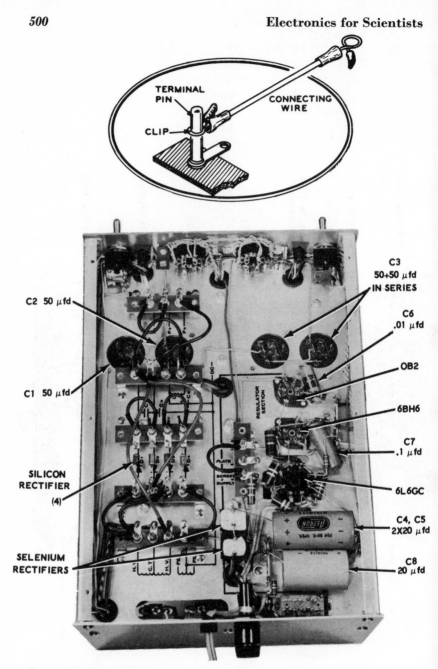

Figure S1-40

Location of Circuit Components. Figure S1-39 is a top view of the power supply, showing the location of tube sockets and major parts. Note the position of the slide switch which connects one side of the a-c power line to one of the three taps on the transformer primary. This allows high or low input voltages to be simulated.

Figure S1-40 is a bottom view of the power supply. *Warning:* Dangerous voltages are exposed when the bottom cover is removed. Even with the switches OFF it is possible to come in contact with line voltage when the unit is plugged in. Note the positions of the quick-connect leads, which are connected in Fig. S1-40 for voltage-doubler operation, as in the schematic.

Circuit Combinations. The block diagrams in Fig. S1-41 illustrate some of the circuit combinations, other than the normal voltage-doubler

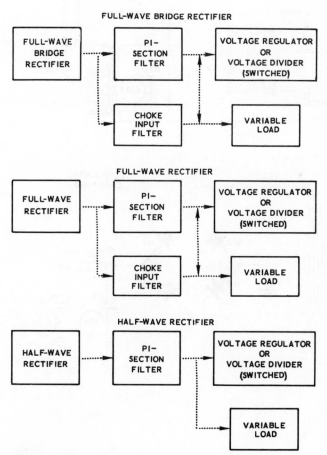

Figure S1-41

circuit, that can be rapidly constructed with the EUW-15 unit. One of specific combinations is shown in Fig. S1-42, with interconnecting clip leads connected to the tie-point posts to provide a bridge rectifier with π-section filter. A full-wave rectifier with choke-input filter is shown in Fig. S1-43.

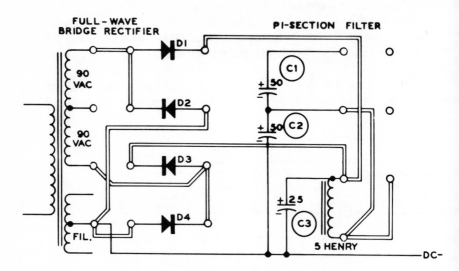

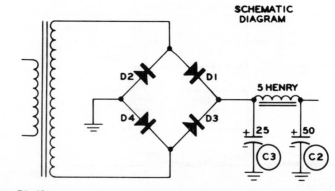

Figure S1-42

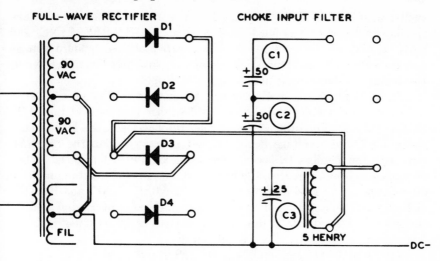

FULL-WAVE RECTIFIER   CHOKE INPUT FILTER

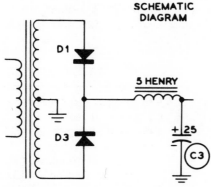

SCHEMATIC
DIAGRAM

Figure S1-43

S1-5 EUW-16. Voltage Reference Source (Zener-Stabilized)

The voltage reference source can be used for many different applications in experimental and development work. The OUTPUT switch selects the mode of operation, allowing the unit to be operated as a standard voltage source or for sum and difference voltage comparisons. The SIGNAL position allows an input signal to be connected directly to the OUTPUT terminals.

In standard voltage (STD VOLT) applications; an accurate d-c voltage, which can be varied from 100 volts to a few tenths of a millivolt, is available at the OUTPUT terminals. The d-c potential at the terminals can be accurately read directly from the COARSE, FINE, and RANGE dials on the front panel. The polarity of this standard voltage may be reversed by the POLARITY switch. Note that this unit is a *voltage* source; it should *not* be used as a power supply.

In SUM-DIFFerence applications, the sum of or difference between the input signal voltage and the standard voltage is present at the OUTPUT terminals. Potentiometer operation is available in the DIFFerence position. The d-c voltage being checked is connected to the SIGNAL terminals, and a null meter is connected to the OUTPUT terminals. When the null meter indicates zero, the two voltages are equal and the unknown d-c voltage can be read directly from the COARSE, FINE, and RANGE dials on the front panel. This is an accurate method of measuring voltage; changes in voltage due to loading are eliminated, since no current is drawn from either voltage supply at the null point.

In the SIGNAL position of the OUTPUT switch, the input signal is connected directly to the OUTPUT terminals. This allows the signal and the standard voltage to be connected to the OUTPUT terminals alternately by merely switching the OUTPUT switch.

Other operating conveniences in this unit include the pushbutton

Specifications

Output voltage	0 to 100 volts d-c, Zener-stabilized
Resolution	0.1 mv on ×1 range
	1 mv on ×10 range
	10 mv on ×100 range
	100 mv on ×1000 range
Accuracy	±1 per cent or 0.1 mv, whichever is larger
Readout	Directly on three dials: COARSE VOLTAGE, FINE VOLTAGE, RANGE
Controls:	
COARSE voltage	0 to 100 mv, in 10-mv steps
FINE voltage	0 to 10 mv, continuous
RANGE	×1, ×10, ×100, ×1000
Output selector	Four positions: AC OFF, SIGNAL, STD VOLTages, SUM-DIFFerence
Polarity switch	NORMAL (SUM) position, or REVERSE (DIFFerence) position
Pushbutton ZERO	Short-circuits OUTPUT terminals together
Power required	25 watts, 117 volts a-c, 50/60 cps
Fuse	$\frac{1}{2}$-amp slow-blow

ZERO switch and the -5 position of the COARSE voltage switch. The ZERO switch short-circuits the OUTPUT terminals together, giving a convenient zero reference voltage to the meter, oscilloscope, or other instrument connected to these terminals.

The minus (-5) position of the COARSE voltage switch provides a continuously variable *minus* $(-)$ to *plus* $(+)$ standard voltage at the OUTPUT terminals. This variable voltage will be in one of the following ranges, depending on the RANGE switch setting: -5 mv to $+5$ mv, -50 mv to $+50$ mv, -0.5 volt to $+0.5$ volt, or -5 volts to $+5$ volts.

Circuit Notes

The voltage reference source consists of three main sections, the Zener-regulated power supply, a precision voltage-divider network, and the output switching circuits. The schematic diagram is shown in Fig. S1-44.

Regulated Power Supply. The a-c line voltage is applied through the ON-OFF switch (on the rear of the OUTPUT switch) and through a slow-blow fuse to the primary of the power transformer. The voltage from the secondary of the power transformer is rectified by a silicon diode in a half-wave circuit. The rectified voltage is then applied to a dual π-section filter, containing two 70-μf capacitors, two 6-watt lamps, and a 10-watt Zener diode.

The 6-watt lamps help keep input line-voltage changes from appearing at the output of the power supply. The resistance of the lamps increases when lamp currents increase and decreases when lamp currents decrease.

The output voltage of the power supply is regulated by the Zener diode, a constant-voltage device, as described in Chap. 2.

Precision Voltage Divider. The regulated output voltage from the filter circuit is applied to the RANGE switch through the calibration control. The calibration control is adjusted to obtain an accurate 100 volts between the arms of the RANGE switch.

The RANGE switch is constructed in two sections to present a constant load to the power supply. It applies the 100 volts directly across the precision voltage divider of the COARSE switch in the $\times$1000 position. In the other RANGE positions, the input voltage is divided by 10, 100, or 1000.

The output of the RANGE switch is coupled directly across the eleven 400-ohm precision resistors of the COARSE switch. Two of these 400-ohm resistors are always shunted by the 800-ohm FINE control, giving a total resistance across this section of 400 ohms; this keeps the total resistance of the divider at 4000 ohms. Thus, if 100 volts is connected across the complete divider, a 10-volt segment is always connected across the

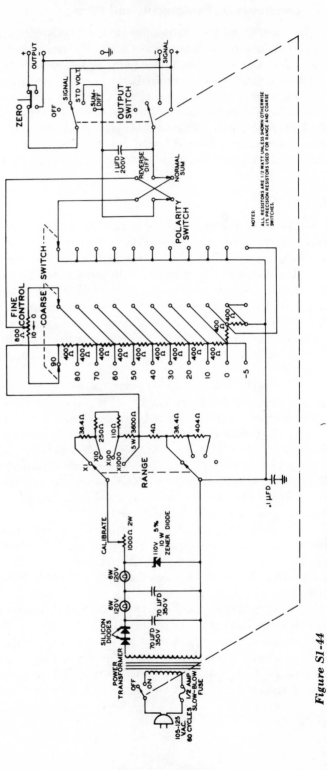

Figure S1-44

FINE voltage control. Which 10-volt segment is selected depends on the setting of the COARSE switch.

For positions 0 through 90 of the COARSE voltage switch, a standard output voltage is taken from between the arm of the FINE voltage control and d-c−.

In the −5 position of the COARSE switch, the FINE control is connected across the last two resistors in the divider. In this position the reference voltage is taken from the center of the last two 400-ohm resistors, instead of from d-c−. As a result, the voltage from the arm of the FINE control now varies above (+5) and below (−5) the reference voltage. The setting of the RANGE switch determines whether this −5 and +5 will be in volts or millivolts.

Output Switching Circuit. The output of the precision voltage-divider network is coupled through the POLARITY switch to the OUT-PUT switch. The OUTPUT switch performs the following operations:

In the SIGNAL position, the SIGNAL terminals are connected directly to the OUTPUT terminals.

In the standard voltage (STD VOLT) position, the output of the precision voltage divider is connected to the OUTPUT terminals.

In the SUM-DIFFerence position the output of the precision voltage divider is connected in series with the voltage at the SIGNAL terminals. Thus, the precision voltage is either added to or subtracted from the SIGNAL voltage, depending on the setting of the POLARITY switch.

The ZERO pushbutton disconnects the OUTPUT switch from the positive OUTPUT terminal and short-circuits the two OUTPUT terminals together.

Front-Panel Controls. The controls are shown in Fig. S1-45. To obtain a standard reference voltage at the output terminals, turn the OUT-PUT switch to STD VOLT position. Turn the RANGE switch to obtain one of the following four voltage ranges:

$$\times 1 \text{ range} = 0 \text{ to } 100 \text{ mv}$$
$$\times 10 \text{ range} = 0 \text{ to } 1000 \text{ mv}$$
$$\times 100 \text{ range} = 0 \text{ to } 10 \text{ volts}$$
$$\times 1000 \text{ range} = 0 \text{ to } 100 \text{ volts}$$

The COARSE switch and FINE control are then adjusted as follows for the desired OUTPUT voltage: The sum of the readings set on the COARSE control and on the 0 to 10 scale of the FINE control will be added together. This sum is then multiplied by the reading of the RANGE switch to give the voltage at the OUTPUT terminals. The −5 range of the COARSE control and the −5, 0, +5 range of the FINE control will be explained separately.

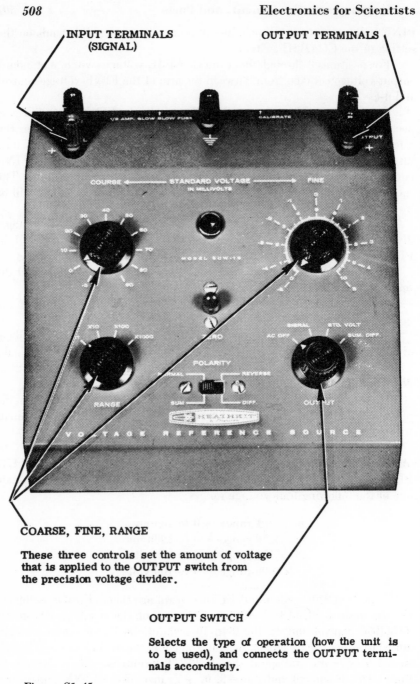

INPUT TERMINALS
(SIGNAL)

OUTPUT TERMINALS

COARSE, FINE, RANGE

These three controls set the amount of voltage
that is applied to the OUTPUT switch from
the precision voltage divider.

OUTPUT SWITCH

Selects the type of operation (how the unit is
to be used), and connects the OUTPUT terminals accordingly.

Figure S1-45

Control-setting examples

Coarse	Fine	Range	Output
(70	+ 3)	× 1	= 73 mv
(40	+ 5)	× 10	= 450 mv, or 0.45 volt
(20	+ 5)	× 100	= 2,500 mv, or 2.5 volts
(30	+ 9)	× 1000	= 39,000 mv, or 39 volts

After the unit is set to give the correct OUTPUT voltage, connect the meter, or other device to which the voltage is to be supplied, to the OUTPUT terminals. *Note:* Do *not* use this unit as a power supply; it has been designed to be used as an accurate voltage source, but it cannot supply appreciable current.

When the POLARITY switch is in the NORMAL position, the output voltage will have the polarity that is marked at the OUTPUT terminals. In the REVERSE position, the polarity of this voltage will be reversed from the way in which it is marked at the terminals. Use the NORMAL switch position for the most quiet operation with low-level OUTPUT signals.

The −5 range of the COARSE control is only used with the −5, 0, +5 range of the FINE control. When these ranges are used, the following voltage ranges become available at the OUTPUT terminals, depending on the RANGE switch setting:

Range switch	Output voltage
×1	−5 mv to +5 mv
×10	−50 mv to +50 mv
×100	−500 mv to +500 mv
×1000	−5 volts to +5 volts

Sum-Difference Operation. When the OUTPUT switch is turned to the SUM-DIFFerence position, a comparison can be made between an external voltage connected to the SIGNAL terminals and the standard voltage of the voltage reference source. The setting of the POLARITY switch determines whether it is the sum of the two voltages or the difference between them that appears at the OUTPUT terminals.

Potentiometer Application

1. Place the OUTPUT switch in the STD VOLT position.

2. Connect the unknown voltage to the SIGNAL terminals, with the polarity as marked at the terminals.

3. Connect a null meter to the OUTPUT terminals. Place the POLARITY switch in the DIFFerence position.

4. Adjust the RANGE, COARSE, and FINE controls to obtain a zero-voltage indication on the null meter. When this point is found, the exact value of the unknown voltage is indicated by these three controls.

The output voltage can be calibrated by setting the output-voltage dials to read the exactly known voltage of a mercury cell or a Weston cell. The mercury or Weston cell is then connected to the VRS as described in the potentiometer application above. A null meter is connected to the output terminals. The calibrate control is then adjusted until the meter reads null. The VRS should be turned on at least $\frac{1}{2}$ hr before calibrating.

In the SIGNAL position of the OUTPUT switch, the SIGNAL terminals are connected directly to the OUTPUT terminals. This allows the input signal and the standard voltage to be connected to the OUTPUT terminals alternately by merely switching the OUTPUT switch between SIGNAL and STD VOLT positions.

S1-6 EUW-17. Transistorized Power Supply

The EUW-17 power supply was designed to supply low operating voltages, especially for operating experimental transistor circuits. Its variable output voltage, compact size, and low ripple make it very useful both in the classroom and the laboratory.

Specifications

Output voltage	0 to 25 volts at maximum current (see Fig. S1-47)
	0 to 35 volts with no load
Ripple	Less than 0.1 per cent at full load
Semiconductors	One R265A transistor
	Two silicon diodes
Circuit type	Full-wave rectifier
Control	VOLTAGE, with ON-OFF switch
Power requirements	105 to 125 volts a-c, 50/60 cps, 9 watts

Circuit Notes

See Fig. 3–61, p. 160, for circuit diagrams.

Front-Panel Controls. Only one rotary control is on the front panel, as shown in Fig. S1-46. This is used as an ON-OFF switch and the voltage control. The control is a 5000-ohm potentiometer that varies the bias of a R265A power transistor, which increases or decreases the effective transistor resistance between emitter and collector. The effective transistor resistance determines the output voltage available across the five-way binding posts. The 3300-ohm resistor acts as a bleeder and provides a current path to the transistor under no-load conditions. The 0.1-μf capacitor filters out noise pulses that might be present at the output of the supply.

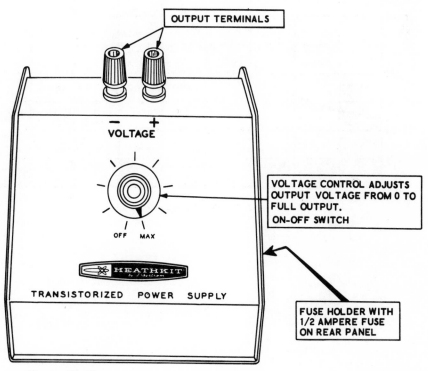

Figure S1-46

Maximum Current. The source is capable of supplying up to 200 ma at voltages above about 19 volts. The maximum current drops off progressively at lower voltages to about 60 ma near 0 volts, as shown in Fig. S1-47. The *maximum load* (minimum resistance) to be used across the output terminals at various output voltages can be determined from Fig. S1-48.

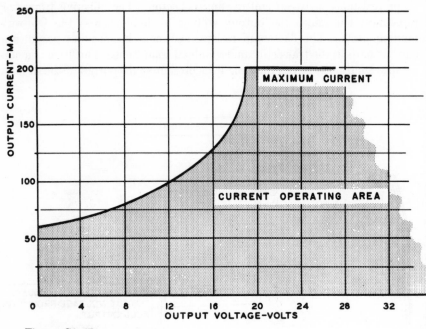

Figure S1-47

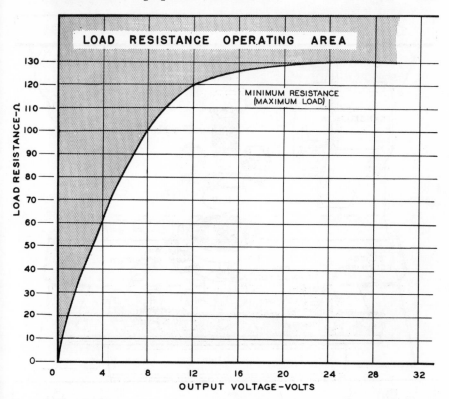

Figure S1-48

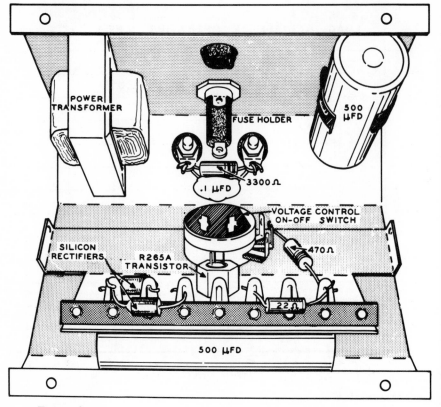

Figure S1-49

Location of Parts. The physical location of the various parts in the chassis is shown in Fig. S1-49.

S1-7   EUW-18.   Laboratory Meter

For many experiments it is useful to have an auxiliary current meter wherein the current range can be readily changed by external plug-in shunts. A convenient meter is a basic 1-ma movement mounted in a sloping-front aluminum case, as shown in Fig. S1-50. The meter terminals are connected to the banana jacks mounted on the top of the case. Dual banana plugs can be used to prepare permanent shunts that are plugged into the jacks on top of the case.

For a 1-ma meter with a 50-ohm resistance the following shunts would be suitable for current ranges of 1.5, 5, 15, and 50 ma and are part of the

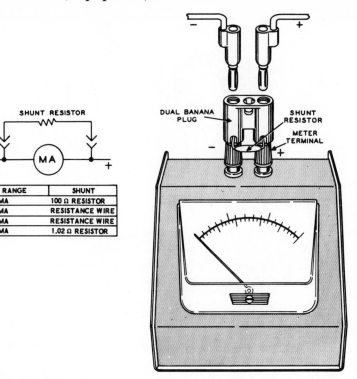

RANGE	SHUNT
1.5 MA	100 Ω RESISTOR
5 MA	RESISTANCE WIRE
15 MA	RESISTANCE WIRE
50 MA	1.02 Ω RESISTOR

Figure S1-50

EUW-18 unit, together with four dual banana plugs:

50-ma range, shunt = 1.02-ohm precision resistor.

1.5-ma range, shunt = 100-ohm precision resistor.

5-ma, 15-ma, and other shunts can be made from resistance wire according to the instructions below. Resistance wire of about 10 ohms/ft is recommended.

Preparation of Shunts on Dual Banana Jacks

1. Calculate the length of resistance wire that is needed for preparing a shunt for a desired range. Cut a length of sleeving 1 in. shorter than this calculated length, and install it over the resistance wire.

2. Install one end of the wire in one of the banana plugs, and tighten the screw. Wrap the sleeving-covered portion around the center of the plug, as shown in Fig. S1-51. Install the other end of the wire in the other banana plug so that the wire is connected slightly shorter than the calculated length. Tighten this screw.

3. Install the banana plug, with its shunt, on the meter. Feed the correct full-scale current through the meter (see Experiments, Chap. 1).

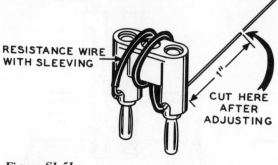

RESISTANCE WIRE
WITH SLEEVING

CUT HERE
AFTER
ADJUSTING

1"

Figure S1-51

Observe the actual meter reading, and estimate how far the wire must be moved to make the meter read exactly at full scale.

4. *Disconnect the power from the meter.* Loosen one of the banana-plug screws, move the wire the estimated distance, and retighten the screw.

5. Reconnect the current source, and check again to see whether or not the meter reads exactly full scale.

Caution: Do not adjust the shunt while the current source is connected, because this could damage the meter.

Note that for convenience a precision resistor can be connected to one of the dual banana jacks, as shown in Fig. S1-52.

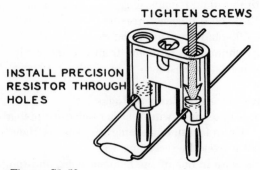

TIGHTEN SCREWS

INSTALL PRECISION
RESISTOR THROUGH
HOLES

Figure S1-52

S1-8 EUW-19. Operational-Amplifier System

The model EUW-19 operational-amplifier system incorporates each of the following units on a single compact chassis: four high-gain operational amplifiers; a high-current booster amplifier; and regulated +300-volt and −300-volt power supplies. It was designed both for convenience and versatility in classroom experiments and for experimental work in research and development laboratories. One of the operational amplifiers can be switched to operate as an inverting amplifier, an unbiased difference amplifier, or as a follower amplifier.

The high gain, low drift, and wide flexibility of this unit make it extremely useful for measurement, control, and computation applications. See Chap. 8 for the application of the system as a constant current source; as a constant voltage source; as a linear-sweep generator; as a servo simulator; or as a precise computer for addition, subtraction, integration, differentiation, and other applications.

The input and output connections of the amplifiers are arranged conveniently on the front panel so that the rapid-connect parts from the EU-13 kit can be quickly connected to perform the desired function. A standard five-prong molded connector socket can also be used to connect components or other units to the amplifier terminals.

An added feature for versatility is a power connector at the rear of the chassis which makes available +300 and −300 volts regulated, which can be used to power auxiliary equipment.

Circuit Notes

Block Diagram. A block diagram illustrating basic units of the operational-amplifier system is shown in Fig. S1-53. Note that amplifiers 1, 2, 3, and 4 are similar except that amplifier 1 can be switched to perform the afore-mentioned functions. Amplifier 5 is a booster amplifier for power applications such as operating relays, etc.

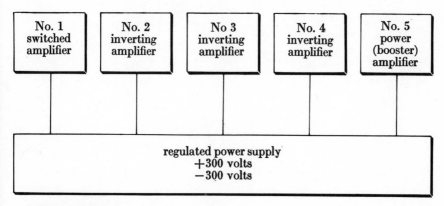

Figure S1-53

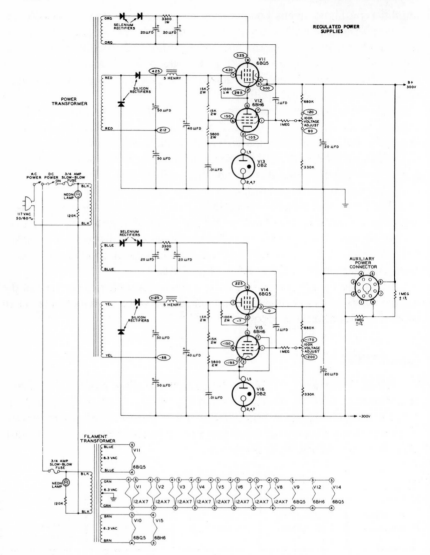

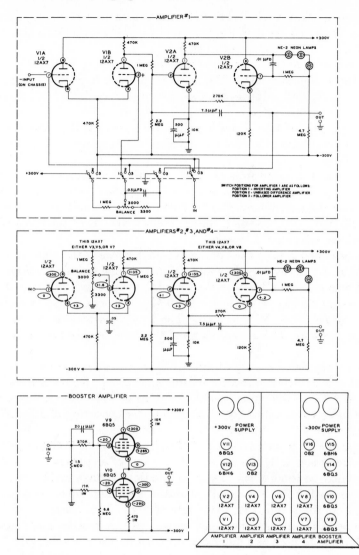

Figure S1-54

Inverting Amplifiers. The following explanation is for amplifier 2 and is also applicable for amplifiers 1, 3, and 4. See the schematic diagram, Fig. S1-54, and the discussion in Chap. 8.

The signal from the input lug of amplifier 2 is connected to the grid of input cathode follower V3A. The cathode of V3A is connected to the cathode of V3B; both cathodes are then returned through a 470-kilohm resistor to −300 volts. The input signal is thus cathode-coupled from V3A to V3B. The grid of V3B is connected to the arm of the BALANCE control. This control is used to eliminate an offset voltage error in the amplifier output voltage.

The signal is coupled from the plate of V3B, through a resistive voltage divider to the grid of V4A, where it is amplified further. From the plate of V4A the signal is coupled by another resistive voltage divider, to the grid of V4B. This resistive voltage divider consists of the three neon lamps and the 4.7-megohm resistor.

The neon lamps keep the voltage constant between the plate of V4A and the grid of V4B; as a result, a larger signal voltage appears between the grid and cathode of V4B, larger than would appear there if a normal resistive voltage divider were used. An 0.01-μf capacitor couples higher-frequency signals from V4A to V4B. The 1-megohm resistor at the grid of V4B prevents the 0.01-μf capacitor and the three neon lamps from oscillating.

The output signal is coupled directly from the cathode of cathode follower V4B. A 270-kilohm resistor returns positive (+) feedback from the cathode of V4B to the cathode of V4A. Correct operating voltages for these cathodes are supplied by a voltage divider consisting of 120-, 270-, and 10-kilohm resistors between −300 volts and ground.

Amplifier 1. In switch position 1, amplifier 1 is an inverting amplifier, and the circuit is exactly the same as the circuits of amplifiers 2, 3, and 4.

In switch position 2, the BALANCE adjust voltage divider is completely removed from the circuit, and the amplifier input terminal is switched from the grid of V1A to the grid of V1B. This causes the output signal to be in phase with the input signal. In this position both inputs are available to be used as a difference amplifier for various unbiased cases.

In switch position 3, the BALANCE adjust voltage divider is connected between −300 volts and the cathode of V2B. The arm of the BALANCE adjust control is connected to the grid of tube V1A. The input terminal is connected to the grid of V1B. This allows the amplifier to be balanced at the grid of V1A when the input signal is connected to V2B.

As explained in Chap. 8, the voltage follower circuit has a very high input impedance ($\sim 10^8$ ohms), a very low output impedance (<1 ohm), and unity gain (1.005).

Booster Amplifier. The booster amplifier is useful when controlled power is to be supplied to a load. Such applications could include relay control, light control, controlled potential electrolysis, small motor control, etc. For loads requiring higher currents, the booster amplifier can be used to provide the base current to a transistor common-collector amplifier.

The booster amplifier is essentially a cathode-follower amplifier (V9) which has a vacuum tube (V10) instead of a cathode resistor. This circuit has the advantage of providing a high dynamic cathode resistance (r_p of V10) without the wasted power of actually using a cathode resistance of such a high value. No more than 20 ma (±50 volts) should be drawn from the booster-amplifier output.

Power-Supply Section. The power-supply section may be divided into three general parts: the regulated $+300$-volt power supply, the regulated -300-volt power supply, and the filament supply. The $+300$-volt supply and the -300-volt supply use exactly the same circuit; so only one of these supplies will be described.

Power is supplied from the 117-volt line to the primary of the filament transformers through the A-C POWER switch and a $\frac{3}{4}$-amp slow-blow fuse. A neon lamp in the primary indicates when the power is applied to this transformer. The three secondary windings of this transformer supply filament current to all tubes.

Power is supplied from the 117-volt line to the primary of the high-voltage transformer through the D-C POWER switch and a $\frac{3}{4}$-amp slow-blow fuse. A neon lamp indicates when d-c power is applied to the unit.

DC+ voltage is supplied from a voltage-doubler circuit that consists of two silicon diodes and two 50-μf electrolytic filter capacitors. Each half of the 60-cps sine wave from the power transformer charges up one of the 50-μf capacitors to its peak voltage. The peak-voltage charges on these two 50-μf capacitors are added together, resulting in a d-c voltage at the output of the voltage doubler. Ripple is filtered by the two 50-μf capacitors, and also by the choke and the 40-μf electrolytic capacitor. Direct-current from this filter is then applied to the regulator circuit.

Positive d-c voltage from the filter is connected to the plate of regulator tube V11. Regulator tube V11 acts like a large variable resistor in series with the positive d-c output of the power supply. The larger this variable resistor becomes, the smaller the output voltage will be; the smaller this variable resistor becomes, the larger the output voltage will be.

The resistance of the regulator tube is controlled by the voltage at its grid, and the voltage at the grid is controlled by the current flowing through the 6BH6 control tube.

The current flowing in the 6BH6 tube is controlled by the setting of the regulator adjustment control in its grid circuit. Thus, when the setting of this control is changed, the resistance of series regulator tube V11 is increased or decreased.

The screen of regulator tube V11 has its own d-c supply voltage. This voltage is obtained from a separate winding on the power transformer; it is then rectified by the selenium diodes. Ripple is removed by a filter that consists of a 3300-ohm 1-watt resistor and two 20-μf electrolytic capacitors.

The regulated (+300 volts) output voltage from the cathode of V11 is connected to pin 6 of the auxiliary power connector. DC— of the +300-volt supply, DC+ of the —300-volt supply, and chassis ground are all connected to pin 4 of the auxiliary power connector. —300 volts is connected to pin 2 of the auxiliary power connector.

One-megohm precision resistors are connected from +300 volts, and from —300 volts, to pin 8 of the auxiliary power connector. These connections on the auxiliary power connector can be used to adjust the +300- and —300-volt power supplies to their correct output voltages.

Operation and Controls. The front-panel controls are shown in Fig. S1-55.

1. Connect the line cord to a 117-volt 50/60-cps a-c outlet. Turn the A-C POWER switch ON; this applies power to all filaments and to the a-c power lamp.

2. Wait 60 sec for the filaments to heat up, and then turn the D-C POWER switch ON. To obtain maximum stability, allow the unit to warm up for $\frac{1}{2}$ hr before putting it into operation.

Warning: Under certain conditions, high voltage may be present at the amplifier pins on the front panel. The safest procedure is to turn the D-C POWER switch off when connections are made to these pins. If it is necessary to make connections with the d-c power ON, be sure to touch the unit with *only one hand* to minimize the danger of electric shock.

See Experiments, Chap. 8, for proper balancing procedure.

Connections can be made to the amplifier pins on the front panel with the quick-connect parts of the universal experimental units, models EU-13 and EU-14.

The hybrid patch cords are convenient for connecting the amplifiers to auxiliary equipment. For more permanent applications, a standard five-prong molded connector socket can be plugged directly onto the amplifier pins.

The three-lug terminals near the top of the front panel are not connected in the system. These lugs provide convenient connecting points for the other ends of parts connected to the amplifier terminals.

An additional input jack is provided for amplifier 1 to allow signals to be connected to both positive and negative inputs at the same time. This additional jack is located on the chassis behind the front panel and is available only in switch position 2. The input terminal on the front panel is the noninverting (+) input; the jack on the chassis is the inverting (—) input.

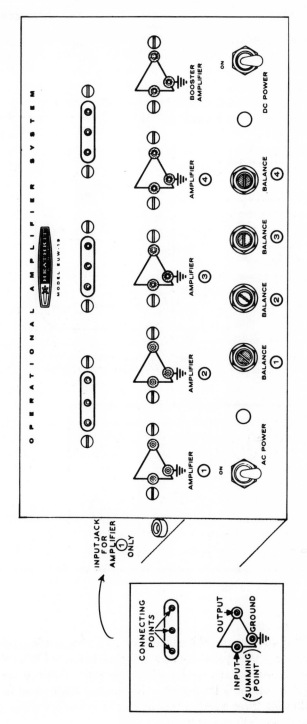

Figure SI-55

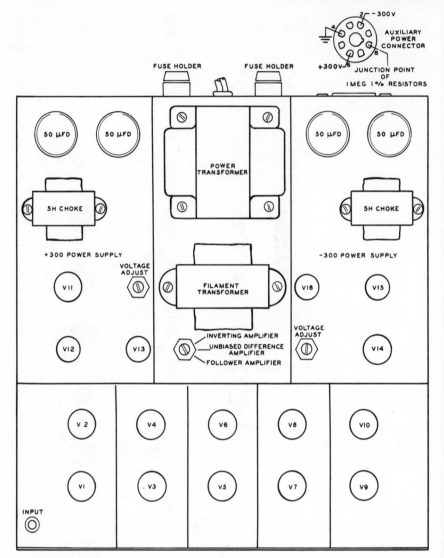

Figure S1-56

Two screwdriver adjust controls and a switch are located on the chassis of the operational amplifier as shown in Fig. S1-56. These controls adjust the voltage of the +300-volt and −300-volt power supplies. The switch, also a screwdriver adjustment, adjusts amplifier 1 to one of the following three modes of operation: inverting amplifier; unbiased difference amplifier; follower amplifier.

One-megohm precision resistors are connected (internally) between lugs 6 and 8, and 8 and 2, of the auxiliary power socket at the rear of the unit. Connecting a d-c voltmeter across these resistors allows the +300-volt and −300-volt power supply to be accurately adjusted by turning the voltage-adjust controls. By adjusting the potential between pin 8 and pin 4 (GND) to a null, the +300- and −300-volt supplies are accurately equalized.

Power to operate auxiliary equipment can also be drawn from the auxiliary power socket. Maximum current is 20 ma when the unit is in normal operation. When all amplifier tubes are removed (V1 to V10), 60 ma can be drawn from each supply.

S1-9 EUW-20. Servo Recorder

The EUW-20 servo recorder is designed to function normally as a laboratory self-balancing potentiometer and also to be used as an instructional device in servomechanisms. The electronic and mechanical systems are laid out so that they are completely exposed by removing a rear panel and snap-on top panels. Therefore, parts can be observed and tested while the unit is operating in its upright position.

The input circuit of the servo is designed with several quick-connect spring clips and posts so that the self-balancing potentiometer circuit can be rapidly rewired to provide a servo constant current supply, a servo controlled-potential source, and other servo systems. As a self-balancing potentiometer the circuit provides nominal spans of 10 and 100 mv. Each range has an individual calibration control. The one span can be adjusted to any value between about 10 to 20 mv and the other span between 100 to 200 mv. Other spans, including a continuously variable span, are easily obtained by modifications of the input circuit. Full-scale zero adjustment and damping adjustment are made by top-panel controls. Scale suppression is accomplished by several methods described in the Experiments of Chap. 7.

The full-scale (10-in.) pen travel requires only 1 sec. Chart speeds can be varied by using different speeds for the interchangeable synchronous motors.

Circuit Notes

Servo-recorder principles are described in Chap. 7, and the specific input circuitry for the potentiometer, constant-current, and controlled-potential applications is illustrated in the Experiments of Chap. 7. Further details can be obtained from the instruction manual. The schematic diagram of the servo is shown in Fig. S1-57.

The tubes in the power supply and amplifier are "on" in the STAND-BY position, but the mercury reference cell, the chopper, and the pen motor

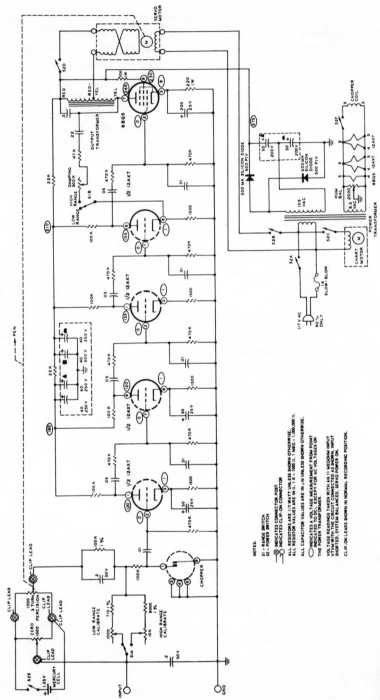

Figure S1-57

are all "off." In this way the recorder is ready for immediate operation when switched to the ON or CHART position, but without the noise, aging, and heat associated with keeping the above components continuously connected. The hum-balancing control across the chopper coil balances the electrostatic noise pickup as described in Sec. 7-4 and illustrated in Fig. 7-12. The hum-balancing control is correctly adjusted when the potentiometer "zero" does not shift in switching from the 100 to the 10 position with a *short circuit* across the recorder input.

The writing pen for the recorder is an inexpensive cartridge fountain pen. The penholder is made specifically to hold the Sheaffer Skrip cartridge pen, but many other pens will also fit in the spring-tension holder.

The voltage amplifier consists of four stages from the two 12AX7 tubes. The 6BQ5 power amplifier uses a 60-cps resonant tank in its plate circuit. The square wave from the chopper is modified to a sine wave through the voltage amplifier, and the phase is determined largely by the 0.01-μf capacitors between the control grids and ground of the 12AX7 tubes.

The damping control provides negative feedback from the plate of the power amplifier to the cathode of the fourth stage of the voltage amplifier.

The synchronous chart motor has a removable gear on its shaft that can be removed and mounted on the shaft of another motor to provide a different chart speed. For rapid change of chart speeds, it is convenient to have other motors with gears already attached. The standard $\frac{1}{2}$-rpm motor provides a chart speed of 2 in./min.

supplement 2

D-C Circuits

The purpose of this supplement is to provide a convenient source for review and reference in the basic relationships of d-c circuits. In addition to a discussion of the common methods of circuit analysis, practical information concerning circuits, components, and signal levels is included.

The simplest electrical circuit is the connection of a material which conducts electrical charge (a conductor) between two points of unequal electrical potential. Charge will flow through the conductor until the potential difference between the two points is zero. If a source of energy is present which maintains a potential difference between the two points (such as at the terminals of a battery) the flow of charge, or current, in the conductor will be continuous.

A circuit diagram which represents a conductor connected between the terminals of a battery is shown in Fig. S2-1. The conducting circuit includes the switch contacts, a light bulb, and the connecting wires. The connecting wires offer very little *resistance* to the flow of charge. The *filament* wire in the light bulb is a less perfect conductor. When the switch contacts are open, the path for the flow of charge is broken and there will be no current in the light bulb. When the switch is closed, there will be a steady flow of charge through the light bulb. This is indicated by the current arrow in Fig. S2-1. The arrow is drawn to indicate the direction of the flow of positive charges according to the prevalent convention. It may be more "graphic" in some cases to indicate the direction of negative

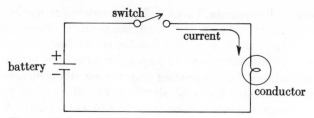

Figure S2-1   A simple d-c circuit.

charge or *electron* flow, but the positive-current convention adopted in this book is the convention used in all college-level texts and scientific journals and is consistent with the arrows in semiconductor symbols.

The magnitude of the current (rate of charge flow) in the circuit depends on the magnitude of the electrical potential and the resistance of the conducting circuit. A measure of current could be the number of electron charge units passing a given point in the circuit every second, but for most circuits this number would be inconveniently large. The common unit for current is the *ampere* (abbreviated A or amp), which corresponds to a charge flow rate of 6.24×10^{18} electrons per second. The common symbols for current are I or i. The resistance to charge flow is measured in *ohms* (abbreviated Ω). A 62-ft length of 22-gauge copper hook-up wire has a resistance of about 1 ohm. The accepted symbol for resistance is R. The *volt* is the standard unit of electrical potential. An electrical potential of 1 volt will cause a current of 1 amp in a resistance of 1 ohm. The symbol for potential is E; volt is often abbreviated V or v.

The current in any resistive circuit is proportional to the potential and inversely proportional to the resistance as given by Ohm's law.

$$I = \frac{E}{R} \tag{S2-1}$$

Thus, in Fig. S2-1, if the potential of the battery is 1.5 volts ($E = 1.5$ volts) and the resistance of the light bulb is 2.5 ohms ($R = 2.5$ ohms), the current will be 1.5 volts/2.5 ohms = 0.60 amp ($I = 0.60$ amp).

S2-1   Resistance

All conductors at normal temperatures offer some resistance to the flow of charge. The resistance of connecting wires and contacts in a circuit should be minimized. However, components made solely for their resistive value are widely used in electronic circuits. Such components are called resistors and often look like Fig. S2-2. They can be obtained in a wide range of resistance values from a few ohms to many million ohms.

Designations of Resistance Value. Most resistors are marked in some way with the nominal value of their resistance in ohms. The present manufacturing practice is either to print the value on the body of the resistor in numbers or to put three colored bands around the body of the resistor which can be translated into a number with two significant figures by using the standard color code. This is illustrated in Fig. S2-2. Each number from 0 to 9 has been assigned a color according to Table S2-1. Note

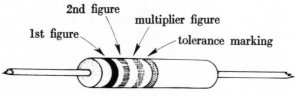

Figure S2-2 *A color-coded resistor.*

Table S2-1

Black	0	Green	5
Brown	1	Blue	6
Red	2	Violet	7
Orange	3	Gray	8
Yellow	4	White	9

that from 2 to 7 the colors follow the spectrum. The color of the band closest to the end of the resistor represents the first figure of the resistance; the second band, the second figure; and the third band, the number of zeros to add to the first two figures to get the total resistance. Thus a resistor whose bands were yellow, purple, and red would be 4700 ohms or 4.7 kilohms. Blue, gray, green would be 6,800,000 ohms or 6.8 megohms, and green, blue, black would be 56 ohms. For resistances between 1 and 10 ohms, gold is used for the third band. Thus orange, white, gold is 3.9 ohms.

The Accuracy of the Nominal Resistance. The limit of accuracy assured by the manufacturer of the resistor is called the tolerance. This is expressed in per cent of the nominal value. For instance, a 100-kilohm resistor with a tolerance of 10 per cent may have any value from 90 to 110 kilohms. In color-coded resistors the tolerance is indicated by the color of the fourth band (Fig. 2-24), silver being 10 per cent, gold being 5 per cent. Closer tolerances are printed on the resistance body.

The 10 per cent tolerance requirement of most common resistor applications has resulted in the somewhat strange values of the resistors manufactured. The standard values of resistances available in 10 per cent tolerance between 1 and 10 kilohms are: 1, 1.2, 1.5, 1.8, 2.2, 2.7, 3.3, 3.9, 4.7, 5.6, 6.8, 8.2, and 10 kilohms. Note that there is a value within 10 per cent of any required resistance. The use of "round" numbers for resistance values would result in an unnecessarily large number of values required to cover the same resistance range. Where 5 per cent tolerance is specified, 5 per cent resistors are supplied in the values 1.1, 1.3, 1.6, 2.0, 2.4, 3.0, 3.6, 4.3, 5.1, 6.2, 7.5, and 9.1 kilohms, in addition to all the standard 10 per cent values. In all other decades, the 5 and 10 per cent values are the same as those listed above. A complete table of standard resistance values is given in Appendix C.

Many factors affect the accuracy of a resistor. For resistors of very low values (less than 10 ohms) the resistance of the connection to the resistor can become a significant part of the total resistance of the circuit. For resistors of very high values (greater than 10 megohms) leakage of current between the contacts on the surface of the resistor may significantly decrease the resistance of the circuit. This effect, which will depend on the ambient humidity, can be reduced through the use of special insulating materials.

Almost all resistors have a temperature coefficient of resistance. The temperature coefficient can be reduced by the use of special resistive materials. If accuracy is not as important as stability, it is often enough to use a resistor having a far greater wattage rating than the circuit requires in order to reduce the temperature changes.

Precision resistors are often coils of resistance wire that are wound on an insulated form. Although they can be wound in such a way that the inductive effect is greatly reduced, it cannot be eliminated altogether. For this reason wire-wound precision resistors lose their accuracy when used in circuits with frequencies over a certain value. This value is usually in the neighborhood of 100 kc for very good resistors. For high-resistance precision resistors, capacitive effects can lower the impedance at high frequencies, and thus high-value precision resistors are precise only at lower frequencies.

Other Resistance Types. Some resistors are made to have an adjustable or variable resistance. This is accomplished by exposing the resistive element so that contact can be made at any point along the resistance by a movable contact, or "wiper." Such a device is called a *rheostat*. The value of the total or maximum resistance is usually stamped on the case of the rheostat. The resistive element is usually either a wound coil of resistance wire or a strip of resistive film.

Resistances which are made to operate "hot" such as tube filaments, heating coils, and light bulbs have a much lower resistance when they are cold than when they are not. A heavy surge of current occurs when the circuit is first closed. This is most often the instant the filament wire "burns out." Sometimes light bulbs are used as resistors in circuits for their stabilizing effect on the current. When the current increases, their temperature increases and their resistance to the current increases.

All components of a circuit introduce some noise into the circuit, as explained in Chap. 4. Noise resulting from resistive components can be reduced by choosing special "low-noise" resistors such as the metal-film type. Ordinary carbon composition resistors should be avoided where the signal level is 10^{-3} volts or less.

S2-2   Current

When the switch of Fig. S2-1 is closed, completing the connection of the light bulb to the battery, there is a current in the circuit. *The current must be the same at every point in the circuit at any instant*, because charge cannot enter any segment of the circuit without an equivalent charge leaving that segment.

This supplement deals only with *direct-current circuits*. A direct current is one which does not change its direction and is essentially constant in magnitude. Circuits where the current reverses direction or varies in magnitude are described in Supplement 3.

Currents in electronic circuits range in magnitude from 10^{-15} amp to several amperes. Circuits having signal currents of microamperes (10^{-6} amp), or less, usually require special care in construction so that noise currents are not of equivalent magnitude. On the other hand, very large currents in the ampere region require heavy wire and special switches.

Work is required to move charge through an element which resists the movement of charge. This work appears as heat in the resistive element. The unit of electrical work is the joule. Power, P, is the time rate of work, i.e., joules per second or watts. The power dissipated in a resistance is given by the expression

$$P = I^2R \tag{S2-2}$$

Substituting in Eq. (S2-2) from Ohm's law, two other equations for power can be obtained.

$$P = EI = \frac{E^2}{R} \tag{S2-3}$$

It is important not to exceed the wattage rating of resistors or other components. Suppose that a 47-kilohm resistor is rated at 1 watt. The maximum current through this resistor is thus $\sqrt{1/47,000} = 5 \times 10^{-3}$ amp, or 5 ma. The maximum voltage which can be applied to the resistor is $\sqrt{1 \times 47{,}000} = 230$ volts. A resistor which is dissipating its maximum rated power can be hot enough to cause burns and must be well ventilated. For cooler and therefore more stable resistance values, a two to ten times overrating of the power dissipation is desirable.

Some devices, like light bulbs, are rated according to the power normally consumed rather than the maximum rated power. For these, the power rating reveals other electrical characteristics. For instance a 110-volt 60-watt light bulb must have a resistance of $(110 \text{ volts})^2/60 \text{ watts} =$ 202 ohms and must carry a current of 60 watts/110 volts = 0.55 amp.

S2-3 Potential

A d-c potential, like a direct current, is invariant in sign and magnitude. Sources of d-c potential may usually be classed as signal sources or power sources. Common d-c power sources are batteries and power supplies, as discussed in Chap. 2.

When current is present in a resistive circuit, there must be a potential across the resistance as given by Ohm's law, $E = IR$. This potential is often referred to as the *IR drop* across a resistance. *In any circuit the algebraic sum of the potential source voltages and the IR drops must be zero.* This is illustrated by Fig. S2-3. Resistances totaling 30 ohms are connected to a potential of 6 volts, resulting in a current of $6/30 = 0.2$ amp. The potential across R_1 is thus $9 \times 0.2 = 1.8$ volts; and across R_2, $21 \times 0.2 = 4.2$ volts, and thus the *IR* drops equal the applied potential.

Suppose that, in Fig. S2-3, R_1 represents the internal resistance of the battery and R_2 represents the normal load for the battery. The voltage supplied to the load is only 4.2 volts instead of 6.0 volts. Yet if a high-resistance voltmeter were used to measure the battery voltage when R_2 (the load) is disconnected, the voltage measured would be 6.0 volts because of the negligibly small *IR* drop across R_1 when the current is so small. The no-load voltage of a potential source is often called the *open-circuit potential*.

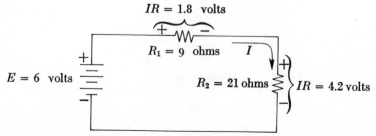

Figure S2-3 IR drops in a d-c circuit.

Common magnitudes of potentials range from microvolts (10^{-6} volts) for very low level signal sources up to several thousand volts for very high voltage power supplies for detectors and indicators. Signals in the submillivolt range require shielding, low noise components, and other considerations discussed in Chap. 4. On the other hand, high voltages of 100 volts or more are a hazard. Care in handling and testing high-voltage equipment is required. Very high voltages in the kilovolt range require special switches, special components, and very heavy insulation to prevent arcing.

S2-4   Series Circuits

The components of Fig. S2-4 are said to be connected *in series*. Note that there is only one current path in the complete circuit so that the current in each component is the same. When switch S is closed, the 100-volt source is connected to the total resistance between points A and F. The total resistance R_T in a series circuit is the sum of the separate resistances.

$$R_T = R_1 + R_2 + R_3 + R_4 + R_5 \qquad \text{(S2-4)}$$

The current $I = E/R_T = 100$ volts$/1000 = 0.10$ amp. The total potential is divided among the separate resistors as in Fig. S2-3. The voltage between any two points can be determined by calculating the IR drop.

$$E_{D,F} = (R_4 + R_5)I = 100 \times 0.10 = 10 \text{ volts}$$

The fraction of the total voltage which appears between points D and F is

$$\frac{E_{D,F}}{E} = \frac{(R_4 + R_5)I}{E} = \frac{R_4 + R_5}{R_T}$$

which is independent of the voltage E. For this reason this circuit is called a *voltage divider*.

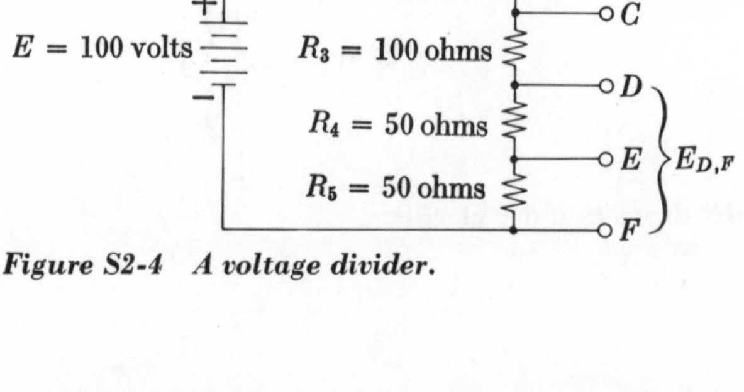

Figure S2-4   A voltage divider.

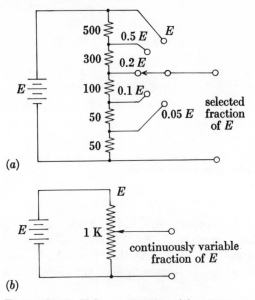

(a)

(b)

Figure S2-5   Voltage dividers: (a) selector switch; (b) potentiometer.

A selector switch may be used to select various fractions of the input voltage, as in Fig. S2-5a. The output-voltage increments may be made as small as desired. Selector switches commonly have up to 11 positions, but switches with more positions are also available. For finer voltage-divider adjustment, a continuously variable resistance is used, as shown in Fig. S2-5b. It is like a rheostat except that it has provision for connecting to *both ends* of the resistive element. This is most often called a *potentiometer*. Precision potentiometers are discussed in Chap. 6.

Since the current in every element of the series circuit is equal, a single switch, placed anywhere in the current path, is sufficient to turn off the current in the entire circuit. Similarly, a single fuse is sufficient to protect all components against excessive current. *The order of components in a series circuit is immaterial.* If any element of the circuit burns out or becomes disconnected, the entire circuit is disabled. This is a common occurrence with the "series-string" Christmas-tree lights and with the series-connected vacuum-tube filaments in inexpensive radios.

Because there is no current in the incomplete series circuit, there will be no *IR* drop in any of the circuit elements. The entire potential-source voltage must then be across the "open"-element terminals, as shown in Fig. S2-6 for the case of the series-wired tube filaments. This is a convenient method for finding the open element, because the potential across every other element will be zero. Another interesting application of this

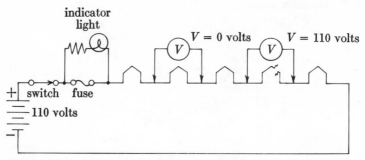

Figure S2-6   Voltages in open series circuit.

principle is the indicator light across the fuse in Fig. S2-6. Assuming that the burned-out tube has been replaced, the full 110 volts will appear across the fuse terminals should the fuse blow, and the "blown-fuse" indicator light would then light. The resistor is used to limit the current to a safe value for the light bulb.

A series circuit may contain more than one potential source. The total potential applied to the circuit is the algebraic sum of the various potential sources. As mentioned before, the algebraic sum of the source potentials and IR drops in the series circuit must be zero.

S2-5   Parallel Circuits

Resistances connected in parallel to a voltage source are shown in Fig. S2-7. Note that the potential E is applied to each resistance. The current through each resistance can be calculated from Ohm's law.

$$I_1 = \frac{E}{R_1} \qquad I_2 = \frac{E}{R_2} \qquad I_3 = \frac{E}{R_3}$$

The total current supplied to the circuit by the battery is $I_1 + I_2 + I_3$.

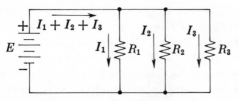

Figure S2-7   A parallel circuit.

The total resistance of the parallel circuit $R_\parallel$ connected to the battery is thus

$$R_\parallel = \frac{E}{I_1 + I_2 + I_3} = \frac{E}{E/R_1 + E/R_2 + E/R_3}$$

Upon rearranging, it is seen that, when resistances are connected in parallel, their total resistance can be found from the relation

$$\frac{1}{R_\parallel} = \frac{1}{R_1} + \frac{1}{R_2} + \frac{1}{R_3} \qquad \text{(S2-5)}$$

For two resistors in parallel

$$R_\parallel = \frac{1}{1/R_1 + 1/R_2} = \frac{R_1 R_2}{R_1 + R_2} \qquad \text{(S2-6)}$$

It is convenient to define a quantity G which is the reciprocal of the resistance and is called the *conductance*. It is seen that, for a parallel network of "conductors," $G_T = G_1 + G_2 + G_3 + \cdots$. In other words, for a series circuit the total resistance is the sum of the separate resistances, and for a parallel circuit the total conductance is the sum of the separate conductances.

From Fig. S2-7 it can be seen that the current through each resistance is independent of the current through all the others. This is because *the potential is the same across each element in a parallel circuit.* In contast to a series circuit, then, the current through each of the parallel components may be different, and each component may be switched off independently without affecting the others.

Potential sources of equal voltage may be connected in parallel to increase the current which can be supplied to the load. *The voltage of parallel-connected sources must be equal*, because the potential across parallel components is the same. Connecting a 3-volt battery in parallel with a 1.5-volt battery will certainly result in damage to one or both batteries.

S2-6 Networks

Practical circuits are often complex combinations of series and parallel circuits. In this section, the methods of analyzing networks to determine the total resistance or the currents and voltages in various branches of the network will be presented.

To find the equivalent resistance of a complex network of resistances, series and parallel combinations can be reduced to single values until only one resistance remains. This procedure is illustrated in Fig. S2-8.

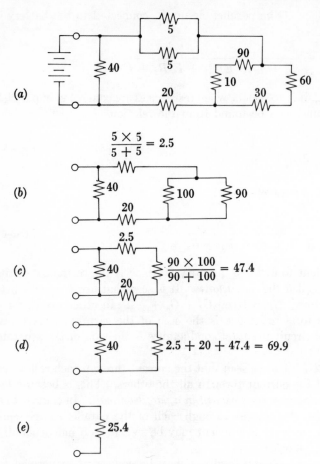

Figure S2-8   Reduction of series-parallel network.

The analysis of the currents and voltages in the network can be made after the reduction of Fig. S2-8. Assume that the potential applied to the network is 10.0 volts. The current through the 40-ohm resistor is thus $10/40 = 0.25$ amp. The current through the 69.9-ohm resistance (part d) is $10/69.9 = 0.143$ amp. The IR drop across the 47.4-ohm resistance (part c) is 0.143 amp $\times$ 47.4 ohms = 6.78 volts, and the current through the 100-ohm branch (part b) is thus 6.78 volts/100 ohms = 0.0678 amp; the 90-ohm branch, 6.78 volts/90 ohms = 0.0752 amp. Continuing in this way, the current through, and the potential across, each circuit element can be found.

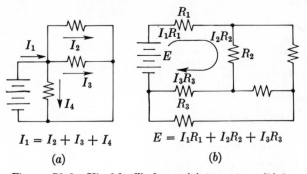

$$I_1 = I_2 + I_3 + I_4 \qquad\qquad E = I_1R_1 + I_2R_2 + I_3R_3$$

(a) (b)

Figure S2-9 Kirchhoff's laws: (a) junction; (b) loop.

Kirchhoff's Laws. Occasionally circuits are encountered where it is not possible to reduce the resistances to simpler circuits. To solve such complex networks, two simple, but very important, laws are used. They are called Kirchhoff's laws, and they are as follows: (1) The algebraic sum of all the currents flowing toward a junction is zero. (2) The algebraic sum of all the potential-source voltages is equal to the algebraic sum of all the IR drops in any loop. (A loop is any closed conducting path in the network.) These laws are illustrated in Fig. S2-9. The use of Kirchhoff's laws to solve a circuit is illustrated for the familiar Wheatstone bridge. The resistance values in ohms are given in Fig. S2-10. The current through each element is numbered and given a direction which seems logical. Note that I_4 is given an arbitrary direction because a knowledge of the actual direction requires a partial solution of the problem.

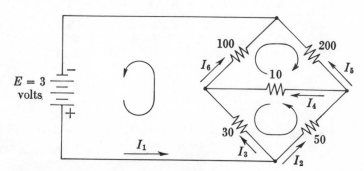

Figure S2-10 A Wheatstone bridge.

From the first law:

$$I_1 = I_2 + I_3$$
$$I_2 = I_4 + I_5$$
$$I_6 = I_3 + I_4$$

From the second law:

$$3 \text{ volts} = 30I_3 + 100I_6$$
$$0 = -30I_3 + 10I_4 + 50I_2$$
$$0 = -200I_5 + 10I_4 + 100I_6$$

Note that for j junctions and n unknown currents there are $j - 1$ independent first-law equations and $n - (j - 1)$ independent second-law equations. These may be solved by the ordinary way of solving simultaneous equations or by the method of determinants illustrated. For the three independent equations

$$ax + by + cz = K$$
$$a'x + b'y + c'z = K'$$
$$a''x + b''y + c''z = K''$$

$$x = \frac{\begin{vmatrix} K & b & c \\ K' & b' & c' \\ K'' & b'' & c'' \end{vmatrix}}{\begin{vmatrix} a & b & c \\ a' & b' & c' \\ a'' & b'' & c'' \end{vmatrix}}$$

$$= \frac{Kb'c'' + bc'K'' + cb''K' - K''b'c - Kb''c' - K'bc''}{ab'c'' + bc'a'' + cb''a' - a''b'c - ab''c' - a'bc''}$$

$$y = \frac{\begin{vmatrix} a & K & c \\ a' & K' & c' \\ a'' & K'' & c'' \end{vmatrix}}{\begin{vmatrix} a & b & c \\ a' & b' & c' \\ a'' & b'' & c'' \end{vmatrix}}$$

and so forth. To solve for any current in the problem given, it is necessary to solve two sixth-order determinants. The total solution involves seven

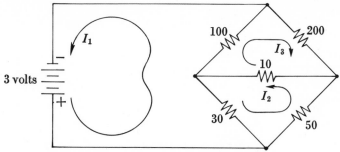

Figure S2-11   Loop currents for bridge analysis.

such determinants. The solution of complex networks can usually be simplified by the use of the loop currents. The problem with six unknown currents (Fig. S2-10) is redrawn (Fig. S2-11).

Remember that there are $n - (j - 1)$ independent loop equations and therefore $n - (j - 1)$ independent loops. The sum of the IR drops must equal the sum of the source potentials in each loop.

$$3 \text{ volts} = 30(I_1 - I_2) + 100(I_1 + I_3)$$

$$0 = 100(I_1 + I_3) + 200I_3 + 10(I_3 + I_2)$$

$$0 = 30(I_2 - I_1) + 50I_2 + 10(I_3 + I_2)$$

Rearranging,

$$3 \text{ volts} = I_1(30 + 100) + I_2(-30) + I_3(100)$$

$$0 = I_1(100) + I_2(10) + I_3(100 + 200 + 10)$$

$$0 = I_1(-30) + I_2(30 + 50 + 10) + I_3(10)$$

$$I_1 = \frac{\begin{vmatrix} 3 & -30 & 100 \\ 0 & 10 & 310 \\ 0 & 90 & 10 \end{vmatrix}}{\begin{vmatrix} 130 & -30 & 100 \\ 100 & 10 & 310 \\ -30 & 90 & 10 \end{vmatrix}} = \frac{300 - 83{,}700}{-2{,}375{,}000} = 35.1 \text{ ma}$$

The current through the 10-ohm resistor is $I_2 + I_3$.

To solve for the current through the 10-ohm resistor only, it is simpler to draw the three loops so that only one loop includes the 10-ohm resistor

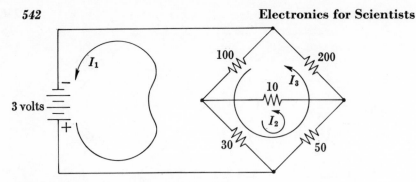

Figure S2-12   Loops for solution of I_2.

and so that the solution of one loop only is required.   This is done in Fig. S2-12.   Now

$$3 \text{ volts} = 30(I_1 - I_2 - I_3) + 100(I_1 - I_3)$$

$$0 = 30(I_2 + I_3 - I_1) + 50(I_2 + I_3) + 10(I_2)$$

$$0 = 100(I_3 - I_1) + 30(I_2 + I_3 - I_1) + 50(I_2 + I_3)$$
$$+ 200(I_3)$$

$$3 \text{ volts} = I_1(30 + 100) + I_2(-30) + I_3(-100 - 30)$$

$$0 = I_1(-30) + I_2(30 + 50 + 10) + I_3(30 + 50)$$

$$0 = I_1(-100 - 30) + I_2(30 + 50)$$
$$+ I_3(100 + 30 + 50 + 200)$$

$$I_2 = \frac{\begin{vmatrix} 130 & 3 & -130 \\ -30 & 0 & 80 \\ -130 & 0 & 380 \end{vmatrix}}{\begin{vmatrix} 130 & -30 & -130 \\ -30 & 90 & 80 \\ -130 & 80 & 380 \end{vmatrix}} = \frac{3000}{2,371,400} = 1.26 \text{ ma}$$

Thévenin's Theorem.   One of the most useful theorems in circuit analysis is Thévenin's theorem.   It states that *any potential source which has only two output terminals and is composed of resistors and batteries can be represented by a series combination of a resistor R and a battery E as in* Fig. S2-13.   From the *Thévenin equivalent circuit*, it can be seen that E is the open-circuit potential of the network and R is the resistance between the output terminals when the battery E is short-circuited, or rather the source resistance of the network as a voltage source.

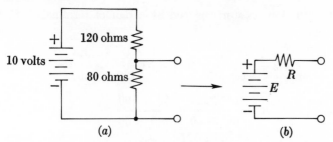

(a)   *(b)*

Figure S2-13   *Thévenin's theorem: (a) voltage divider; (b) equivalent circuit.*

The network shown in Fig. S2-13 is a voltage divider as discussed in Sec. S2-4. The open-circuit potential E is

$$E = 10 \text{ volts} \times \frac{80}{80 + 120} = 4.0 \text{ volts}$$

When the 10-volt battery is replaced by a short circuit, the resistance between the output terminals is the parallel combination of the 80-ohm and 120-ohm resistors.

$$R = \frac{80 \times 120}{80 + 120} = 48 \text{ ohms}$$

This particular voltage divider is thus electrically identical to a battery of 4.0 volts in series with a resistor of 48 ohms. The actual output of the divider for any load resistance connected to the output terminals can be readily calculated. In fact, through the use of this theorem, the calculation of the output voltage, under load, of *any* voltage source is no more complicated than that of Fig. S2-3.

A further proof of the usefulness of Thévenin's theorem is shown in Fig. S2-14. The network which is being solved will be recognized as the

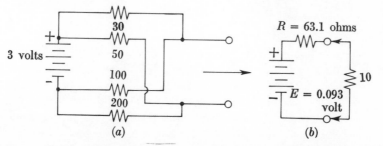

(a)   *(b)*

Figure S2-14   *Thévenin's theorem: (a) bridge circuit; (b) equivalent circuit.*

bridge with the 10-ohm resistor replaced by a pair of terminals. E, the open-circuit voltage, is

$$\frac{30}{100 + 30} \times 3 - \frac{50}{200 + 50} \times 3 = 3\left(\frac{30}{130} - \frac{50}{250}\right) = 0.093 \text{ volt}$$

and
$$R = \frac{50 \times 200}{200 + 50} + \frac{30 \times 100}{100 + 30}$$

$$= 63.1 \text{ ohms}$$

The current through the 10-ohm resistor in the bridge is simply

$$I = \frac{E}{R + 10} = \frac{0.093}{73.1} = 1.26 \text{ ma}$$

This theorem is particularly useful where the solution of only one element is desired. Note that the solution is independent of the value of the applied element until the last step.

supplement 3

Electrical Signals and Reactive Circuits

Information about nuclear disintegrations, light intensity, pressure, sound, temperature, relative position, mass, and essentially all physical and chemical properties and quantities can be converted (transduced) into electrical currents or voltages called signals.   In other words, an *electrical signal* can be considered a current or voltage that contains information.   This information may simply be related to the *amplitude* of the current or voltage, such as the relationship of light intensity to the output voltage of a photovoltaic cell.   It may be related to the precise way in which the amplitude varies with time or the *frequency* of the variations, as radio signals which contain sound information.   The number or time relationship of short bursts of electrical energy may relate directly to nuclear reactions or other processes.

One basic problem in electronics is how to convert the electrical signal to a form whose relationship to the desired information is precise and easily recognized.   Sometimes only distortion-free amplification is required.   In other cases the signal must be filtered to eliminate unwanted signal components, or compared or added to other signals, or integrated with respect to time in order to obtain the desired information from the signal.   There is a great tendency in electronics to focus attention on the action of the diodes, vacuum tubes, and transistors in a circuit. However, except for rectification and amplification, most variations of the signal are performed by simple circuits of resistance, capacitance, and inductance, which *react* in various ways to changes in the signal amplitude. Because of their great importance in electronic circuits, the effects of reactive circuits on various types of signals are presented in this supplement. The following sections provide review and reference material which can be profitably referred to both before and during the reading of the chapters in the book.

Capacitance and inductance are found in virtually all practical circuit components. Therefore *reactance* is an inherent property of all circuits. The discussion of reactance set forth in this supplement will aid in the choice of circuits and components for a desired effect, and also demonstrate the methods of calculating the amount by which signals will be distorted by unavoidable reactances.

S3-1   Introduction to Signals and Reactive Components

Reactance to changes in signal level are either capacitive or inductive. Intentionally reactive components are called capacitors or inductors. The way in which each of these components reacts is introduced in this section. Characteristic variations in signal amplitude are identified and analyzed.

Capacitance. Capacitance is the ability to store electrical charge. A capacitor is composed of two conductors separated by a *dielectric*, or *insulator*. When a capacitor is connected to a voltage source, as shown in Fig. S3-1, electrons from the upper conductor or *plate* are attracted to the positive terminal of the battery while the same number of electrons is supplied to the lower plate by the voltage source. (At any given time the current in a series circuit must be the same at every point.) The current in this circuit will continue only until the capacitor is *charged* to the potential equal to that of the voltage source. The quantity of electricity q necessary

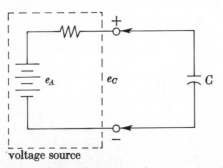

voltage source

Figure S3-1   Capacitor charging circuit.

to charge the capacitor is directly proportional to the potential e_C across the capacitor:

$$q = Ce_C \qquad \text{(S3-1)}$$

The quantity of electricity q is called the charge on the capacitor and has the units coulombs. A *coulomb* is approximately 6.24×10^{18} electrons and is defined as *the charge passing a given point during 1 second when the current is 1 ampere.* The proportionality constant C is the *capacitance* of the capacitor, the ratio of charge to voltage, or the measure of its effectiveness as a charge storage device. The unit of capacitance is the *farad.* A capacitor has a capacitance of 1 farad when 1 coulomb charges it to 1 volt.

Suppose that the potential of the voltage source in Fig. S3-1 varies with time. According to Eq. (S3-1), the potential across the capacitor cannot change without a change in charge, and therefore a current is required. The current i is equal to the rate of charge flow dq/dt. Substituting from Eq. (S3-1) for q,

$$i = \frac{dq}{dt} = C\frac{de_C}{dt} \qquad \text{(S3-2)}$$

Rewriting Eq. (S3-2) as $de_C = (1/C)i\,dt$, it is obvious that *the potential across a capacitor cannot change instantly* because an infinite current would be required. The larger the capacitance C and the larger the resistance to current the slower the potential change across the capacitor. *The capacitor reacts against a change in potential across it.* For the circuit in Fig. S3-1, if a potential e_A is suddenly applied across an uncharged capacitor C, the potential e_C across the capacitor will be zero at the instant e_A is applied, and then e_C will increase toward e_A at a rate proportional to the instantaneous current i and the reciprocal of the capacitance, as shown by Eq. (S3-2). Note that the potential e_C across the capacitor opposes the applied potential e_A, and there will be no current when the two are equal. In other words, current cannot continue in a circuit like Fig. S3-1 if the applied potential remains constant. Therefore, the capacitor is said to offer an *open circuit* to a d-c voltage.

Practical capacitors and their characteristics are described in Sec. S3-2, and the effects of capacitive circuits on various signals are discussed in Secs. S3-4 and S3-5.

Inductance. Inductance is that property of a device which resists a change in the current through the device. Inductors work on the principle that a varying magnetic field *induces* a potential or *electromotive force* (emf) in any conductor within that field. A practical inductor may simply be a coil of wire, as in Fig. S3-2. The current in each loop of wire generates a magnetic field which passes through its neighboring loops. If the current through the coil is constant, the magnetic field is constant; that is, the mag-

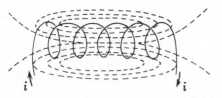

Figure S3-2   Coil and magnetic field.

netic field is not changing with respect to the coil, and no action takes place. If the current increases, the magnetic field expands, and the motion of the magnetic field with respect to the coil generates an emf in each loop which is counter to the applied potential.   This counter emf tends to impede or react against a change of current through the coil.   The greater the rate of change of the magnetic field the greater will be the counter emf.   In most inductors the magnetic field strength is proportional to the current and therefore,

$$\text{Counter emf} = L\,\frac{di}{dt} \tag{S3-3}$$

where L is a measure of the inductance of the coil and has the units henrys. An inductance of *1 henry will induce a counter emf of 1 volt when the current is changing at the rate of 1 ampere per second.*

The inductor reacts against a change in current through itself by storing electrical energy in the magnetic field.   Work is required to increase the magnetic field; therefore, *the current in an inductive circuit cannot change instantaneously.*   Equation (S3-3) shows that an attempt to change the current abruptly will be opposed by an infinite emf induced in the coil.   If the applied potential in an inductive circuit decreases, the energy stored in the magnetic field returns to the circuit in the form of an emf which tends to maintain the previous current level.

In a perfect inductor, there is no opposition to a steady current (d-c) because $di/dt = 0$.

Practical inductors and their characteristics are described in Sec. S3-3, and the effects of inductive circuits on various signals are discussed in Secs. S3-4 and S3-5.

Sine-Wave Signals.   A sine-wave signal is, of course, a voltage or current which varies sinusoidally with time.   The sine wave is of great importance in physics and electronics.   *It is the simplest periodic waveform.* Objects whose displacement is a sinusoidal function of time are undergoing "simple harmonic motion" and are very common in nature.   Sinusoidal current is produced by rotating a wire loop in a uniform magnetic field, as in a power generator.   The sine-wave signal is the only true single-frequency periodic waveform.

The generation of a sine wave from a rotating vector of magnitude A_p is illustrated in Fig. S3-3. The sine wave results from the projection of the vector on the vertical axis as the vector rotates counterclockwise with a uniform *angular velocity* ω. If the vector is rotating at the rate of one revolution per second, the sine wave repeats itself periodically once every second. One revolution of the vector produces one *cycle* every second. The time interval required to produce one cycle is called the *period T*. Since a cycle is generated each time the vector sweeps through 360°, or 2π radians, the time axis is conveniently expressed in angles. The *frequency f* with which each cycle recurs is related to the period T. Since the vector sweeps one cycle every T seconds

$$f = \frac{1}{T} \tag{S3-4}$$

and the vector is rotating at a rate of 2π radians per T seconds, so

$$\omega = \frac{2\pi}{T} = 2\pi f \tag{S3-5}$$

If the instantaneous amplitude of the sine wave is designated a_t and the maximum or *peak* amplitude is designated A_p, the equation of a sine wave is

$$a_t = A_p \sin \omega t = A_p \sin 2\pi f t$$

If the vector represents a current or voltage, the instantaneous current i or voltage e can be given as

$$i = I_p \sin \omega t$$
$$e = E_p \sin \omega t \tag{S3-6}$$

where I_p and E_p are the *peak* current and voltage, respectively.

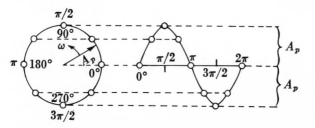

Figure S3-3 *Development of sine wave from the projection of a rotating vector.*

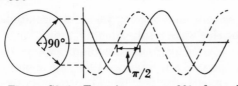

Figure S3-4   Two sine waves, 90° phase difference.

If two voltages have the same frequency but start from zero at different times, they are said to be out of *phase*. This difference in time may be expressed in terms of angles (fractions of a cycle) called the *phase angle, θ*.[1] The phase angle arises from one vector *leading* or *lagging* another vector, as shown in Fig. S3-4. A sine wave which is 90° ($\pi/2$) out of phase with another sine wave could be called a "cosine wave." However, the *waveform* is still sinusoidal and may be written as $\cos \omega t = \sin (\omega t + \pi/2)$. A generalized current sine wave is therefore

$$i = I_p \sin (\omega t + \theta) \tag{S3-7}$$

where θ is referred to some reference sine wave.

Since the sine wave is such a simple waveform, there are only two pieces of information obtainable from a sine-wave signal: the frequency and the amplitude. If another signal of the same frequency is available for a time reference, the phase angle between them may contain information.

A-C Signals. The concept of an a-c signal as one in which the charge flow actually reverses direction periodically is too confining. In electronics it is useful to define an a-c signal as that part of the signal current or voltage which varies with time. The average value, about which the a-c signal varies, is called the d-c signal level. Figure S3-5 shows a signal with a sinusoidal variation of E_p volts about an average signal value of E_{d-c}. The total signal may actually be considered as the sum of the steady or d-c voltage and the variant or a-c voltage. If E_{d-c} were zero, the flow of charge would reverse direction and the potential would change sign, as in

[1] In some books and in some chapters of this book the symbol ϕ is used for phase angle.

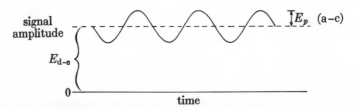

Figure S3-5   A-c and d-c signal components.

the conventional concept of alternating current. An a-c signal is readily isolated from a d-c component in an electronic circuit.

Nonsinusoidal Periodic Signals. If the pattern of voltage or current variation is repeated at regular intervals, the signal is said to be periodic. The sine wave is one example of a periodic waveform. The rectangular wave shown in Fig. S3-6a is a *train* of regularly recurring pulses. If the width of the positive and negative "half-cycles" are identical, the waveform is called a *square wave*. A square wave is shown in Fig. S3-6b. (Frequently rectangular waves are called square waves, if the asymmetry is not too great.) A *ramp* and *sawtooth* wave are also pictured in Fig. S3-6c and d.

All the waveforms illustrated in Fig. S3-6 have the same *period* and *repetition frequency*. The period of any given periodic waveform is the time interval required for each repetition. The *repetition frequency* is the number of periods which occur in 1 second. Technically, the term "frequency" should be reserved for sine waves, but usage has established the interchangeability of the terms. The frequency, or repetition frequency, is

$$f = \frac{1}{T}$$

For rectangular waves the frequency is often expressed as the *pulse repetition frequency*, or PRF.

All the waveforms of Fig. S3-6 have the same amplitude, or peak-to-

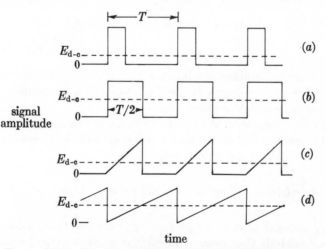

Figure S3-6   Nonsinusoidal, periodic signals: (a) rectangular wave; (b) square wave; (c) ramp; (d) sawtooth.

peak value. Although the waveforms are shown as voltages, the same general considerations apply to currents.

The average d-c voltage of each of the waveforms shown is not, however, the same in every case. The average value is that d-c level above and below which the voltage-time or current-time areas are equal. This value is called $E_{\text{d-c}}$ or $I_{\text{d-c}}$. ($E_{\text{d-c}}$ is shown on Fig. S3-6.) These areas may be found graphically or by integration. The d-c level is a basic characteristic of all periodic waveforms.

Fourier-Series Waveform Analysis. In music the quality of a tone or the *timbre* of a note is dependent upon the *harmonic content* of the tone. A distinct difference is detectable in the timbre of an A produced by a violin and an A produced by an oboe, even though the note is identical. The difference is attributable to the number and magnitudes of the harmonics produced by the different instruments. The basic frequency which distinguishes one note from another is called the fundamental. The sound from a violin not only contains information about the note being played (the fundamental), but also that it is a violin, and, to a trained ear, information about the quality of the instrument and the player. Periodic waveforms such as those shown in Fig. S3-6 have a fundamental frequency or repetition rate, and they also contain a great deal more information than just the fundamental frequency and amplitude.

It has been proved mathematically that any single-valued periodic function can be represented by a *Fourier series expansion*, which is a summation of the fundamental frequency and its harmonics in various amplitudes and phase relationships.

The general form of Fourier series for a voltage waveform is

$$e(t) = E_{\text{d-c}} + E_1 \sin(\omega t + \theta_1) + E_2 \sin(2\omega t + \theta_2)$$

$$+ \cdots + E_n \sin(n\omega t + \theta_n) \quad \text{(S3-8)}$$

where $e(t)$ is the desired voltage as a function of time, $E_{\text{d-c}}$ is the d-c level, $E_1 \cdots E_n$ are the peak voltages of the first through n harmonics, and $\theta_1 \cdots \theta_n$ are the corresponding phase angles.

The harmonic composition of a square wave can be visualized from Fig. S3-7. The fundamental and first three *odd* harmonics of the Fourier series for a square wave with no d-c component,

$$e(t) = \frac{4E}{\pi}(\sin \omega t + \tfrac{1}{3} \sin 3\omega t + \tfrac{1}{5} \sin 5\omega t + \tfrac{1}{7} \sin 7\omega t + \cdots)$$

are graphically added to produce a waveform approaching the actual square wave. Fourier analysis thus demonstrates that a nonsinusoidal signal is not a single frequency but a spectrum of frequencies and that in order to preserve the signal waveform a circuit must be able to pass the entire fre-

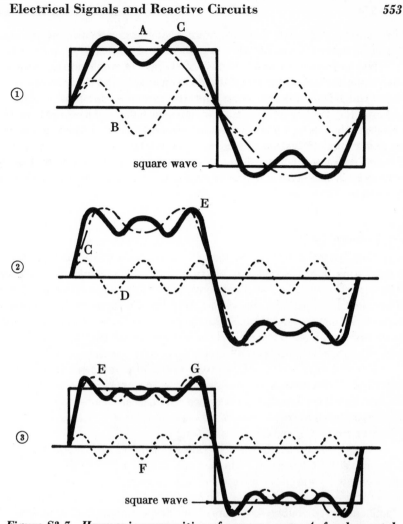

*Figure S3-7 Harmonic composition of a square wave: A, fundamental;
B, 3rd harmonic; C, fundamental plus 3rd harmonic;
D, 5th harmonic; E, fundamental plus 3rd and 5th harmonics; F, 7th harmonic; G, fundamental plus 3rd, 5th,
and 7th harmonics. (From "Radar Electronic Fundamentals," NAVSHIPS 900,016, U.S. Government Printing
Office, Washington, D.C., 1944.)*

quency spectrum without changing the amplitude or phase relationship of
the various components.

As shown in Fig. S3-7, the higher frequency components are required to
produce the abrupt changes in the signal at the leading and trailing edges of

the square wave. It is true in general that the greater the rate of signal-voltage change, the higher the frequencies will be in the signal spectrum.

Nonperiodic Signals. Signals often vary in amplitude or shape from one to the next or do not recur at regular intervals. Such signals cannot be represented by a Fourier series, but the generalizations made above regarding the frequency spectrum of nonsinusoidal signals apply to them equally well. In fact, the Fourier analysis should not be taken too literally in either case. While it is true that all the frequencies indicated in the Fourier series will be found in the complex waveform, a circuit that will pass only those frequencies will often distort the signal, as will be shown in Sec. S3-5.

S3-2 Capacitors

The simplest capacitor consists of two sheets of metal foil separated by a dielectric. The dielectric can be paper, oil, mica, ceramic, or plastic film. The whole "sandwich" can then be rolled, folded, or otherwise compacted. Then the unit is sealed from the effects of the atmosphere. The larger the area of the foil and the thinner the dielectric sheet, the higher the capacitance value will be. However, if the voltage across the capacitor is made high enough, the dielectric will break down and a discharge will occur between the two foil sheets. This often results in permanent damage to the capacitor. The breakdown voltage rating may be increased by using a thicker dielectric, but the capacitance will be correspondingly decreased. The capacitance of these units varies from about 0.001 to 1 μf, and they are the most frequently observed capacitors.

Capacitors can be obtained in various tolerance ratings, usually 20, 10, or 3 per cent. Capacitors of higher accuracy can be obtained for special applications. Capacitors have some temperature coefficient, but they do not generate appreciable heat. They can be made quite free of spurious effects and are probably the "purest" electrical components available. In some very critical circuits it is necessary to consider the leakage current through the capacitor dielectric. A capacitor constructed for especially high leakage resistance may have a leakage resistance-capacitance product of 10^6 megohm-microfarad.

Electrolytic capacitors are made of a metal foil with a surface that has an anodic formation of metal oxide film. The anodized foil is in an electrolytic solution. The oxide film is the dielectric between the metal and the solution. Because the dielectric is so thin, a high capacitance can be obtained in a small space. The electrolytic capacitor has the following disadvantages. It must be used in a circuit where the polarity is always in one direction. If the polarity is reversed, the oxide will be reduced, thus destroying the dielectric; gas will be evolved at the cathode; and the capacitor will *explode*. The electrolytic capacitor, unlike other types of capacitors, deteriorates with time. It has a relatively low resistance dielectric, causing some leakage current. These capacitors are generally used for filtering and transistor applications where poor dielectric can be tolerated and where large capacitance in a small space is essential. They are generally rated from about 1μf to thousands of microfarads. The physical size of the capacitor increases with increased capacitance and voltage rating.

Variable capacitors are usually small-valued capacitors not exceeding about 1000 picofarads (pf). When larger variations are desired, a switch is often used to put various fixed-value capacitors into the circuit. There are two common types of variable capacitors, the mica trimmer capacitor and the variable air capacitor.

The mica trimmer capacitor is composed of two sheets of metal sandwiching a sheet of mica. The spacing between the metal sheets, and thus the capacitance, is adjusted by turning a machine screw. This kind of variable capacitor is used when adjustment is only occasionally necessary and when knowledge of the actual value of the capacitance is unimportant.

The variable air capacitors are adjusted from zero to full capacitance by turning a shaft 180°. If the movable plates are semicircular, the capacitance is nearly a linear function of the angular position of the shaft. End effects cause a small deviation from linearity at both limits of rotation.

The main considerations when choosing a capacitor for a given circuit are the value of the capacitance, the voltage rating of the capacitor, and the resistance of the dielectric employed. No power is dissipated by a capacitor, so there is no power rating.

S3-3 Inductors

Inductors are never pure inductances because there is always some resistance in the coil windings and some capacitance between the coil windings. When choosing an inductor (choke) for a specific application it is necessary to consider the value of the inductance, the d-c resistance of the coil, the current-carrying capacity of the coil windings, the breakdown voltage between the coil and the frame, and the frequency range in which the coil is designed to operate.

Inductors are available with values ranging from several hundred henrys down to a few microhenrys. To obtain a very high inductance it is necessary to have a coil of many turns. The inductance may further be increased by winding the coil on a closed-loop iron core. To obtain as pure an inductance as possible, it is desirable to reduce the d-c resistance of the windings to a minimum. This can only be done by increasing the wire size, which, of course, will increase the size of the choke. The size of the wire also determines the current-handling capacity of the choke. As was pointed out in Supplement 2, the work done in forcing a current through a resistance is converted to heat in the resistance. Magnetic losses in an iron core also account for some heating, and this heating restricts any choke to a certain safe operating current. The windings of the coil must be insulated from the frame as well as from each other. Heavier insulation, which necessarily makes the choke more bulky, is used in applications where a high voltage will be present between the frame and the winding.

The losses sustained in the iron core increase as the frequency increases. They become so large at about 15 kc (the symbol kc is understood to mean "kilocycles per second"; Mc is used to represent "megacycles per second"; cps is used for cycles per second) that the iron core must be abandoned. This results in coils of reduced coupling efficiency, but fortunately very large inductance values are not used at high frequencies. Thus iron-core chokes are restricted to low-frequency applications.

The use of precision inductors is rather uncommon. However, they are available and restrictions with respect to frequency, temperature, etc., must be taken into account.

Variable Inductors. A variable inductor is one in which the magnetic coupling between the windings of the coil is varied in order to change the total inductance value. This is accomplished by one of two methods. The magnetic coupling is physically moved in and out of a cylinder upon which the choke has been wound, or the coupling is changed by varying the orientation of part of the coil winding.

Another type of variable choke is called the swinging choke. The inductance of this choke increases with decreasing current. This type of choke is used to advantage in certain power-supply circuits.

Large inductors, rated in henries (h), are used principally in power applications. The frequency in these circuits is relatively low and is generally 60 cps or low multiples thereof. In high-frequency circuits, such as those found in FM radios and TV sets, very small inductors are frequently observed. These frequencies are generally in the 10 to 1000 Mc region and the chokes are of the order of microhenries (μh). In radio-frequency applications (broadcast band) chokes are frequently rated in millihenries (mh).

S3-4 Sine-Wave Signals and Reactive Circuits

The importance of sinusoidal signals was introduced in Sec. S3-1. In the present section the discussion of sine waves will be extended, and the effect of various reactive circuits on sinusoidal signals will be studied.

Measures of Sine-Wave Amplitude. Sine-wave voltage and current amplitudes are commonly described in four ways: the peak value, the peak-to-peak value, the average value, and the rms (or *root-mean-square*)

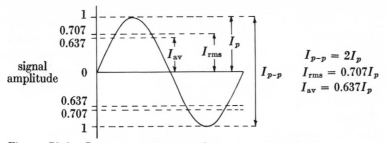

Figure S3-8 Common measures of sine-wave amplitude.

value. The particular description used depends on the application. Measuring instruments such as vacuum-tube voltmeters and oscilloscopes *respond* to the peak-to-peak value which for a sine wave is merely twice the peak value. Moving-coil meters *respond* to the average value (effective rectified d-c value), and the rms value is mostly used for the measurement of *power* in an a-c circuit. Figure S3-8 graphically summarizes the four commonly used measures.

Average Value. Moving-coil meters respond to the average value of the current through them. The mechanism by which the meters operate is discussed in Chap. 1. The average value is that current above and below which the current-time areas of a half cycle are equal. This is illustrated graphically in Fig. S3-9. The average value may be obtained by integrating the area over a half-cycle.

$$I_{\mathrm{av}} = \frac{1}{\pi} \int_0^\pi I_p \sin \omega t \, dt$$

$$= \frac{2I_p}{\pi} = 0.637 I_p \tag{S3-9}$$

In practice, the sine wave must be rectified (full-wave) to obtain meter readings corresponding to Eq. (S3-9).

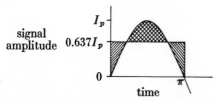

Figure S3-9 Determination of the average value of a sinusoidal signal.

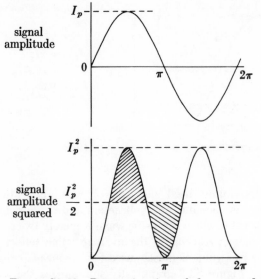

Figure S3-10   Determination of the rms value of a sinusoidal signal.

RMS Value.   The rms value is the *effective* value needed in power calculations.   The rms value of a sine-wave current will produce the same heating (power) in a resistor as an identical d-c current.   In other words, 1 rms a-c ampere produces the same amount of heat in a resistor in a given time as 1 ampere of d-c current.   The rms value is obtained by taking the *square root* of the *mean* (average) of the *squared* values of the current.   This operation is shown graphically in Fig. S3-10.   The square of the sine wave $(I_p{}^2 \sin^2 \omega t)$ is plotted directly below the sine wave, because the heating effect of a current is directly proportional to the square of the current.   The result is another "sine wave" which is completely above zero and twice the frequency.   The mean or average value of this "sine wave" is clearly $I_p{}^2/2$. On taking the square root,

$$I_{\text{rms}} = \sqrt{\frac{I_p{}^2}{2}} = \frac{I_p}{2} \sqrt{2} = 0.707 I_p \tag{S3-10}$$

The relation between the effective emf and the peak emf is the same as for effective and peak current.   Thus, $E_{\text{rms}} = 0.707 E_p$.   Calculations of voltages and currents in a-c circuits provide self-consistent values; e.g., if rms voltages are used, the currents will have rms values, etc.   Note that peak values are obtained by multiplying the rms values by the reciprocal of 0.707 (1.414), so that

$$I_p = 1.414 I_{\mathrm{rms}}$$

$$E_p = 1.414 E_{\mathrm{rms}}$$

Series RC Circuit. To begin the analysis of the effect of reactive circuits on sine-wave signals, consider the series RC circuit and the sine-wave signal source as shown in Fig. S3-11. The instantaneous current in the series circuit must be the same in all elements of the circuit.

$$i = I_p \sin \omega t \tag{S3-11}$$

The instantaneous potential e_R across the resistor will simply be

$$e_R = iR = I_p R \sin \omega t \tag{S3-12}$$

which is a sine wave of the same phase as the current and of peak amplitude $E_{pR} = I_p R$. The expression for the potential across the capacitor e_C can be obtained from Eqs. (S3-2) and (S3-11).

$$i = C \frac{de_C}{dt} = I_p \sin \omega t$$

Integrating,

$$e_C = \frac{I_p}{C} \int \sin \omega t \, dt = \frac{I_p}{\omega C} (-\cos \omega t) \tag{S3-13}$$

Thus e_C is also sinusoidal, but the $-\cos \omega t$ indicates that the potential across the capacitor *lags* the current through it by 90°, or $\pi/2$. This is a fundamental property of capacitance. The peak value of capacitor potential E_{pC} from Eq. (S3-13) is $I_p/\omega C$. In resistive circuits the ratio of the potential to the current is the resistance. In this case the ratio of E_{pC} to I_p,

$$\frac{E_{pC}}{I_p} = \frac{1}{\omega C} = \frac{1}{2\pi f C} = X_C \tag{S3-14}$$

is the *capacitive reactance* X_C, as shown in Eq. (S3-14). The capacitive reactance is a measure of the *impedance* to the flow of charge offered by the

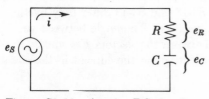

Figure S3-11   A series RC circuit.

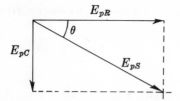

Figure S3-12   Potential vectors for a series RC circuit.

capacitor. The unit of reactance is the ohm, as in resistance. Note that capacitive reactance is frequency-dependent; the higher the frequency, the less reactance or impedance to the current.

It is now possible to solve for the sine-wave source potential e_S. The sum of all the potentials in the circuit at any instant must be zero ($e_S = e_R + e_C$). However, it is *not* true that the peak potentials are additive, because the peak value does not occur across all components simultaneously. The potential e_R is in phase with the current while the potential e_C lags by 90°. The quantities E_{pR} and E_{pC} can thus be added by representing E_{pC} as a vector quantity at right angles to E_{pR}. This is shown in Fig. S3-12. The sum of the two vectors, E_{pS}, is thus

$$E_{pS} = \sqrt{E_{pR}^2 + E_{pC}^2} \tag{S3-15}$$

The 90° angle between the vectors E_{pR} and E_{pC} of Fig. S3-12 is the phase difference between the two potentials e_R and e_C. In the same way, the angle θ between E_{pR} and E_{pS} is the phase difference between the potentials e_R and e_S. Since e_R is in phase with i, θ *is the phase angle between the applied potential e_S and the current i.* From Fig. S3-12 it can be seen that $\tan \theta = E_{pC}/E_{pR}$.

The total impedance Z of the combination of R and C must be E_{pS}/I_p. If all three quantities in Fig. S3-12 are divided by I_p, the vector diagram for impedances (Fig. S3-13) is obtained. From this it can be seen that

$$Z = \sqrt{R^2 + X_C^2} \tag{S3-16}$$

Impedance, symbolized by Z, is a general term which may be resistance, reactance, or, as in this case, a mixture. Impedance also has the units ohms.

The vector diagrams in Figs. S3-12 and S3-13 differ only by the constant factor I_p in the length of the vectors. The angle between vectors R and Z must then be θ, the angle between the vectors E_{pR} and E_{pS}. The phase angle between the applied potential and the current in the circuit is thus

$$\tan \theta = \frac{X_C}{R} \tag{S3-17}$$

The use of the above relationship is illustrated by the following example. Suppose that in Fig. S3-11 $R = 10$ kilohms, $C = 0.02$ μf, and the signal source has an output potential of 25 volts rms and a frequency of 500 cps. The capacitive reactance is thus

$$X_C = \frac{1}{2\pi(500 \text{ cps})(2 \times 10^{-8}f)} = 1.59 \times 10^4 \text{ ohms}$$

The total impedance is

$$Z = \sqrt{(15.9K)^2 + (10K)^2} = 18.8K$$

The rms value of the current is

$$i_{\text{rms}} = 25 \text{ volts}/18.8 \text{ kilohms} = 1.33 \text{ ma}$$

The phase angle θ between the current and the applied voltage is

$$\theta = \arctan(15.9/10) = 57.8°$$

with the current *leading* the voltage. The potential across the resistor is

$$e_R = iR = 1.33 \times 10^{-3} \times 10^4 = 13.3 \text{ volts rms}$$

and across the capacitor it is

$$e_C = iX_C = 1.33 \times 10^{-3} \times 15.9 \times 10^3 = 21.2 \text{ volts rms}$$

Note that the sum of the rms potentials in the circuit does not follow Kirchhoff's law. The power dissipated in the resistor P_R is simply

$$P_R = (i_{\text{rms}})^2 R = (1.33 \times 10^{-3})^2 \times 10^4 = 1.77 \times 10^{-2} \text{ watt}$$

The power dissipated by the capacitor is the current-voltage product, but it cannot be obtained by simple multiplication because the current and voltage are vector quantities at right angles to each other. The product of two vectors is the product of the scalar quantities times the cosine of the angle between them. Since the cosine of 90° is zero, *the power dissipated in the capacitor is zero.*

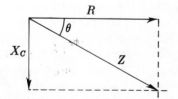

Figure S3-13 Impedance vectors for a series RC circuit.

The *apparent power* supplied by the potential source is

$$\text{Apparent power} = e_{rms} \times i_{rms} \tag{S3-18}$$

In this case, the apparent power is $(1.33 \times 10^{-3}) \times 25 = 3.33 \times 10^{-2}$ watts, but the *actual power* dissipated in the circuit as shown above is only 1.77×10^{-2} watt. Another way to find the actual power dissipated is to take the *vector* product of the current and potential supplied by the source.

$$\text{Actual power} = e_{rms} \times i_{rms} \times \cos\theta \tag{S3-19}$$

where θ is the phase angle as given in Eq. (S3-17). For the above example the actual power, calculated from Eq. (S3-19), is $3.33 \times 10^{-2} \times \cos 57.8° = 1.77 \times 10^{-2}$ watt. The ratio of the actual power to the apparent power is called the *power factor*. From Eqs. (S3-19) and (S3-18),

$$\text{Power factor} = \frac{\text{actual power}}{\text{apparent power}}$$

$$= \frac{e_{rms} \times i_{rms} \times \cos\theta}{e_{rms} \times i_{rms}} = \cos\theta \tag{S3-20}$$

The above equation is usually stated

$$\text{Actual power } P = e_{rms} \times i_{rms} \, (\cos\theta) \tag{S3-21}$$

which shows that $(\cos\theta)$ is the factor used to obtain the real power from the apparent power.

In the above example it was shown that the a-c potential from the source in Fig. S3-11 is divided between the resistor and capacitor in much the same way as the d-c voltage divider described in Supplement 2. Figure S3-14 shows two configurations of an RC, a-c voltage divider. Both are of great importance in electronics. In Fig. S3-14a the output is taken across the resistance. The fraction of e_S to be found across R depends upon the ratio of R to the total impedance.

$$e_R = e_S \frac{R}{\sqrt{R^2 + X_C^2}} \tag{S3-22}$$

When X_C is small compared to R (i.e., when the capacitance or the *frequency* is large) e_R is very nearly equal to e_S. But as the frequency decreases, X_C increases and the fraction of e_S found across R approaches zero. This circuit is often called a *high-pass filter* because only high-frequency signals will be passed unattenuated. Note also that any d-c component in the signal source will not be passed by C and cannot appear across R. The potential across R *leads* the potential of the signal by the angle $\theta = \arctan$

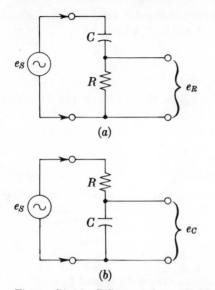

(a)

(b)

Figure S3-14   RC, a-c voltage dividers: (a) high-pass filter; (b) low-pass filter.

(X_C/R) as shown in Fig. S3-12 and given in Eq. (S3-17). The phase difference between e_R and e_S increases with decreasing frequency.

When the signal frequency is such that $X_C = R$, the power dissipated in R is exactly half the apparent power, the output potential $e_R = 0.707e_S$, and the phase angle is 45°. This frequency is called the lower cutoff frequency, f_1. If $R = 1/(2\pi f_1 C)$,

$$f_1 = \frac{1}{2\pi RC} \qquad (S3-23)$$

The potential across the capacitor in Fig. S3-14b is

$$e_C = e_S \frac{X_C}{\sqrt{R^2 + X_C{}^2}} \qquad (S3-24)$$

This circuit is called a *low-pass filter* because e_C decreases as the frequency increases. The potential across the capacitor *lags* the signal potential by $90° - \theta$, as shown in Fig. S3-12. The phase shift for this filter is thus

$$\text{Phase shift} = \arctan(R/X_C) \qquad (S3-25)$$

When the frequency is low (X_C high) the phase shift is small. The frequency at which $X_C = R$ is called the *upper cutoff frequency*, f_2, for a low-pass filter. The equation is the same as Eq. (S3-23).

$$f_2 = \frac{1}{2\pi RC} \tag{S3-26}$$

This circuit is used extensively to remove the components in the signal above f_2.

The reactance of capacitors in series ($X_{C \text{ series}}$) is the sum of the separate reactances.

$$X_{C \text{ series}} = X_{C_1} + X_{C_2} + X_{C_3} + \cdots \tag{S3-27}$$

The resulting capacitance of a series combination of capacitors can be found by substituting $1/(2\pi fC)$ for X_C in Eq. (S3-27).

$$\frac{1}{C_{\text{series}}} = \frac{1}{C_1} + \frac{1}{C_2} + \frac{1}{C_3} + \cdots \tag{S3-28}$$

The capacitance of a series combination of capacitors must be smaller than that of the smallest capacitor in the series.

Series *LR* Circuit.   The effect of inductive reactance in a series circuit can be analyzed in much the same way as that of capacitive reactance above. A series *LR* circuit is shown in Fig. S3-15. As in the case of Fig. S3-11, $i = I_p \sin \omega t$ and $e_R = I_p R \sin \omega t$. From Eqs. (S3-3) and (S3-11),

$$e_L = L \frac{di}{dt} = I_p L \omega \cos \omega t \tag{S3-29}$$

Thus e_L is sinusoidal and the cos ωt indicates that the potential across the inductor *leads* the current through it by 90°. This is a fundamental property of inductance. The ratio of the peak potential E_{pL} to the peak current is

$$E_{pL}/I_p = \omega L = 2\pi fL = X_L \tag{S3-30}$$

where X_L is the inductive reactance. Note that inductive reactance, too, is frequency-dependent; the higher the frequency, the greater the reactance.

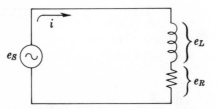

Figure S3-15   A series LR circuit.

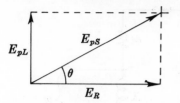

Figure S3-16   Potential vectors for a series LR circuit.

The vector diagram of the potentials is drawn as shown in Fig. S3-16. Note that the vector quantity E_{pL} is drawn pointing up to indicate that the potential across the inductor leads the potential across the resistor. The source voltage is then

$$E_{pS} = \sqrt{E_{pR}^2 + E_{pL}^2} \tag{S3-31}$$

and the phase angle θ between the applied potential and the current is the angle whose tangent is E_{pL}/E_{pR}. The impedance vector diagram is shown in Fig. S3-17. The impedance is seen to be

$$Z = \sqrt{R^2 + X_L{}^2} \tag{S3-32}$$

and the phase angle is

$$\tan \theta = \frac{X_L}{R} \tag{S3-33}$$

The discussion of power in the *RC* circuit applies directly to the *RL* case. The only actual power is dissipated in the resistance of the circuit. The discrepancy between the power dissipated and the rms current-voltage product of the signal source is accounted for by the power factor, $\cos \theta$.

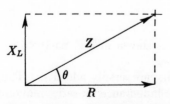

Figure S3-17   Impedance vectors for a series LR circuit.

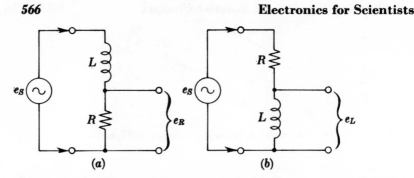

Figure S3-18   LR, a-c voltage dividers: (a) low-pass filter; (b) high-pass filter.

Two LR a-c potential dividers are shown in Fig. S3-18. The fraction of e_S to be found across R depends upon the ratio of R to the total impedance,

$$e_R = e_S \frac{R}{\sqrt{R^2 + X_L^2}} \tag{S3-34}$$

When X_L is small compared to R, nearly the full signal potential appears across R. This condition will be met at low frequencies, which means that Fig. S3-18a is a low-pass filter. The upper-frequency cutoff, f_2, where $X_L = R$, is

$$f_2 = \frac{R}{2\pi L} \tag{S3-35}$$

The phase difference between the input potential e_S and the output potential e_R is θ, as given by Eq. (S3-33) and shown in Fig. S3-16. The output voltage leads the input signal voltage.

The potential e_L in Fig. S3-18b is

$$e_L = e_S \frac{X_L}{\sqrt{R^2 + X_L^2}} \tag{S3-36}$$

Since X_L increases with increasing frequency, this circuit is a high-pass filter. The lower cutoff frequency, f_1, where $X_L = R$, is

$$f_1 = \frac{R}{2\pi L} \tag{S3-37}$$

The phase difference between e_S and e_L is shown in Fig. S3-16 to be $90°$ $- \theta$. In this case the potential e_L leads e_S.

The reactances of inductors in series are simply additive. That is, $X_{L\,\text{series}} = X_{L_1} + X_{L_2} + \cdots$, so that the inductance for series inductors is

$$L_{\text{series}} = L_1 + L_2 + L_3 + \cdots \tag{S3-38}$$

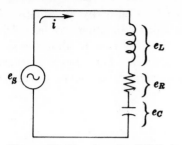

Figure S3-19   A series LRC circuit.

Series *LRC* Circuit. In general, a series *LRC* circuit is a simple combination of the *RC* and *LR* circuits already discussed. An *LRC* circuit is shown in Fig. S3-19. The potential across each element is found by multiplying the current in the circuit by the reactance of the element. The total impedance is found by vector addition, as shown in Fig. S3-20. In the case shown, X_L is larger than X_C, so that the circuit has a net inductive effect. The total impedance of the circuit is seen to be

$$Z = \sqrt{R^2 + (X_L - X_C)^2} \tag{S3-39}$$

There is a special case of the *LRC* circuit worth noting; that is, when $X_C = X_L$. From Eq. (S3-39) it is apparent that when $X_C = X_L$ the impedance is simply R. The signal-source potential is in phase with the current and the current is simply e_S/R. The potential across the inductor is thus

$$e_L = iX_L = \frac{e_S}{R} X_L \tag{S3-40}$$

e_C must equal e_L since $X_C = X_L$, but of course e_L is 180° out of phase with e_C. Note that if R is less than X_L, the potential across the inductor (or capacitor) will be greater than the signal potential! (Kirchhoff's law is still

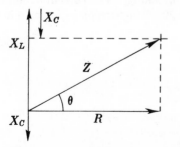

Figure S3-20   Impedance vectors for a series LRC circuit.

obeyed because the high potential across C is offset by an equally high potential across L, but opposite in polarity.) In other words, a large, single-frequency potential can be obtained across L or C while the signal source supplies only the power dissipated in R. This circuit is called a *series resonant* circuit. The resonant frequency, f_o, is found by equating X_C and X_L.

$$f_o = \frac{1}{2\pi\sqrt{LC}} \tag{S3-41}$$

The magnitude of the potential across either L or C falls off rapidly either side of f_o, making this circuit a selective frequency filter. To increase the selectivity and response of the resonant circuit it is desirable to minimize R. Usually R can be reduced to the resistance of the wire in the inductor. The ratio of inductive reactance to resistance of a coil is called the quality Q.

$$Q = \frac{X_L}{R} \tag{S3-42}$$

At resonance the potential e_L [from Eq. (S3-40)] is then

$$e_L = e_S Q \tag{S3-43}$$

Common values for Q are between 10 and 100.

When R is made to be small, the total impedance of the RLC circuit at resonance is small.

Parallel RC Circuits. A parallel combination of resistance and capacitance is connected to a signal source as shown in Fig. S3-21. Recall that in a parallel circuit, the potential across each component is the same; that is, $e_C = e_R = e_S$. The currents are then

$$i_C = \frac{e_S}{X_C} \quad \text{and} \quad i_R = \frac{e_S}{R} \tag{S3-44}$$

The total current i is the vector sum of i_C and i_R. The current vector diagram for this circuit is shown in Fig. S3-22. The current i_C is drawn in the

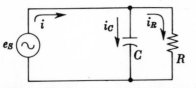

Figure S3-21   A parallel RC circuit.

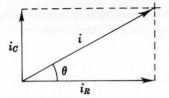

Figure S3-22   Current vectors for a parallel RC circuit.

upward position because the current *leads* the potential in a capacitor. From the vector diagram,

$$i = \sqrt{\left(\frac{e_S}{X_C}\right)^2 + \left(\frac{e_S}{R}\right)^2} = e_S \sqrt{\left(\frac{1}{X_C}\right)^2 + \left(\frac{1}{R}\right)^2} \tag{S3-45}$$

The phase difference between the applied voltage and current is θ. From Fig. S3-22,

$$\tan \theta = \frac{i_C}{i_R} = \frac{R}{X_C} \tag{S3-46}$$

The current leads the applied potential.

The total impedance of the parallel combination of R and C is e_S/i. From Eq. (S3-45),

$$Z = \frac{e_S}{i} = \frac{1}{\sqrt{\left(\frac{1}{X_C}\right)^2 + \left(\frac{1}{R}\right)^2}} \tag{S3-47}$$

The impedance of this circuit decreases as the frequency increases. A vector diagram may be drawn for the addition of parallel impedances as shown in Fig. S3-23.

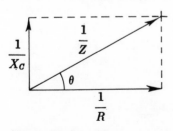

Figure S3-23   Admittance vectors for a parallel RC circuit.

From Eq. (S3-47) and Fig. S3-23 it is apparent that it is convenient to define a set of quantities which are the reciprocals of the impedance.

$$\text{Admittance:} \qquad\qquad Y = \frac{1}{Z}$$

$$\text{Capacitive susceptance:} \; B_C = \frac{1}{X_C} \qquad\qquad \text{(S3-48)}$$

$$\text{Conductance:} \qquad\qquad G = \frac{1}{R}$$

All three quantities have the units ohms^{-1} (mhos). Equation (S3-47) is then simply

$$Y = \sqrt{B_C{}^2 + G^2} \qquad\qquad\qquad \text{(S3-49)}$$

If there are two or more capacitors in parallel, their susceptances are additive.

$$B_{C\,\text{parallel}} = B_{C_1} + B_{C_2} + \cdots \qquad\qquad \text{(S3-50)}$$

Substituting $2\pi f C$ for B_C it is seen that the capacitances are also additive.

$$C_{\text{parallel}} = C_1 + C_2 + \cdots \qquad\qquad\qquad \text{(S3-51)}$$

Parallel _LR_ Circuits. The parallel combinations of inductance and resistance shown in Fig. S3-24 can be analyzed in the same way as the _RL_ circuit above. From the admittance diagram (Fig. S3-25) it can be seen that

$$Z = \frac{1}{\sqrt{\left(\dfrac{1}{X_L}\right)^2 + \left(\dfrac{1}{R}\right)^2}} \qquad\qquad \text{(S3-52)}$$

and

$$\tan\theta = \frac{R}{X_L} \qquad\qquad\qquad \text{(S3-53)}$$

The impedance of this circuit increases as the frequency increases. The current lags the potential by the angle θ.

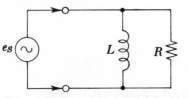

Figure S3-24   _A parallel LR circuit._

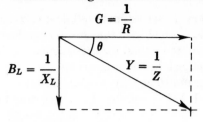

Figure S3-25   Admittance vectors for a parallel LR circuit.

The susceptances of inductors in parallel are additive.

$$B_{L \text{ parallel}} = B_{L_1} + B_{L_2} + \cdots \tag{S3-54}$$

Substituting $1/(2\pi fL)$ for B_L,

$$\frac{1}{L_{\text{parallel}}} = \frac{1}{L_1} + \frac{1}{L_2} + \cdots \tag{S3-55}$$

The total inductance of inductors in parallel cannot be greater than the smallest inductance.

Parallel *RLC* Circuits.   A parallel combination of resistance, inductance, and capacitance is simply a combination of the parallel *RC* and *RL* circuits already discussed.   If $B_L > B_C$ ($X_C > X_L$), the circuit will have a net inductive character.   The admittance is

$$Y = \sqrt{(B_L - B_C)^2 + G^2} \tag{S3-56}$$

The special case of the resonant circuit, $X_L = X_C$, is as interesting in parallel circuits as in series circuits.   From Eq. (S3-56) it is seen that at resonance $Y = G$ or $Z = R$.   If there is no parallel resistance, that is, if there are only L and C in parallel, the impedance is theoretically infinite. The current required by this circuit at resonance will be negligibly small.

A practical parallel resonant circuit will have an actual circuit as shown in Fig. S3-26, where R is the resistance in the inductor.   This circuit is

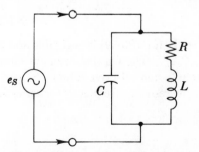

Figure S3-26   A parallel resonant circuit.

seen to be a series-parallel combination of components. While it is possible to solve such circuits by the graphical method used thus far, the method of complex notation is a quick and accurate method for determining the impedance algebraically. When an impedance is represented in complex numbers, the reactive component is multiplied by j. Algebraically, j is treated as $\sqrt{-1}$. Therefore $j^2 = -1, 1/j = -j$, etc. Inductive reactance in complex numbers is

$$\overline{X}_L = jX_L = j\omega L \tag{S3-57}$$

and capacitive reactance is

$$\overline{X}_C = -jX_C = \frac{-j}{\omega C} \tag{S3-58}$$

where the bar indicates that the vector or complex quantity is meant. The difference in the sign of the complex notation for capacitive and inductive reactance corresponds to the difference in the direction of the reactance vectors in the impedance diagrams.

The impedance of a series combination of an inductance and resistance is thus

$$\overline{Z}_{LR} = R + jX_L$$

The parallel combination of the above impedance and $\overline{X}_C$ is

$$\frac{1}{\overline{Z}} = \frac{1}{\overline{X}_C} + \frac{1}{\overline{Z}_{LR}}$$

$$\overline{Z} = \frac{(-jX_C)(R + jX_L)}{R + jX_L - jX_C}$$

At resonance, $X_C = X_L = X$:

$$\overline{Z} = \frac{-jX(R + jX)}{R} = \frac{X^2}{R} - jX$$

Recall that $Q = X_L/R$ for the inductor.

$$\overline{Z} = QX - jX = X(Q - j) \tag{S3-59}$$

If Q is greater than 10, the reactive term in Eq. (S3-59) is negligible and the impedance is approximately equal to QX_L. The parallel resonant circuit is very common in tuned amplifier circuits and selective filters. Since the conditions for resonance are the same, the resonant frequency for series and parallel resonant circuits is the same.

$$f_o = \frac{1}{2\pi\sqrt{LC}}$$

Another example of the use of complex numbers to solve reactive circuits is given in Sec. 6-5.

S3-5   Nonsinusoidal Signals and Reactive Circuits

The previous section was concerned only with the response of reactive circuits to sinusoidal (single-frequency) signals. The methods of analysis used for the reactive circuits with sinusoidal signals cannot easily be applied when the signal contains a spectrum of frequencies. Of all the nonsinusoidal signals, the most useful and perhaps the most characteristic one to study is the *step* signal. A step signal is an instantaneous change from one steady signal level to another. Such a signal is a good test of the response speed of a circuit or instrument as well as being very important in pulse and digital circuitry.

Series *RC* Response to Step Signals. Consider the circuit of Fig. S3-27. Assume that the switch is in position *B* and that the capacitor is completely discharged. The switch is thrown to position *A* and the capacitor begins to charge through *R* to the potential *E*. During the charging process $e_R = iR$ and $e_C = q/C$. From Kirchhoff's law,

$$E = iR + \frac{q}{C} \tag{S3-60}$$

From this equation it is seen that as the charge q on the capacitor increases, i decreases and the rate of charging is thereby decreased. The exact expression for e_C as a function of time can be obtained by substituting dQ/dt for i in Eq. (S3-60) and integrating. The result is that

$$e_C = E(1 - e^{-t/RC}) \tag{S3-61}$$

which shows that $e_C = 0$ when $t = 0$, and that e_C approaches E exponen-

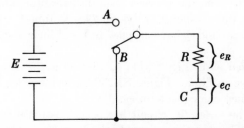

Figure S3-27   A series RC circuit and step signal source.

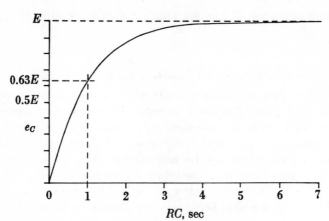

Figure S3-28   Charging curve for a series RC circuit.

tially as t approaches infinity. The charging curve is shown in Fig. S3-28.
Note that the time scale is calibrated in units of RC. The product RC has
the units of seconds $\left(\dfrac{\text{volts}}{\text{coulombs/sec}} \; \dfrac{\text{coulombs}}{\text{volts}} = \text{sec} \right)$ and is called the *time
constant* of the circuit. At the end of one time constant, the charge is within
$1/e$, or 0.37, of its final value.

When the output signal is taken as e_C, the circuit is a low-pass filter
(Fig. S3-14b). Figure S3-28 shows the response of the low-pass circuit to a
step change in the input potential. It is clear that the high-frequency components of the signal (the region of the greatest rate of change) have been
filtered out. This illustrates the effect on the response speed of a circuit
when a capacitance is connected across a signal source. As was stated previously, the potential across a capacitor cannot be instantly changed.

The expression for the current or e_R as a function of time can be obtained from Eqs. (S3-60) and (S3-61).

$$e_R = E - e_C = Ee^{-t/RC} \qquad\qquad\qquad\qquad (\text{S3-62})$$

When $t = 0$, the full potential E is developed across the resistor. The current and e_R then decrease with time and are zero when the capacitor is fully
charged. The plot of e_R vs. time is shown in Fig. S3-29. At time $t = RC$
(one time constant), the current and e_R have dropped to $1/e$ of their original
value.

If the circuit is arranged as in Fig. S3-14a so that e_R is the output
signal, the circuit is a high-pass filter. Figure S3-29 clearly indicates the
presence of the high-frequency components in e_R.

The step response of the series RC circuit has been illustrated for a
step from zero to E volts. The situation is exactly the same for a step between any two potentials. When the switch in Fig. S3-27 is returned to

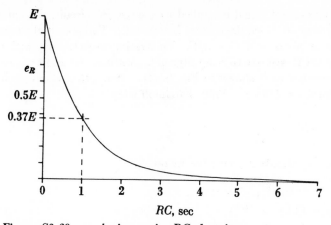

Figure S3-29 e_R *during series RC charging.*

position B, the potential steps from E back to zero. The potentials e_R and e_C approach their final values exponentially, as shown in Fig. S3-30.

If the capacitance is large and the resistance is small in the circuit of Fig. S3-27, the current peak when the switch is thrown can be very large. Occasionally it is necessary to put a switch or relay contacts directly in parallel with a fairly large capacitor. In such cases it may be necessary to use a switch or relay specifically designed for such use or put a protecting resistor in series with the contacts.

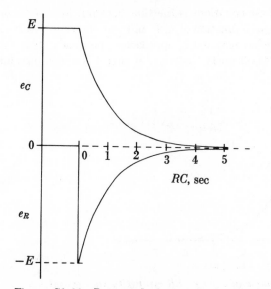

Figure S3-30 *Potentials during discharge of a series RC circuit.*

If a step-current signal is applied to a series RC circuit, the potential e_R is constant at iR, since the current is constant. The potential across the capacitor is simply $e_C = q/C = it/C$. Thus e_C increases linearly with time.

Series LR Response to Step Signals. A series LR circuit with a test step potential source is shown in Fig. S3-31. When the switch is closed, $e_R = iR$ and $e_L = L\, di/dt$. From Kirchhoff's law,

$$E = iR + L\frac{di}{dt} \tag{S3-63}$$

Integrating this equation yields the following:

$$e_L = Ee^{-tR/L} \tag{S3-64}$$

$$e_R = E(1 - e^{-tR/L}) \tag{S3-65}$$

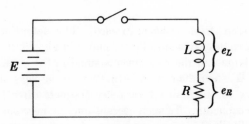

Figure S3-31　A series LR circuit and step signal source.

The quantity L/R in these equations is the time constant for LR circuits. The curves for e_L and e_R as a function of L/R units are shown in Fig. S3-32. The potential e_L approaches zero and e_R approaches the steady-state value E. The curves of Fig. S3-32 verify that the LR circuit is a high-pass filter

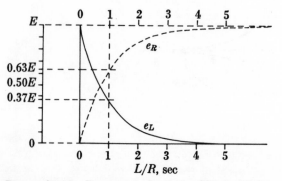

Figure S3-32　Response of a series LR circuit to step signal.

when the output is taken across L and a low-pass filter when the output signal is e_R.

Reactive Circuit Response to Pulse Signals.   A pulse is a step signal which remains at the new value for a brief period and then returns to the normal value.   A signal which is a series of pulses is shown in Fig. S3-33. T is the pulse *width* in seconds.   The response of high-pass and low-

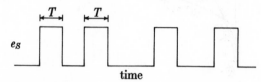

e_S

time

Figure S3-33   A succession of pulses.

pass circuits to pulse signals is of interest because of the importance of accurate pulse measurements in current research.

The response of a low-pass circuit for a single pulse is shown in Fig. S3-34 for various ratios of the time constant to the pulse width.   It can be seen that the low-pass circuit distorts the leading and trailing edges of the pulse and tends to *delay* the pulse (shift it to later time).   A very short time constant is obviously required for low distortion.   For the longer time

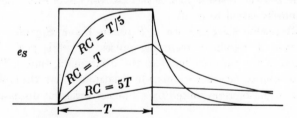

e_S

$RC = T/5$

$RC = T$

$RC = 5T$

T

Figure S3-34   Response of a low-pass circuit to a pulse signal.

constants it is seen that the pulse height is reduced, and that the output pulse height will be a function of the pulse width.   The latter effect is bad if a measure of pulse amplitude is desired, but it can be used to advantage in measuring the pulse width.

At very long time constants the output potential of the low-pass circuit is almost linear for the duration of the pulse.   Because the output thus approximates the time integral of the input signal, it is often called an integrator.

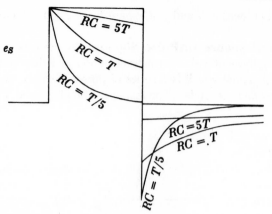

Figure S3-35   Response of a high-pass circuit to a pulse signal.

The response of a high-pass circuit for a single pulse is shown in Fig. S3-35 for various ratios of the time constant to the pulse width. The high-pass circuit distorts the nonchanging or continuous part of the signal. Note that only for very *long* time constants is a semblance of the pulse passed. A short time constant, high-pass circuit is sometimes called a "peaking circuit," or differentiator, because peaks are produced during rapid changes in the signal amplitude. It can be shown from Eq. (S3-2) that the potential across the resistor in a series RC circuit of short time constant is approximately equal to de/dt.

Response of Reactive Circuits to a Square-Wave Signal. A square wave is a series of regularly recurring pulses. If it is perfectly "square" the duration of the pulse is equal to the intervening time. The only reason for giving the square wave separate treatment from the pulse is that the square wave can be represented by a Fourier series, as discussed in Sec. S3-1.

The Fourier analysis showed that a 1000-cps square wave could be considered to be the sum of a 1000-cps sine wave and its harmonics in a certain amplitude and phase relation. Equation (S3-23) gives the formula for the low-frequency cutoff of a high-pass filter as $f_1 = 1/(2\pi RC)$. A high-pass filter with a time constant of 170 μsec will pass a 1000-cps sine wave with an attenuation of only 0.707, but *half* a cycle is 500 μsec long. The amplitude of a square wave subjected to this filter would drop to a small fraction of its initial value during each half cycle. The response curves of high-pass circuits of 170 μsec and 5 msec time constants to a 1000-cps square wave are shown in Fig. S3-36. Even when $f_1 = 30$ cps, there is a definite slope or "tilt" to the square wave. The percentage tilt, P, can be determined from the following expression:

$$P = 100\pi \frac{f_1}{f} \qquad (S3\text{-}66)$$

where f is the frequency of the square wave. For a 10 per cent tilt on a 1000-cps square wave,

$$f_1 = \frac{1000 \times 10}{100\pi} = 32 \text{ cps}$$

If only 1 per cent distortion can be tolerated, the low-frequency response of the circuit must extend to 3.2 cps. This could not have been concluded from the Fourier construction of the square wave shown in Fig. S3-7. The square wave thus illustrates the very exacting demands on the frequency response of a circuit which is expected to pass a nonsinusoidal waveform. The more rapid the rate of change of the signal, the higher must be f_2. The longer the level remains constant, the lower f_1 must be.

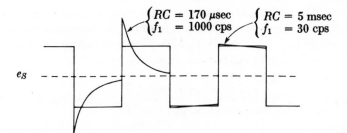

Figure S3-36 *Response of a high-pass circuit to a square-wave signal.*

S3-6 Mutual Inductance

The changing magnetic field around a coil which is in an a-c circuit can be "intercepted" by a second coil placed in proximity to the first coil. Consider two inductors placed so that each lies within the magnetic field generated by the other, as shown in Fig. S3-37. When the current in coil 1 changes, the movement of the magnetic field through the turns of coil 2 will induce an emf across coil 2. The magnitude of the emf which is induced is increased with an increased number of turns of coil 2, an increased magnetic coupling between coils 1 and 2, and an increased rate of change of the current in coil 1. If a load is connected to the terminals of coil 2, a current will flow in coil 2 and the load because of the induced emf from the magnetic field of coil 1. The increasing current in coil 2 generates a

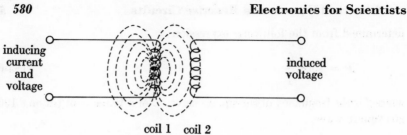

coil 1   coil 2

Figure S3-37   Mutual inductance.

changing magnetic field which opposes the magnetic field generated by coil 1. This would have the tendency to reduce the counter emf generated by self-induction in coil 1, but the counter emf must always equal the applied potential. Thus the current through coil 1 must increase in order to maintain the same net magnetic flux through the turns of coil 1.

In this way energy in the form of a changing current is transferred from coil 1 to coil 2. A device containing two or more coils whose magnetic fields interact is called a transformer. A d-c current in coil 1 induces no emf in coil 2 except when the current in coil 1 is turned on or off. The efficiency of a transformer depends on the degree of coupling between the coils. If the magnetic coupling between the coils is unity (the maximum possible) and if there are no losses in the coils and coupling medium, the power supplied to coil 1 will be equal to the power consumed by the load connected to coil 2.

$$\text{emf in coil 2} = \frac{\text{number of turns in coil 2}}{\text{number of turns in coil 1}} \times \text{emf in coil 1} \quad \text{(S3-67)}$$

The coil to which the power is supplied is called the primary. The coil to to which the load is connected is called the secondary.

As explained above, the load placed across the secondary coil affects the current in the primary coil. In other words, the impedance of the primary coil Z_p depends upon the impedance of the load Z_s connected to the secondary. The relationship is the following:

$$Z_p = Z_s N^2 \quad \text{(S3-68)}$$

N is the turns ratio, primary to secondary.

Transformers are specially designed for each type of duty. In general, the same limitations with regard to the resistance of the windings, the current capacity of the windings, the breakdown potential between the windings and the frame, and the frequency limitations apply to transformers as well as to the inductors discussed in Sec. S3-3.

References

"Radar Electronics Fundamentals," NAVSHIPS 900,016, U.S. Government Printing Office, Washington, D.C., 1944. Includes a basic presentation of some of the material in this supplement.

"Radio Amateur's Handbook," published annually by the American Radio Relay League, West Hartford, Conn. Contains basic laws of a-c circuits and information on practical components and applications.

Any text in a-c circuit analysis may be referred to for the use of vectors and complex numbers in the solution of a-c networks.

For a discussion of the frequency analysis of signals see S. Goldman, "Frequency Analysis, Modulation, and Noise," McGraw-Hill, New York, 1948.

Appendixes

appendix A

Transistor Parameter Equivalents and Interconversion Tables

Hybrid parameters, conversion table

From CE to CB	From CE to CC	From CB to CE	From CB to CC
$h_{ib} = \dfrac{h_{ie}}{1 + \alpha_{fe}}$	$h_{ic} = h_{ie}$	$h_{ie} = \dfrac{h_{ib}}{1 + \alpha_{fb}}$	$h_{ic} = \dfrac{h_{ib}}{1 + \alpha_{fb}}$
$\mu_{rb} = \dfrac{h_{ie}h_{oe}}{1 + \alpha_{fe}} - \mu_{re}$	$\mu_{rc} = 1 - \mu_{re} \cong 1$	$\mu_{re} = \dfrac{h_{ib}h_{ob}}{1 + \alpha_{fe}} - \mu_{rb}$	$\mu_{rc} = \dfrac{1 = h_{ib}h_{ob}}{1 + \alpha_{fb}} + \mu_{rb}$
$\alpha_{fb} = \dfrac{-\alpha_{fe}}{1 + \alpha_{fe}}$	$\alpha_{fc} = -(1 + \alpha_{fe})$	$\alpha_{fe} = \dfrac{-\alpha_{fb}}{1 + \alpha_{fb}}$	$\alpha_{fc} = \dfrac{-1}{1 + \alpha_{fb}}$
$h_{ob} = \dfrac{h_{oe}}{1 + \alpha_{fe}}$	$h_{oc} = h_{oe}$	$h_{oe} = \dfrac{h_{ob}}{1 + \alpha_{fb}}$	$h_{oc} = \dfrac{h_{ob}}{1 + \alpha_{fb}}$

[*Source:* "Basic Theory and Applications of Transistors," U. S. Army Technical Manual TM 11-690.]

Other notations used for hybrid parameters

Parameter	Configuration														
	Common emitter					Common base					Common collector				
	1	2	3	4	5	1	2	3	4	5	1	2	3	4	5
1. Input resistance with output shorted	h_{ie}	h_{11e}	$\dfrac{1}{r_{11e}}$	h_{bb}	h_{ie}	h_{ib}	h_{11b}	$\dfrac{1}{r_{11b}}$	h_{ec}	h_{ib}	h_{ic}	h_{11c}	$\dfrac{1}{r_{11c}}$	h_{bb}	h_{ic}
2. Reverse open-circuit voltage amplification factor	μ_{re}	h_{12e}	μ_{bc}	h_{bc}	h_{re}	μ_{rb}	h_{12b}	μ_{ec}	h_{ec}	h_{rb}	μ_{rc}	h_{12c}	μ_{be}	h_{be}	h_{rc}
3. Forward short-circuit amplification factor	α_{fe}	h_{21e}	α_{cb}	h_{cb}	h_{fe}	α_{fb}	h_{21b}	α_{ce}	h_{ce}	h_{fb}	α_{fc}	h_{21c}	α_{eb}	h_{eb}	h_{fc}
4. Output conductance with input open	h_{oe}	h_{22e}	$\dfrac{1}{r_{22e}}$	h_{cc}	h_{oe}	h_{ob}	h_{22b}	$\dfrac{1}{r_{22b}}$	h_{cc}	h_{ob}	h_{oc}	h_{22c}	$\dfrac{1}{r_{22c}}$	h_{ee}	h_{oc}

[*Source:* "Basic Theory and Applications of Transistors," U. S. Army Technical Manual TM 11-690.]

Open-circuit, short-circuit, and hybrid-parameter conversion table

From hybrid parameters to open-circuit parameters	From hybrid parameters to short-circuit parameters	From open-circuit parameters to hybrid parameters
$r_{ie} = h_{ie} - \dfrac{\mu_{re}\alpha_{fe}}{h_{oe}}$	$g_{ie} = \dfrac{1}{h_{ie}}$	$h_{ie} = r_{ie} - \dfrac{r_{re}r_{fe}}{r_{oe}}$
$r_{re} = \dfrac{\mu_{re}}{h_{oe}}$	$g_{re} = \dfrac{-\mu_{re}}{h_{ie}}$	$\mu_{re} = \dfrac{r_{re}}{r_{oe}}$
$r_{fe} = \dfrac{-\alpha_{fe}}{h_{oe}}$	$g_{fe} = \dfrac{\alpha_{fe}}{h_{ie}}$	$\alpha_{fe} = \dfrac{r_{fe}}{r_{oe}}$
$r_{oe} = \dfrac{1}{h_{oe}}$	$g_{oe} = h_{oe} - \dfrac{\mu_{re}\alpha_{fe}}{h_{ie}}$	$h_{oe} = \dfrac{1}{r_{oe}}$

Note: The above formulas apply directly to the *CE* configuration. These formulas can be made to apply to the *CB* or the *CC* configuration by changing each subscript letter *e* to *b* or *c*, respectively.
[*Source:* "Basic Theory and Applications of Transistors," U. S. Army Technical Manual TM 11-690.]

appendix B

Vacuum-Tube Characteristic
Curves

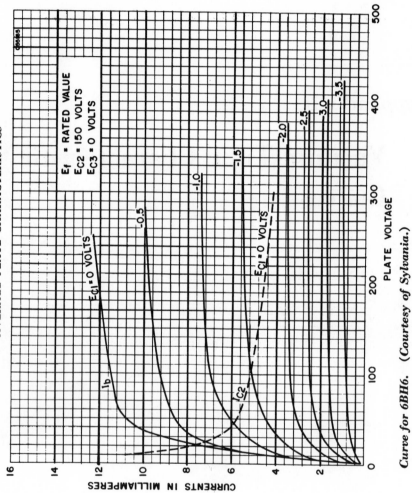

AVERAGE PLATE CHARACTERISTICS

E_f = RATED VALUE
E_{C2} = 150 VOLTS
E_{C3} = 0 VOLTS

CURRENTS IN MILLIAMPERES

PLATE VOLTAGE

Curve for 6BH6. (Courtesy of Sylvania.)

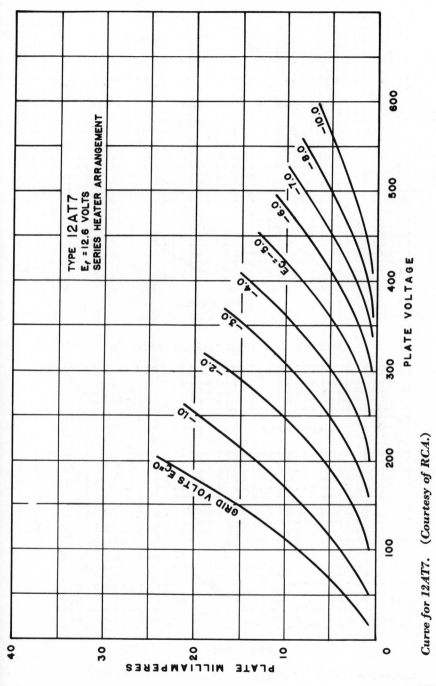

Curve for 12AT7. (Courtesy of RCA.)

591

AVERAGE PLATE CHARACTERISTICS

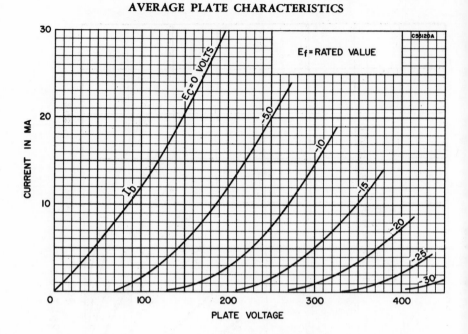

AVERAGE TRANSFER CHARACTERISTICS

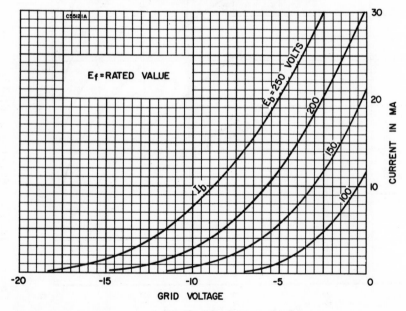

Curves for 12AU7. (*Courtesy of Sylvania.*)

AVERAGE PLATE CHARACTERISTICS

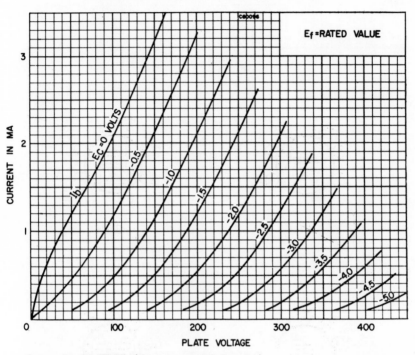

Curve for 12AX7.   (Courtesy of Sylvania.)

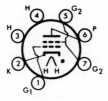

2D21

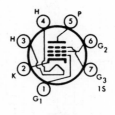

6BH6

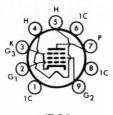

6BQ5

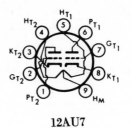

12AU7
12AX7

appendix C

Resistors (EIA-JAN Values)

10% Resistors

Ohms	Ohms	Ohms	Ohms	Ohms	Ohms	Ohms	Ohms	Ohms	Ohms	Ohms	Ohms
0.27	1.2	5.6	27	120	560	2,700	12,000	56,000	0.27 meg	1.2 meg	5.6 meg
0.33	1.5	6.8	33	150	680	3,300	15,000	68,000	0.33 meg	1.5 meg	6.8 meg
0.39	1.8	8.2	39	180	820	3,900	18,000	82,000	0.39 meg	1.8 meg	8.2 meg
0.47	2.2	10	47	220	1,000	4,700	22,000	0.1 meg	0.47 meg	2.2 meg	10 meg
0.56	2.7	12	56	270	1,200	5,600	27,000	0.12 meg	0.56 meg	2.7 meg	12 meg
0.68	3.3	15	68	330	1,500	6,800	33,000	0.15 meg	0.68 meg	3.3 meg	15 meg
0.82	3.0	18	82	390	1,800	8,200	39,000	0.18 meg	0.82 meg	3.9 meg	18 meg
1.0	4.7	22	100	470	2,200	10,000	47,000	0.22 meg	1.0 meg	4.7 meg	22 meg

5% Resistors

Ohms	Ohms	Ohms	Ohms	Ohms	Ohms	Ohms	Ohms	Ohms	Ohms	Ohms	Ohms
0.24	1.1	5.1	24	110	510	2,400	11,000	51,000	0.24 meg	1.1 meg	5.1 meg
0.27	1.2	5.6	27	120	560	2,700	12,000	56,000	0.27 meg	1.2 meg	5.6 meg
0.30	1.3	6.2	30	130	620	3,000	13,000	62,000	0.30 meg	1.3 meg	6.2 meg
0.33	1.5	6.8	33	150	680	3,300	15,000	68,000	0.33 meg	1.5 meg	6.8 meg
0.36	1.6	7.5	36	160	750	3,600	16,000	75,000	0.36 meg	1.6 meg	7.5 meg
0.39	1.8	8.2	39	180	820	3,900	18,000	82,000	0.39 meg	1.8 meg	8.2 meg
0.43	2.0	9.1	43	200	910	4,300	20,000	91,000	0.43 meg	2.0 meg	9.1 meg
0.47	2.2	10	47	220	1,000	4,700	22,000	0.1 meg	0.47 meg	2.2 meg	10 meg
0.51	2.4	11	51	240	1,100	5,100	24,000	0.11 meg	0.51 meg	2.4 meg	11 meg
0.56	2.7	12	56	270	1,200	5,600	27,000	0.12 meg	0.56 meg	2.7 meg	12 meg
0.62	3.0	13	62	300	1,300	6,200	30,000	0.13 meg	0.62 meg	3.0 meg	13 meg
0.68	3.3	15	68	330	1,500	6,800	33,000	0.16 meg	0.68 meg	3.3 meg	15 meg
0.75	3.6	16	75	360	1,600	7,500	36,000	0.16 meg	0.75 meg	3.6 meg	16 meg
0.82	3.9	18	82	390	1,800	8,200	39,000	0.18 meg	0.82 meg	3.9 meg	18 meg
0.91	4.3	20	91	430	2,000	9,100	43,000	0.20 meg	0.91 meg	4.3 meg	20 meg
1.0	4.7	22	100	470	2,200	10,000	47,000	0.22 meg	1.0 meg	4.7 meg	22 meg

appendix D

Power-Transformer Color Code

Black—primary
Red—high-voltage secondary
Red-yellow (striped)—high-voltage center tap
Green—heater secondary
Green-yellow—heater center tap
Yellow—rectifier filament

Index

Index

Boldface entries indicate definitions.

Boldface entries indicate definitions.